THEORY OF ALTERNATING-CURRENT MACHINERY

THEORY OF
ALTERNATING-CURRENT MACHINERY

ALEXANDER S. LANGSDORF, M.M.E., D.Sc.

*Dean Emeritus, Schools of Engineering and Architecture
and Professor Emeritus of Electrical Engineering, Washington University
Fellow, American Institute of Electrical Engineers
Member, American Society of Mechanical Engineers*

SECOND EDITION

McGRAW-HILL BOOK COMPANY, INC.

New York   Toronto   London

1955

THE MAPLE PRESS COMPANY, YORK, PA.

To

ELSIE H. LANGSDORF

PREFACE

Since the publication of the first edition of this book, the many developments in the science and art of electrical engineering have been reflected in engineering curricula by a marked increase in the emphasis upon electronics and related topics and a correspondingly decreased allocation of time to the formal presentation of power machinery. Circuit and field theory and kindred topics, which were formerly lumped with the study of machines, are now taught in introductory courses much earlier than was considered possible when a disproportionate amount of time was devoted to subjects now regarded as of minor importance. For these reasons, circuit theory, which was included in the first three chapters of the first edition, has been eliminated, and attention has been confined to the properties of machines.

Further, because of the fact that the time available for courses on power machinery is in many institutions severely limited, the chapter arrangement of the material dealing with each of the major types has been planned to make a clear distinction between fundamental principles, on the one hand, and the structural, design, and operational features, on the other. In this way, time may be conserved by the judicious omission or deferment of topics which are not essential to mastery of basic principles, while at the same time continuity is not seriously impaired.

Just as in the first edition, the transformer has been given priority in the order of presentation, not only because it is the simplest type of electromagnetic apparatus, but also because the fundamental principles are immediately applicable to all types of generators and motors. The transformer material has been arranged in three chapters so that portions of Chaps. 2 and 3 may be the more readily omitted in an introductory course.

Chapters 4 and 5, of which the greater part was incorporated in later chapters of the first edition, have been inserted at this stage because they summarize the essential principles which underlie the performance of all types of rotating machinery, both synchronous and asynchronous. It is believed that when these two chapters have been thoroughly mastered the remaining chapters of the book may be taken up in whatever order may seem preferable.

Actually, however, these chapters have been followed by the treatment of induction machines, partly for the reason that many experienced teachers believe that this order is a natural development of transformer theory, partly for the reason that much of the theory of synchronous machines follows as a logical consequence of induction machine theory. Nevertheless, it is possible to proceed from Chap. 4 to the synchronous generator, Chap. 10, with only occasional references to intervening material.

At the time the first edition was written, electronic devices were just beginning to have an important impact upon the power field; so it was decided to omit any treatment of the mercury-arc rectifier in a book avowedly devoted to electromagnetic machines. In the meantime, however, the mercury-arc rectifier has been developed to such an extent as to make the synchronous converter almost obsolescent; hence this edition includes a new chapter on power rectifiers and inverters.

In deference to the trend toward the use of mks units, all derivations of essential formulas have been presented in terms of the rationalized mks system of units. For the same reason, the terms *vector* and *vector diagram* have been changed to read *phasor* and *phasor diagram*, as recommended by the American Standards Association.

Illustrative problems have been inserted in the text to a greater extent than in the first edition, and the problem material at the end of the book has been considerably enlarged.

In planning the selection and arrangement of material in this book, the author has had the benefit of the advice and criticism of several friends, especially Professor Harry G. Hake and Mr. Olle Elgerd of Washington University and Professor Edward Erdelyi of Syracuse University. To the latter he is particularly indebted for valued assistance in the preparation of problem material and for critical comments on portions of the text. To these gentlemen he extends his grateful thanks, as well as to friends in the General Electric Company, the Westinghouse Electric Corporation, the Allis-Chalmers Manufacturing Company, and the Wagner Electric Corporation, for photographs and technical data.

ALEXANDER S. LANGSDORF

CONTENTS

TABLE OF SYMBOLS

a cross section, cir mils
instantaneous armature mmf
number of parallel paths in armature
ratio of transformation

A cross section
amplitude of armature mmf
radiating area

A_1 amplitude of fundamental mmf

A_r amplitude of rth harmonic mmf

A_x mmf equivalent to armature leakage reactance

b flux density
pole arc
width of coil

B flux density
susceptance

B_0 exciting susceptance

B_g average airgap flux density

B_m maximum flux density

d, D diameter

e instantaneous emf

e_r arc drop in rectifier

E effective (rms) emf

E_1 primary induced emf

E_2 secondary induced emf

E_m maximum value of emf

E_a armature mmf
rms voltage impressed upon rectifier anodes

E_d emf equivalent to direct-axis armature mmf
average of rectified voltage

E_q emf equivalent to quadrature-axis armature mmf

E_r rotational (speed) emf

E_t transformer (induced) emf

E_{rr} rotational emf due to speed field

E_{rt} transformer emf due to speed field

E_{tr} rotational emf due to transformer field

E_{tt} transformer emf due to transformer field

f frequency

f_s slip frequency
tooth frequency

F field excitation
force
watts per lb

F_R resultant field excitation

g conductance

G_0 exciting conductance

h cir mils per amp
height

H magnetizing force

i instantaneous current

I_0 primary no-load current
zero-sequence component

I_1 primary current

I_2 secondary current

I_2', I_{2e} secondary current reduced to terms of primary

I_a armature current
rms value of anode current

I_d direct-axis component of armature current
d-c output of rectifier

I_q quadrature-axis component of armature current

I_n negative-sequence component of current

I_p positive-sequence component of current

I_s current at standstill

I_{h+e} power component of no-load current

I_{sc} short-circuit current

I_ϕ magnetizing component of no-load current

J polar moment of inertia

k constant

k_b breadth or spread factor of winding

k_e eddy-current loss coefficient

k_h hysteresis loss coefficient

k_p pitch factor of winding

k_r combined winding factor for rth harmonic

K ratio of eddy-current loss to copper loss at 75°C

l length in general; length of core

L inductance in general

L_1 primary inductance

L_2 secondary inductance

L_{2e} secondary inductance in terms of primary

m number of phases

m_1 number of phases in primary

m_2 number of phases in secondary

M mass
coefficient of mutual inductance
cir mils per amp (Chap. 3)

n revolutions per unit time
number of rectifier anodes

n_1 synchronous speed corresponding to primary frequency

n_2 actual speed of rotor

N number of turns in series

N_1 primary turns per phase

N_2 secondary turns per phase

N_p armature turns per pole per phase

p number of poles

P power
permeance

P_0 no-load power

P_e eddy-current loss

P_h hysteresis loss

P_{h+e} core loss

q slots per pole per phase
amp-conductors per in. of periphery

r order of space harmonic

r_{pc} per cent resistance

r_{pu} per-unit resistance

R resistance

R_0 exciting resistance

R_1 primary resistance

R_2 secondary resistance

R_{2e} secondary resistance in terms of primary

R_e equivalent resistance at short circuit

R_a armature resistance

s slip
order of time harmonic

s_p slots per pair of poles

S speed in terms of synchronous speed as unity
total number of slots
amp per sq in. of conductor

t time, sec
temperature, °C
thickness of laminations

T time of one cycle
average length of turn
torque

T_l load torque

T_s standstill torque

v instantaneous value of impressed voltage
velocity

V rms value of impressed voltage

V_1 primary impressed voltage

V_2 secondary terminal voltage

V_e impedance drop in transformer

V_n negative-sequence component of voltage

V_p positive-sequence component of voltage

V_0 zero-sequence component of voltage

V_s voltage impressed at standstill

w turns of winding per coil

w_b width of rotor bar

w_s width of rotor slot

W work or energy
weight, lb

x_{pc} per cent reactance

x_{pu} per-unit reactance

x_0 zero-sequence reactance

x_2 negative-sequence reactance

X reactance in general

X_0 exciting (magnetizing) reactance

X_1 primary leakage reactance

X_2 secondary leakage reactance

X_{2e} secondary leakage reactance in terms of primary

X_a armature leakage reactance

X_A armature reaction reactance

X_d direct-axis reactance
differential leakage reactance

X_e short-circuit reactance

X_{end} end-connection leakage reactance

X_{rd} reaction reactance, direct axis

X_{rq} reaction reactance, quadrature axis

X_s synchronous reactance

X_q quadrature axis reactance

X_d'	transient direct-axis reactance		length of airgap
X_d''	subtransient direct-axis react-		torque angle
	ance	ϵ	angle
Y	admittance		eddy-current-loss constant
Y_0	exciting admittance	ζ	angle
z_0	zero-sequence impedance	η	efficiency
z_2	negative-sequence impedance		hysteresis-loss constant
z_{pc}	per cent impedance	θ	angle
z_{pu}	per-unit impedance		angular phase displacement
Z	impedance in general		temperature
	number of armature conductors	λ	linkages
Z_1, Z_2	primary and secondary leakage	ξ	output coefficient
	impedance	ρ	resistivity
Z_0	exciting impedance		angle
Z_a	armature leakage impedance	σ	specific heat
Z_e	short-circuit impedance		current density
	equivalent impedance		leakage factor
Z_d	direct-axis impedance	τ	pole pitch
Z_q	quadrature-axis impedance	φ, ϕ	instantaneous flux
Z_r	number of rotor bars in squirrel	φ	phase angle
	cage		angle of overlap in rectifier
Z_s	synchronous impedance	φ_1	primary leakage flux
α	space angle	φ_2	secondary leakage flux
	angle of hysteretic advance	Φ	flux per pole
	angular acceleration	Φ_m	maximum value of alternating
	emissivity		flux
	angle of delay in rectifier phase	Φ_r	harmonic flux, order r
	control		rotational (speed) flux
β	angle, phase angle	Φ_t	flux in transformer axis
γ	angle between slots, electrical	ψ	angle of phase displacement
	degrees		angular spread of winding belt
δ	angle		angle of skew
	density	ω	angular velocity

FUNDAMENTAL PRINCIPLES OF THE TRANSFORMER

1-1. Electromagnetic Induction. Oersted's discovery, first published in 1820, showed that a current flowing in a wire deflects a compass needle suitably placed in its immediate vicinity and thereby demonstrated that a magnetic field is invariably associated with an electric current. This fact led a number of experimenters, of whom Michael Faraday was one, to surmise that it should be possible to make a magnetic field produce an electric current, but it was not until 1831, after eleven years of experimentation, that Faraday was able to prove the truth of this converse proposition. In so doing, he established the principle of *electromagnetic induction*.

Faraday's apparatus consisted of a ring of soft bar-iron on which were wound two coils of insulated copper wire, P and S, as in Fig. 1-1. On opening and closing the switch which connected coil P to a battery, the galvanometer G connected to coil S showed a deflection which was in one direction on closing the switch and in the opposite direction on opening it. So long as the current through coil P remained constant, no current was induced in coil S.

In terms of the concept of lines of force (or lines of induction) as envisaged by Faraday, these phenomena may be accounted for in the following manner: Assume that on closing the switch the current through P, originally zero, increases in the direction indicated in Fig. 1-1. A magnetic flux is thereby established through the iron core in the clockwise direction, in accordance with Ampère's rule, and an increasing flux of lines of induction becomes linked with the turns of coil S. Since no flux was originally linked with S, the effect is the same as though lines of induction indicated by the arrow B were sweeping into the iron core from the outside, which amounts to the same thing as a relative movement of a wire, such as A, outward across the lines of induction B. Fleming's right-hand rule then indicates that an emf and a corresponding current will be induced in wires like A in the direction shown by the arrowheads. On opening the switch, the current in coil P decreases, and the magnetic flux collapses, which is equivalent to an outward movement of the lines of induction across wires A; hence, the emf and current in coil S reverse their direction.

It will be noted that when the current in coil P is increasing, the induced current in coil S is so directed as to tend to produce a counterclockwise flux through the iron core in opposition to the inducing flux. This result checks with Lenz's law, which states that an induced current always opposes the action which produces it. In like manner, the collapse of the magnetic field, which occurs when the switch is opened, automatically causes the reversed current in coil S to tend to maintain the flux in its original direction.

In general, the development of an induced emf and current in the secondary coil S is seen to be the result of the *changing magnetic flux* linked with it because of the excitation produced by the changing current

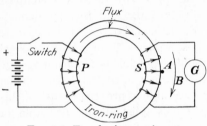

FIG. 1-1. Faraday's experiment.

in the primary coil P. Energy is therefore transferred from the primary to the secondary through the intervention of the magnetic flux which links with both of them. In order that this transfer of energy may be continuous, it is obvious that the primary must be supplied with emf and current which alternate periodically, and it is therefore obvious that the frequency of alternation of secondary emf and current will be the same as that of the primary.

Faraday's apparatus (Fig. 1-1) was the forerunner of the a-c transformer (sometimes referred to as the static transformer because of the absence of moving parts). The modern transformer differs from it only in constructional details. In its simplest form, the transformer consists essentially of two insulated windings so disposed with respect to each other that a current through one of them will set up a magnetic flux linking more or less completely with the turns of the other. The emf induced in the secondary has the frequency of the primary, and its magnitude is proportional to the flux linking the secondary and to the number of turns of the latter. The secondary emf may therefore be greater, equal to, or less than that of the primary; if it is greater, the transformer is a *step-up* transformer; if less, it is a *step-down* transformer; if primary and secondary voltages are equal, the transformer is said to have a one-to-one ratio. One-to-one transformers are used when it is necessary or desirable to insulate the secondary side of the circuit from the primary circuit; for though both circuits will then have the same difference of potential between their terminals, they will not necessarily have the same difference of potential to ground.

Either of the two windings may be the primary, while the other then serves as the secondary. The primary may therefore be best defined as the winding which receives energy from the supply source, and the secondary as the winding which delivers energy to the load. In general, however, the windings are designated simply as the high-tension (H.T.) and the low-tension (L.T.) windings, respectively.

In order to ensure the most effective magnetic linkage of the two windings, the core which serves to support them mechanically as well as to carry their mutual magnetic flux is usually made of a highly permeable iron or steel alloy designed to have a low reluctance. However, in special cases the magnetic circuit linking the windings may be made of non-magnetic material, in which case the transformer is referred to as an air-core transformer. The air-core transformer is of interest chiefly in radio devices and in certain types of measuring and testing instruments. An intermediate type, exemplified by induction coils of the Ruhmkorff model and by the small transformers used in the talking circuits of telephone systems, utilizes a straight core made of a bundle of iron wires on which the primary and secondary coils are wound one over the other.

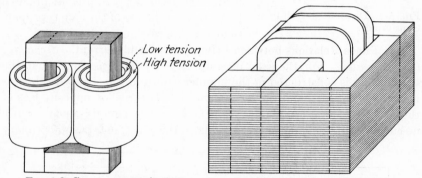

Fig. 1-2. Core-type transformer. Fig. 1-3. Shell-type transformer.

1-2. Core- and Shell-type Transformers. The relative arrangement of the core and windings of a transformer is determined by considerations of economy of material, simplicity and ease of construction of the parts, provision of insulation to withstand electrical stresses, mechanical strength to resist the forces caused by heavy short-circuit currents, and ventilation to get rid of the heat due to the losses in the core and coils. There are two principal types which embody these requirements to a greater or lesser degree, one of them, called the *core type*, being indicated by Fig. 1-2, the other, called the *shell type*, being shown in Fig. 1-3. The distinction between the two types may be summed up in the statement that in the core type the windings encircle the core, while in the shell type the core encircles the windings. An intermediate type of construction, called the distributed-shell type, is shown in Fig. 1-4.

The sheet-steel punchings used in building up the core are commonly of the form indicated in Fig. 1-5, successive layers being built up so that the joints overlap in the manner indicated by the two parts of the drawing. Other types of construction in general use are described in Chap. 3.

The choice between the core and the shell types of construction depends

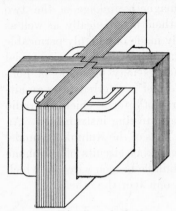

in any given case upon considerations of design, which are not within the scope of this book. In general, it may be said that while both types can be designed to be equally satisfactory with respect to their ability to withstand both electrical and mechanical stresses, the shell type requires more specialized fabrication facilities than the core type, and the latter offers the additional advantages of permitting visual inspection of the coils in case of trouble and of greater ease in making repairs in the field. For these reasons, present practice

FIG. 1-4. Distributed shell-type transformer.

tends toward the use of the core type, particularly in large, high-voltage units.

1-3. Phase Relations between Primary EMF and Current. *Secondary Open-circuited.* For the sake of simplicity, let it be assumed that the transformer is constructed in the manner shown in Fig. 1-6, with the primary P of N_1 turns and the secondary S of N_2 turns, on opposite legs of the core;* also let it be assumed that the secondary circuit is open. Since no current will then flow in the secondary, the effect, so far as the primary

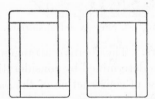

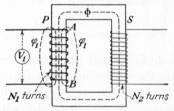

FIG. 1-5. Successive layers of laminations.   FIG. 1-6. Diagram of elementary transformer.

is concerned, is the same as though the secondary winding were not present; hence the transformer under these conditions is nothing more or less than a reactance coil, and the current I_0 set up in the primary by an impressed voltage V_1 will be determined by the impedance of the primary winding. Assuming that the impressed voltage V_1 varies harmonically with a frequency f cps, the complete determination of the magnitude of I_0 and its phase relation to V_1 can be worked out by assuming certain ideal conditions to begin with and then introducing one by one the factors

---

* In practice, core-type transformers are constructed with half of the primary winding and half of the secondary winding on each leg of the core.

originally omitted. Thus, let the following conditions be initially assumed:

1. That the flux Φ in the core is proportional to the mmf which produces it, in other words, that the core is unsaturated and that the permeability of the material of the magnetic circuit is constant.

2. That there are no iron losses (hysteresis and eddy currents) in the core.

3. That all the flux set up by the primary current lies within the magnetic core and that it therefore links with all the turns of both windings.

4. That the primary winding has zero resistance.

The assumption of zero primary resistance might at first thought lead to the conclusion that the primary current would increase without limit. But it must be remembered that as the current increases from its initial zero value the flux Φ increases in direct proportion, and its alternations, in step with those of the current, will in accordance with Lenz's law induce in the primary an emf that opposes the increase of current and is therefore in opposition to the impressed voltage. Since by hypothesis the primary has no resistance, the ohmic drop in the primary is zero, so that the primary winding is the seat of only two opposing emfs, namely, the impressed voltage and the counter emf induced by the alternating flux; and in accordance with Kirchhoff's second law these two emfs must at every instant be equal and opposite.

The assumption that the impressed voltage varies harmonically with respect to time then imposes the requirement that the counter emf must likewise vary harmonically; and this in turn requires that the flux must also be harmonic. For if the flux at any instant t is represented by the equation

$$\varphi = \Phi_m \sin \omega t = \Phi_m \sin 2\pi f t \qquad (1\text{-}1)$$

where Φ_m is the maximum value of the flux, in webers, it follows that the corresponding instantaneous emf induced in the N_1 turns of the primary is

$$e_1 = -N_1 \frac{d\varphi}{dt} = -2\pi f N_1 \Phi_m \cos \omega t = 2\pi f N_1 \Phi_m \sin \left(\omega t - \frac{\pi}{2} \right) \qquad (1\text{-}2)$$

It will thus be seen that the sinusoidal flux induces a sinusoidal emf which lags 90° in time phase behind the flux.

The maximum value of the induced emf is

$$E_{1m} = 2\pi f N_1 \Phi_m$$

and its effective, or rms, value, which under the foregoing assumptions is also the effective value of the impressed voltage V_1, is

$$E_1 = V_1 = \sqrt{2}\, \pi f N_1 \Phi_m = 4.44 f N_1 \Phi_m \qquad (1\text{-}3)$$

If the flux is represented by the phasor* Φ_m of Fig. 1-7, the emf E_1 will be represented by the phasor OE_1 lagging 90° behind the flux, in accordance with the relations demanded by Eqs. 1-1 and 1-2. The impressed voltage is OV_1, equal and opposite to OE_1; and the current I_0, since it is at every instant proportional to the flux it produces, must be in time phase with Φ_m and is therefore represented by the phasor OI_0.

Figure 1-7 shows that the current I_0 lags 90° behind V_1 and that the power supplied from the line, or $V_1I_0 \cos 90°$, is accordingly equal to zero. This result is a natural consequence of the assumed conditions, there being neither ohmic nor iron losses to be supplied. It follows that such an ideal transformer, under open-circuit conditions, is a pure reactance X_0, such that $X_0 = V_1/I_0$ ohms.

The assumption of a linear relation between flux and mmf is not particularly violent so long as the maximum flux density in the core is kept low, but if the bend in the magnetization curve of the core material is passed, the assumed proportionality no longer holds true, and in that case

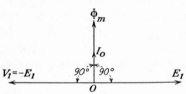

FIG. 1-7. Phasor diagram of ideal transformer, secondary open circuited.

if the flux varies harmonically as in Eq. 1-1 the current will not at every instant be proportional to the corresponding value of the flux; hence, it will not be sinusoidal. This means that the current cannot be represented accurately by a simple phasor as in Fig. 1-7, but it is still permissible to represent the actual nonsinusoidal current by an equivalent sine current having the same effective value as the distorted current. The nature of the distortion caused by varying permeability will be discussed in greater detail in Art. 1-20.

The time-phase relations shown in Fig. 1-7 were based upon the assumed absence of hysteresis and eddy currents in the iron core; actually, however, such losses are always present to some extent when a ferromagnetic core is subjected to an alternating flux, even though the core is laminated to reduce eddy currents and hysteresis is minimized by the use of high-grade material. It follows, therefore, that even though there is no secondary load the primary must supply sufficient power to overcome the core losses, which means that I_0 cannot lag behind V_1 by 90° but must lead the flux Φ_m by a small angle, α, called the *angle of hysteretic advance*, as shown in Fig. 1-8. Accordingly, the no-load primary current

---

* The word *phasor* is defined as a quantity the magnitude of which can be expressed by a complex number. It replaces the term *vector*, formerly used to designate the graphical representation of alternating currents, voltages, etc., in order that the word vector may be reserved to designate directed quantities like forces and velocities. Similarly, the term *phasor diagram* replaces the previously used term *vector diagram*. (See American Standards Association ASA Z10.8, Par. 9.)

may be considered to be the resultant of two components, one of which, I_ϕ, in phase with Φ_m, is the true *magnetizing current*, while the other component, I_{h+e}, in phase with the component $-E_1$ of the impressed voltage, is the power component.

The mmf due to the current in the primary produces a difference of magnetic potential between the ends of the winding, i.e., between points A and B of Fig. 1-6. This difference of magnetic potential will set up the *leakage flux* indicated by φ_1 in that figure, the distinctive feature of this flux being that it links with the primary but not with the secondary and that its path is so largely in air that it may be considered to be directly proportional to, and in phase with, the current I_0 producing it. In just the same way that the mutual flux Φ_m induces in the primary an emf proportional to, and lagging 90° behind, that flux, so also does the leakage flux induce in the primary a *leakage-reactance emf* lagging 90° behind φ_1 and proportional to φ_1, and therefore nearly proportional to I_0. This emf is

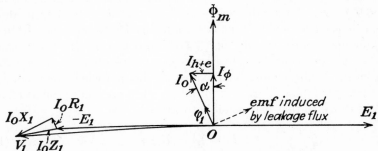

FIG. 1-8. Phasor diagram of transformer, secondary open circuited.

shown as a dashed line in Fig. 1-8. The quantity I_0X_1, leading I_0 by 90°, then represents the component of the impressed voltage required to balance it. The factor X_1 is the proportionality constant between the current and the leakage-reactance emf due to it, and this constant is clearly of the nature of reactance, expressible in ohms.

Finally, on introducing the ohmic resistance R_1 of the primary, previously omitted in accordance with the initial assumptions, it is evident that the impressed voltage V_1 must contain as one component the potential drop I_0R_1, in phase with I_0, as shown in Fig. 1-8. Consequently, the total impressed voltage V_1 must be the geometrical sum of (1) the component $(-E_1)$ equal and opposite to the emf induced by the mutual flux Φ_m; (2) I_0X_1, the leakage-reactance drop, equal and opposite to the emf induced by the leakage flux φ_1; and (3) the ohmic drop I_0R_1, in phase with I_0. The geometrical sum of I_0R_1 and I_0X_1 is I_0Z_1, where Z_1 is called the *leakage impedance* of the primary.

1-4. Exciting Impedance and Admittance. With the exception of a few special types to be considered later, most transformers are designed to operate with nominally constant impressed voltage V_1. The phasor diagram (Fig. 1-8) shows that when the secondary is open-circuited the counter emf E_1 induced by the mutual flux Φ_m differs geometrically from V_1 by the no-load impedance drop $I_0 Z_1$, which ordinarily amounts to a fraction of 1 per cent of V_1. If the secondary supplies a load circuit, the additional power required will cause the primary current to increase from I_0 to a larger value and the primary leakage-impedance drop will increase proportionally. Within the limits of normal loading, the primary leakage-impedance drop will seldom exceed 3 to 5 per cent of V_1, which leads to the conclusion that if V_1 is constant, E_1 remains substantially constant within normal operating limits; and Fig. 1-8 shows that Φ_m, to which E_1 is directly proportional, will also remain constant to the same degree as does E_1.

Since the maximum flux density is ordinarily not much beyond the knee of the magnetization curve, the relation between flux density and magnetizing force is fairly represented by the nearly straight portion of the BH curve, so that the magnetizing current I_ϕ (Fig. 1-8) is almost proportional to Φ_m and like the latter remains nearly constant within the working limits of the transformer. The component I_{h+e} likewise remains nearly constant, since both hysteresis and eddy-current losses are functions of the frequency and the flux density, both of which are practically constant. It follows that I_0 is for all practical purposes proportional to Φ_m and to E_1, so that it is possible to write

$$I_0 = \frac{E_1}{Z_0} = E_1 Y_0 \tag{1-4}$$

where Z_0 = exciting impedance, ohms

Y_0 = exciting admittance, siemens (mhos)

In Eq. 1-4, Z_0 and Y_0 are both proportionality constants which define the assumed linear relation between I_0 and E_1. The exciting impedance Z_0 is relatively large, while its reciprocal Y_0 is correspondingly small. In complex notation, Eq. 1-4 becomes

$$\mathbf{I}_0 = \frac{-\mathbf{E}_1}{Z_0} = \frac{-\mathbf{E}_1}{R_0 + jX_0} \tag{1-5}$$

or
$$\mathbf{I}_0 = -\mathbf{E}_1 Y_0 = -\mathbf{E}_1 (G_0 - jB_0) \tag{1-6}$$

the negative sign of E_1 indicating that I_0 may be considered to be produced by the component of V_1 which balances the induced emf E_1, as in Fig. 1-8.

In Fig. 1-8, the emf E_1 is drawn as a horizontal line, so that

$$\mathbf{E}_1 = E_1 + j0 \tag{1-7}$$

and Eq. 1-6 may then be written

$$\mathbf{I}_0 = -G_0 \mathbf{E}_1 + jB_0 \mathbf{E}_1 \tag{1-8}$$

The term $-G_0\mathbf{E}_1$ represents the component of exciting current in phase with $-\mathbf{E}_1$ and is therefore the same as I_{h+e}; similarly, $jB_0\mathbf{E}_1$ is the component of no-load current in quadrature with $-\mathbf{E}_1$ and is shown as I_ϕ in Fig. 1-8. Hence Eq. 1-8 is the same as

$$\mathbf{I}_0 = \mathbf{I}_{h+e} + \mathbf{I}_\phi \tag{1-9}$$

which checks with the construction of Fig. 1-8.

In the expressions

$$Z_0 = R_0 + jX_0$$

and

$$Y_0 = G_0 - jB_0$$

R_0 and X_0 are, respectively, the *exciting resistance* and the *exciting reactance*, and G_0 and B_0 are, respectively, the *exciting conductance* and the *exciting susceptance*. Since

$$Z_0 = R_0 + jX_0 = \frac{1}{Y_0} = \frac{1}{G_0 - jB_0}$$

it follows that

$$R_0 = \frac{G_0}{G_0^2 + B_0^2} \qquad G_0 = \frac{R_0}{R_0^2 + X_0^2}$$
$$X_0 = \frac{B_0}{G_0^2 + B_0^2} \qquad B_0 = \frac{X_0}{R_0^2 + X_0^2} \tag{1-10}$$

1-5. Phasor Diagram of Transformer under Load Conditions. When the secondary of a transformer is open-circuited, as in Fig. 1-6, the mutual flux Φ_m induces in the secondary wind-ing an emf of effective value E_2 such that

$$E_2 = \sqrt{2}\,\pi f N_2 \Phi_m \tag{1-11}$$

the derivation of which is obtained in the same manner as Eq. 1-3; further-more, the time phase of E_2 is 90° be-hind that of Φ_m, just as in the case of E_1. The ratio of E_1 and E_2 is

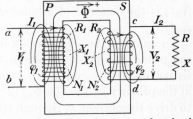

Fig. 1-9. Transformer under load conditions.

$$\frac{E_1}{E_2} = \frac{N_1}{N_2} = a \tag{1-12}$$

and this is called the *ratio of transformation*.

When the external circuit of the secondary is closed through the impedance represented by $Z = R + jX$ in Fig. 1-9, the induced emf E_2 will set up in the secondary a current

$$\mathbf{I}_2 = \frac{\mathbf{E}_2}{(R_2 + R) + j(X_2 + X)} \tag{1-13}$$

and this current will differ in phase from E_2 by an angle ψ_2 determined by the equation

$$\tan \psi_2 = \frac{X_2 + X}{R_2 + R} \tag{1-14}$$

as shown in the diagram (Fig. 1-10a).

Referring to Fig. 1-9, it will be seen that if the primary current at a given instant has the direction indicated by the arrowhead on the primary winding, the secondary current must in general be so directed, in accordance with Lenz's law, as to oppose the magnetizing action of the primary; in other words, the effect of the induced secondary current is demagnetizing.   But the flux Φ_m must remain nearly the same as under open-circuit conditions for the reasons cited in Art. 1-4.   Hence, *the demagnetizing effect of the secondary current must be balanced by an automatic increase of primary current to such an extent that the resultant of the primary and secondary mmfs (or ampere-turns) will be just sufficient to maintain the flux at a value corresponding to the counter emf E_1 demanded by the new conditions.*

Because of these considerations, Fig. 1-10a has been drawn with the same flux Φ_m as in Fig. 1-8, but the exciting current I_0 of that figure has been replaced by the primary exciting ampere-turns $N_1 I_0$, proportional to and in phase with I_0, in order to facilitate the construction whereby $N_1 I_0$ must be the resultant (i.e., the geometrical sum) of the primary and secondary ampere-turns.   The secondary ampere-turns are represented by $N_2 I_2$, in time phase with I_2, and therefore displaced from E_2 by the angle ψ_2.   The primary ampere-turns $N_1 I_1$ must then be so drawn that $N_1 I_0$ is the diagonal of a parallelogram the sides of which are $N_2 I_2$ and $N_1 I_1$.*

To complete the construction shown in Fig. 1-10a, it must be noted that the primary impressed voltage V_1 is the resultant of components consisting of (1) the emf $-E_1$, equal and opposite to the emf E_1 induced in the primary by the flux Φ_m; (2) the emf $I_1 R_1$, in phase with I_1, required to drive the current I_1 through the resistance R_1; and (3) the emf $I_1 X_1$, in quadrature with and leading the primary current by 90°, required to overcome the primary leakage reactance.

The dominant feature of the construction of Fig. 1-10a is the geometrical addition of the primary and secondary mmf phasors to fix the resultant mmf, which is in turn responsible for the mutual flux.   This procedure differs from the method used in many early treatments of the magnetic circuit, where it was assumed that each component mmf acted separately to produce its own flux and that these component fluxes then

---

* The justification of this geometrical combination of $N_1 I_1$ and $N_2 I_2$ is that by virtue of the construction the instantaneous value of the resultant mmf (equal to $N_1 i_0$) is always the *algebraic* sum of the corresponding instantaneous values of primary and secondary mmfs, $N_1 i_1$ and $N_2 i_2$, as demanded by Kirchhoff's law applied to magnetic circuits.

combined to yield the single resultant. This method may easily lead to erroneous results, especially if the component mmfs, or some of them, are so large that the fluxes they would separately produce are in the range of saturation; in that case, it is not true that the combination of the separate hypothetical fluxes will give the actual resultant flux. For consider the case of a specimen of cast iron subjected first to a tensile load and then, separately, to an equal compressive load; the elongation produced by the tension acting alone is greater than the shortening caused by the compression acting alone; but if both tension and compression are applied simultaneously, it is obvious that the resultant deformation is zero instead of the net lengthening called for by combining the deformations produced by the forces acting independently. In general, if two or more mmfs act upon the same magnetic circuit, it is legitimate to assume that each mmf sets up its own component of flux, and that these components then combine to produce a single resultant, *only* on condition that the individual

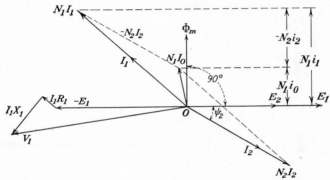

Fig. 1-10a. Phasor diagram of transformer under load conditions.

fluxes are all within the saturation limit; or, more precisely, that there is a linear relationship between flux and mmf. Under such circumstances, the law of superposition holds true, but not otherwise.

It is important to understand that the time-phase relations shown in Fig. 1-10a follow logically from the space relations of Fig. 1-9 provided that a positive direction through the magnetic circuit of that diagram is arbitrarily assumed, as, for example, by drawing the arrow marked with a plus sign. Consistency then requires that a given mmf (and the current corresponding thereto) must be considered positive if, when acting alone, it would produce a positively directed flux; and that an emf or an impressed voltage must be treated as positive if it acts in the direction of a positive current. From this point of view, it must be concluded that since I_1 and I_2 magnetize in opposite directions through the core, they must in general be in phase opposition; and V_1 and E_2 must also be nearly opposite in phase.

There is, however, a different approach to the problem of fixing time-phase relations between primary and secondary currents and voltages. Instead of concentrating attention upon an assumed positive direction through the magnetic circuit, let it be noted that at the instant corresponding to the conditions shown in Fig. 1-9 the primary terminal a is positive with respect to b, whereas the secondary terminal d is simultaneously positive with respect to c. It follows that if terminals a and b, in that order, are connected to the terminals of an oscillograph, the V_1 voltage wave observed on the screen will be approximately in phase with the V_2 voltage wave obtained by connecting terminals d and c, in that order, to the homologous terminals of an identical oscillograph. Similar observations would show that the current entering terminal a is nearly in phase with the current leaving terminal d. The end result of these considerations, which are based upon the relative polarities of primary and secondary terminals, is the phasor diagram of Fig. 1-10b, which, though it appears to contradict Fig. 1-10a, is merely another aspect of the same realities viewed from a different standpoint.

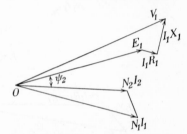

FIG. 1-10b. Alternative form of phasor diagram.

Since the terminals of the primary and secondary windings are brought to the outside of the enclosing case through insulating bushings, it would not be possible, in the absence of identifying markings (unless a test were made), to say with certainty whether the primary and secondary currents and voltages are to be considered as being in phase opposition or in phase coincidence. Either alternative might be correct; but in that case a reversal of the terminals of either winding would establish the validity of the other alternative. In order to overcome this ambiguity, it is standard practice to mark the transformer terminals so that the relative polarities of primary and secondary are clearly defined.*

1-6. Reduction Factors. In constructing Fig. 1-10, the several phasors have been drawn without special attention to their actual magnitudes; in fact, the scale of some has been purposely exaggerated for the sake of clarity. In actual practice, the ratio of transformation is commonly so large that primary and secondary quantities, as, for example, the emfs E_1 and E_2, cannot readily be represented to scale in a single diagram. The same thing is true of the primary and secondary currents I_1 and I_2; for it may be seen from Fig. 1-10 that since $N_1 I_0$ is usually very small in comparison with either $N_1 I_1$ or $N_2 I_2$, it follows that

$$N_1 I_1 = N_2 I_2 \qquad \text{nearly} \qquad (1\text{-}15)$$

or
$$I_1 = \frac{N_2}{N_1} I_2 = \frac{1}{a} I_2 \qquad \text{nearly} \qquad (1\text{-}16)$$

* For details, see Art. 2-1.

From Eq. 1-12, $E_1 = aE_2$; hence,

$$E_1 I_1 = E_2 I_2 \qquad \text{nearly} \tag{1-17}$$

and it follows that *the volt-amperes usefully supplied to the primary are substantially equal to the volt-amperes developed in the secondary.*

If in Fig. 1-10 each of the three mmfs $N_1 I_1$, $N_2 I_2$, and $N_1 I_0$ is divided by the scalar factor N_1, they become, respectively, I_1, $(N_2/N_1)I_2$, and I_0, which are the magnitudes of current phasors which preserve among themselves the same phase relations as obtain between the mmfs of Fig. 1-10. While $(N_2/N_1)I_2$ is almost equal to I_1, as indicated by the approximate Eq. 1-16, it is not exactly equal to I_1 and this expression may be written

$$\frac{N_2}{N_1} I_2 = \frac{1}{a} I_2 = I_2' \tag{1-18}$$

where I_2' represents the magnitude of the secondary current if the ratio of transformation were unity; the quantity I_2' is referred to as the *secondary current reduced to terms of the primary.*

Similarly, the secondary emf E_2, when reduced to terms of the primary, becomes

$$E_2' = \frac{N_1}{N_2} E_2 = aE_2 \tag{1-19}$$

In other words, the actual secondary current must be divided, and the actual secondary emf must be multiplied, by the ratio of transformation to convert them to terms of primary quantities.

To find the factors for reducing secondary resistance, reactance, and impedance to terms of the primary, consider a term like $I_2 R_2$, the actual ohmic drop in the secondary, which is to be converted to an equivalent primary value $I_2' R_2'$, where I_2' and R_2' are, respectively, the secondary current and secondary resistance, each expressed in terms of the primary. Since $I_2 R_2$ is a potential drop expressed in volts, it is seen from Eq. 1-19 that

$$I_2' R_2' = a(I_2 R_2)$$

and since $I_2' = I_2/a$, it follows that

$$R_2' = a^2 R_2$$

Exactly the same considerations apply to reactances and impedances; hence, the reduction factor for these quantities is likewise a^2, and

$$X_2' = a^2 X_2$$
$$Z_2' = a^2 Z_2$$

In the solution of some problems, it is sometimes convenient to deal with secondary quantities instead of primary quantities. In that case, primary quantities can be expressed in terms of the secondary by using

reduction factors which are the reciprocals of those given above. Thus, the equivalent primary quantities, referred to the secondary, are

$$I_1' = aI_1 \qquad R_1' = \frac{1}{a^2} R_1$$

$$E_1' = \frac{1}{a} E_1 \qquad X_1' = \frac{1}{a^2} X_1$$

$$Z_1' = \frac{1}{a^2} Z_1$$

Example. A 10-kva 440/110-volt 60-cycle transformer has a primary resistance of 0.50 ohm, a secondary resistance of 0.032 ohm, and primary and secondary leakage reactances of 0.90 and 0.06 ohm, respectively. The ratio of transformation is 4; hence,

Secondary resistance referred to the primary = $0.032 \times 4^2 = 0.512$
Secondary reactance referred to the primary = $0.06 \ \times 4^2 = 0.96$

1-7. General Phasor Diagram. Because of the inconvenience of using primed symbols to indicate conversion to a primary (or secondary) basis, it is simpler to proceed on the tacit assumption that the ratio of transformation is unity and to make the necessary reductions later if calculations are to be made. In other words, quantities like E_1, E_2, I_1, I_2,

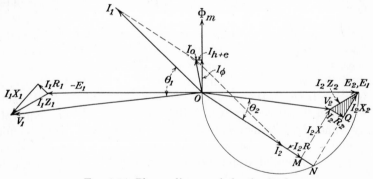

FIG. 1-11. Phasor diagram, inductive load.

$I_1 R_1$, etc., are to be understood as equivalent magnitudes expressed in terms either of the primary or of the secondary.

The phasor diagram of Fig. 1-10 can then be drawn in the manner indicated in Fig. 1-11, which represents the case of an inductive secondary load. If a semicircle is drawn on OE_2 as a diameter and the secondary current I_2 is extended until it intersects the circle, the intercept ON is the total ohmic drop in the secondary circuit, or $I_2(R_2 + R)$; similarly, the chord NE_2 is the total reactive drop $I_2(X_2 + X)$. Dividing ON into parts such that $OM = I_2R$ and $MN = I_2R_2$, and dividing NE_2 into parts $NQ = I_2X$ and $QE_2 = I_2X_2$, then drawing MV_2 and QV_2, it is seen that OV_2 is the secondary terminal voltage since it is the geo-

metrical sum of I_2R and I_2X. The side V_2Q of the small right triangle V_2QE_2 represents the ohmic drop I_2R_2 in the secondary winding, QE_2 represents the *secondary leakage-reactance* drop I_2X_2, and the hypotenuse V_2E_2 is the *secondary leakage-impedance* drop I_2Z_2.

The phasor diagram of Fig. 1-12 represents the case of capacitative load, the secondary current leading E_2 instead of lagging behind it. The two diagrams, Figs. 1-11 and 1-12, differ considerably so far as their general appearance goes, but on comparing them line for line it is easily seen that they conform to the same basic principles. It should be noted that whereas the load-reactance drop I_2X and the secondary leakage-reactance drop I_2X_2 are in phase with each other in Fig. 1-11 because both reactances are inductive, they are in phase opposition in Fig. 1-12, where the load reactance is capacitative while the secondary leakage reactance remains inductive.

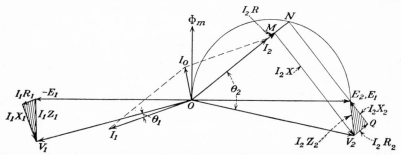

Fig. 1-12. Phasor diagram, capacitative load.

If the scale of Fig. 1-12 is sufficiently altered to make OV_1 the same in length as in Fig. 1-11, it will be observed that the secondary terminal voltage V_2 becomes considerably larger when the load is capacitative than when it is inductive. In other words, while an inductive load always results in a secondary terminal voltage (expressed in terms of the primary) which is smaller than the primary impressed voltage, a capacitative load may cause the corresponding secondary terminal voltage to exceed that of the primary.

1-8. Mathematical Relations and the Equivalent Circuit. From Eqs. 1-5, 1-6, and 1-13,

$$\mathbf{I}_0 = \frac{-\mathbf{E}_1}{Z_0} = -\mathbf{E}_1 Y_0$$

and

$$\mathbf{I}_2 = \frac{\mathbf{E}_2}{(R_2 + R) + j(X_2 + X)}$$

Assuming that all secondary quantities have been reduced to terms of the primary, it follows that $\mathbf{E}_2 = \mathbf{E}_1$; hence, Eq. 1-13 becomes

$$\mathbf{I}_2 = \frac{\mathbf{E}_1}{(R_2 + R) + j(X_2 + X)} \tag{1-20}$$

The construction of Figs. 1-11 and 1-12 shows that I_0 is the geometrical sum of I_1 and I_2; hence,

$$\mathbf{I}_1 = \mathbf{I}_0 - \mathbf{I}_2 \tag{1-21}$$

which, on substituting the above values for $\mathbf{I}_0$ and $\mathbf{I}_2$, becomes

$$\mathbf{I}_1 = -\mathbf{E}_1 Y_0 - \frac{\mathbf{E}_1}{(R_2 + R) + j(X_2 + X)}$$

$$= -\mathbf{E}_1 \left[Y_0 + \frac{1}{(R_2 + R) + j(X_2 + X)} \right] \tag{1-22}$$

The phasor diagrams also show that V_1 is the geometrical sum of $-E_1$, $I_1 R_1$, and $I_1 X_1$, a relation expressible in complex notation as

$$\mathbf{V}_1 = -\mathbf{E}_1 + \mathbf{I}_1 (R_1 + j X_1) \tag{1-23}$$

From Eq. 1-22 we have

$$-\mathbf{E}_1 = \frac{\mathbf{I}_1}{Y_0 + \dfrac{1}{(R_2 + R) + j(X_2 + X)}} \tag{1-24}$$

and, on substituting Eq. 1-24 in 1-23 and transposing, there results

$$\mathbf{V}_1 = \mathbf{I}_1 \left[(R_1 + jX_1) + \frac{1}{Y_0 + \dfrac{1}{(R_2 + R) + j(X_2 + X)}} \right] \tag{1-25}$$

The last equation gives the primary current of the transformer (the dependent variable) in terms of the independent variables R and X and the constants of the transformer. It shows, moreover, the nature of the *equivalent circuit* of the transformer, i.e., the combination of fixed and variable resistances and reactances, which will exactly imitate the performance of the actual transformer so far as the magnitude and phase of the primary current are concerned. The interpretation of Eq. 1-25 may be understood from the following analysis:

In the first place, the quantity in the brackets in Eq. 1-25 is clearly of the nature of an impedance (ohms) since when multiplied by $\mathbf{I}_1$ (amperes) it gives $\mathbf{V}_1$ (volts). This quantity is representative of the entire transformer and its connected secondary load, hence may be called the *total equivalent impedance*. It is plain that it includes the impedance represented by the denominator of the last partial fraction, or

$$(R_2 + R) + j(X_2 + X)$$

this being the sum of the impedances of the internal and external parts of the secondary circuit. The reciprocal of this impedance is an admittance, and the fact that this is added to Y_0 indicates that the circuit characterized by admittance Y_0 is in parallel with the other; in other words, referring to Fig. 1-13, the exciting admittance Y_0, constituted of conductance G_0 and susceptance B_0, is in parallel with the impedance characteristic of the secondary circuit. The reciprocal of the sum of these two admittances is obviously an impedance, and since it is added directly to the primary leakage impedance $R_1 + jX_1$, it follows that the latter must be considered to be in series with the two parallel branches represented by the remaining terms. The circuit diagram shown in Fig. 1-13 therefore represents the *equivalent circuit* of the transformer, R and X being the independent vari-

ables characteristic of the external circuit, the other quantities being the constants of the transformer itself.

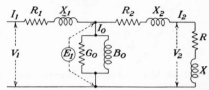

FIG. 1-13. Equivalent circuit of the transformer.

1-9. Approximate Equivalent Circuit. It has been pointed out in the preceding analysis that E_1 (or, more strictly, $-E_1$) differs from the constant impressed voltage V_1 only by the small amount due to the drop of potential through the primary leakage impedance. Furthermore, the exciting current I_0 amounts to only a few per cent of the full-load primary current, so that I_2, in terms of the primary, is practically equal to I_1. Consequently no appreciable error will be introduced by transferring the exciting admittance Y_0 from the position indicated in Fig. 1-13 to the one shown in Fig. 1-14, which then becomes the *approximate equivalent circuit* of the transformer. It should be borne in mind that in these diagrams the secondary quantities are to be considered as reduced to terms of the primary, or vice versa.

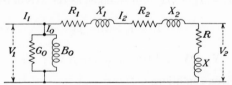

FIG. 1-14. Approximate equivalent circuit.

Referring to Fig. 1-11, it will be noted that if the left-hand side of the diagram is rotated through 180° the two OE_1 phasors will coincide. The resultant diagram, omitting the phasors representing Φ_m and I_0, will then appear as in Fig. 1-15. The currents I_1 and I_2 differ slightly in magnitude and in phase because of the fact that their resultant, I_0, is not identically zero, and for the same reason the homologous sides of the primary and secondary leakage-impedance triangles are not strictly parallel to each other. But in the approximate circuit diagram of Fig. 1-14 the primary and secondary leakage impedances are grouped in series, which is equivalent to assuming that the same current flows in both of them (subject, of course, to the understanding that one circuit has been reduced to terms of the other). This means that if the phasor diagram is to be brought into agreement with the approximate circuit of Fig. 1-14, the exciting current I_0 in Fig. 1-15 must be ignored, thereby giving rise to the simplified phasor diagram, Fig. 1-16, which then corresponds with the circuit diagram, Fig. 1-14.

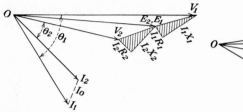

FIG. 1-15. Modified phasor diagram (see Fig. 1-11).

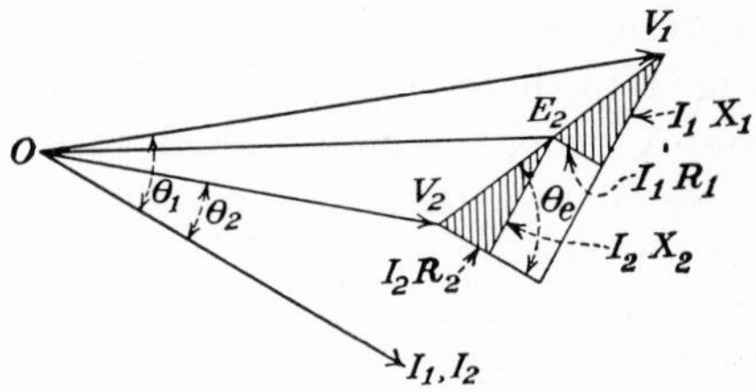

FIG. 1-16. Simplified phasor diagram of approximate equivalent circuit.

Example. A 10-kva single-phase transformer designed for 2,000/400 volts has the following constants: $R_1 = 5.5$; $R_2 = 0.2$; $X_1 = 12$; $X_2 = 0.45$. Calculate the approximate value of the secondary terminal voltage at full load, 80 per cent power factor (lagging), when the primary supply voltage is 2,000 volts.

Solution. Referring to Fig. 1-16, let all quantities be expressed in terms of the primary, so that

$$I_1 = I_2 = \frac{10,000}{2,000} = 5 \text{ amp}$$

$$a = \frac{2,000}{400} = 5$$

$$R_1 + R_2 = 5.5 + 5^2 \times 0.2 = 10.5 \text{ ohms}$$
$$X_1 + X_2 = 12 + 5^2 \times 0.45 = 23.25 \text{ ohms}$$

Let the current $I_1 = I_2$ in Fig. 1-16 be taken as the axis of reference, so that in complex notation

$$\mathbf{I}_1 = \mathbf{I}_2 = 5 + j0$$

It follows that

$$\mathbf{V}_1 = \mathbf{V}_2 + \mathbf{I}_2[(R_1 + R_2) + j(X_1 + X_2)]$$

and since by the given conditions

$$\mathbf{V}_2 = (0.8 + j0.6)V_2$$

we have $\mathbf{V}_1 = (0.8 + j0.6)V_2 + 5(10.5 + j23.25)$
or $\mathbf{V}_1 = (0.8V_2 + 52.5) + j(0.6V_2 + 116.25)$
from which,

$$V_1^2 = 2,000^2 = (0.8V_2 + 52.5)^2 + (0.6V_2 + 116.25)^2$$

and $V_2 = 1,887.25$ volts in terms of the primary

and its actual value is

$$V_2 = \frac{1,887.25}{5} = 377.45 \text{ volts}$$

1-10. Relative Magnitudes of Primary and Secondary Leakage Impedances. It will have been observed that in Fig. 1-16 the leakage-impedance triangles (indicated by hatched lines) have been drawn equal in size and with their hypotenuses in the same straight line. In order that this may be correct, it is necessary that the primary and secondary resistances and leakage reactances be related by the expression

$$\frac{X_1}{R_1} = \frac{X_2}{R_2}$$

or

$$\frac{R_1}{R_2} = \frac{X_1}{X_2}$$

where, as before, the secondary quantities are expressed in terms of the primary. These relations are not necessarily exact, but that they are approximately correct will be evident from the following considerations:

The copper loss in the primary is given by $I_1^2 R_1$, and in the secondary by $I_2^2 R_2$. In each case, this loss will produce a rise of temperature which will depend upon the facility with which the heat is dissipated. The H.T. winding is the more thoroughly insulated and therefore tends to hold its heat more than the L.T. winding, but this is in part counterbalanced, at least in core-type transformers, by the greater surface of the H.T. coil exposed to the cooling medium. The rise of temperature should be the same in both windings in order that the active material in both of them may be utilized as fully as possible, and if we may assume approximately equal radiation for both windings, it follows that the copper losses should be approximately equal, or $I_1^2 R_1 \cong I_2^2 R_2$, from which

$$\frac{R_1}{R_2} = \frac{I_2^2}{I_1^2}$$

But since $I_1 \cong I_2$ (secondary quantities in terms of primary), this means that $R_1 \cong R_2$.

So far as the leakage reactances X_1 and X_2 are concerned, it is to be noted that in each case the reactance is equivalent to the product of ω ($= 2\pi f$) and an inductance which may be represented by L_1 for the primary and by L_2 for the secondary. The inductance is defined as the flux linkages (in weber-turns) per ampere. Referring to the construction of Fig. 1-9, it is seen that the paths of the leakage fluxes of primary and secondary have substantially the same reluctance; hence, the flux per ampere-turn, say, ϕ, will be nearly the same in each case. The actual leakage flux per ampere linking with the primary will be $N_1 \phi$, and the number of flux linkages per ampere will then be $N_1^2 \phi$. Similarly, the number of flux linkages per ampere will be $N_2^2 \phi$ in the case of the secondary. It follows, then, that the *actual* values of X_1 and X_2 will be, respectively,

$$X_1 = \omega N_1^2 \phi$$
$$X_2 = \omega N_2^2 \phi$$

and

$$\frac{X_1}{X_2} = \frac{N_1^2}{N_2^2} = a^2$$

But in the diagram of Fig. 1-16, where secondary quantities are expressed in terms of the primary, the value of X_2 that has been used is the actual value of X_2 multiplied by a^2, and by the above relation $X_2a^2 = X_1$. Hence, the leakage reactances are nearly equal when reduced values are used, just as has been found to be the case with respect to the resistances; therefore,

$$\frac{R_1}{R_2} = \frac{X_1}{X_2} \qquad \text{nearly}$$

thus justifying the construction of the leakage-impedance triangles of Fig. 1-16.

1-11. The Circle Diagram for Noninductive Load. When the external secondary load is noninductive, in the manner illustrated in Fig. 1-17, the corresponding modification of the phasor diagram is interesting, not only because of the geometrical relations between the phasors, but because the circuit diagram and the phasor diagram for this special case are directly applicable to the study of the polyphase induction motor, as shown later in Chap. 6. From Fig. 1-17, it follows that

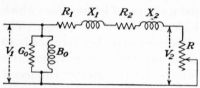

FIG. 1-17. Equivalent circuit, noninductive load.

$$I_2 = \frac{V_1}{\sqrt{(R_1 + R_2 + R)^2 + (X_1 + X_2)^2}} \tag{1-26}$$

and since $\sin \theta_2 = \dfrac{X_1 + X_2}{\sqrt{(R_1 + R_2 + R)^2 + (X_1 + X_2)^2}}$ (1-27)

we have $\qquad I_2 = \dfrac{V_1}{X_1 + X_2} \sin \theta_2$ (1-28)

The coefficient $V_1/(X_1 + X_2)$ is constant in magnitude and represents the current that would flow through the secondary circuit if the total

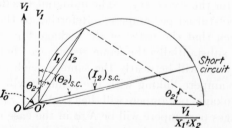

FIG. 1-18. Circle diagram, noninductive load.

resistance were reduced to zero. It is therefore represented by a phasor lagging 90° behind V_1, as in Fig. 1-18, and from Eq. 1-28 it follows that the locus of the current I_2 is a semicircle constructed on $V_1/(X_1 + X_2)$ as a diameter. Since the secondary resistance cannot be reduced below the value $R_1 + R_2$, it follows that the maximum secondary current that can flow on completely short-circuiting the secondary terminals is given by

$$(I_2)_{sc} = \frac{V_1}{\sqrt{(R_1 + R_2)^2 + (X_1 + X_2)^2}} \tag{1-29}$$

and the corresponding phasor is shown in Fig. 1-18, the angle of lag with respect to V_1 being given by

$$\tan (\theta_2)_{sc} = \frac{X_1 + X_2}{R_1 + R_2} \tag{1-30}$$

Under the conditions determined by the approximate equivalent circuit of Fig. 1-17, the exciting current I_0 will have the constant value

$$I_0 = V_1 \sqrt{G_0^2 + B_0^2} = V_0 Y_0 \tag{1-31}$$

lagging behind V_1 by the constant angle θ_0 determined by the relation

$$\tan \theta_0 = \frac{B_0}{G_0}$$

and the line current I_1 is then the geometrical sum of I_0 and I_2. The locus of I_1 is then the same semicircle as before, but the origin of current I_1 is at O, whereas the origin of I_2 is at O'.

1-12. Measurement of Transformer Constants. Open-circuit and Short-circuit Tests. *a. Open-circuit Test.* Inspection of the equivalent circuit, Fig. 1-13, shows that if the secondary circuit is open, the impressed voltage acts upon a circuit consisting of the primary leakage impedance $Z_1 = R_1 + jX_1$ in series with the exciting impedance

$$Z_0 = R_0 + jX_0$$

the latter being the reciprocal of the exciting admittance

$$Y_0 = G_0 - jB_0$$

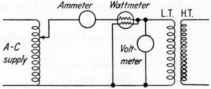

FIG. 1-19. Open-circuit test of transformer.

Since Z_1 is very small in comparison with Z_0, it is usually sufficiently accurate to ignore Z_1 under the specified conditions; or, what amounts to the same thing, the circuit may be assumed to be represented by the approximate diagram, Fig. 1-14, where, if the secondary is open, there remains in circuit only the exciting admittance Y_0 or the equivalent exciting impedance Z_0.

These considerations indicate that if the secondary of a transformer is open-circuited, a voltmeter, ammeter, and wattmeter suitably connected to the supply circuit will suffice to make direct measurements of G_0 and B_0 or the corresponding values of R_0 and X_0. The diagram of connections for making the open-circuit test is shown in Fig. 1-19, which reinforces the physical fact, obvious from Fig. 1-13, that the only losses present are the hysteresis and eddy-current losses in the core and the very small copper loss due to the flow of the no-load current I_0 through the ohmic resistance of the primary.

These open-circuit measurements are most conveniently made by impressing the supply voltage on the L.T. winding, both because the normal rated voltage of the L.T. side is more likely to be within the range of the usual instruments, and because of the lesser hazard of working with the L.T. side. It must of course be remembered that in making this test the H.T. side is "hot," and its terminals must be carefully insulated.

When the instruments are connected as in Fig. 1-19 and simultaneous readings of all three of them are taken, the ammeter will read too high, because in addition to carrying the exciting current of the transformer it also carries the current taken by the voltmeter and by the potential coil of the wattmeter; accordingly, the true exciting (no-load) current can be measured only if the voltmeter and the potential coil of the watt-meter are disconnected. Further, when the voltmeter and ammeter are fully connected, the wattmeter reading will include the power consumed in the voltmeter and in the potential coil of the wattmeter itself, so that corrections must be made.

For reasons to be explained later (Art. 1-19), it is important that the core-loss measurement be made with sinusoidal impressed voltage. If the available sinusoidal supply circuit has a voltage that differs from the rated L.T. voltage of the transformer under test, the best procedure is to step the supply voltage up or down, as required, by means of an auto-transformer with adjustable taps or by another transformer equipped with suitable taps.

If the corrected instrument readings are

V_1 = impressed voltage
I_0 = no-load current
P_0 = core loss

it follows that

$$P_0 = V_1 I_0 \cos \theta_0 = I_0^2 R_0$$

whence

$$R_0 = \frac{P_0}{I_0^2}$$

$$X_0 = R_0 \tan \theta_0$$

$$G_0 = \frac{R_0}{R_0^2 + X_0^2}$$

$$B_0 = \frac{X_0}{R_0^2 + X_0^2}$$

The preceding discussion assumes that the open-circuit test is made with an impressed voltage exactly equal to the rated voltage of the L.T.

side of the transformer. If the test conditions make it impossible to adjust the voltage to the exact value desired, it is best to take a series of readings with values of V_1 covering a range on either side of the rated voltage, and then to interpolate. On plotting the core loss as a function of V_1, a core-loss curve will be obtained which shows that core loss increases nearly as the square of the impressed voltage. Further discussion of this curve, and of core loss in general, is reserved for subsequent articles (Arts. 1-15 and 1-16).

b. *Short-circuit Test.* The short-circuit current referred to in Art. 1-11 and shown in the circle diagram of Fig. 1-18 is the current that would flow through the primary if full voltage were maintained at its terminals. This current would be so greatly in excess of the carrying capacity of the windings of both primary and secondary as seriously to injure the insulation because of the heat developed; it is therefore out of the question to

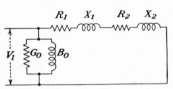

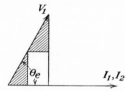

FIG. 1-20. Short-circuit test of transformer.

FIG. 1-21. Phase relations, short-circuit test.

measure this current directly, both for this reason and because of the fact that instruments of suitable range are not as a rule available. If, however, the impressed voltage V_1 is reduced to such a value that normal full-load current flows in the primary (and consequently also in the secondary), the windings cannot become overheated. Under these conditions, as will be evident from Fig. 1-20, the current flow will be determined by the joint leakage impedance of primary and secondary,

$$(R_1 + R_2) + j(X_1 + X_2)$$

since this is small compared with the impedance of the exciting circuit, with which it is in parallel. The extent to which the impressed voltage must be reduced to circulate full-load current under short-circuit conditions will be appreciated on referring to Fig. 1-16; for on short-circuiting the secondary terminals the secondary terminal voltage V_2 becomes zero, and the hypotenuse of the combined leakage-impedance triangle becomes the same as V_1, in the manner indicated in Fig. 1-21.

The impressed voltage under these conditions, being merely that required to overcome the joint leakage impedance of the windings, is only a few per cent of the normal value; consequently, the mutual flux Φ_m is likewise very small, and the iron losses in the core are negligibly small. A wattmeter connected in the supply circuit, as in Fig. 1-22, will therefore indicate the copper losses corresponding to the current flowing (after suitably correcting the reading for the power consumed in the voltmeter, and, if necessary, in the potential coil of the wattmeter).   The short circuit is most conveniently made by short-circuiting the L.T. winding, for this means that the current to be measured will be the moderate amount corresponding to full load on the H.T. side; and at the same time the voltage to be supplied will be only a small fraction of the normal voltage of the H.T. winding, therefore within the range of ordinary instruments.

If the corrected values of a simultaneous set of readings of wattmeter, voltmeter, and ammeter are P, V_e, and I, respectively, we have

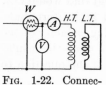

FIG. 1-22. Connections for short-circuit test.

$$P = I^2(R_1 + R_2)$$

$$\cos \theta_{sc} = \frac{P}{V_e I}$$

$$V_e = I \sqrt{(R_1 + R_2)^2 + (X_1 + X_2)^2}$$

$$X_1 + X_2 = (R_1 + R_2) \tan \theta_{sc}$$

from which it is possible to find $R_1 + R_2$ and $X_1 + X_2$.

It is customary to assume that if the measured impedance voltage V_e produces full-load current I_1 under short-circuit conditions, full voltage V_1 would produce a proportionately larger current; in other words, the short-circuit current I_{sc} of Fig. 1-18 is computed from the relation

$$I_{sc} = I_1 \frac{V_1}{V_e}$$

This assumption, and the further assumption that $R_1 + R_2$ and $X_1 + X_2$, determined as above by measurement at reduced voltage, may be taken to be the same as under normal conditions, are not in strict accordance with actual facts.   The mutual flux Φ_m being negligibly small under the conditions of the short-circuit test, the leakage flux is not distributed in exactly the same way as under normal conditions, with the result that the calculated leakage reactance is not necessarily the same as under load. The changed distribution of the leakage flux likewise alters the magnitude of the eddy-current losses in the windings, thereby influencing the *effective* values of resistance calculated from the measurements; for it should be particularly noted that the value of $R_1 + R_2$ determined by the short-circuit method is not the same as the pure ohmic resistance but is greater than the latter by an amount due to the nonuniform distribution of current over the cross section of the conductors; the increase, expressed in terms of the pure ohmic resistance, may be anywhere from 10 to 30 per cent, or even higher, if the conductors are solid and of large cross section; for this reason, if large cross section is required to carry the full-load current, the conductors are subdivided into two or more parts connected in parallel, but with insulation between adjacent surfaces.

The measurement of the pure ohmic resistances of primary and secondary, as distinguished from the somewhat higher effective resistances, is usually made by the drop-of-potential method, i.e., by measuring the voltage required to circulate a given direct current through the winding. The current to be used for this purpose should approximate as nearly as possible the full-load current of the winding to be measured, and readings should be taken only after the winding has attained its working temperature. Care must be exercised in taking the simultaneous readings of current and potential drop, for because of the highly inductive nature of the circuit an appreciable time is required for the current to reach its final value after closing the switch in the supply circuit; if the readings are taken before steady conditions have been reached, the computed value of resistance will be seriously in error. For the same reason, it is very important to disconnect the voltmeter before opening the circuit; otherwise the high voltage induced on breaking the circuit will burn out the voltmeter.

1-13. Voltage Regulation. The simplified phasor diagram of Fig. 1-16 has been redrawn as Fig. 1-23a and b, part a representing the case of inductive loading, part b that of capacitative loading. In both diagrams, the impressed voltage V_1 is the same, corresponding to normal operating conditions; but the current $I = I_1 = I_2$, while numerically the same in both, is shown lagging behind V_2 in part a and leading it in part b. The impedance drop in the transformer as a whole,

$$V_e = I \sqrt{(R_1 + R_2)^2 + (X_1 + X_2)^2}$$

is therefore the same in both cases so far as its magnitude is concerned, but its time-phase positions are quite different since the components $I(R_1 + R_2)$ and $I(X_1 + X_2)$ must be, respectively, in phase with, and in quadrature with, the current I. The effect of these changes upon the magnitude of V_2 is clearly indicated.

Inspection of Fig. 1-23a and b shows that the relative phase positions of V_1 and V_2 are determined by the impedance drop V_e, which is proportional to the current I, but which remains constant in magnitude only so long as the load current remains the same. Consequently, since V_1 is fixed, the locus of the terminal point of OV_2 for a given value of load current will be a circle of radius V_e with its center at the fixed terminal point of OV_1, as in Fig. 1-24. The latter diagram is constructed to show the manner in which the terminal voltage of the secondary changes as the phase angle θ_2 of the secondary load goes through the complete range from 90° lag to 90° lead. The size of the phasor V_e is purposely exaggerated in both Figs. 1-23 and 1-24 in order that the geometrical relations may be more easily visualized.

The construction of Fig. 1-24 is based upon considerations readily deduced from Fig. 1-23. For if in the latter figure a perpendicular is dropped from the terminal point of OV_1 to OV_2 (the latter prolonged, if necessary) it will be seen that the phase angle β between V_1 and V_2 is defined by the equation

$$\sin \beta = \frac{V_e \sin (\theta_e - \theta_2)}{V_1} \tag{1-32}$$

where θ_2 is to be taken as positive in the case of lagging secondary power factor and negative in the case of leading secondary power factor. Furthermore, a positive value of the angle β is to be interpreted to mean

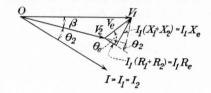

(a) Inductive load

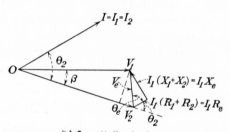

(b) Capacitative load

Fig. 1-23. Variation of secondary voltage with load power factor.

that V_2 lags behind V_1, whereas a negative value of β indicates that V_2 leads V_1. Hence, if $\theta_2 = 90°$ lagging, Eq. (1-32) becomes

$$\sin \beta = \frac{V_e \sin \left(\theta_e - \dfrac{\pi}{2}\right)}{V_1} = - \frac{V_e \cos \theta_e}{V_1} = - \frac{I(R_1 + R_2)}{V_1} \tag{1-33}$$

and if $\theta_2 = 90°$ leading,

$$\sin \beta = \frac{V_e \sin \left(\theta_e + \dfrac{\pi}{2}\right)}{V_1} = \frac{V_e \cos \theta_e}{V_1} = \frac{I(R_1 + R_2)}{V_1} \tag{1-34}$$

These relations suggest the construction of Fig. 1-24 as follows: With the terminal point of phasor V_1 as center, draw circles having radii $I(R_1 + R_2)$ and V_e. On OV_1 as a diameter, draw a circle intersecting the smaller of the other two circles in points P_1 and P_2, and connect these points to the origin O. The straight lines OP_1 and OP_2 intersect circle V_e at points Q_1 and Q_2, respectively, and OQ_1 and OQ_2 are then the values of V_2 corresponding to fully inductive and to fully capacitative loads, respectively. In actual practice, the term $I(R_1 + R_2)$ is so small that it may be neglected, so that V_2 is nearly equal to $V_1 - V_e$ for zero-power-factor lagging load, and to $V_1 + V_e$ for the corresponding leading load.

It will be seen that in general, therefore, the secondary voltage varies with the magnitude and power factor of the load, though the extent of this variation can be held within narrow limits by so designing the trans-former that the impedance drop V_e is a small per cent of the impressed voltage V_1. Transformers intended to be used in circuits supplying incandescent lamps must regulate closely to prevent objectionable changes in candlepower. In any case, the *regulation* of a transformer is an important item in its over-all characteristics.

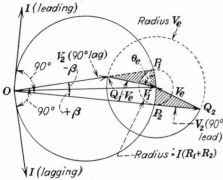

Fig. 1-24. Variation of V_2 from zero power factor lagging to zero power factor leading.

The regulation of a constant-potential transformer is defined* as "the change in secondary voltage, expressed in per cent of rated secondary voltage, which occurs when rated kva output at a specified power factor is reduced to zero, with the primary impressed voltage maintained con-stant." Thus, if the rated secondary voltage is V_1/a, where a is the ratio of transformation, and $(V_2)_l$ is the actual secondary voltage at rated kva load, the regulation is

$$\frac{V_1/a - (V_2)_l}{V_1/a} \times 100\%$$

which may be written

$$\frac{V_1 - V_2}{V_1} \times 100\%$$

where $V_2 = a(V_2)_l$ is the secondary terminal voltage, under load condi-tions, expressed in terms of the primary.

* American Standards for Transformers, Regulators and Reactors, ASA C57.1 to 57.3 Standard 1.065, 1942.

Reference to Fig. 1-23 shows that

$$V_1^2 = [V_2 + V_e \cos (\theta_e - \theta_2)]^2 + [V_e \sin (\theta_e - \theta_2)]^2 \qquad (1\text{-}35)$$

from which V_2, and therefore also the per cent regulation, can be computed.

On expanding the trigonometric terms in Eq. 1-35 and observing that $V_e \cos \theta_e = I_1 R_e$ and $V_e \sin \theta_e = I_1 X_e$, Eq. 1-35 becomes

$$V_1^2 = (V_2 + I_1 R_e \cos \theta_2 + I_1 X_e \sin \theta_2)^2$$
$$+ (I_1 X_e \cos \theta_2 - I_1 R_e \sin \theta_2)^2 \qquad (1\text{-}36)$$

a result which is in agreement with the geometry of Fig. 1-23a and b if it is understood that an angle of lag is to be treated as essentially positive and an angle of lead as negative.

Example. A 5-kva transformer has a nominal voltage rating of 1,100/110 volts. With the low-voltage winding short-circuited, it is found by experiment that 33 volts is required to circulate rated full-load current, and the corresponding power input is 85 watts. It is required to find the per cent regulation when the load takes rated current at a power factor of 80 per cent, lagging.

Solution a   (based upon Eq. 1-35).   From the given data

$$I_1 = \frac{5,000}{1,100} = 4.55 \text{ amp}$$

$$\cos \theta_e = \frac{85}{33 \times 4.55} = 0.567$$

$$\theta_e = 55°29'$$

$$\cos \theta_2 = 0.8$$

$$\theta_2 = 36°52'$$

$$V_e \cos (\theta_e - \theta_2) = 33 \cos 18°37' = 31.27$$

$$V_e \sin (\theta_e - \theta_2) = 33 \sin 18°37' = 10.53$$

$$1,100^2 = (V_2 + 31.27)^2 + 10.53^2$$

$$V_2 = 1,068.7$$

$$\text{Regulation} = \frac{1,100 - 1,068.7}{1,100} \times 100 = 2.85\%$$

Solution b   (based upon Eq. 1-36).

$$I_1 = \frac{5,000}{1,100} = 4.55 \text{ amp}$$

$$Z_e = \frac{33}{4.55} = 7.25 \text{ ohms}$$

$$R_e = \frac{85}{4.55^2} = 4.125 \text{ ohms}$$

$$X_e = \sqrt{7.25^2 - 4.125^2} = 5.96 \text{ ohms}$$

$$1,100^2 = (V_2 + 4.55 \times 4.125 \times 0.8 + 4.55 \times 5.96 \times 0.6)^2$$
$$+ (4.55 \times 5.96 \times 0.8 - 4.55 \times 4.125 \times 0.6)^2$$

$$1,100^2 - 10.44^2 = (V_2 + 15.0 + 16.3)^2$$

$$V_2 = 1,068.7$$

$$\text{Regulation} = \frac{1,100 - 1,068.7}{1,100} \times 100 = 2.85\%$$

1-14. Per Cent and Per-unit Methods of Expressing Magnitudes.
Equations 1-35 and 1-36, and the solutions of the illustrative problem
based upon them, have the disadvantage that each of the several terms
involves magnitudes which pertain to a particular transformer; so it is not
at once evident how the performance of this transformer will compare
with that of another which is designed for different voltage and load
ratings. This objection can be overcome by noting that Eq. 1-36 may
be written

$$V_1 \left[1 - \left(\frac{I_1 X_e \cos \theta_2 - I_1 R_e \sin \theta_2}{V_1} \right)^2 \right]^{\frac{1}{2}}$$
$$= V_2 + I_1 R_e \cos \theta_2 + I_1 X_e \sin \theta_2$$

which, on expanding the radical by the binomial theorem and dropping
terms of higher order, may be transformed to

$$\frac{V_1 - V_2}{V_1} = \frac{I_1 R_e}{V_1} \cos \theta_2 + \frac{I_1 X_e}{V_1} \sin \theta_2 + \frac{1}{2} \left(\frac{I_1 X_e}{V_1} \cos \theta_2 - \frac{I_1 R_e}{V_1} \sin \theta_2 \right)^2$$
$$(1\text{-}37)$$

The significant feature of Eq. 1-37 is that the terms $(V_1 - V_2)/V_1$,
$I_1 R_e/V_1$, $I_1 X_e/V_1$ are all pure ratios, so that the equation as a whole is
dimensionless. If all the terms of Eq. 1-37 are multiplied by 100, they
become

$$\frac{V_1 - V_2}{V_1} \times 100 = \% \text{ regulation}$$

$$\frac{I_1 R_e}{V_1} \times 100 = r_{pc} = \% \text{ resistance drop}$$

$$\frac{I_1 X_e}{V_1} \times 100 = x_{pc} = \% \text{ reactance drop}$$

and Eq. 1-37 becomes

$$\% \text{ regulation} = r_{pc} \cos \theta_2 + x_{pc} \sin \theta_2 + \frac{(x_{pc} \cos \theta_2 - r_{pc} \sin \theta_2)^2}{200} \quad (1\text{-}38)$$

with the result that calculations may be made in terms of the per cent
drops due to internal resistance and reactance; the magnitude of one or
both of these per cent drops is commonly stamped on the name plate of
commercial transformers.

Example. The data specified in the illustrative problem of Art. 1-13 yield the
following tabulation:

$$r_{pc} = \frac{I_1 R_e}{V_1} \times 100 = \frac{I_1 Z_e \cos \theta_2}{V_1} \times 100 = \frac{33 \times 0.567}{1,100} \times 100 = 1.70$$

$$x_{pc} = \frac{I_1 X_e}{V_1} \times 100 = \frac{I_1 Z_e \sin \theta_2}{V_1} \times 100 = \frac{33 \times 0.823}{1,100} \times 100 = 2.47$$

$$\cos \theta_2 = 0.8 \qquad \sin \theta_2 = 0.6$$

whence

$$\% \text{ regulation} = 1.70 \times 0.8 + 2.47 \times 0.6 + \frac{(2.47 \times 0.8 - 1.70 \times 0.6)^2}{200} = 2.85$$

The introduction of the factor 100 in order to reduce the calculations to a percentage basis is clearly not necessary; for it is just as easy to use $(V_1 - V_2)/V_1$, and the coefficients appearing in Eq. 1-37, as decimals which express these magnitudes in terms of V_1 as unity; for this reason, these ratios are called *per-unit* quantities. Thus, if

$$\frac{V_1 - V_2}{V_1} = \text{per-unit regulation}$$

$$\frac{I_1 R_e}{V_1} = r_{pu} = \text{per-unit resistance drop}$$

$$\frac{I_1 X_e}{V_1} = x_{pu} = \text{per-unit reactance drop}$$

it follows from Eq. 1-37 that

$$\text{Per-unit regulation} = r_{pu} \cos \theta_2 + x_{pu} \sin \theta_2 + \frac{(x_{pu} \cos \theta_2 - r_{pu} \sin \theta_2)^2}{2}$$

$$(1-39)$$

In the illustrative problem used in Art. 1-13, $r_{pu} = 0.017$, $x_{pu} = 0.0247$, $z_{pu} = 0.03$, results which are obviously obtainable from the corresponding per cent values by shifting the decimal point two places to the left.

Thus far, the per-unit values which have been considered have been computed in terms of the impressed voltage V_1 as the unit of voltage. But it will be noted that in the relation

$$z_{pu} = \frac{I_1 Z_e}{V_1} = \frac{Z_e}{V_1/I_1}$$

the per-unit impedance is the ratio between the actual impedance (in the case here considered expressed in terms of the primary) and a *fictitious unit* impedance V_1/I_1, which is itself equal to the *unit voltage* V_1 divided by the *unit current* I_1, the latter being the rated full-load current. Thus, in the example used above,

$$\text{Unit impedance} = \frac{V_1}{I_1} = \frac{1,100}{4.55} = 242 \text{ ohms}$$

and since the actual leakage impedance (in terms of the primary) is

$$Z_e = \frac{V_e}{I_1} = \frac{33}{4.55} = 7.26 \text{ ohms}$$

it follows that

$$z_{pu} = \frac{7.26}{242} = 0.03$$

which checks with the value previously obtained.

It will thus be seen that any of the quantities which enter into performance calculations can be expressed as a pure numeric which is in each case equal to the number of times the actual magnitude of the quantity is contained in the rated unit value. In the example cited, all voltages are expressed in terms of 1,100 volts as the unit; currents in terms of 4.55 amp as the unit; resistances, reactances, and impedances in terms of 242 ohms as the unit. In the same way, kva load would be expressed in terms of 5 kva as the unit.

Example. Let it be required to find the per-unit regulation of the same transformer as before when the secondary load, at unity power factor, draws a primary current amounting to a 25 per cent overload.

Solution. Since the values of r_{pu} and x_{pu} previously determined were based upon full-load current as the unit of current, it will be seen from Eq. 1-37 that an additional factor of 1.25 must be introduced into the terms on the right-hand side of Eq. 1-39, to take account of the 25 per cent overload, whence

$$\text{Per-unit regulation} = 1.25 \times 0.017 + \tfrac{1}{2} (1.25 \times 0.0247)^2 = 0.0217$$

1-15. Transformer Losses. The losses in a transformer are made up of three parts:

a. The *copper loss* $(I^2 R)$, which includes, in addition to the pure ohmic loss, the load loss caused by nonuniform distribution of the current density in the conductors. This nonuniformity of current density may be thought of as due to the flow of eddy currents superimposed upon the theoretically uniform current density which of itself would result in the pure ohmic loss.

b. The *hysteresis loss*, caused by something akin to molecular friction as the ultimate particles of the core tend to align themselves first in one direction, then in the other, as the magnetic flux alternates periodically.

c. The *eddy-current loss* in the core, caused by the flow of currents induced in the same way as the working current is induced in the windings of the transformer.

Each of these component losses will now be discussed separately.

a. Copper Loss. The resistance of a copper conductor is directly proportional to its length l and inversely proportional to its cross section a in accordance with the formula

$$R = \rho \frac{l}{a} \qquad \text{ohms}$$

where ρ, the proportionality constant called the resistivity, is the resistance of a specimen having unit length and unit cross section. The resistivity ρ is itself a function of the temperature of the conductor as given by

$$\rho = \rho_0 \left(1 + \frac{t}{234.5} \right)$$

where t = temperature, °C

ρ_0 = resistivity at 0°C

The numerical value of ρ_0 in ohms is given in the following table:

Unit of measurement	ρ_0, ohms
Cubic meter	1.7241×10^{-8}
Cubic centimeter	1.7241×10^{-6}
Cubic inch	0.6787×10^{-6}
Circular mil-foot*	9.56

* At the standard operating temperature of 75°C, the resistivity is slightly greater than 12 ohms per cir mil-ft, or approximately 1 ohm per cir mil-in.

From the general formula for R, it follows that if R_{t_1} and R_{t_2} are the resistances of a conductor at temperatures t_1 and t_2, respectively,

$$\frac{R_{t_2}}{R_{t_1}} = \frac{t_2 + 234.5}{t_1 + 234.5}$$

from which it is a simple matter to compute the resistance at a specified temperature t_2 if the resistance at some other temperature, t_1, is known. Moreover, the above equation can be written

$$t_2 - t_1 = \frac{R_{t_2} - R_{t_1}}{R_{t_1}} (t_1 + 234.5) \qquad (1\text{-}40)$$

which makes it possible to compute the rise of temperature of a winding if its resistance is measured at a known temperature t_1 and at the unknown temperature t_2.

The resistance computed by the above formulas corresponds to the condition of uniform current density over the entire cross section of the conductor. Subject to this condition, the corresponding I^2R loss is directly proportional to the resistance.

In actual transformer windings, the current density is never quite uniform. The leakage fluxes illustrated in Fig. 1-9 do not link equally with all parts of the cross section of a given conductor, with the result that some portions become the seat of induced emfs which are greater or less than in others, and differences of potential are accordingly set up from point to point of the cross section. The currents thereby established are eddy currents superimposed upon the average uniformly distributed current, and they result in additional load losses which may amount to anywhere from 10 to 30 per cent of the pure ohmic loss, and they may considerably exceed the higher figure. This load loss is minimized by using windings made of two or more conductors (usually of strip or ribbon wire) in parallel, lightly insulated from one another except, of course, at their terminals. The outer wire, if there are two in parallel, will in general develop an emf which differs somewhat from that of the inner wire, and if this condition is not compensated, a circulating current will flow to equalize the potential differences and so cause a loss; this difficulty can be avoided by transposing the two parts of the coil, the outer wire of the winding on one leg of the core being connected to the inner wire of the other half of the winding. The transition can easily be made at the crossover connection between the two parts of the winding. If the conductor is made of three wires in parallel, the middle wire is not transposed, but the other two are interchanged as in the two-conductor case.

The load loss due to eddy currents in the windings is clearly inversely proportional to the resistance of the winding, and therefore decreases with increasing temperature, whereas the major part of the I^2R loss, for a given value of current, increases with temperature.

Example. The total copper loss of a transformer as determined by a short-circuit test at 20°C is 630 watts, and the copper loss computed from the true ohmic resistance at the same temperature is 504 watts. What is the load loss at the working temperature of 75°C?

Solution:

Eddy-current loss at 20°C $= 630 - 504 = 126$ watts

True copper loss at 75°C $= 504 \times \dfrac{75 + 234.5}{20 + 234.5} = 613$ watts

Eddy-current loss at 75°C $= 126 \times \dfrac{20 + 234.5}{75 + 234.5} = 104$ watts

Load loss at 75°C $= 613 + 104 = 717$ watts

b. Hysteresis Loss. Assume that the cross section* of an iron core is A, that the length of its magnetic circuit is l, and that it is wound with a coil of N turns. As the exciting current varies cyclically from $-I_m$ to $+I_m$, the flux will vary from $-\Phi_m$ to $+\Phi_m$ in the manner shown in Fig. 1-25. On the ascending curve ab, a change in excitation from Ni to $N(i + di)$ in the time dt will be accompanied by an increase in the flux $d\varphi$, and the emf thereby induced in the winding is

$$e = -N \frac{d\varphi}{dt}$$

which must be balanced by an equal and opposite component of impressed voltage if the current is to be maintained. The instantaneous power supplied by the exciting circuit is therefore equal to $(-e)i$, and in the interval dt the energy supplied is

$$dW = (-e)i\, dt = Ni\, d\varphi \qquad \text{joules}$$

which is proportional to the area of the crosshatched element in Fig. 1-25; hence, the energy consumed as the loop is traversed from a to b is represented by the area $Oabp$.

When the excitation is reduced to zero, the flux follows the curve bc, that is, it decreases while the current retains its original direction. The induced emf changes sign; hence, energy is returned to the supply circuit

---

* Rationalized mks units are assumed.

by an amount proportional to area bpc. Proceeding similarly from point to point around the loop until the starting point is reached, the net energy consumed per complete cycle is represented by the area enclosed by the loop, or

$$W = \int_{-\Phi_m}^{+\Phi_m} Ni \, d\varphi \qquad \text{joules} \qquad (1\text{-}41)$$

In the rationalized mks system of units, $d\varphi = A \, dB$ and $Ni = Hl$, where B is the flux density in webers per square meter and H is the magnetizing force in ampere-turns per meter. Hence, Eq. 1-41 can be written

$$W = Al \int_{-B_m}^{+B_m} H \, dB \qquad \text{joules} \qquad (1\text{-}41a)$$

which shows that the hysteresis loss is proportional to the volume of the core ($= Al$) and to the area of the hysteresis loop when plotted in terms of B and H.

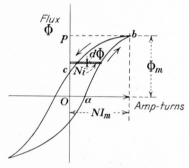

FIG. 1-25. Hysteresis loop.

The integral appearing in Eqs. 1-41 and 1-41a cannot be evaluated by mathematical methods because the functional relation between the variables is unknown; but experiment leads to the result, first discovered by Charles P. Steinmetz, that the area of the hysteresis loop is in general proportional to B_m^x. The value of x for the low-carbon steel used in Steinmetz's experiments was found to be 1.6; but the silicon steel now used is characterized by values of x ranging from 1.7 to somewhat more than 2.0.

The term Al in Eq. 1-41a may be replaced by M/δ, where M is the mass of the core and δ is the density of the core material. Consequently, if the frequency of alternation of the flux is f cps, the hysteresis loss is

$$P_h = \eta \frac{M}{\delta} f B_m^x \qquad \text{watts} \qquad (1\text{-}42)$$

where η is a proportionality constant characteristic of the core material, its magnitude depending upon the units in which M, δ, and B_m are expressed.

c. Eddy-current Loss. Figure 1-26 represents a cross section of one of the laminations of the core, its thickness being t and its width ct, where c is a factor considerably greater than unity. Let the length of the lamination (in the direction perpendicular to the cross section) be unity, and let it be assumed that the flux density is uniformly distributed over the cross section, that it varies harmonically with time, and that its maximum value is B_m.

The cross section may be considered to be built up of a set of elements bounded by similar rectangles, of which the inner one has sides $2x$ and $2cx$, and the outer one has sides $2(x + dx)$ and $2c(x + dx)$. The alternation of the flux within the inner rectangle will set up an emf in the elementary path, and this emf will in turn give rise to the current under consideration. The maximum flux linked with the one-turn element is $B_m \times 4cx^2$, and the total change of flux per cycle will be four times this amount, or $16B_mcx^2$; the total flux

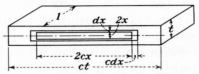

FIG. 1-26. Idealized path of eddy-current flow.

cut per second will therefore be $16fB_mcx^2$, where f is the number of cycles per second. If all quantities are expressed in mks units, the average emf induced in the element will be

$$E_{av} = 16fB_mcx^2$$

and the effective emf will be

$$E = \frac{\pi}{2\sqrt{2}} E_{av} = \frac{8\pi}{\sqrt{2}} fB_mcx^2 \qquad \text{volts}$$

This emf acts in the elementary path which has the resistance

$$\rho\left(\frac{4cx}{dx} + \frac{4x}{c\,dx}\right) = \frac{4\rho x}{dx}\frac{c^2 + 1}{c}$$

where ρ is the resistivity of the material; hence, the loss in the element is

$$dP = \frac{E^2}{\dfrac{4\rho x}{dx}\dfrac{c^2 + 1}{c}} = \frac{8\pi^2 f^2 B^2 x^3\,dx}{\rho}\frac{c^3}{c^2 + 1}$$

and the total loss is

$$P_e = \frac{8\pi^2 f^2 B_m^2}{\rho}\frac{c^3}{c^2 + 1}\int_0^{t/2} x^3\,dx$$
$$= \frac{\pi^2 f^2 B_m^2}{8\rho}\frac{c^3 t^4}{c^2 + 1}$$

The volume of the iron in which this loss occurs is $V = M/\delta = t \times ct \times 1$; hence,

$$P_e = \frac{\pi^2}{8\rho}\frac{M}{\delta} f^2 B_m^2 t^2 \frac{c^2}{c^2 + 1} \qquad \text{watts}$$

and since c is much greater than unity, it may be assumed that

$$\frac{c^2}{(c^2 + 1)} = 1$$

whence $\qquad\qquad\qquad P_e = \epsilon\,\dfrac{M}{\delta} f^2 B_m^2 t^2 \qquad\qquad\qquad\qquad (1\text{-}43)$

where ϵ, the proportionality constant which must be determined experimentally, is usually considerably larger than the theoretical value indicated by the foregoing derivation. The difference between the actual and the theoretical value of the constant is in part accounted for by the fact that the flux density is not uniformly distributed over the cross section as has been assumed, but tends to be crowded toward the outer surface of the laminations; and in part by the fact that the insulation between the laminations is not perfect, with the result that the actual paths of the currents are not so simple as those assumed.

The crowding of the flux toward the outer surface of the laminations is due to the fact that the eddy currents exert a demagnetizing, or screening, action which becomes greater as the center of the cross section is approached from the surface. This demagnetizing action of the eddy currents is similar to the demagnetizing action of the secondary winding upon the primary winding, and leads to the conclusion that the eddy-current paths are equivalent to an auxiliary (but useless and wasteful) secondary in addition to the main secondary winding.

The derivation of the basic formula shows that the eddy-current loss is inversely proportional to the resistivity of the core material. This accounts in large part for the use of silicon steel in building transformer cores, its resistivity being greater than that of the low-carbon steel originally used. Silicon steel has the further advantage that it is free from the "aging" effect which causes the core loss of low-carbon steel to increase with use.

1-16. Separation of Hysteresis and Eddy-current Losses. It follows from Eqs. 1-42 and 1-43 that the total core loss of a transformer is

$$P_{h+e} = \frac{M}{\delta} \left(\eta f B_m^x + \epsilon t^2 f^2 B_m^2 \right)$$

which, for given values of M, δ, and t, may be written

$$P_{h+e} = k_h f B_m^x + k_e f^2 B_m^2 \tag{1-44}$$

The coefficients k_h and k_e and the exponent x must therefore be found if the measured total core loss is to be broken down into the constituent parts P_h and P_e. Since there are three unknown quantities, three independent equations are necessary to evaluate them.

Let the total core loss be measured (1) at frequency f_1 and flux density B_1; (2) at frequency f_2 and flux density B_2; (3) at frequency f_1 and flux density B_2. If the corresponding measured values of total core loss are, respectively, P_1, P_2, and P_3,

$$P_1 = k_h f_1 B_1^x + k_e f_1^2 B_1^2$$
$$P_2 = k_h f_2 B_2^x + k_e f_2^2 B_2^2$$
$$P_3 = k_h f_1 B_2^x + k_e f_1^2 B_2^2$$

which, when solved as simultaneous equations, yield the results (where $a = f_2/f_1$)

$$x = \frac{\log\left[\dfrac{B_2^2(P_2 - a^2P_3)}{(P_2 - aP_3)B_1^2 - a(a - 1)P_1B_2^2}\right]}{\log(B_2/B_1)} \tag{1-45}$$

$$k_h = \frac{P_2 - a^2P_3}{f_2(1 - a)B_2^x} \tag{1-46}$$

$$k_e = \frac{P_2 - aP_3}{f_2^2B_2^2}\frac{a}{a - 1} \tag{1-47}$$

Example. Number 29 gage sheet steel designated as U.S.S. Transformer 52 yields the following data:

Frequency	Flux density, kilogauss	Core loss, watts per lb
30	8	0.135
60	12	0.75
30	12	0.31

Substituting in Eqs. 1-45, 1-46, and 1-47,

$$x = 2.06$$
$$k_h = 489 \times 10^{-7}$$
$$k_e = 501 \times 10^{-9}$$

The computed hysteresis and eddy-current losses are then as shown in the following tabulation:

f	B, kilogauss	P_h, watts per lb	P_e, watts per lb
30	8	0.106	0.029
60	12	0.490	0.260
30	12	0.245	0.065

The results of these calculations show that the eddy-current loss is the smaller of the two parts of the core loss; it is usually between 20 and 50 per cent of the total core loss.

Figure 1-27 is typical of the functional relation between core loss and (maximum) flux density. The two curves* show this relation for the frequencies commonly used in the United States. Since the curves appear to have parabolic form, one may assume that the variables are related by the equation

$$P_{h+e} = kB^z \tag{1-48}$$

or
$$\log P_{h+e} = \log k + z \log B \tag{1-49}$$

* Data taken from U.S.S. Electrical Sheet Steel, *Eng. Manual* 3 (Carnegie-Illinois Steel Corporation), 1949.

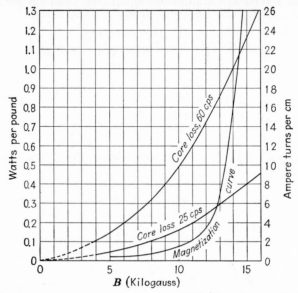

Fig. 1-27. Core loss and magnetization curves, U.S.S. Transformer 52, No. 29 gage.

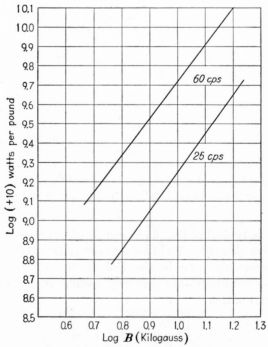

Fig. 1-28. Logarithmic equivalent of Fig. 1-27.

which, if valid, would indicate that log P_{h+e} and log B should plot as a straight line with the exponent z as its slope. The results, illustrated in Fig. 1-28, show that the empirical equation 1-48 is reasonably accurate, and in this particular case the exponent z turns out to be very nearly equal to 2.

Transformers are usually designed to operate at normal voltage with a value of flux density somewhat beyond the knee of the magnetization curve.* The maximum permissible value of B is determined in part by the necessity of keeping the core loss below the thermal operating limit, and in part by the consideration that if B is pushed too high the magnetizing current becomes excessive because of saturation.

The design of transformers is conditioned further by the following considerations: When the working value of B_m has been fixed, thereby fixing the core loss per pound of material, the over-all permissible value of core loss will in turn determine the volume, weight, and cost of the core, and thus indirectly the cross section A of the core, and the total flux $\Phi = AB$. Since, from Eq. 1-3, $E = \text{constant} \times \text{turns} \times \text{flux}$, the number of turns is determined, and thus also the weight and cost of the copper. Since it is desirable to keep the total cost of the materials at a minimum, the final choice of B, A, and N will depend upon the considerations of cost and the thermal properties determined by the combined core and copper losses.

1-17. Efficiency. The efficiency of a transformer is the ratio of output to input, expressed in per cent; i.e., the efficiency is

$$\eta = \frac{\text{output}}{\text{input}} \times 100 = \frac{\text{output}}{\text{output} + \text{losses}} \times 100 = \frac{\text{input} - \text{losses}}{\text{input}} \times 100$$

The losses, corresponding to the working temperature of 75°C, consist of the hysteresis and eddy-current losses in the core, and the copper losses in the windings; mechanical losses encountered in other types of electromagnetic machines are absent since there are no moving parts. The efficiency of transformers is therefore in general very high, being higher in units of large rating than in smaller ones. Knowledge of the efficiency is in itself of less importance than the losses themselves, and it is now usual practice to specify the no-load loss and the full-load losses rather than the efficiency at some particular load.

The expression for the efficiency as given above may be written

$$\eta = \frac{V_2 I_2 \cos \theta_2}{V_2 I_2 \cos \theta_2 + P_{h+e} + I_2^2(R_2 + R_1/a^2)} \tag{1-50}$$

---

* The flux density in the core depends upon the kva rating if hot-rolled steel is used; thus, for transformers rated at 25 kva and below, the flux density is 11 kilogauss; for ratings between 37.5 and 100 kva, it is 12 kilogauss; and for ratings of 150 to 200 kva, it is 12.5 kilogauss. Transformers utilizing cold-rolled steel are normally operated at a flux density of 14 kilogauss.

where $\cos\theta_2$ is the power factor of the load and all other symbols represent actual values. Assuming that V_2 remains practically constant, it will be seen that the losses consist of the nearly constant term P_{h+e} (hysteresis and eddy-current loss) and a term $I_2^2(R_2 + R_1/a^2)$ which varies approximately as the square of the load. For a given value of $\cos\theta_2$, the efficiency will have its maximum value when $d\eta/dI_2 = 0$; hence, on differentiating Eq. 1-50 and equating the result to zero,

$$\left[V_2I_2\cos\theta_2 + P_{h+e} + I_2^2\left(R_2 + \frac{R_1}{a^2}\right)\right]V_2\cos\theta_2$$
$$= V_2I_2\cos\theta_2\left[V_2\cos\theta_2 + 2I_2\left(R_2 + \frac{R_1}{a^2}\right)\right]$$

whence
$$I_2^2\left(R_2 + \frac{R_1}{a^2}\right) = P_{h+e}$$

which means that *maximum efficiency occurs when the variable copper loss is equal to the fixed core loss.*

It is possible, by suitable designing, to fix the relative magnitudes of core loss and copper loss so that maximum efficiency will occur at any desired fraction of full-load rating; obviously, this should be the average load if the transformer is continuously under load. Thus, let the kva rating of the transformer be P, and let the core loss be xP and the copper loss (at full-load rating) be yP. The efficiency at full-load rating will then be

$$\eta = \frac{1}{1 + x + y}$$

At any other load, pP, the core loss will still be xP, but the copper loss which varies as the square of p, will be $p^2(yP)$. For maximum efficiency, it is necessary that

$$p^2yP = xP$$

or maximum efficiency will occur at that fractional part of full-load rating determined by the relation

$$p = \sqrt{\frac{x}{y}} \tag{1-51}$$

If x is greater than y (i.e., core loss greater than full-load copper loss), p will be greater than unity, or maximum efficiency will occur beyond full-load rating; if x is less than y (core loss less than full-load copper loss), p will be less than unity, or maximum efficiency will occur at less than full load.

The *all-day efficiency* of a transformer is the ratio of the total energy output (kilowatthours) in a 24-hr day to the total energy input during the same time.   Since transformers on distribution circuits are connected permanently to the line, the core loss goes on continuously, so that it is important to design such transformers with the lowest core loss consistent with other requirements.   In general, low core loss means keeping down the flux density, which can be brought about either by using a relatively large number of turns in the winding, or by increasing the cross section of the core, or in both ways.   The apportionment of the losses as between core loss on the one hand and copper loss on the other is therefore of much importance in determining all-day efficiency.

Example.   A 50-kva 2,200/220 volt 60-cycle transformer has a core loss, determined by the open-circuit test, of 350 watts and a copper loss, at rated current, of 630 watts, determined by the short-circuit test.   Find the efficiency

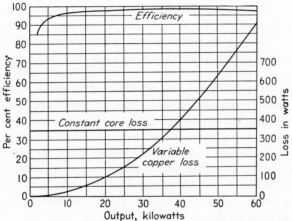

FIG. 1-29. Efficiency curves, 50-kva transformer.

(a) at full load, unity power factor; (b) at three-fourths load, unity power factor; (c) at full kva rating, 80 per cent power factor; (d) at three-fourths of rated kva, 80 per cent power factor.

Solution:

(a) $$\frac{50{,}000}{50{,}000 + 350 + 630} = 98.1\%$$

(b) $$\frac{\frac{3}{4}(50{,}000)}{\frac{3}{4}(50{,}000) + 350 + (\frac{3}{4})^2 630} = 98.2\%$$

(c) $$\frac{50{,}000 \times 0.80}{50{,}000 \times 0.80 + 350 + 630} = 97.6\%$$

(d) $$\frac{\frac{3}{4}(50{,}000 \times 0.80)}{\frac{3}{4}(50{,}000 \times 0.80) + 350 + (\frac{3}{4})^2 630} = 97.7\%$$

The variation of efficiency with load is illustrated in Fig. 1-29, which likewise shows the constant and variable components of the total loss. The abscissas in this figure represent output in kilowatts, and since kilowatt output is proportional to the current, the curve showing the variable copper loss (I^2R) is a parabola. The intersection of this curve with the constant-loss line occurs at a point where the efficiency is a maximum. It will be seen that the efficiency changes very little over the greater part of the operating range.

1-18. Calculation of Leakage Reactance. The performance characteristics of a transformer are determined by the excitation requirements, the losses in the core, the winding resistance, and particularly by the leakage reactances of the primary and secondary. All these parameters are in turn related to the physical dimensions of the component parts of the structure and to the nature of the materials used. The detailed considerations which lead to the dimensions of the core, the number of winding turns, and the cross sections of the conductors are treated in texts on the design of electrical machinery. For present purposes, it is sufficient to point out that in accordance with the fundamental formula, Eq. 1-3, the product of winding turns and maximum flux is substantially constant when the impressed voltage and frequency are specified. It follows that if the flux (and therefore also the cross section of the core) is large, the number of winding turns will be correspondingly small, and vice versa. Somewhere between the two extremes there will be a pair of values of flux and turns for which the total cost of steel and copper will be a minimum; but the final choice of dimensions will also be influenced by the consideration that the volts per turn in the winding must lie within practical limits of insulation strength, and that the winding space in the core window must be sufficient to accommodate the coils and their insulation and allow for the use of current density in the conductors which permits effective utilization of the copper.

The major dimensions having been established, the ohmic resistances of the primary and secondary windings can be computed in the manner indicated in Art. 1-15; and by applying a factor, ordinarily between 1.1 and 1.3, based upon experience with similar types of construction, the effective resistances can be calculated.

It has been indicated in Art. 1-3, and illustrated in Fig. 1-6, that the primary leakage reactance is due to the leakage flux, φ_1, which links with the primary winding but not with the secondary. Similarly, the secondary leakage reactance is due to a leakage flux φ_2 which links with the secondary but not with the primary. The calculation of the leakage reactances therefore reduces to the problem of analyzing the magnitude and distribution of the corresponding leakage fluxes and their linkages with the turns of their respective windings. In the interest of clarity, it is desirable to consider separately the conditions presented (a) in the core-type transformer, (b) in the shell-type transformer.

a. Core-type Transformer. Consider first the construction shown in Fig. 1-30, in which the high-voltage winding H and the low-voltage winding L each consists of two coils built up as concentric cylinders. Let N_{1c} and N_{2c} be the number of turns per coil in H and L, respectively, the corresponding oppositely directed currents being I_1 and I_2. If the exciting current is neglected, it follows that $N_{1c}I_1 \cong N_{2c}I_2$, from which it may be concluded that the magnetizing effect is the same as though the adjacent sections of each pair have the same number of turns and carry equal currents; in other words, they may be regarded as opposite sides of a coil lying outside the core, as in Fig. 1-31, which sets up leakage flux in the manner there indicated.

For the sake of simplicity, it is assumed that the tubes of induction follow straight lines within the limits of the coil sections. In the case of winding L, the lines of induction complete their paths through the negligible reluctance of the core, while the return path of the lines linked with H is through the walls of the enclosing case. The two return paths do not necessarily have the same negligible reluctance, but because the

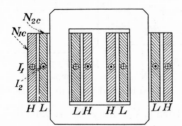

FIG. 1-30. Core-type transformer.

cross section of the return path associated with H is large, the difference is not great, and it is sufficiently accurate to assume that the dividing line between primary and secondary leakage lies midway between the coil sections, as indicated by the line marked Y in Fig. 1-31.

The ordinates of the trapezoidal diagram at the lower left-hand corner of Fig. 1-31 show the distribution of mmf (in ampere-turns) which is effective in producing the leakage fluxes. The mmf has maximum value $N_{1c}I_1 = N_{2c}I_2$ in the space b, and decreases linearly to zero at the two extremes. It is to be noted that the dimensions b, b_1, and b_2 are fixed by the boundary lines of the copper of the winding, exclusive of the insulation around the coils.

Starting with these considerations, the leakage reactance can be found by either of two methods, of which the first utilizes the fact that the inductance of a coil is defined as the number of flux linkages (in weber-turns) per ampere, and that the reactance is equal to the inductance multiplied by $2\pi f$, while the second method is based upon the fact that the energy stored in the magnetic field of a coil is given by the expression $W = \frac{1}{2}LI^2$, and that at a point in a magnetic field where the magnetizing force is H and the flux density is B the energy stored in an elementary volume dv is

$$dW = \tfrac{1}{2}HB \, dv \qquad (1\text{-}52)^*$$

all quantities being expressed in rationalized mks units.

METHOD 1.   LEAKAGE REACTANCE BY METHOD OF LINKAGES.   Referring to Fig. 1-31, it will be noted that the equality $N_{1c}I_1 = N_{2c}I_2$ implies

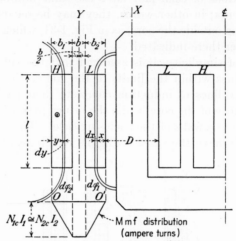

FIG. 1-31. Idealized paths of leakage flux.

that the secondary turns N_{2c} may be replaced by N_{1c} provided the secondary current I_2 is at the same time replaced by I_1.   The effect of these substitutions is merely to make the subsequent calculations of

* This formula may be derived as follows: Assume that a toroidal ring of non-magnetic material has a cross section A and a mean circumferential length l, and that it is uniformly wound with a coil of N turns.   The magnetizing force due to a coil current of I amp is

$$H = \frac{NI}{l} \qquad \text{amp-turns per m}$$

and the corresponding flux density is

$$B = \mu_0 \frac{NI}{l} \qquad \text{webers per sq m}$$

where $\mu_0 = 4\pi \times 10^{-7}$.   The total flux in the cross section A is

$$\phi = AB = \mu_0 \frac{ANI}{l} \qquad \text{webers}$$

and the flux linkages per ampere, equal by definition to the coil inductance in henrys, is

$$L = \frac{\lambda}{I} = \frac{N\phi}{I} = \mu_0 \frac{A}{l} N^2 \qquad \text{henrys}$$

The energy stored in the magnetic field is therefore

$$W = \frac{1}{2} LI^2 = \frac{1}{2} \mu_0 \frac{A}{l} N^2 I^2 = \frac{1}{2} HB \times Al \qquad \text{joules}$$

from which, since Al is the volume of the core, the energy stored per unit volume, or dW/dv, is

$$\frac{dW}{dv} = \frac{1}{2} HB \qquad \text{joules per cu m}$$

secondary leakage flux and leakage reactance come out in terms of primary quantities.

In terms of this substitution, the flux in the elementary tube of width dx is equal to the quotient obtained by dividing the mmf of the $(x/b_2)N_{1c}$ turns (which lie to the right of element dx) by the reluctance of the tube; the latter is given by the expression

$$\frac{\text{Length of path}}{\text{Permeability} \times \text{section of path}} = \frac{kl}{\mu_0\pi(D + 2x)\, dx}$$

where k is a factor greater than unity to take account of the fact that the effective length of path is somewhat greater than l, and $\pi(D + 2x)$ is the perimeter of the cylindrical tube having X as its axis. The resultant elementary flux per ampere is

$$\frac{d\varphi}{I_1} = \frac{xN_{1c}}{b_2} \frac{\mu_0\pi(D + 2x)\, dx}{kl}$$

and this flux links with the $(x/b_2)N_{1c}$ turns lying to the right of element dx. The total number of partial linkages (per ampere) is found by integrating over the width b_2 of the coil, in accordance with the expression

$$\lambda'_L = \int_0^{b_2} \frac{x}{b_2} N_{1c} \frac{d\varphi}{I_1} = \int_0^{b_2} \left(\frac{x}{b_2} N_{1c}\right)^2 \frac{\mu_0\pi(D + 2x)\, dx}{kl}$$

$$= N_{1c}^2 \frac{\mu_0\pi}{kl} \left(D\frac{b_2}{3} + \frac{b_2^2}{2}\right) \tag{1-53}$$

Beyond $x = b_2$, and up to the line of separation represented by Y, where $x = b_2 + \tfrac{1}{2}b$, the mmf is $N_{1c}I_1$, and the corresponding elementary flux links with all of the N_{1c} turns. Hence, the number of flux linkages per ampere due to this part of the flux is

$$\lambda''_L = \int_{b_2}^{b_2+\frac{1}{2}b} N_{1c}^2 \frac{\mu_0\pi(D + 2x)\, dx}{kl} = N_{1c}^2 \frac{\mu_0\pi}{kl} \left(D\frac{b}{2} + b_2 b + \frac{b^2}{4}\right) \tag{1-54}$$

Proceeding similarly to find the linkages per ampere with coil H in Fig. 1-31, it will be seen that when the variable y lies between zero and b_1,

$$\lambda'_H = \int_0^{b_1} \left(\frac{y}{b_1} N_{1c}\right)^2 \frac{\mu_0\pi(D + 2b_2 + 2b + 2b_1 - 2y)}{kl}\, dy$$

$$= N_{1c}^2 \frac{\mu_0\pi}{kl} \left[(D + 2b_2 + 2b + 2b_1)\frac{b_1}{3} - \frac{b_1^2}{2}\right] \tag{1-55}$$

while beyond $y = b_1$ and up to $y = b_1 + \tfrac{1}{2}b$ the linkages are

$$\lambda''_H = \int_{b_1}^{b_1+\frac{1}{2}b} N_{1c}^2 \frac{\mu_0\pi(D + 2b_2 + 2b + 2b_1 - 2y)\, dy}{kl}$$

$$= N_{1c}^2 \frac{\mu_0\pi}{kl} \left[(D + 2b_2 + 2b)\frac{b}{2} - \frac{b^2}{4}\right] \tag{1-56}$$

On adding Eqs. 1-53, 1-54, 1-55, and 1-56, the result is the total inductance of the primary and secondary coils on one leg of the core. The inductance of primary and secondary for the transformer as a whole is double this amount; hence, the total primary and secondary leakage reactance is

$$X_1 + X_2 = 2\pi f \times 2(\lambda'_L + \lambda''_L + \lambda'_H + \lambda''_H)$$

and on performing the operations indicated it is found that the result differs from

$$X_1 + X_2 = 4\pi f N_{1c}^2 \frac{\mu_0 \pi}{kl} (D + 2b_2 + b) \left(b + \frac{b_1 + b_2}{3} \right) \qquad (1\text{-}57)$$

by an amount equal to

$$\Delta = 4\pi f N_{1c}^2 \frac{\mu_0 \pi}{kl} \left[\frac{b_1^2 - b_2^2}{6} + \frac{b}{3} (b_1 - b_2) \right]$$

which becomes zero if b_1 and b_2 are equal, and is negligible if b_1 and b_2 are approximately equal.

Reference to Fig. 1-31 will show that the term

$$\pi(D + 2b_2 + b) = T$$

which appears in Eq. 1-57 is the circumference of a circle centered at axis X and passing through axis Y. The quantity T is therefore the *mean length of turn* of the windings. Finally, on substituting $\mu_0 = 4\pi \times 10^{-7}$ and $N_{1c} = \frac{1}{2}N_1$, Eq. 1-57 becomes

$$X_1 + X_2 = \frac{4\pi^2}{3 \times 10^7} \frac{N_1^2 f T}{kl} (b_1 + b_2 + 3b) \qquad (1\text{-}58)$$

where all dimensions are in meters.

If dimensions are expressed in centimeters, the factor 10^7 in Eq. 1-58 becomes 10^9; and if dimensions are in inches, the numerical coefficient in Eq. 1-58 becomes $3.34/10^8$.

METHOD 2. LEAKAGE REACTANCE BY METHOD OF ENERGY STORAGE. The tube of induction of width dx which passes through coil L in Fig. 1-31 represents energy storage to the extent of $dW_{b_2} = \frac{1}{2}HB\,dv$ in accordance with Eq. 1-52, where

$$H = \frac{x}{b_2} \frac{N_{1c} I_1}{kl}$$
$$B = \mu_0 H$$
$$dv = \pi(D + 2x)\,dx\,kl$$

It is, however, sufficiently accurate to replace the perimeter $\pi(D + 2x)$ by the mean length of turn, T, of the entire winding for the same reason that was found to be permissible in Method 1. Consequently, the total energy represented by the linkages with coil L is

$$W_{b_2} = \int_0^{b_2} \frac{\mu_0}{2} \left(\frac{x}{b_2} \frac{N_{1c}I_1}{kl} \right)^2 Tkl \, dx = \frac{\mu_0}{2} \frac{N_{1c}^2 I_1^2}{kl} T \frac{b_2}{3} \qquad (1\text{-}59)$$

In the same way, the energy stored in the space b is

$$W_b = \frac{\mu_0}{2} \frac{N_{1c}^2 I_1^2}{kl} Tb \qquad (1\text{-}60)$$

while in the space b_1 the stored energy is

$$W_{b_1} = \int_0^{b_1} \frac{\mu_0}{2} \left(\frac{y}{b_1} \frac{N_{1c}I_1}{kl} \right)^2 Tkl \, dy = \frac{\mu_0}{2} \frac{N_{1c}^2 I_1^2}{kl} T \frac{b_1}{3} \qquad (1\text{-}61)$$

The total energy of the leakage field for the single side of the transformer here considered is

$$W = W_{b_2} + W_b + W_{b_1}$$

and double this amount is accordingly equal to the quantity

$$\frac{1}{2} LI_1^2 = \frac{1}{2} \frac{X_1 + X_2}{2\pi f} I_1^2$$

which is the energy stored in the leakage field of the transformer as a whole. It follows that

$$\frac{1}{2} \frac{X_1 + X_2}{2\pi f} I_1^2 = 2 \frac{\mu_0}{2} \frac{N_{1c}^2 I_1^2}{kl} T \left(b + \frac{b_1 + b_2}{3} \right)$$

and on substituting $\mu_0 = 4\pi \times 10^{-7}$ and $N_{1c} = \frac{1}{2} N_1$ the result is

$$X_1 + X_2 = \frac{4\pi^2}{3 \times 10^7} \frac{N_1^2 fT}{kl} (b_1 + b_2 + 3b)$$

which is the same as Eq. 1-58.

b. *Effect of Subdivision of Windings, Core-type Transformers.* Where close voltage regulation is essential, as in distribution transformers for lighting circuits, it is necessary to make the leakage reactance small. The obvious way to reduce magnetic leakage is to interlace the primary and secondary windings, which can be accomplished by "sandwiching" sections of one winding between sections of the other. This is illustrated in Fig. 1-32, which shows a type of construction commonly used. The diagram shows that for purposes of analysis the actual arrangement of the windings on each leg of the core can be considered to consist of two groups of coils connected in series. In each group, the number of turns in the primary and secondary are $\frac{1}{2} N_{1c} = \frac{1}{4} N_1$ and $\frac{1}{2} N_{2c} = \frac{1}{4} N_2$ turns, respectively, while the corresponding coil widths are $\frac{1}{2} b_1$ and $\frac{1}{2} b_2$, and their separation remains b. Referring then to Eq. 1-58, the reactance of each group is proportional to $(\frac{1}{4} N_1)^2$ instead of to N_1^2, though the parentheses $(b_1 + b_2 + 3b)$ must be replaced by $[\frac{1}{2}(b_1 + b_2) + 3b]$ in order to agree with the modified widths of the coils. The result must further be multiplied by 2 to take into account the two series-connected groups on each leg of the core; hence, the combined primary and secondary leakage reactance (in terms of the primary) is

$$X_1 + X_2 = \frac{\pi^2}{3 \times 10^7} \frac{N_1^2 fT}{kl} (b_1 + b_2 + 6b) \tag{1-62}$$

where all dimensions are in meters. It will be seen by comparing Eqs. 1-58 and 1-62 that the effect of interlacing the coils is to reduce the leakage reactance to nearly one-fourth of its original value.

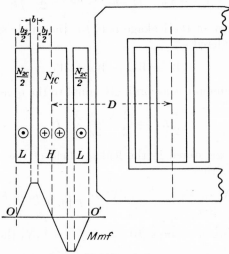

FIG. 1-32. Subdivided coils, core type.

c. *Shell-type Transformers, Concentric Coils.* Figure 1-33 shows a cross section of the usual construction of a shell-type transformer having concentric coils, the high-voltage winding being surrounded by the two halves of the low-voltage winding. Just as in the above case b, the arrangement is equivalent to two groups of coils in series, each group containing $N_{1c} = \frac{1}{2}N_1$ turns (in terms of the primary), the widths of the coils being $\frac{1}{2}b_1$ and $\frac{1}{2}b_2$ and their separation being b. It follows from Eqs. 1-59 to 1-61 that the energy storage of both groups is

$$W = 2 \times \frac{\mu_0}{2} \frac{N_{1c}^2 I_1^2}{kl} T \left[b + \frac{\frac{1}{2}(b_1 + b_2)}{3} \right]$$

where $T = \pi D$, and since W is equal to $\frac{1}{2}LI_1^2 = \frac{1}{2} \frac{X_1 + X_2}{2\pi f} I_1^2$,

$$X_1 + X_2 = \frac{\pi^2}{15 \times 10^6} \frac{N_1^2 fT}{kl} (b_1 + b_2 + 6b) \tag{1-63}$$

where all dimensions are in meters.

d. Shell-type Transformers, Pancake Coils. In Fig. 1-34, the coils may be subdivided into four groups, each of which may be treated in accordance with the methods described in the preceding derivations. In general, if there are q such groups, each having N_1/q turns per coil, the total energy stored in the leakage field will be

$$W = q \frac{\mu_0}{2} \frac{(N_1/q)^2 I_1^2}{kl} T \left[b + \frac{\frac{1}{2}(b_1 + b_2)}{3} \right]$$

from which $X_1 + X_2 = \dfrac{4\pi^2}{3 \times 10^7} \dfrac{1}{q} \dfrac{N_1^2 fT}{kl} (b_1 + b_2 + 6b)$ (1-64)

where, as before, all dimensions are in meters.

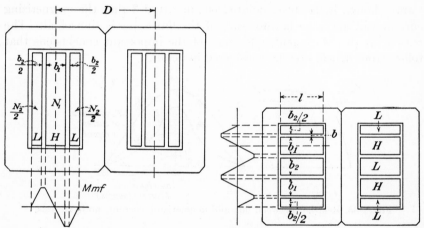

FIG. 1-33. Subdivided concentric coils, shell type.

FIG. 1-34. Subdivided pancake coils, shell type.

1-19. Effect of Reactance upon Transformer Performance.* The preceding formulas show that reactance is proportional to the square of the number of turns and inversely proportional to the length of the coil (and therefore to the length of the core window). It is also affected by the distance between primary and secondary windings, but this dimension is more or less fixed by insulation requirements; hence, other things being the same, a high-voltage design implies larger reactance than a low-voltage design.

The fundamental formula $E = kfN\Phi$ shows that, for a given arrangement of windings and a given voltage, any reduction in the number of turns for the purpose of reducing the reactance must be accompanied by an increase of flux and correspondingly increased cross section of the core. Reduced reactance can also be secured by lengthening the core,

* Based upon an article by R. E. Coates and H. C. Holderness in *Distribution* (General Electric Company), **8**(3):12 (July, 1946).

but in either case, or by a combination of both, the conclusion follows that a low-reactance design involves larger volume and weight of core, larger core loss, and larger exciting current than is the case when the per cent reactance is higher.

Otherwise stated, increased reactance implies more copper and less iron; decreased reactance implies less copper and more iron. There will be some particular value of reactance for which the total cost of material will be a minimum. In any case, low reactance is not consistent with low weight and low core loss.

1-20. Nonsinusoidal Wave Forms: Secondary Open-circuited. Thus far it has been assumed that the various voltages, currents, and fluxes concerned in the operation of the transformer have sinusoidal wave forms, though it has been pointed out in Art. 1-3 that the magnetizing current will not vary harmonically if the flux wave is sinusoidal. The reason for this statement, and some of the important conclusions that follow from it, will now be considered in detail.

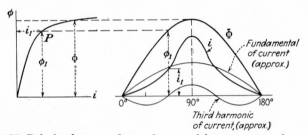

FIG. 1-35. Relation between flux and magnetizing current, no hysteresis.

It is well-known that when an iron core is subjected to a magnetizing force, the resultant magnetization tends to approach a limit as the magnetizing force is increased; in other words, the iron approaches a condition of saturation. This is represented in Fig. 1-35, which is nothing more nor less than the usual BH curve drawn to such a scale that ordinates represent the total flux Φ instead of B, and abscissas represent the magnetizing current I instead of $H = NI/l$. If it is assumed that there is no hysteresis loss in the core, the coordinates of any point P on the magnetization curve must then represent simultaneous values of the flux in the core and the magnetizing current producing the flux, and this must be true without regard to the manner of time variation of either one of the coordinates; but if one of them varies with time in any arbitrarily assumed manner, then the time variation of the other is definitely fixed.

For example, let it be assumed that the flux Φ varies as a harmonic function of time, as indicated by the sine curve, Φ, of Fig. 1-35. When the flux has a value indicated by ϕ_1, the current must necessarily be i_1, as fixed by the magnetization curve. Proceeding in this way for a sufficient number of additional points, the time variation of the current is found to be a curve which is not sinusoidal but tends to become more and more peaked as the iron approaches saturation. The current curve remains symmetrical with respect to the middle of the loop. On resolving a curve of this type into a series of component sine curves, in accordance with Fourier's theorem, it is found that it is equivalent to a sine curve of fundamental frequency (i.e., of the same frequency as the flux curve) and a series of odd harmonics, with the third harmonic dominant to such an extent that the others, of higher order, may usually be neglected. The fundamental and third-harmonic constituents of curve i of Fig. 1-35 are indicated in light lines.

Considering the case where hysteresis is present, the relation between flux and current now becomes the familiar loop shown in Fig. 1-36, with its cusps lying on the original magnetization curve of Fig. 1-35 as indicated by the dashed curve.

If the flux is again assumed to vary harmonically, the current-time curve will have the form shown, the method of constructing it being the

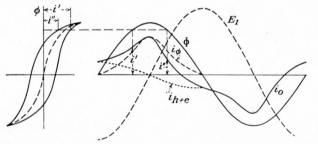

FIG. 1-36. Effect of hysteresis upon wave form of no-load current (sinusoidal flux).

same as before. The general shape of the curve is much the same as in Fig. 1-35, but it is no longer symmetrical about the peak. It may be resolved into a fundamental and harmonics as before, with the third harmonic again dominant. The dotted curve marked i_ϕ in Fig. 1-36 is the same as curve i of Fig. 1-35 and may be considered to be the current which supplies the magnetizing force, in phase with Φ, while curve i_{h+e}, the ordinates of which are equal to the difference between the corresponding ordinates of i and i_ϕ, supplies the loss due to hysteresis. It is seen that curve i_{h+e} is in quadrature with the equivalent sine curve corresponding to i_ϕ, which circumstance is in agreement with the phasor diagram of Fig. 1-8.

Since the flux Φ has been assumed to vary harmonically, the emf induced by it in the winding will also vary harmonically and will lag 90° behind the flux, as shown by the dashed curve marked E_1 in Fig. 1-36. To maintain the flow of current through the winding, it is therefore necessary to impress upon the terminals a voltage which must contain as components:

1. An emf at all times equal and opposite to E_1.

2. An emf in phase with the current, and at each instant equal to iR_1.

3. An emf at all times equal and opposite to the emf due to leakage reactance, the latter being expressed by $-L_1\,di/dt$, where $L_1 = X_1/2\pi f$.

These three components of the impressed voltage V_1 are indicated in Fig. 1-37, though for the sake of clearness they are not all drawn to the

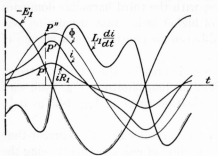

same scale, those included under items (2) and (3) being exaggerated. Under the conditions obtaining in the usual transformer, the latter two will be quite small compared with E_1, but the point is that they are not sinusoidal; hence, the wave form of V_1 is likewise not quite sinusoidal, though it is nearly so if the current is small and the leakage impedance is within usual limits. If then the

Fig. 1-37. Effect of distorted current upon components of impressed voltage.

drops due to resistance and leakage reactance are ignored, it may be said that a sinusoidal impressed voltage will result in a sinusoidal flux, but the current will be nonsinusoidal, with a prominent third harmonic.

Conversely, if the exciting current is assumed to be sinusoidal, the flux wave will be distorted in the manner shown in Fig. 1-38, which is constructed in accordance with the same principle used in Fig. 1-36. The emf induced by the distorted wave of flux will also be distorted in such

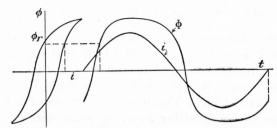

Fig. 1-38. Effect of hysteresis upon flux (sinusoidal current).

manner that the emf at any instant is proportional to the rate of change of the flux, and, with a reversal of sign, in accordance with the general formula

$$e = -N\frac{d\varphi}{dt}$$

As a further example of the effect of nonsinusoidal wave forms, consider the case of a transformer upon which there is impressed a line voltage represented by

$$e = E_1 \sin \omega t + E_3 \sin 3\omega t$$

where E_1 and E_3 are both essentially positive.   It follows from the relation $e = -N \, d\varphi/dt$ that

$$\varphi = \frac{E_1}{\omega N} \cos \omega t + \frac{E_3}{3\omega N} \cos 3\omega t$$

and the wave forms showing the time variations of e and φ are shown in Fig. 1-39.   It will be observed that whereas the wave form of emf is flat-topped, that of the flux is peaked.

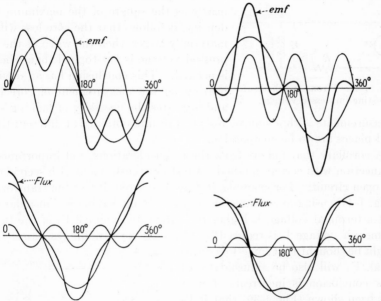

FIG. 1-39. Flat-topped emf and the corresponding peaked flux.

FIG. 1-40. Peaked emf and the corresponding flat-topped flux.

If on the other hand the emf is represented by

$$e = E_1 \sin \omega t - E_3 \sin 3\omega t$$

which is equivalent to the peaked wave shown in Fig. 1-40, the flux is given by

$$\varphi = \frac{E_1}{\omega N} \cos \omega t - \frac{E_3}{3\omega N} \cos 3\omega t$$

which is a flat-topped wave.

In both cases illustrated in Figs. 1-39 and 1-40, the emf waves, though differing widely in appearance and in their maximum values, are the resultants of components which have the same amplitudes.   But it is known that the effective (rms) value of a periodic function is

$$E = \sqrt{E_1^2 + E_2^2 + E_3^2 + \cdots}$$

where E_1, E_2, E_3, etc., are the effective values of the fundamental and the higher harmonics. The value of E remains the same without regard to the signs of the amplitudes and without regard to the phase positions of the components. It follows, therefore, that the emf waves in Figs. 1-39 and 1-40 have the same effective values, which means that in both cases a voltmeter connected across the supply circuit would give the same reading. But in the case of the flat-topped wave of emf, Fig. 1-39, the flux in the core reaches a considerably higher maximum value than in the other case, Fig. 1-40, where the emf wave is peaked; and since core loss varies

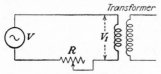

FIG. 1-41. Wrong method of adjusting impressed voltage.

nearly as the square of the maximum flux density, it follows that the core loss will be materially larger when the wave of the impressed voltage is flat-topped than when it is peaked. This conclusion has an obvious bearing on the measurement of core loss, and indicates the necessity of making such measurements with a sinusoidal emf if results obtained at different times and places are to be comparable.

A corollary that follows from these considerations is of importance in connection with certain methods of testing transformers with secondaries on open circuit. For example, it may be desired to test the transformer (Fig. 1-41), using as a source of power a circuit having a sinusoidal emf but a terminal voltage V higher than the rated voltage V_1 of the transformer; if voltage V is reduced by inserting the variable resistance R, it might be thought that since V is sinusoidal, V_1 will also be sinusoidal, but this conclusion is incorrect. For it has been shown (Fig. 1-36) that if V_1 is sinusoidal, the no-load current of the transformer will contain a third harmonic, and since the resultant nonsinusoidal current flows through R, the drop of potential in the latter will also be nonsinusoidal. The resultant wave, obtained by combining the sinusoidal voltage V_1 and the nonsinusoidal drop in R, will then be distorted,

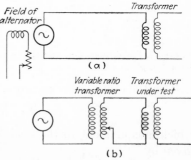

FIG. 1-42. Correct method of adjusting impressed voltage.

which contradicts the assumption that V is sinusoidal. Hence, if V is sinusoidal, V_1 will not be sinusoidal, and the amount of the distortion will be different for each setting of the resistor R. Consequently, if core loss is to be measured at various values of impressed voltage, the rheostatic control shown in Fig. 1-41 must not be used. The proper method is to regulate the generator voltage either by means of a rheostat in its field circuit, as in Fig. 1-42a, or by interposing a transformer (or autotransformer) which has a variable ratio of transformation, as in Fig. 1-42b.

1-21. Effect of Load upon Current Distortion. The considerations discussed in the preceding article apply to the case of open-circuited secondary, and the distortion of current therefore occurs in the wave form of the no-load or exciting current. Assuming that the flux varies harmonically, which means that the wave form of the emf induced in the secondary is sinusoidal (and that the wave form of primary impressed voltage is substantially sinusoidal), the secondary current will generally be sinusoidal also, unless the secondary circuit is itself of such nature as to introduce disturbances. For example, it is conceivable that the secondary load may consist of one or more translating devices containing iron cores worked at high flux density, in which case the effect of the widely varying permeability and the hysteresis loss would bring about the same type of distortion of secondary current already described for the case of the primary circuit; or the load may consist of arc welders, which also have the effect of introducing harmonics into the current wave. Ordinarily, however, the secondary load will be characterized by circuit constants which are independent of the current value, as in circuits containing incandescent lamps and induction motors, in which case the wave form of secondary current will follow that of the secondary induced emf.

Since the primary current is at any instant equal to the sum of the corresponding values of exciting current and of the secondary current reversed, it follows that if the latter is sinusoidal and of full-load value, the resultant primary current will be only slightly distorted, since the harmonics of the exciting current constitute only a small percentage of the total current. In other words, the effect of increasing the load is to smooth out the primary current, provided, of course, that the load is of the passive nature mentioned in the preceding paragraph.

1-22. Transient Starting Current.* The relations between voltage, current, and flux thus far discussed, and illustrated, for instance, in Fig. 1-36, have been based upon the tacit assumption that steady conditions of operation obtain in the circuit and that the cycle of changes represented in the diagrams is repeated over and over. To each instantaneous value of impressed voltage there corresponds one, and only one, value of each of the other quantities, such as flux and exciting current. But if a transformer (with open secondary) is connected to the supply circuit by closing the line switch at the moment when the voltage has the value indicated by point P in Fig. 1-37, the exciting current, instead of having the value indicated by ordinate P', is zero, and the adjustment necessary to bring about the permanent relations must be effected by a flow of current which for a greater or less period of time departs from the permanent or final wave form.

The problem is complicated by the fact that at the moment of closing

* See C. P. Steinmetz, "Transient Electric Phenomena and Oscillations," p. 179, McGraw Pub. Co. (1909).

the switch the flux may not have the value P'' corresponding, under permanent conditions, to the given value of impressed voltage, P. When a transformer has been in use, and the circuit is broken, the flux does not necessarily disappear, but may persist for a considerable time at the remanent value, ϕ_r in Fig. 1-38, which corresponds to zero excitation; thus, at the moment of again connecting the transformer to the line, the flux may have the value ϕ_r or something between ϕ_r and zero, and it may be either positive or negative. It follows, therefore, that the current will start without a transient effect only on condition that the switch is closed at the precise moment that the emf has the value normally corresponding to zero current, and also that the remanent flux has the proper sign—negative if the current starts in the positive direction, positive if the current starts in the negative direction.

Reference to Fig. 1-36 will show that the initial disturbance may be expected to be most pronounced if the circuit is closed at or near the moment when the impressed voltage is passing through its zero value, for at this moment the current should have its maximum (absolute) value, whereas in reality it is zero. At the same time, the flux, which should have a value of, say, $-\Phi$, may actually be $+\phi_r$. During the first half cycle, the flux would normally vary between $-\Phi$ and $+\Phi$, that is, the range of values would be 2Φ; under the actual conditions, but neglecting the leakage-impedance drop, the total change in the flux must still be 2Φ in order to develop the requisite counter emf, and since the initial value may be $+\phi_r$, it follows that under the worst conditions the flux may increase to $2\Phi + \phi_r$, or far beyond the knee of the magnetization curve.

For example, let Fig. 1-43 represent the magnetization curve and the normal hysteresis loop of the transformer; the normal range of flux density in gauss is from $B = -10,000$ to $B = +10,000$, and that of the exciting current is from -4 to $+4$ amp. If the circuit is closed at the instant when B should be $-10,000$ and the actual value corresponding to ϕ_r is $+7,500$, the maximum flux density will then reach a value of $27,500$ at the end of the first half cycle if the leakage-impedance drop is neglected. Corresponding to this extreme value of flux density is a current value of approximately $1,800$ amp, or 450 times as great as the normal maximum. Obviously, with such a large value of current the impedance drop is not negligible; hence, the counter emf cannot be considered to be equal in magnitude to the impressed voltage, the actual range of value of the flux will not be so great as 2Φ, as was tentatively assumed, and the current will not reach the extreme value determined roughly as above. In any case, however, it is clear that under the assumed conditions the initial rush of current may be excessive.

Assume, then, that at the end of the first half cycle the flux has reached the value indicated by point 1 of Fig. 1-43, or somewhat less than $B = 27,500$. During the next half cycle, the range of flux must again be

20,000 if the impedance drop is neglected, or something less than this amount if the drop is taken into account, the conditions at the end of this half cycle being then represented by point 2. At the end of succeeding half cycles, the conditions will be represented successively by points 3, 4, 5, etc. It will be observed that the maximum value of current is all the while becoming less, and that as the maximum current, and consequently also the drop, decreases, the range of flux approaches more and more to the final value of 20,000. The rate of approach to normal conditions will obviously be greater the higher the effective resistance of the circuit.

It is plain from Fig. 1-43 that during the first few cycles the flux is mainly of one sign, i.e., it is virtually unidirectional, though pulsating at line frequency. The same is true with regard to the current. As time goes on, the originally large positive half loops become smaller, and the small negative loops become larger, until the symmetry of permanent conditions is attained.

The effects here described are more pronounced in 25-cycle than in 60-cycle transformers for the reason that the flux densities used in the former are higher than in the latter. They are likewise

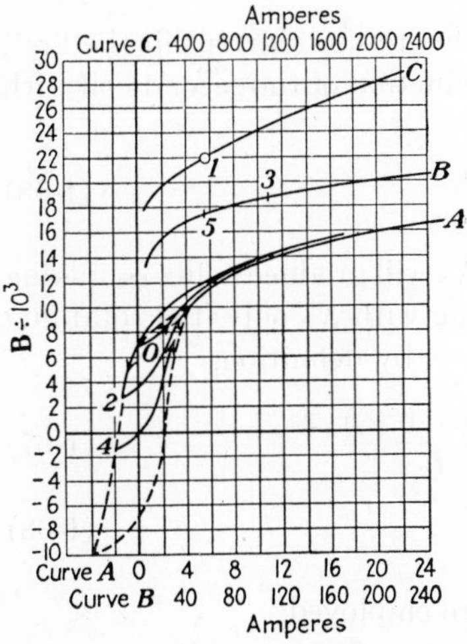

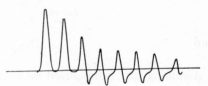

FIG. 1-43. Cyclic change of flux during starting period of transformer.

FIG. 1-44. Typical oscillogram of starting current of a transformer.

more pronounced with cores made of silicon steel than with the black sheet steel formerly used, because the smaller losses in the former permit the use of higher flux densities.

Figure 1-44 is typical of the oscillogram of the starting current of a 25-cycle transformer and illustrates the points that have here been discussed.

1-23. The Two-winding Transformer from the Standpoint of Self- and Mutual Induction. The analysis of transformer operation in terms of the mutual flux linking the windings, and the two leakage fluxes associated with them, constitutes the so-called engineering approach. The method has numerous advantages in the case of transformers for power purposes, but it is not so useful in communication circuits, where it is found to be advantageous to work with the coefficients of self-induction, L_1 and L_2, of the two windings, and their coefficient of mutual induction, M. It is therefore desirable to compare the two methods of analysis, and to show that both lead to the same results.

Consider, for example, a pair of coils having N_1 and N_2 turns, respectively, wound on a nonmagnetic core in the manner indicated in Fig. 1-9. Let the coils be so disposed that a current I_1 amp in the first coil sets up a flux ϕ_1 (webers) which links with both N_1 and N_2, and in addition a flux φ_1 which links with N_1 alone. The total flux linked with N_1 is then $\Phi_1 = \phi_1 + \varphi_1$. The coefficient of self-induction of the first coil, being by definition equal to the flux linkages per ampere, is

$$L_1 = \frac{N_1\Phi_1}{I_1} = \frac{N_1(\phi_1 + \varphi_1)}{I_1} \qquad (1\text{-}65)$$

The flux linkages with the second coil, due to unit current in the first, is by definition the coefficient of mutual induction of the second coil with respect to the first; hence,

$$M_{21} = \frac{N_2\phi_1}{I_1} \qquad (1\text{-}66)$$

In the same way, a current of I_2 amp in N_2 will produce a flux ϕ_2 linking with both N_2 and N_1, and a flux φ_2 linking with N_2 only, the total flux linked with N_2 being $\Phi_2 = \phi_2 + \varphi_2$. Hence, by definition,

$$L_2 = \frac{N_2\Phi_2}{I_2} = \frac{N_2(\phi_2 + \varphi_2)}{I_2} \qquad (1\text{-}67)$$

and

$$M_{12} = \frac{N_1\phi_2}{I_2} \qquad (1\text{-}68)$$

Assuming that rationalized mks units are employed,

$$\phi_1 = N_1 I_1 P_0 \qquad \varphi_1 = N_1 I_1 P_1$$
$$\phi_2 = N_2 I_2 P_0 \qquad \varphi_2 = N_2 I_2 P_2$$

where P_0, P_1, and P_2 are the respective permeances of the magnetic circuit common to both coils, the primary leakage path, and the secondary leakage path. In general,

$$\text{Permeance} = \mu_0 \frac{\text{cross section of path}}{\text{length of path}}$$

where $\mu_0 = 4\pi \times 10^{-7}$ and linear dimensions are expressed in meters. It follows that

$$L_1 = N_1^2(P_0 + P_1)$$
$$L_2 = N_2^2(P_0 + P_2) \qquad (1\text{-}69)$$
$$M = M_{12} = M_{21} = N_1 N_2 P_0$$

The assumption of a nonmagnetic core (such as air) is equivalent to the assumption that L_1, L_2, and M remain constant for all values of the current flowing in the coils.   There can be no hysteresis under the assumed conditions, and if any metal parts are so constructed as to preclude eddy currents, the only losses that can occur are those due to the ohmic resistances of the coils themselves.

Let the primary winding be supplied from a source of alternating current such that the primary impressed voltage is

$$v_1 = V_{1m} \sin (\omega t + \alpha) \tag{1-70}$$

V_{1m} being assumed to be constant; and let the secondary winding be connected to an external circuit having resistance R and inductance L, so that the instantaneous secondary terminal voltage is

$$v_2 = i_2 R + L \frac{di_2}{dt} \tag{1-71}$$

Kirchhoff's law applied to the primary and the secondary then leads to the pair of simultaneous differential equations

$$v_1 = i_1 R_1 + L_1 \frac{di_1}{dt} + M \frac{di_2}{dt} \tag{1-72}$$

$$0 = i_2(R_2 + R) + (L_2 + L) \frac{di_2}{dt} + M \frac{di_1}{dt} \tag{1-73}$$

where $R_2 + R$ = total secondary resistance = R_s
$\qquad L_2 + L$ = total secondary inductance = L_s
Reference to Eq. 1-71 shows that Eq. 1-73 can be written

$$-v_2 = i_2 R_2 + L_2 \frac{di_2}{dt} + M \frac{di_1}{dt} \tag{1-74}$$

in which form it becomes symmetrical with Eq. 1-72, except that $-v_2$ takes the place of $+v_1$.   This reversal of sign of v_2 is the expression of the physical fact that v_1 and v_2 are in general in phase opposition.

The pair of equations 1-72 and 1-73 can be written

$$v_1 = i_1 R_1 + L_1 \frac{di_1}{dt} + M \frac{di_2}{dt} \tag{1-75}$$

$$0 = i_2 R_s + L_s \frac{di_2}{dt} + M \frac{di_1}{dt} \tag{1-76}$$

which are readily solvable for i_1 and i_2.   Thus, differentiating each of them with respect to t,

$$L_1 \frac{d^2 i_1}{dt^2} + R_1 \frac{di_1}{dt} + M \frac{d^2 i_2}{dt^2} = \frac{dv_1}{dt} \tag{1-77}$$

$$L_s \frac{d^2 i_2}{dt^2} + R_s \frac{di_2}{dt} + M \frac{d^2 i_1}{dt^2} = 0 \tag{1-78}$$

Multiplying Eq. 1-77 by L_s, and Eq. 1-78 by M, and subtracting,

$$(L_1L_s - M^2)\frac{d^2i_1}{dt^2} + R_1L_s\frac{di_1}{dt} - MR_s\frac{di_2}{dt} = L_s\frac{dv_1}{dt} \qquad (1\text{-}79)$$

The term involving di_2/dt can be eliminated by observing from Eq. 1-72 that

$$MR_s\frac{di_2}{dt} = v_1R_s - i_1R_1R_s - L_1R_s\frac{di_1}{dt}$$

whence Eq. 1-79 becomes

$$(L_1L_s - M^2)\frac{d^2i_1}{dt} + (R_1L_s + R_sL_1)\frac{di_1}{dt} + R_1R_si_1 = v_1R_s + L_s\frac{dv_1}{dt} \quad (1\text{-}80)$$

A similar procedure serves to eliminate i_1 in Eqs. 1-77 and 1-78, the result being

$$(L_1L_s - M^2)\frac{d^2i_2}{dt^2} + (R_1L_s + R_sL_1)\frac{di_2}{dt} + R_1R_si_2 = -M\frac{dv_1}{dt} \quad (1\text{-}81)$$

Equations 1-80 and 1-81 are both linear differential equations of the second order and first degree, in which the coefficients are constant, and both can be solved by standard methods. In both cases, the integral is of the form

$$i = Ae^{m_1t} + Be^{m_2t} + \text{a function of } t$$

where the exponential terms represent transient currents which disappear in a relatively short time, leaving as the permanent, or steady-state, solution a function of the time, t. The constants of integration, A and B, are determined by the initial conditions in the circuit, and the exponents m_1 and m_2 are found to be

$$m_1 = -\frac{L_1R_s + L_sR_1}{2(L_1L_s - M^2)} + \frac{\sqrt{(L_1R_s + L_sR_1)^2 - 4R_1R_s(L_1L_s - M^2)}}{2(L_1L_s - M^2)}$$

$$m_2 = -\frac{L_1R_s + L_sR_1}{2(L_1L_s - M^2)} - \frac{\sqrt{(L_1R_s + L_sR_1)^2 - 4R_1R_s(L_1L_s - M^2)}}{2(L_1L_s - M^2)}$$

In these expressions, all the quantities on the right-hand side are essentially positive; hence, the values of m_1 and m_2 are both essentially negative, and the transient currents accordingly decay in a logarithmic manner.

The steady-state solution for i_1 is found to be

$$i_1 = \frac{V_{1m}\sqrt{R_s^2 + \omega^2L_s^2}}{[R_1R_s - \omega^2(L_1L_s - M^2)]^2 + \omega^2(L_1R_s + L_sR_1)^2}$$
$$\sin[\omega t + \alpha - (\beta - \beta_2)] \quad (1\text{-}82)$$

where
$$\tan\beta = \frac{\omega(L_1R_s + L_sR_1)}{R_1R_s - \omega^2(L_1L_s - M^2)}$$

$$\tan\beta_2 = \frac{\omega L_s}{R_s} \qquad\qquad (1\text{-}83)$$

and the solution for i_2 is

$$i_2 = -\frac{\omega M V_{1m}}{\sqrt{[R_1 R_s - \omega^2(L_1 L_s - M^2)]^2 + \omega^2(L_1 R_s + L_s R_1)^2}} \sin(\omega t + \alpha - \gamma) \quad (1\text{-}84)$$

where

$$\tan \gamma = \frac{\omega^2(L_1 L_s - M^2) - R_1 R_s}{\omega(L_1 R_s + L_s R_1)} \quad (1\text{-}85)$$

In Eqs. 1-82 and 1-84, the coefficients of the trigonometric terms represent the maximum values of the harmonically varying currents in the primary and secondary; and their ratio is therefore equal to the ratio of the corresponding effective values of these currents; i.e.,

$$\frac{I_2}{I_1} = \frac{\omega M}{\sqrt{R_s^2 + \omega^2 L_s^2}} = \frac{\omega M}{Z_s} \quad (1\text{-}86)$$

where Z_s is the total impedance of the entire secondary circuit, and I_2/I_1 is substantially equal to the ratio of transformation heretofore designated as a. Reference to Eq. 1-82 shows that the equivalent impedance of the transformer, in terms of the primary, is

$$Z_{1e} = \frac{\sqrt{[R_1 R_s - \omega^2(L_1 L_s - M^2)]^2 + \omega^2(L_1 R_s + L_s R_1)^2}}{Z_s} \quad (1\text{-}87)$$

which can be reduced to the form

$$Z_{1e} = \sqrt{(R_1 + a^2 R_s)^2 + (\omega L_1 - a^2 \omega L_s)^2} \quad (1\text{-}88)$$

The last expression contains the term $R_1 + a^2 R_s$, which calls to mind the corresponding term that appears in the expression for the equivalent impedance based upon the circuit of Fig. 1-14; but the other term in Eq. 1-88 has an unfamiliar aspect, and it is desirable to investigate whether it will reduce to a form comparable with that of the theory presented in the first part of this chapter.

The initial pair of differential equations, 1-72 and 1-74, which show the relations between the instantaneous values of the variables, may be written in the form

$$v_1 = i_1 R_1 + L_1 \frac{di_1}{dt} + M \frac{di_2}{dt}$$

$$-v_2 = i_2 R_2 + L_2 \frac{di_2}{dt} + M \frac{di_1}{dt}$$

The primary impressed voltage has been assumed to vary harmonically, as in Eq. 1-70, and the solution of the differential equations shows that the steady-state variation of both i_1 and i_2 (and therefore of v_2) is likewise harmonic. Consequently, the instantaneous values of v_1, v_2, i_1, and i_2 may be regarded as proportional to the projections on a fixed reference axis of the corresponding phasors represented in complex notation by the effective values of $\mathbf{V}_1$, $\mathbf{V}_2$, $\mathbf{I}_1$, and $\mathbf{I}_2$.   But if

$$i_1 = I_{1m} \sin (\omega t \pm \varphi)$$

we have $$\frac{di_1}{dt} = \omega I_{1m} \cos (\omega t \pm \varphi) = I_{1m} \sin \left(\omega t \pm \varphi + \frac{\pi}{2}\right)$$

which means that a derivative of a variable like i_1 is equivalent to a phasor of effective value ωI_1 which is 90° in advance of I_1.   The two fundamental differential equations may therefore be written

$$\mathbf{V}_1 = \mathbf{I}_1 R_1 + j\omega L_1 \mathbf{I}_1 + j\omega M \mathbf{I}_2 \tag{1-89}$$
$$-\mathbf{V}_2 = \mathbf{I}_2 R_2 + j\omega L_2 \mathbf{I}_2 + j\omega M \mathbf{I}_1 \tag{1-90}$$

with the understanding that the solution of this pair of equations will yield the steady-state solution only.

On substituting in Eqs. 1-89 and 1-90 the values of L_1, L_2, and M from Eqs. 1-69, there are obtained

$$\mathbf{V}_1 = \mathbf{I}_1(R_1 + j\omega N_1^2 P_1) + j\omega N_1(N_1 \mathbf{I}_1 + N_2 \mathbf{I}_2)P_0 \tag{1-91}$$
$$-\mathbf{V}_2 = \mathbf{I}_2(R_2 + j\omega N_2^2 P_2) + j\omega N_2(N_1 \mathbf{I}_1 + N_2 \mathbf{I}_2)P_0 \tag{1-92}$$

In Eq. 1-91, the term $N_1 \mathbf{I}_1 + N_2 \mathbf{I}_2$ is clearly the resultant mmf acting upon the common magnetic circuit when both primary and secondary are carrying current, and the product of this term by P_0 is the effective value of the mutual flux Φ.   The additional factors ω and N_1 serve to convert the term as a whole to the counter emf induced by the mutual flux, and the symbol j means that this emf leads the flux by 90°, so that the term is the same as what was called $-E_1$ in Fig. 1-10.   In the same way, the final term in Eq. 1-92 is equal to $-E_2$; and the expressions $\omega N_1^2 P_1$ and $\omega N_2^2 P_2$ are the leakage reactances, X_1 and X_2, respectively.

Equations 1-91 and 1-92 therefore reduce to the forms

$$\mathbf{V}_1 - \mathbf{I}_1(R_1 + jX_1) = -\mathbf{E}_1$$
$$\mathbf{V}_2 - \mathbf{I}_2(R_2 + jX_2) = \mathbf{E}_2$$

which agree with the original theory as embodied in Fig. 1-10 and the diagrams that follow it.

An additional check upon the identity of the results of the two methods of analysis follows from consideration of Eqs. 1-89 and 1-90, which may be written

$$\mathbf{V}_1 = \mathbf{I}_1 R_1 + j\omega L_1 \mathbf{I}_1 + j\omega M \mathbf{I}_2$$
$$0 = \mathbf{I}_2 R_2 + j\omega L_s \mathbf{I}_2 + j\omega M \mathbf{I}_1$$

On eliminating $\mathbf{I}_2$ between these two equations, it is found that

$$\mathbf{V}_1 = \mathbf{I}_1 \left(R_1 + j\omega L_1 + \frac{\omega^2 M^2}{R_s + j\omega L_s}\right)$$

and the term in parentheses is then the equivalent impedance of the transformer, which has previously been designated as Z_{1e}; hence,

$$Z_{1e} = R_1 + j\omega L_1 + \frac{\omega^2 M^2}{(R_2 + R) + j\omega(L_2 + L)}$$
$$= R_1 + j\omega L_1 + \frac{\omega^2 M^2}{Z + R_2 + j\omega L_2} \qquad (1\text{-}93)$$

where $Z = R + j\omega L$ is the impedance of the load on the secondary.

Reference to Eqs. 1-69 shows that if N_2 is made equal to N_1, which is equivalent to reducing all secondary quantities to terms of the primary, we have

$$\omega L_1 = X_1 + X_0$$
$$\omega L_2 = X_2 + X_0$$
$$\omega M = X_0$$

and on substituting these relations in Eq. 1-93 the result is

$$Z_{1e} = R_1 + j(X_1 + X_0) + \frac{X_0^2}{Z + R_2 + j(X_2 + X_0)}$$
$$= R_1 + jX_1 + \frac{1}{\dfrac{1}{jX_0} + \dfrac{1}{Z + (R_2 + jX_2)}} \qquad (1\text{-}94)$$

The last expression is the same as that derived in Eq. 1-25, Art. 1-8, except that $1/jX_0$ appears instead of $Y_0 = 1/(R_0 + jX_0)$. The omission of R_0 in Eq. 1-94 is a natural consequence of the initial assumption of zero core loss; hence, with this exception the two methods lead to identical results.

CHAPTER 2

TRANSFORMER CONNECTIONS AND OPERATION

2-1. Polarity.   Each of the two primary terminals of a transformer is alternately positive and negative with respect to the other, and the same thing is of course true with respect to the secondary terminals.   But it is obvious that if two or more transformers are to be connected in parallel in a single-phase network, or if they are to be interconnected in a poly-phase system, it is necessary to know the relative polarities, at any instant, of the primary and secondary terminals if the connections are to be made correctly.   This information is readily obtainable by making the simple *polarity test* illustrated in Fig. 2-1, where, on facing the high-tension side of the enclosing case, the left-hand terminals of the H.T. and L.T. windings are connected.   The H.T. winding is then energized by impress-

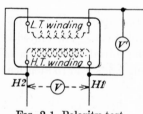

FIG. 2-1. Polarity test.

ing a moderate voltage V, within the range of an ordinary voltmeter.   Voltage V' will then be either greater or less than V by an amount equal to the emf induced in the L.T. winding; if $V' > V$, the emfs in the two windings have an additive relation and the transformer is said to have *additive polarity;* but if $V' < V$, the two emfs are subtractive and the transformer is said to have *subtractive polarity.*

The obvious need for a systematic identification of transformer polar-ities has led to the adoption by the American Standards Association (ASA) of a standard method of marking the terminals.   The high-tension terminals are designated H1, H2, H3, etc., the H1 terminal being on the right-hand side of the case when facing the high-voltage side.   The low-tension terminals are similarly designated X1, X2, X3, etc., but X1 may be on either side, adjacent to H1 or diagonally opposite.   The numbers must be so arranged that the difference of potential between any two leads of the same set, taken in the order from smaller to larger numbers, must be of the same sign as that between any other pair of the set taken in the same order.   It is further specified that when the instantaneous voltage is directed from H1 to H2, it is simultaneously directed from X1 to X2. It follows, therefore, that when the terminals are arranged as in Fig. 2-2*a* the transformer has subtractive polarity, while the arrangement of Fig. 2-2*b* represents additive polarity.

The American Standards specify that single-phase transformers in sizes up to and including 200 kva, which are designed for high-tension voltages up to and including 8,660 volts, shall have additive polarity. Subtractive polarity is standard for all other single-phase transformers. Subtractive polarity reduces the voltage stress between adjacent leads.

2-2. Transformer Connections in Single-phase Circuits. Standard distribution transformers are usually built with both high- and low-voltage windings in two equal sections, though single-coil secondaries are also made. When both H.T. and L.T. windings

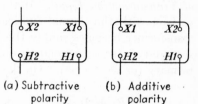

(a) Subtractive polarity (b) Additive polarity

Fig. 2-2. Subtractive and additive polarity.

have two equal parts, the four pairs of terminals are either brought out through suitably bushed openings in the enclosing case or they are brought to a readily accessible connection board inside the cover. Thus, in a transformer for 2,300-volt primary and 230-volt secondary, each half of the H.T. winding is designed for 1,150 volts, and each half of the L.T. winding for 115 volts. The terminals may then be grouped in any of the combinations indicated in Fig. 2-3. Though six arrangements are shown,

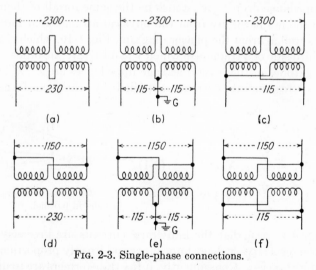

Fig. 2-3. Single-phase connections.

part *b* differs from *a*, and *e* from *d*, only in the addition of a neutral wire to form a three-wire secondary system, permitting the use of 230-volt power devices between the outer wires and 115-volt lighting fixtures or their equivalent between the neutral and each of the outer wires. Note that when a neutral wire is used it must be grounded so that the potential difference between any part of the secondary system and ground may not exceed 115 volts. In a two-wire secondary circuit, one of the wires is grounded as a precaution against the possibility of a breakdown of insulation between the H.T. and L.T. windings, which, if it occurred, would subject the secondary to the high potential of the primary.

2-3. Division of Load between Transformers in Parallel. *a. Ratios of Transformation Equal.* If the exciting current is neglected in comparison with the normal full-load current, the equivalent circuit of a transformer becomes simply the leakage impedance of the primary and secondary in series, secondary quantities being expressed in terms of the primary (or vice versa). On the basis of this approximation, the equivalent circuit of three transformers in parallel is shown in Fig. 2-4. It is assumed that all of the transformers have the same ratio of transformation, and that all connections are made with due regard to the polarity of the windings. Since the magnitude and phase of the primary voltage V_1, and likewise of the secondary voltage V_2, must necessarily be the same for each of the transformers by virtue of the method of connecting them, the leakage-impedance drop V_e must also be the same for all of them. This conclusion follows naturally from the physical arrangement indicated in Fig. 2-4, as well as from the phasor diagram, Fig. 1-16, which shows that V_e is the third side of a triangle in which V_1 and V_2 are the other two sides. If the magnitudes of the several leakage impedances are Z', Z'', and Z''', etc., the corresponding currents supplied by the transformers are, respectively,

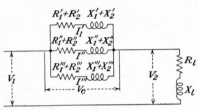

FIG. 2-4. Approximate equivalent circuit, transformers in parallel.

$$\mathbf{I}' = \frac{\mathbf{V}_e}{Z'} = \mathbf{V}_e Y'$$

$$\mathbf{I}'' = \frac{\mathbf{V}_e}{Z''} = \mathbf{V}_e Y'' \qquad (2\text{-}1)$$

$$\mathbf{I}''' = \frac{\mathbf{V}_e}{Z'''} = \mathbf{V}_e Y'''$$

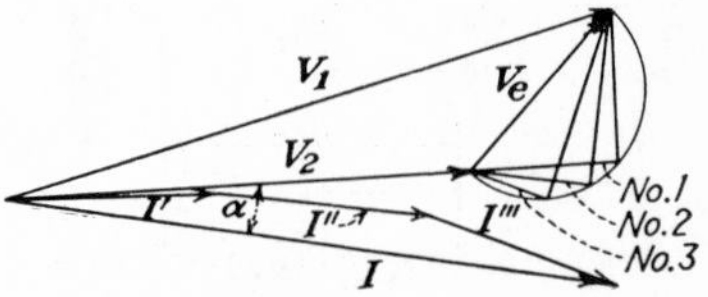

FIG. 2-5. Phasor diagram, transformers in parallel.

from which it is seen that the individual currents are inversely proportional to the respective leakage impedances or directly proportional to the leakage admittances. Consequently, if the transformers are to divide the total load (in amperes) in proportion to their kva ratings, it is necessary that the leakage impedances be inversely proportional to the respective kva ratings; this conclusion is in no way dependent upon the power factor of the external load.

Figure 2-5 illustrates a case in which the impedance triangles are all different because of differing ratios of reactance to resistance in the several transformers. The currents supplied by the three transformers are therefore not in phase with one another, though it must of course be true that

$$\mathbf{I} = \mathbf{I}' + \mathbf{I}'' + \mathbf{I}''' \tag{2-2}$$

Substituting Eq. 2-1 in Eq. 2-2,

$$\mathbf{I} = \mathbf{V}_e(Y' + Y'' + Y''') = \mathbf{V}_e Y \tag{2-3}$$

where $Y = Y' + Y'' + Y'''$ is the joint admittance equivalent to the three transformers in parallel. Hence, from Eqs. 2-3 and 2-1,

$$\mathbf{I}' = \frac{Y'}{Y}\mathbf{I}$$

$$\mathbf{I}'' = \frac{Y''}{Y}\mathbf{I} \tag{2-4}$$

$$\mathbf{I}''' = \frac{Y'''}{Y}\mathbf{I}$$

In the ideal case, the current should divide between the individual transformers in such a manner that the several currents are not only in direct proportion to the respective ratings but also in phase with one another and with the total current. The obvious condition for this agreement in phase relations is that

$$\frac{X_1' + X_2'}{R_1' + R_2'} = \frac{X_1'' + X_2''}{R_1'' + R_2''} = \frac{X_1''' + X_2'''}{R_1''' + R_2'''} \tag{2-5}$$

which means that the three separate impedance triangles of Fig. 2-5 coalesce into one. In other words, the effective resistances and leakage reactances should, like the leakage impedances, be severally inversely proportional to the kva ratings.

The relations indicated in Eq. 2-5 will not in general be satisfied; hence, the several transformers will not operate with the same power factor, as will be clear from Fig. 2-5. Thus, if the three leakage admittances Y', Y'', and Y''' are represented by

$$Y' = G' - jB' = Y'e^{-j\theta_e'}$$
$$Y'' = G'' - jB'' = Y''e^{-j\theta_e''} \tag{2-6}$$
$$Y''' = G''' - jB''' = Y'''e^{-j\theta_e'''}$$

and

$$Y = G - jB = (G' + G'' + G''') - j(B' + B'' + B''') = Ye^{-j\theta} \tag{2-7}$$

where

$$\tan \theta_e' = \frac{B'}{G'} \qquad \tan \theta_e'' = \frac{B''}{G''} \qquad \tan \theta_e''' = \frac{B'''}{G'''} \qquad \tan \theta = \frac{B}{G} \tag{2-8}$$

it follows that

$$\mathbf{I}' = \mathbf{I}\,\frac{Y'}{Y}\,e^{-j(\theta_e'-\theta)}$$

$$\mathbf{I}'' = \mathbf{I}\,\frac{Y''}{Y}\,e^{-j(\theta_e''-\theta)} \tag{2-9}$$

$$\mathbf{I}''' = \mathbf{I}\,\frac{Y'''}{Y}\,e^{-j(\theta_e'''-\theta)}$$

from which it is seen that I' lags behind I by angle $(\theta_e' - \theta)$, or leads by $(\theta - \theta_e')$, and similarly for the others. Therefore, if the power factor of the external load is cos α (see Fig. 2-5), the power factor of transformer 1, referred to the secondary side, is cos $(\alpha + \theta_e' - \theta)$, that of the second is cos $(\alpha + \theta_e'' - \theta)$, and that of the third is cos $(\alpha + \theta_e''' - \theta)$.

In case the resistances and reactances of the transformers to be operated in parallel do not satisfy the relations indicated in Eq. 2-5, it is possible to restore these relations by the insertion of suitable impedances on either the primary or the secondary sides. In this way, the currents may be brought into phase agreement, thus making it possible to utilize the full capacity of all the transformers, whereas otherwise they could only be used up to that load at which one of the transformers reaches its safe limit of heating.

b. Ratios of Transformation Not Equal. It is to be understood, of course, that transformers having widely different ratios of transformation cannot be operated in parallel unless special devices are used to equalize the primary and secondary voltages, as by interposing booster transformers or autotransformers. But it may happen that transformers having the same nominal voltage ratings of primary and secondary differ slightly as to the exact values of the ratios of transformation. Thus, if the desired ratio of transformation is $\sqrt{3}/2 = 0.866$, the ratio of the integers representing the actual number of turns might conceivably be $70\!\!/\!\!81$, or $65\!\!/\!\!75$, or $45\!\!/\!\!52$, etc., which, while nearly the same, are not actually identical. Such small differences in the ratio of transformation do not seriously affect parallel operation, but it is evident that under no-load conditions, for instance, the slight discrepancies in the values of secondary induced emfs must be equalized by the flow of current in the internal circuits formed by the windings themselves.

In this case, as in (*a*), the primary and secondary terminal voltages of all the transformers are necessarily equal and in phase, but since the ratios of transformation are different, the phasor diagram of Fig. 2-5 no longer applies. If primary quantities are expressed in terms of the secondary, the reduced values of the primary voltage, which has the actual value V_1, must be considered to be V_1/a_1, V_1/a_2, V_1/a_3, etc., for the transformers the ratios of transformation of which are, respectively, a_1, a_2, a_3, etc. The impedance drops, being in each case the geometrical difference between

V_1/a_k and V_2 (where the subscript k takes the values 1, 2, 3, etc.), are then given by

$$\frac{V_1}{a_1} - V_2 = I'Z' = \frac{I'}{Y'}$$

$$\frac{V_1}{a_2} - V_2 = I''Z'' = \frac{I''}{Y''} \qquad (2\text{-}10)$$

$$\frac{V_1}{a_3} - V_2 = I'''Z''' = \frac{I'''}{Y'''}$$

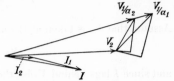

FIG. 2-6. Phasor diagram, unequal ratios of transformation.

as illustrated in Fig. 2-6, whence

$$I = I' + I'' + I''' = V_1 \sum \frac{Y_k}{a_k} - V_2 \sum Y_k$$

where $\Sigma Y_k = Y' + Y'' + Y'''$, and therefore

$$V_1 = \frac{V_2 \Sigma Y_k + I}{\Sigma (Y_k/a_k)} \qquad (2\text{-}11)$$

Any one of the currents I', I'', and I''' can be found by eliminating V_2 between Eq. 2-11 and that one of the group in Eq. 2-10 which contains the current to be evaluated; thus, solving for I', it is found that

$$I' = \frac{I + V_1[(\Sigma Y_k/a_1) - \Sigma (Y_k/a_k)]}{Z' \Sigma Y_k} \qquad (2\text{-}12)$$

Example. Two transformers, connected in parallel on both the high- and low-voltage sides, are characterized by the following data, where the impedances and resistances are given in terms of the low-voltage sides:

Unit	Kva rating	Voltage	Impedance, ohms	Resistance, ohms
A	100	4,600/230	0.027	0.008
B	200	4,610/225	0.013	0.003

The load, connected to the low-voltage side, takes 150 kw at a lagging power factor of 0.85, and the terminal voltage is 235 volts. It is required to find the primary voltage and the current supplied by each transformer.

Solution:

Transformer A

$a_1 = 4,600/230 = 20$

$Z' = 0.008 + j0.027$

$Y' = 10.08 - j34.05$

$\dfrac{Y'}{a_1} = 0.504 - j1.702$

Transformer B

$a_2 = 4,610/225 = 20.49$

$Z'' = 0.003 + j0.013$

$Y'' = 16.85 - j73.03$

$\dfrac{Y''}{a_2} = 0.822 - j3.563$

$$\sum Y_k = 26.93 - j107.08$$

$$\sum \frac{Y_k}{a_k} = 1.326 - j5.265$$

From the given data,

$$I = \frac{150,000}{225 \times 0.85} = 784 \text{ amp}$$

Assume that V_2 is taken as the axis of reference so that

$$\mathbf{V}_2 = V_2 + j0 = 225$$

and since I lags behind V_2 by the angle $\cos^{-1} 0.85$ or $\sin^{-1} 0.527$,

$$\mathbf{I} = 784(0.85 - j0.527) = 666.4 - j413.17$$

It follows from Eq. 2-11 that

$$\mathbf{V}_1 = \frac{225(26.93 - j107.08) + 784(0.85 - j0.527)}{1.326 - j5.265}$$

$$= \frac{6,725.6 - j24,506}{1.326 - j5.265} = \frac{25,411\underline{/-74°39.16'}}{5.428\underline{/-75°51.85'}}$$

$$= 4,681\underline{/1°12.7'}$$

From Eq. 2-12,

$$\mathbf{I}' = \frac{784(0.85 - j0.527) + 4,681\underline{/1°12.7'}\left[\dfrac{26.93 - j107.08}{20} - (1.326 - j5.265)\right]}{(0.008 + j0.027)(26.93 - j107.08)}$$

$$= 363.8\underline{/-44°38'} = 258.9 - j255.7$$

and therefore

$$\mathbf{I}'' = \mathbf{I} - \mathbf{I}' = 407.5 - j157.47 = 436.9\underline{/-21°7.7'}$$

These results show that transformer A is loaded to 83.5 per cent of its current rating, while transformer B is loaded only to 49.3 per cent of its rated current.

It appears from Eq. 2-12 that the current through any one of the parallel transformers consists of two components, one of which is proportional to I and therefore variable with the load, the other of which is proportional to V_1 and is therefore constant. The latter component, in combination with the corresponding constant components of the other parallel transformers, circulates in the local circuit between them and so represents an objectionable constant loss.

2-4. Single-phase Transformers in Two-phase Circuits. In the simplest form of the two-phase system, each of the two phases consists of an independent single-phase system, as in Fig. 2-7a. Some economy in secondary copper is effected by the three-wire arrangement shown in Fig. 2-7b, but it must be remembered that the middle wire is in that case not a neutral, as in Fig. 2-3b, since for equal loads on the two phases it must carry a current equal to $\sqrt{2}$ times the current in either phase; furthermore, the voltage between the outer wires is $\sqrt{2}$ times the voltage per phase. Figure 2-7c shows a five-wire arrangement with a neutral in each phase, but only one of these neutrals can be grounded.

Figure 2-8a shows two identical transformers supplied on the primary sides by a two-phase source, so that the two secondary voltages $X_1' X_2'$

and $X_1''X_2''$ are equal and in time quadrature; the latter voltage is shown leading the former, but it could be made to lag by reversing the primary terminals of phase 2. The middle points of the two secondaries are connected, as indicated in both Fig. 2-8a and b; the latter diagram is marked with small arrows to indicate the arbitrarily assumed positive directions through the windings in conformity with the polarity markings of the terminals. To fix the magnitude and phase of the voltage between, say, X_1'' and X_2', it will be noted that in tracing through the circuit $X_1''OX_2'$ in Fig. 2-8b the portions $X_1''O$ and OX_2' are both traversed in the assumed

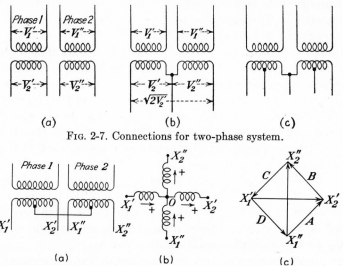

(a)   (b)   (c)
Fig. 2-7. Connections for two-phase system.

(a)   (b)   (c)
Fig. 2-8. Quarter-phase connection of two transformers.

positive direction; the emf phasors pertaining to these two partial windings, each amounting to half of the central phasors in Fig. 2-8c, must then be combined without any change in the assumed phase positions of these partial emfs. The resultant is the phasor marked A in Fig. 2-8c; this phasor leads phasor $X_1'X_2'$ by 45° and lags behind phasor $X_1''X_2''$ by the same amount. Each of the other line-to-line voltages can be fixed as to magnitude and phase by a similar procedure,* and it will be seen that

* The time-phase relations between voltages (and current) in a polyphase system can always be determined with ease and accuracy by applying the three rules stated below, each of them being a natural consequence of the physical meaning that attaches to the use of phasor diagrams.

1. Assume a positive direction through each part of the interlinked circuit with due consideration to the fact that in a balanced polyphase circuit the order of connections must be such as to make the system symmetrical as a whole.

2. Designate the terminals in accordance with a *cyclical* system of notation.

3. In tracing through the circuit from one terminal *to the next in cyclical order*, the phasors corresponding to parts traversed in the positive direction must be used in the sense in which they appear in the given phasor diagram; but if the part is traversed in the negative direction, the phasor corresponding thereto must be reversed before combining it with others.

as a whole they constitute a four-phase arrangement, each voltage being displaced 90° from its neighbor on following the terminals of Fig. 2-8b in cyclical order. The secondary connections of Fig. 2-8a are said to constitute a *quarter-phase* system.

2-5. Three Transformers in Three-phase Circuits. There are four possible ways in which the primary and secondary windings of a group of three transformers may be connected together to transfer energy from one three-phase circuit to another. They are

1. Primaries in Y, secondaries in Y.
2. Primaries in Δ, secondaries in Δ.
3. Primaries in Y, secondaries in Δ.
4. Primaries in Δ, secondaries in Y.

Since these connections are all symmetrical, it follows that if the three transformers have identical characteristics and ratings, and if the primary impressed voltages are balanced, the secondary voltages will also be balanced provided the load is the same on each of the phases. Omitting for the present the consideration of operating characteristics under unbalanced load conditions, it is desirable to investigate the time-phase relations between primary and secondary voltages for each of these four combinations, subject to the assumption of balanced loads.

1. *The Y-Y Connection.* The diagram of connections of the three transformers is shown in Fig. 2-9a, the marking of the terminals indicating subtractive polarity in accordance with the standard conventions described in Art. 2-1. The three primary leads are designated A, B, C, while the corresponding secondary leads are a, b, c.

If the phase voltages of the three primaries are represented by the phasors OA, OB, OC, the corresponding phase voltages of the secondaries are $O'a$, $O'b$, and $O'c$, as indicated in Fig. 2-9b and c.

In order to fix the time-phase positions of the line voltages, it must be noted that the cyclical order of the primary line terminals is ABC; so in accordance with the procedure indicated in the footnote on page 71, to find the time phase of the voltage between terminals A and B, it is necessary to trace through the circuit AOB in that order, and in so doing the part AO is traversed in the positive direction, and OB in the negative direction. Consequently, on reversing phasor OB and combining it geometrically with OA, the resultant is BA. The other primary line phasors are similarly determined, and likewise for the secondary line voltages.

It must be borne clearly in mind that phasor diagrams like Fig. 2-9b and c show *time-phase* relations between the quantities represented and that they are not to be confused with such *space* diagrams as Fig. 2-9a. For example, suppose that the points O and A of Fig. 2-9a are connected, respectively, to the plus and minus terminals of an oscillograph element, and that at the same time points B and A are connected to the corresponding terminals of an identical oscillograph element; of the two wave forms thus obtained, that of voltage OA will lead that of BA by 30°. Otherwise stated, the phasor diagrams, Fig. 2-9b and c, must be considered to be rotating counterclockwise at synchronous angular velocity, so that the projection of each phasor upon an axis of reference is at every instant proportional to its instantaneous value. From this point of view, the sum of the instantaneous voltages BA, AC, and CB is always zero.

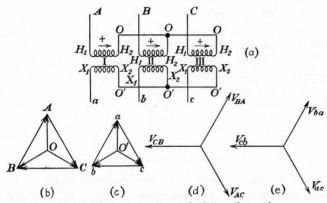

FIG. 2-9. Y-Y connection, polarities subtractive.

In order to eliminate any lingering belief that voltages BA, AC, and CB are chasing each other around a circuit in short-circuit fashion, the triangular diagrams ABC and abc may be replaced by the star arrangements of Fig. 2-9d and e.

Comparison of the phasor diagrams of Fig. 2-9 shows that there is zero angular displacement between the primary and secondary line voltages; actually, there will be a slight displacement because of the effects of leakage impedance and magnetizing current, but this angular shift is quite small.

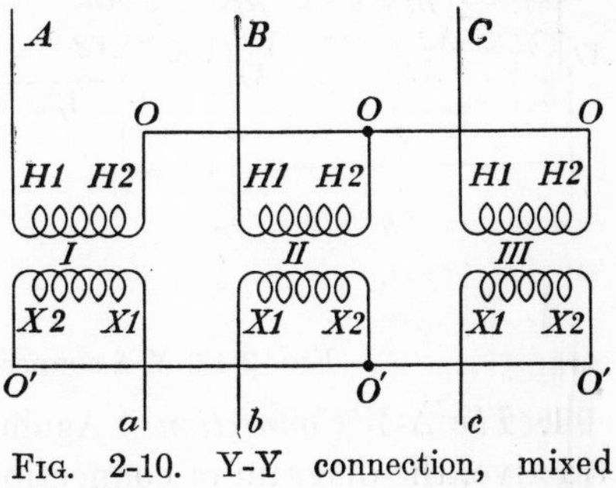

It will be noted that if the primary and secondary line voltages are V_1 and V_2, the primary and secondary voltages of the individual transformers must be $V_1/\sqrt{3}$ and $V_2/\sqrt{3}$, respectively.

FIG. 2-10. Y-Y connection, mixed polarities.

In Fig. 2-9a, all three transformers have subtractive polarity. It may happen, however, that one of the three transformers, such as transformer I in Fig. 2-10, has additive polarity, while the other two have subtractive polarity; in that case, the secondary terminals of transformer I must be interchanged. Similar considerations apply to other possible combinations of additive and subtractive polarities.

2. *The Δ-Δ Connection.* Figure 2-11 shows three transformers, all having subtractive polarity, connected in Δ on both primary and secondary sides. All primary windings must be designed for the full line voltage V_1, and all secondary windings for the full secondary line voltage V_2. As in the case of the Y-Y connection, there is no angular displacement between primary and secondary line voltages, except the small amount due to leakage reactance and magnetizing current.

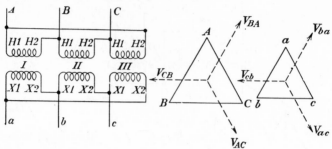

FIG. 2-11. Δ-Δ connection, polarities subtractive.

3. *The Y-Δ Connection.* The diagram of connections for the case where all polarities are subtractive is indicated in Fig. 2-12, and the relative phases of line and phase voltages are also shown. It will be noted that there is a 30° phase shift between the primary and secondary line voltages. If the line voltages are V_1 and V_2, as before, the transformers must be designed for a primary voltage $V_1/\sqrt{3}$ and a secondary voltage V_2.

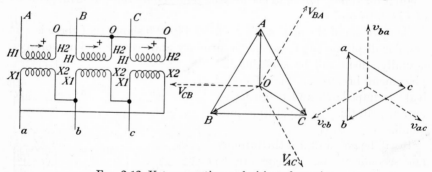

FIG. 2-12. Y-Δ connection, polarities subtractive.

4. *The Δ-Y Connection.* Again assuming that all polarities are subtractive, the diagram of connections is shown in Fig. 2-13, also the time-phase relations between primary and secondary voltages. There is a 30° phase shift between primary and secondary line voltages, but in a direction opposite to that in Fig. 2-12. The transformers must be designed for a primary voltage V_1 and a secondary voltage $V_2/\sqrt{3}$.

2-6. Operating Characteristics of the Y-Y Connection. For a given voltage V between lines, the voltage across the terminals of a Y-connected transformer is $V/\sqrt{3}$, whereas in the case of Δ-connected trans-

formers the coil voltage is V, or 73 per cent greater; the coil current of
the Y-connected transformer is equal to the line current I, while that of
the Δ-connected transformer is $I/\sqrt{3}$, or 58 per cent of the line current.
Consequently, other things being equal, the winding of the Y-connected
transformer will have fewer turns, will require a conductor of larger cross

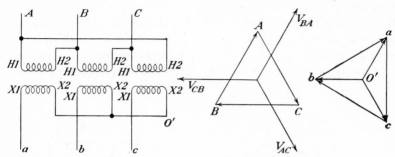

FIG. 2-13. Δ-Y connection, polarities subtractive.

section than an equivalent Δ-connected transformer, and will be somewhat less expensive to build.   The heavier construction makes the winding mechanically strong and therefore better able to withstand the
stresses due to large short-circuit current; and the lower voltage reduces
the dielectric stress on the insulation.   For these reasons, the Y-Y connection presents advantages when two systems, both of relatively high
voltage, are to be tied together; and
there is the further consideration,
which may sometimes be desirable,
that there is no phase shift between
primary and secondary voltages.   On
the other hand, there are some disadvantages, as explained in what
follows.

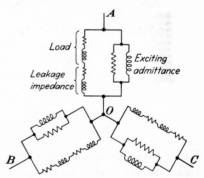

FIG. 2-14. Equivalent circuit, Y-Y connection.

The secondary loads supplied by
the Y-Y transformers may be connected either in Δ or in Y, and may
be balanced or unbalanced; but if the
loads are Δ-connected, they may always be replaced by an equivalent
set of Y-connected loads, so that the circuit equivalent to the entire combination of transformers and their loads will have the form shown in
Fig. 2-14.

If the common junction points of the transformers and of the loads
are insulated, it is apparent that the potential of point O in Fig. 2-14 is
not fixed with respect to the line potentials, but may take any position
relative to the triangle that represents the voltages between lines A, B,
and C.

Suppose, for example, that transformer 1 in Fig. 2-15a is short-circuited. The drop across its terminals will be only the small amount due to the flow of current through the leakage impedance; hence, the potential of the neutral point becomes nearly the same as that of line A, and the other transformers, 2 and 3, are subjected to almost the entire Δ voltage, or nearly 73 per cent above normal.

If only one phase is loaded, the others being on open circuit, the equivalent circuit reduces to the form shown in Fig. 2-15b, from which it will be seen that the only current that can flow in the loaded transformer, 1, is the geometrical sum of the exciting currents of transformers 2 and 3.

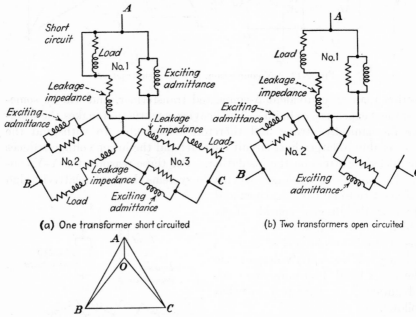

(a) One transformer short circuited   (b) Two transformers open circuited

Fig. 2-15. Y-Y connection, unbalanced loading.

Under these circumstances, the load impedance of transformer 1 may be varied through wide limits, from open circuit to short circuit, without materially affecting the resultant current.

These two extreme cases are sufficient to show the instability of the secondary neutral if its potential is not otherwise fixed; but even with moderate unbalance between the loads on the three phases, the neutral will shift considerably.

Example. Three identical transformers are connected in Y on both H.T. and L.T. sides. Each transformer is rated at 100 kva, 11,500/230 volts, 60 cycles. On open-circuit test, each unit consumes 560 watts at a power factor of 0.155. On short-circuit test, 217.5 volts impressed upon the H.T. winding circulates 8.7 amp, and the power consumed is 1,135 watts.

A balanced three-phase voltage of 15,000 volts, line to line, is impressed upon the H.T. side of the Y-connected group. The L.T. terminals are connected to a star-connected set of three reactors, each having an impedance of 0.6 ohm, but one of them is noninductive, another has a lagging power factor of 0.866, and the third a leading power factor of 0.500.

It is required to compute the current and voltage in each branch of the load.

Solution. From the short-circuit data,

$$\text{Power factor} = \cos \theta_e = \frac{1{,}135}{217.5 \times 8.7} = 0.6$$

$$\sin \theta_e = 0.8$$

$$\text{Ratio of transformation} = a = \frac{11{,}500}{230} = 50$$

The equivalent impedance, resistance, and reactance of each transformer are then

In terms of H.T. side $\qquad$ In terms of L.T. side

$$Z = \frac{217.5}{8.7} = 25 \qquad Z = \frac{25}{a^2} = 0.010$$

$$R = Z \cos \theta_e = 15 \qquad R = \frac{15}{a^2} = 0.006$$

$$X = Z \sin \theta_e = 20 \qquad X = \frac{20}{a^2} = 0.008$$

The primary (H.T.) impressed voltage of 15,000 volts, line to line, is equivalent to a L.T. line voltage of 300 volts between lines. Consequently, the equivalent circuit, neglecting the exciting current, is of the type shown in Fig. 2-16a, all quantities being expressed in terms of the L.T. side.

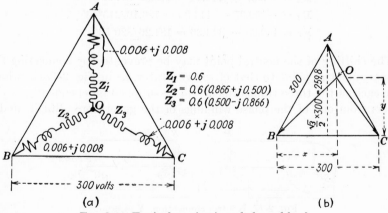

FIG. 2-16. Equivalent circuit, unbalanced load.

In Fig. 2-16b, the phase voltages *OA*, *OB*, *OC* depend upon the potential of the common junction point *O*, which is defined, relative to point *B*, by the unknown coordinates x and y. Thus,

$$\mathbf{E}_A = -(x - 150) + j(259.8 - y)$$
$$\mathbf{E}_B = -x - jy$$
$$\mathbf{E}_C = (300 - x) - jy$$

The phase currents are therefore

$$\mathbf{I}_A = \frac{-(x - 150) + j(259.8 - y)}{0.606 + j0.008}$$

$$\mathbf{I}_B = \frac{-x - jy}{0.526 + j0.308}$$

$$\mathbf{I}_C = \frac{(300 - x) - jy}{0.306 - j0.512}$$

On rationalizing these expressions for the three currents, the results are

$$\mathbf{I}_A = -1.649x - 0.0218y + 253.01 + j(425.14 - 1.649y + 0.0218x)$$
$$\mathbf{I}_B = -1.415x - 0.829y + j(0.829x - 1.415y)$$
$$\mathbf{I}_C = -0.860x + 1.439y + 258 + j(-1.439x - 0.860y + 431.7)$$

Since $\mathbf{I}_A + \mathbf{I}_B + \mathbf{I}_C = 0$, the real and the imaginary terms of the summation must each be identically zero; hence,

$$-3.924x + 0.588y + 511.01 = 0$$
$$-0.588x - 3.924y + 856.84 = 0$$

from which

$$x = 159.37$$
$$y = 114.36$$

$$\mathbf{I}_A = -12.28 + j240.03 = 240.34\underline{/92°56'}$$
$$\mathbf{I}_B = -320.31 - j29.70 = 321.7\underline{/185°18'}$$
$$\mathbf{I}_C = 285.51 + j104 = 303.86\underline{/20°1'}$$
$$\mathbf{E}_A = -9.37 + j115.44 = 115.82\underline{/94°38'}$$
$$\mathbf{E}_B = -159.37 - j114.36 = 196.16\underline{/215°40'}$$
$$\mathbf{E}_C = 140.63 - j114.36 = 181.26\underline{/320°53'}$$

The shifting of the neutral point may be prevented by connecting the primary neutral point to that of the generator, as in Fig. 2-17, in which case each of the three transformers will be supplied independently of the others from one of the phase windings of the generator.   But if, under

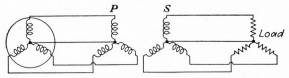

FIG. 2-17. Neutral connection, Y system.

these conditions, there is a third harmonic in the wave form of the generator phase voltage, this third harmonic will appear in the secondary phase voltages, and there will be a corresponding triple-frequency current in each of the secondary circuits.   In the neutral wire, all of these triple-frequency currents are in phase with one another, hence they add directly; and if the secondary neutral is grounded, as it usually is, the triple-frequency current will be likely to interfere with neighboring telephone circuits.

It has been shown in Art. 1-19 that a transformer supplied with a sinusoidally varying voltage will take an exciting current having a third harmonic as a component. With the primary neutral point connected to that of the generator as in Fig. 2-17, these triple-frequency components of the exciting currents have a return path in which all three of them are in phase. In the absence of the primary neutral connection, there is no return path for the triple-frequency component of exciting current; hence, the flux wave is distorted, and a third harmonic appears in the phase voltage of each transformer between neutral and line; this is true with respect to both primary and secondary. If now the secondary neutral is grounded, triple harmonic currents will be set up in the secondary circuits, and since all of them are in phase, they will be directly additive in the neutral or ground return, thus tending to produce inductive interference with neighboring telephone circuits. These triple-frequency currents in the secondary windings take the place of the missing triple-frequency

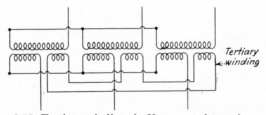

Fig. 2-18. Tertiary windings in Y-connected transformers.

components of primary current and restore harmonic variation to the fluxes. Finally, if the neutrals of both primary and secondary sides are insulated, there will be a triple harmonic in the voltage wave of each transformer, though this is of itself not objectionable.

It appears, therefore, that if the neutral points are insulated, the voltage regulation of the several phases will be very poor if the load is unbalanced; if the primary neutral is tied to that of the generator, a third harmonic in the generator phase voltage will appear in the secondary phase voltages; and if the secondary neutral is grounded, objectionable triple-frequency currents will flow and perhaps give telephone trouble.

These triple-frequency secondary currents can be suppressed by providing each transformer with an auxiliary, or *tertiary*, winding and connecting the tertiary windings in a closed Δ, as in Fig. 2-18. The emfs of fundamental or line frequency induced in these windings will be 120° apart, and will therefore balance; but the induced emfs of triple frequency will be in time phase around the closed circuit, and the resultant triple-frequency current will supply the small magnetizing component that cannot flow in the primaries. Since the entire magnetizing mmf amounts to less than

2 per cent of the primary mmf at normal load, it would appear that the kva rating of the tertiary winding need be only a very small fraction of that of the main transformer; but because of possible short-circuit conditions the tertiary is usually designed to have a rating about one-third that of the main windings. The number of turns in the tertiary winding, and therefore the emf induced in it, is immaterial because the larger the number of turns the smaller will be the triple-frequency magnetizing current. At the same time, the excess capacity in the tertiary makes it possible to supply an auxiliary load at any desired voltage, thus justifying the extra cost of the tertiary as an offset to the saving due to the use of Y-connected, rather than Δ-connected, main windings.

2-7. The Open-Δ, or V, Connection. It is apparent from the connection diagram of the Δ-Δ arrangement, Fig. 2-11, shown also diagrammatically in Fig. 2-19, that each transformer is excited directly from the generator or other source of supply. This arrangement is extensively used, for it has the advantage that one transformer can be removed entirely without interfering with the operation of the system except to the extent that the ultimate capacity is less with the two remaining transformers than with the original three; there is also in that case some unbalancing of the secondary voltages, as will be shown later. When one transformer is thus removed, as in the diagram of connections Fig. 2-20, the transformers are said to be *V-connected*, or to be in *open* Δ.

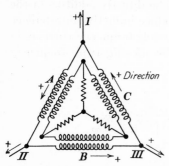

Fig. 2-19. Δ-connected transformers.

In order that three transformers may operate satisfactorily when in Δ, they should each have the same impedance, for if this condition is not satisfied, the currents will not be quite balanced even with balanced load. Thus, if in Fig. 2-19 the three line currents are I_I, I_{II}, and I_{III}, and the transformer or Δ currents (expressed in terms of the primary) are I_A, I_B, and I_C, it follows from Kirchhoff's law that

$$\mathbf{I}_I = \mathbf{I}_C - \mathbf{I}_A \tag{2-13}$$
$$\mathbf{I}_{II} = \mathbf{I}_A - \mathbf{I}_B \tag{2-14}$$
$$\mathbf{I}_{III} = \mathbf{I}_B - \mathbf{I}_C \tag{2-15}$$

If the three primary line voltages are V'_A, V'_B, and V'_C, and the three secondary line voltages (expressed in terms of the primary) are V''_A, V''_B, and V''_C, it is necessarily true that

$$\mathbf{V}'_A + \mathbf{V}'_B + \mathbf{V}'_C = 0$$
$$\mathbf{V}''_A + \mathbf{V}''_B + \mathbf{V}''_C = 0$$

whence $$(\mathbf{V}'_A - \mathbf{V}''_A) + (\mathbf{V}'_B - \mathbf{V}''_B) + (\mathbf{V}'_C - \mathbf{V}''_C) = 0$$

But the three terms in the last equation represent the impedance drops, so that

$$\mathbf{I}_A Z_A + \mathbf{I}_B Z_B + \mathbf{I}_C Z_C = 0 \tag{2-16}$$

where Z_A, Z_B, and Z_C are the leakage impedances of the three transformers, likewise expressed in terms of the primary. From Eq. 2-14, $\mathbf{I}_B = \mathbf{I}_A - \mathbf{I}_{II}$; from Eq. 2-13, $\mathbf{I}_C = \mathbf{I}_I + \mathbf{I}_A$; substituting these values in Eq. 2-16, and collecting terms,

$$\mathbf{I}_A = \frac{\mathbf{I}_{II} Z_B - \mathbf{I}_I Z_C}{Z_A + Z_B + Z_C} \tag{2-17}$$

Similarly,
$$\mathbf{I}_B = \frac{\mathbf{I}_{III} Z_C - \mathbf{I}_{II} Z_A}{Z_A + Z_B + Z_C} \tag{2-18}$$

$$\mathbf{I}_C = \frac{\mathbf{I}_I Z_A - \mathbf{I}_{III} Z_B}{Z_A + Z_B + Z_C} \tag{2-19}$$

If now one of the three leakage impedances, say, Z_C, is placed equal to infinity, which means physically that transformer C is removed entirely from the circuit, the connections will be as in Fig. 2-20 and the three equations 2-17, 2-18, and 2-19 become

$$\mathbf{I}_A = -\mathbf{I}_I$$
$$\mathbf{I}_B = +\mathbf{I}_{III}$$
$$\mathbf{I}_C = 0$$

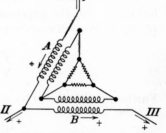

FIG. 2-20. Transformers in open-Δ, or V, connection.

These relations check with the conclusion, obvious from Fig. 2-20, that the currents in windings A and B must be numerically the same as in lines I and III, respectively. The negative sign in the relation $\mathbf{I}_A = -\mathbf{I}_I$ means merely that a positive current in A, or from line I to line II, is the same as a negative current in line I.

If each of the three transformers in a closed-Δ system is rated at V volts and I amp, the line current will be $\sqrt{3}\ I$ when all three transformers are in use; but when one transformer is removed, as in the open-Δ, or V, connection, the line current may not exceed I amp if the current in each of the two remaining transformers is to be the rated value. Hence, the combined rating of the two V-connected transformers amounts to only 58 per cent ($I/\sqrt{3}\ I$) of the rating of the original three transformers, whereas one might have supposed that the two transformers would yield two-thirds, or 67 per cent, of the original rating. In other words, the output that can be obtained from the two transformers in open Δ is 58/67, or 86.6 per cent, of the available capacity of these two transformers; or, to obtain two-thirds of the output of the original closed Δ, each transformer in the open delta must have a rating of $^{67}\!/_{58}$, or 115 per cent, of the original rating.

To determine the voltage regulation of two identical transformers in open Δ, it is convenient first to replace the schematic diagram of Fig. 2-20 by the equivalent circuit diagram, Fig. 2-21. In the latter, it is assumed that the no-load current may be neglected and that each transformer may be represented by its equivalent leakage impedance Z (in terms of the primary). It is also assumed that the impressed voltages are balanced and that the source of supply has negligible impedance (i.e., that the

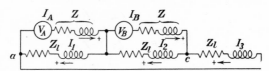

FIG. 2-21. Equivalent circuit, transformers in open Δ, loads in Δ.

source may be considered as an "infinite bus"). The three branches of the load, assumed to be balanced, have equal impedances, Z_l, referred to terms of the primary.

Applying Kirchhoff's second law to the closed loops including (1) transformer A and the adjacent branch of the load carrying current I_1 and (2) transformer B and the branch of the load carrying current I_2, we have

$$\mathbf{V}_A - \mathbf{I}_A Z - \mathbf{I}_1 Z_l = 0 \qquad (2\text{-}20)$$
$$\mathbf{V}_B - \mathbf{I}_B Z - \mathbf{I}_2 Z_l = 0 \qquad (2\text{-}21)$$

Further, in the closed loop formed by the three branches of the load,

$$\mathbf{I}_1 Z_l + \mathbf{I}_2 Z_l + \mathbf{I}_3 Z_l = 0$$
or
$$\mathbf{I}_1 + \mathbf{I}_2 + \mathbf{I}_3 = 0 \qquad (2\text{-}22)$$

Applying Kirchhoff's first law to the junction points a and c, and noting from Eq. 2-22 that $-\mathbf{I}_3 = \mathbf{I}_1 + \mathbf{I}_2$,

$$\mathbf{I}_A = \mathbf{I}_1 - \mathbf{I}_3 = 2\mathbf{I}_1 + \mathbf{I}_2 \qquad (2\text{-}23)$$
$$\mathbf{I}_B = \mathbf{I}_2 - \mathbf{I}_3 = \mathbf{I}_1 + 2\mathbf{I}_2 \qquad (2\text{-}24)$$

Substituting Eqs. 2-23 and 2-24 in Eqs. 2-20 and 2-21,

$$\mathbf{I}_1 = \frac{\mathbf{V}_A(Z_l + 2Z) - \mathbf{V}_B Z}{(Z_l + 3Z)(Z_l + Z)} \qquad (2\text{-}25)$$

$$\mathbf{I}_2 = \frac{\mathbf{V}_B(Z_l + 2Z) - \mathbf{V}_A Z}{(Z_l + 3Z)(Z_l + Z)} \qquad (2\text{-}26)$$

$$\mathbf{I}_A = \frac{\mathbf{V}_A(2Z_l + 3Z) + \mathbf{V}_B Z_l}{(Z_l + 3Z)(Z_l + Z)} \qquad (2\text{-}27)$$

$$\mathbf{I}_B = \frac{\mathbf{V}_A Z_l + \mathbf{V}_B(2Z_l + 3Z)}{(Z_l + 3Z)(Z_l + Z)} \qquad (2\text{-}28)$$

Example. To obtain an idea of the relative magnitudes and phase relations of the various currents and voltages, assume that two 10-kva 2,200/220-volt transformers each has an impedance $Z = R + jX = 8 + j12$ ohms and that they are connected in open Δ to a noninductive load as in Fig. 2-21, where

$$Z_l = R_l + j0 = 500 \text{ ohms},$$

all quantities being expressed in terms of the primary.

Noting that $\mathbf{V}_B = \mathbf{V}_A \underline{/120°} = \mathbf{V}_A(-0.5 + j0.866)$,

$$\mathbf{I}_1 = \mathbf{V}_A \frac{(500 + 16 + \overline{j24}) - (-0.5 + j0.866)(8 + j12)}{(500 + 24 + j36)(500 + 8 + j12)}$$

$$= \mathbf{V}_A \frac{530.39 + j23.07}{265,760 + j24,576} = \frac{\mathbf{V}_A}{502.72} \underline{/-2°47.6'}$$

$$\mathbf{I}_2 = \mathbf{V}_A \frac{(-0.5 + j0.866)(500 + 16 + j24) - (8 + j12)}{265,760 + j24,576} = \frac{\mathbf{V}_A}{522.36} \underline{/118°51.7'}$$

$$\mathbf{I}_3 = -\mathbf{I}_1 - \mathbf{I}_2 = \frac{\mathbf{V}_A}{525.2} \underline{/236°4.2'}$$

$$\mathbf{I}_A = \mathbf{V}_A \frac{(1,000 + 24 + j36) + (-0.5 + j0.866)500}{265,760 + j24,576} = \frac{\mathbf{V}_A}{294.9} \underline{/25°55.8'}$$

$$\mathbf{I}_B = \mathbf{V}_A \frac{500 + (-0.5 + j0.866)(1,024 + j36)}{265,760 + j24,576} = \frac{\mathbf{V}_A}{306.8} \underline{/87°33.7'}$$

These results are plotted in Fig. 2-22, which shows clearly the severe unbalancing of the currents, as to phase relations, in the supply lines.

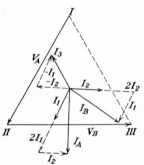

FIG. 2-22. Phase relations of voltages and currents, open-Δ connection.

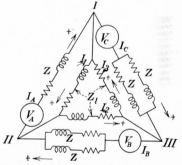

FIG. 2-23. Equivalent circuit, closed-Δ and open-Δ transformers in parallel.

2-8. Parallel Operation of Open- and Closed-Δ Transformers. If two identical banks of transformers, each consisting of three identical transformers in Δ, are operating in parallel and one transformer is removed from one of the two banks, the equivalent circuit will take the form shown in Fig. 2-23. If each transformer has a leakage impedance Z, one side of the Δ will have an impedance Z, while each of the other two sides will have an impedance $Z/2$. Assume that the primary impressed voltages V_A, V_B, and V_C are balanced and that the load is also balanced, each branch having impedance Z_l. It is desired to find the current carried by each transformer and the capacity of the system as compared with that of the original set of six transformers.

Applying Kirchhoff's laws (a) to the circuit of each transformer, (b) to the closed Δ of the load impedances, and (c) to the junction points I and II, we have

$$\mathbf{V}_A - \mathbf{I}_A Z - \mathbf{I}_1 Z_l = 0$$

$$\mathbf{V}_B - \mathbf{I}_B \frac{Z}{2} - \mathbf{I}_2 Z_l = 0$$

$$\mathbf{V}_C - \mathbf{I}_C \frac{Z}{2} - \mathbf{I}_3 Z_l = 0$$

$$\mathbf{I}_1 + \mathbf{I}_2 + \mathbf{I}_3 = 0$$

$$\mathbf{I}_1 - \mathbf{I}_3 = \mathbf{I}_A - \mathbf{I}_C$$

$$\mathbf{I}_2 - \mathbf{I}_1 = \mathbf{I}_B - \mathbf{I}_A$$

From these six equations, it is possible to solve for the six quantities I_1, I_2, I_3 and I_A, I_B, I_C. The solution is facilitated by noting that

$$\mathbf{V}_B = \mathbf{V}_A \underline{/120°} = \mathbf{V}_A\left(-\frac{1}{2} + j\frac{\sqrt{3}}{2}\right)$$

$$\mathbf{V}_C = \mathbf{V}_A \underline{/240°} = \mathbf{V}_A\left(-\frac{1}{2} - j\frac{\sqrt{3}}{2}\right)$$

The results are

$$\mathbf{I}_1 = \frac{4\mathbf{V}_A}{4Z_l + 3Z} \tag{2-29}$$

$$\mathbf{I}_2 = \frac{-(4Z_l + 2Z) + j\sqrt{3}\,(4Z_l + 3Z)}{(4Z_l + 3Z)(2Z_l + Z)}\mathbf{V}_A \tag{2-30}$$

$$\mathbf{I}_3 = \frac{-(4Z_l + 2Z) - j\sqrt{3}\,(4Z_l + 3Z)}{(4Z_l + 3Z)(2Z_l + Z)}\mathbf{V}_A \tag{2-31}$$

$$\mathbf{I}_A = \frac{3\mathbf{V}_A}{4Z_l + 3Z} \tag{2-32}$$

$$\mathbf{I}_B = \frac{-3(2Z_l + Z) + j\sqrt{3}\,(4Z_l + 3Z)}{(4Z_l + 3Z)(2Z_l + Z)}\mathbf{V}_A \tag{2-33}$$

$$\mathbf{I}_C = \frac{-3(2Z_l + Z) - j\sqrt{3}\,(4Z_l + 3Z)}{(4Z_l + 3Z)(2Z_l + Z)}\mathbf{V}_A \tag{2-34}$$

Under full-load conditions, Z may be neglected in comparison with Z_l; hence, approximately,

$$\mathbf{I}_A = \frac{3}{4}\frac{\mathbf{V}_A}{Z_l}$$

$$\mathbf{I}_B = \frac{-3 + j2\sqrt{3}}{4}\frac{\mathbf{V}_A}{Z_l}$$

$$\mathbf{I}_C = \frac{-3 - j2\sqrt{3}}{4}\frac{\mathbf{V}_A}{Z_l}$$

from which it follows that the actual values of these three currents are

$$I_A = \frac{3}{4}\frac{V_A}{Z_l} = 0.75\,\frac{V_A}{Z_l}$$

$$I_B = \frac{\sqrt{21}\,V_A}{4Z_l} = 1.146\,\frac{V_A}{Z_l}$$

$$I_C = \frac{\sqrt{21}\,V_A}{4Z_l} = 1.146\,\frac{V_A}{Z_l}$$

Referring to Fig. 2-23, it will be seen that if I_A is the full rated current (100 per cent) of the single transformer in branch A, the current in each of the two transformers in branch B will be only $\dfrac{\frac{1}{2}(1.146)}{0.75} \times 100 = 76.4$ per cent of their rated currents. The same thing is true with respect to the two transformers in branch C. The total output of the five transformers is then $1 \times 100 + 4 \times 76.4 = 405.6$ per cent of the available capacity of 500 per cent, so that the utilization factor is only 81 per cent. The three transformers comprising the closed Δ would, if they were alone in service, contribute an output of 300 per cent; hence, the increment added by the parallel open Δ is only $(405.6 - 300)/300$, or about 35 per cent.

2-9. Operating Characteristics of Δ-Y and Y-Δ Connections. These connections are particularly well adapted to transformers in high-voltage systems, the Δ-Y connection being used for stepping up and the Y-Δ for stepping down the voltage. The use of the Y connection on the high-voltage side permits the grounding of the neutral point, thereby limiting the potential on any one line to the Y voltage of the system, and at the same time reducing the cost of the high-voltage windings for the reasons previously pointed out.

The grounding of the neutral point of the Δ-Y step-up transformers does not introduce any difficulty because of third harmonics, because the third-harmonic component of the exciting current can flow in the primary. In the case of the step-down transformer, connected Y-Δ, the triple-harmonic component of exciting current cannot flow in the primary windings, but it appears in the secondary Δ circuit, where all three of the triple-harmonic currents are in phase around the delta. In other words, the main Δ winding takes the place of the tertiary winding referred to in connection with the Y-Y grouping.

If the wave form of the voltage impressed on the primary of a Y-Δ bank contains harmonics, the wave form on the secondary side will not be the same as on the primary side. For example, suppose that the voltage between line and neutral on the primary side contains a fifth harmonic, as in Fig. 2-24, which shows the harmonic so placed with respect to the fundamental that the resultant Y voltage is peaked. The secondary voltage induced in each phase of the Δ will then be of the same form, i.e., also peaked. But the wave form on the primary side (line to line) is the resultant of two such waves having their fundamentals 60° apart, and the diagram shows that it is of the flat-topped variety. In other words, a flat-topped wave form of voltage between primary lines gives in general a peaked wave form of voltage between secondary lines, and vice versa.

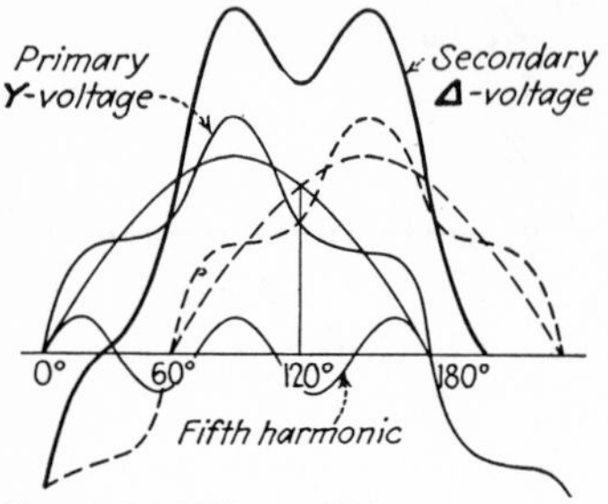

FIG. 2-24. Effect of Y-Δ connection upon wave form.

2-10. Parallel Operation of Y-Y, Δ-Δ, Y-Δ, and Δ-Y Connections. It is evident without analysis that two banks of transformers, each connected Y-Y and having the same individual ratios of transformation, will operate in parallel. This is true because the phasor diagrams of primary and secondary voltages superpose directly.

Inspection of the phasor diagrams of Figs. 2-9 and 2-11 shows that three transformers connected Y-Y will parallel with a bank connected Δ-Δ since in this case the phasor diagrams of primary and secondary voltage likewise superpose exactly, provided, of course, that the line-to-line voltages of both sets are the same.

A bank of transformers connected Y-Y or Δ-Δ cannot be paralleled with another bank connected either Y-Δ or Δ-Y, for when the two sets of primary leads are connected to the same supply circuit, there will always be a phase displacement between the two sets of secondary leads. Thus, comparing the secondary phase relations of the Y-Y group, Fig. 2-9, with those of the Δ-Y group, Fig. 2-13, it is seen that the two sets of secondary voltages are 30° apart; if the secondaries were connected in parallel under these conditions, a partial short circuit would result.

Taking up next the case of two transformer banks, one connected Y-Δ and the other Δ-Y, both designed for the same line voltages on the primary and the secondary sides, it is not immediately apparent whether parallel operation is possible. In order to analyze conditions, the diagrams showing the connections as well as the phase relations between the voltages, which are shown in Figs. 2-12 and 2-13, are essentially reproduced for convenience as Fig. 2-25a and b. It will be seen that when the primary line voltages are the same in both groups, the secondary line voltages of the Δ-Y bank, Fig. 2-25b, lag 60° behind the corresponding secondary voltages of the Y-Δ bank, Fig. 2-25a. This fact suggests that if the secondary line voltages in Fig. 2-25b can each be shifted in the backward (lagging) direction by an additional 120°, the two sets of secondary line voltages will then be exactly in phase opposition; and a further shift of 180° will bring the two sets into phase coincidence, in which case the two banks can be paralleled.

The initial shift of 120° in the secondary line voltages of Fig. 2-25b can be accomplished by a cyclical interchange of the primary leads, in the manner indicated in Fig. 2-25c, thus giving rise to secondary line voltages that are in phase opposition to those of Fig. 2-25a. By reversing the terminals of all three primary windings, as indicated in Fig. 2-25d, all three secondary phase voltages are also reversed, thereby bringing the

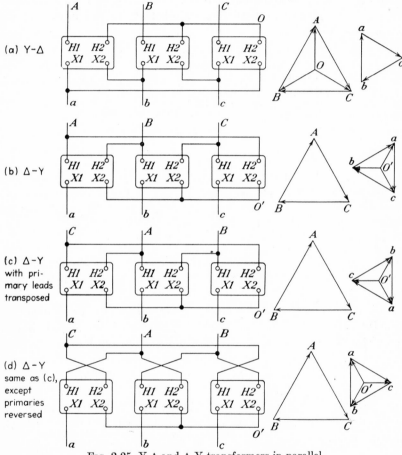

FIG. 2-25. Y-Δ and Δ-Y transformers in parallel.

secondary line voltages into coincidence with those of the Y-Δ group, Fig. 2-25a. The two sets of transformers, Fig. 2-25a and d, may then be paralleled.

The voltage ratings of the Y-Δ group must be $(V_1/\sqrt{3})/V_2$, while those of the Δ-Y group must be $V_1/(V_2/\sqrt{3})$.

2-11. The T Connection in Three-phase Systems. Transformation from one voltage to another in a three-phase system may be accomplished economically by means of two transformers connected in T, in the manner indicated in Fig. 2-26a. One transformer, the primary of which is connected to terminals A and B of a balanced three-phase supply system ABC, is called the *main* transformer; the primary of the other transformer, called the *teaser*, is connected to the mid-point O of the main primary and to the third terminal C of the supply circuit. It will be seen from Fig. 2-26b that the primary voltage V_{OC} impressed upon the teaser transformer must be equal to $(\sqrt{3}/2)V_{AB} = 0.866V_{AB}$, and that V_{OC} is in time quadrature with V_{AB}. Both transformers have the same ratio of transformation.

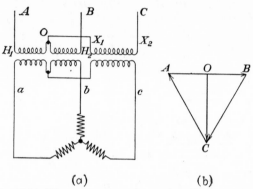

(a)   (b)

Fig. 2-26. Three-phase transformation, T connection.

If the no-load currents are neglected, the equivalent circuit that represents the entire combination takes the form shown in Fig. 2-27a, where all quantities are expressed in terms of the primary (or of the secondary, if that is more convenient). Z_A and Z_B represent the leakage impedances of the two halves of the main transformer, while Z_C is the leakage impedance of the teaser transformer. Z_A and Z_B may each be taken as one-half of the leakage impedance of the main transformer as a whole. The impedance of each branch of the balanced Y-connected load is Z.

The arrows in Fig. 2-27a indicate the arbitrarily assumed positive directions in the various branches of the circuit. Kirchhoff's laws, applied to the junction point O, and to the closed circuits BOC and COA, yield the following relations:

$$\mathbf{I}_A + \mathbf{I}_B + \mathbf{I}_C = 0 \tag{2-35}$$

$$\mathbf{V}_{BO} + \mathbf{V}_{OC} + \mathbf{I}_B(Z_B + Z) - \mathbf{I}_C(Z_C + Z) = 0 \tag{2-36}$$

$$\mathbf{V}_{CO} + \mathbf{V}_{OA} + \mathbf{I}_C(Z_C + Z) - \mathbf{I}_A(Z_A + Z) = 0 \tag{2-37}$$

It is to be noted from Fig. 2-26b that

$$\mathbf{V}_{BO} + \mathbf{V}_{OC} = \mathbf{V}_{BC} = \mathbf{V}_{AB}\left(-\frac{1}{2} - j\frac{\sqrt{3}}{2}\right)$$

and

$$\mathbf{V}_{CO} + \mathbf{V}_{OA} = \mathbf{V}_{CA} = \mathbf{V}_{AB}\left(-\frac{1}{2} + j\frac{\sqrt{3}}{2}\right)$$

so that it becomes possible to solve Eqs. 2-35, 2-36, and 2-37 for $\mathbf{I}_A$, $\mathbf{I}_B$, and $\mathbf{I}_C$. Since Z_A, Z_B, and Z_C are usually small in comparison with Z, they may be neglected without appreciable error, and in that case

$$\mathbf{I}_A = \frac{\mathbf{V}_{AB}}{\sqrt{3}\,Z}\left(-\frac{\sqrt{3}}{2} + j\frac{1}{2}\right) = \frac{\mathbf{V}_{AB}}{\sqrt{3}\,Z}\,\underline{/150^\circ} \qquad (2\text{-}38)$$

$$\mathbf{I}_B = \frac{\mathbf{V}_{AB}}{\sqrt{3}\,Z}\left(+\frac{\sqrt{3}}{2} + j\frac{1}{2}\right) = \frac{\mathbf{V}_{AB}}{\sqrt{3}\,Z}\,\underline{/30^\circ} \qquad (2\text{-}39)$$

$$\mathbf{I}_C = -j\frac{\mathbf{V}_{AB}}{\sqrt{3}\,Z} = \frac{\mathbf{V}_{AB}}{\sqrt{3}\,Z}\,\underline{/-90^\circ} \qquad (2\text{-}40)$$

The last equation means that I_C is 90° behind V_{AB}, or it is in phase with the teaser voltage V_{OC}. The fact that I_A leads V_{AB} by 150° is to be interpreted to mean that I_A leads by 30° its half of the main voltage,

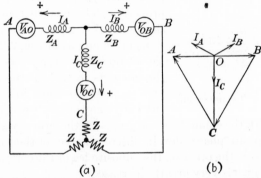

Fig. 2-27. Equivalent circuit and phase relations, three-phase T connection, noninductive load.

V_{OA}; and I_B lags by 30° behind its half voltage V_{OB}. These phase relations are shown in Fig. 2-27b. If the loads are inductive, say, with a power factor $\cos\varphi$, $Z = |Z|\underline{/\varphi}$, where $|Z|$ is the actual value of Z in ohms, and in that case

$$\mathbf{I}_A = \frac{\mathbf{V}_{AB}}{\sqrt{3}\,|Z|}\,\underline{/150 - \varphi} \qquad (2\text{-}41)$$

$$\mathbf{I}_B = \frac{\mathbf{V}_{AB}}{\sqrt{3}\,|Z|}\,\underline{/30 - \varphi} \qquad (2\text{-}42)$$

$$\mathbf{I}_C = \frac{\mathbf{V}_{AB}}{\sqrt{3}\,|Z|}\,\underline{/-90 - \varphi} \qquad (2\text{-}43)$$

The preceding analysis has been based upon the assumption that the teaser transformer is designed for a rated voltage equal to 0.866 times the line voltage V of the three-phase system. If the rated line current is I, the combined volt-ampere rating of the two transformers is $VI(1 + 0.866)$, whereas the output is $\sqrt{3}\,VI$; the utilization factor is therefore $\sqrt{3}/(1 + 0.866) = 0.926$, which is better than that of the V connection.

It is of course possible to design the teaser transformer for the full line voltage V, in which case it will be identical with the main transformer. Since the actual teaser voltage is $(\sqrt{3}/2)V$, its core loss will be approximately three-fourths of normal; so it will develop a temperature rise somewhat less than that of the main transformer. The utilization factor is then $\sqrt{3}/2 = 0.866$.

On the other hand, the teaser transformer may be designed for the line voltage V, but with taps on the H.T. and L.T. sides at the 86.6 per cent points. In that case, the teaser transformer will have normal core loss, but 13.4 per cent of its winding will be idle.

It is important to note that if the secondary connections of the teaser transformer are reversed, without at the same time reversing the primary connections, the system will not operate properly. The incorrect connections are shown in Fig. 2-28. When the connections are made as in Fig. 2-26, the polarities of both transformers being standard, the currents in each of the halves of the main transformer flow in opposite directions, as in any ordinary single-phase trans-

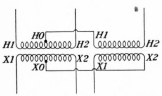

FIG. 2-28. Incorrect T connection.

former; but with the connections of Fig. 2-28, the primary and secondary currents of opposite phases flow in different halves of the winding, one on one leg of the core, the other on the opposite leg of the core, and hence the leakage impedance is very greatly increased.

2-12. Transformation from Two- to Three-phase Circuits. *Scott Connection.** Starting with a polyphase system having two or more phases, it is possible to transform to any other number of phases by means of static transformers suitably interconnected. The earliest example of actual use of such transformation, from two- to three-phase, dates back to 1894, the arrangement being known as the Scott connection in honor of the inventor, Charles F. Scott. The diagram of connections is shown in Fig. 2-29a, transformer I being provided with a secondary designed to give the desired three-phase voltage, with a tap at its middle point; transformer II, which is usually wound for the same total secondary voltage as I, has a tap at a point corresponding to 86.6 per cent of this voltage, and this tap is connected to the third line of the three-phase circuit. Usually both transformers are alike, i.e., each of them is provided with taps at the middle point and at the 86.6 per cent point, so that they may be used interchangeably.

If the primary voltages have the phase relations shown in Fig. 2-29b, the secondary voltages, in their proper phase relation to those of the pri-

* *Elec. Jour.*, **16**:28 (1919).

mary, will be as shown in Fig. 2-29c, the constructions following the rules previously indicated. In case the wave form of the voltage impressed on the primary (two-phase) side contains harmonics, the wave form of the secondary voltage of phase ab will be the same as that of the primary, but the wave forms of phases bc and ca will differ from it and from each other.

It is obvious that the connections of Fig. 2-29 may be used reversibly for transforming from three-phase to two-phase. If the middle points of

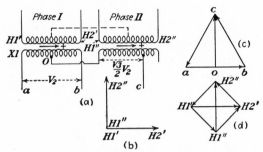

FIG. 2-29. Two- to three-phase transformation, T connection.

the windings H1′H2′ and H1″H2″ are connected, an interlinked two-phase system results, and quarter-phase relations will exist between voltages H1′H1″, H1″H2′, H2′H2″, and H2″H1′, as shown in Fig. 2-29d.

The Scott connection, because of its asymmetry, will not give perfectly balanced conditions on the secondary side. The actual relations can be worked out in the manner already explained for the T connection.

2-13. Third Harmonics in T-connected Transformers. Let Fig. 2-30 represent a three-phase Y-connected generator supplying two identical

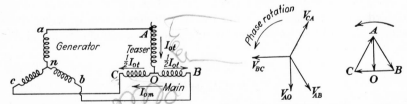

FIG. 2-30. T-connected transformers.   FIG. 2-31. Voltage phase relations, T connection.

T-connected transformers, which in turn supply a two-phase circuit. The main transformer, BC, has a tap at its mid-point to which is connected one terminal of the teaser transformer AO; the tap at point A is so placed that the number of turns between O and A is 86.6 per cent of the total turns of the teaser primary, and likewise 86.6 per cent of the number of turns in the primary of the main transformer.

The voltages impressed between the terminals A, B, and C constitute a balanced three-phase set, as indicated in Fig. 2-31, which also shows the phase of voltage AO with respect to voltage BC.

Under the assumed conditions, the number of volts per turn will be the same in both transformers; hence, the magnetic flux and the core loss will also be the same in both. It follows that the exciting mmf, in ampere-turns, will be the same in both transformers, but since the ratio of turns in the teaser to the turns in the main transformer is 0.866,

$$I_{0m} = 0.866 I_{0t} \qquad (2\text{-}44)$$

where I_{0m} = rms value of no-load current in main transformer

I_{0t} = rms value of no-load current in teaser transformer

Both I_{0m} and I_{0t} will in general be nonsinusoidal because of hysteresis loss and variable permeability, and they can both be resolved into a fundamental and higher harmonics, though in this case only the fundamental

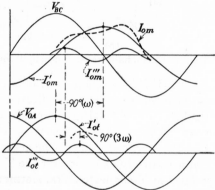

Fig. 2-32. Phase relations of fundamental and third harmonic currents, T connection.

and third harmonics need be considered. Because the maximum flux density is the same in both transformers, the wave forms of I_{0m} and I_{0t} will be similar, so that

$$I'_{0m} = 0.866 I'_{0t} \qquad (2\text{-}45)$$
$$I'''_{0m} = 0.866 I'''_{0t} \qquad (2\text{-}46)$$

where I'_{0m}, I'''_{0m} = rms values of fundamental and third harmonics, respectively, in main transformer

I'_{0t}, I'''_{0t} = rms values of fundamental and third harmonics, respectively, in teaser transformer

Both I'_{0m} and I'_{0t} will lag by nearly 90° behind the voltages impressed upon their respective primaries, as shown in Fig. 2-32. The third harmonics, I'''_{0m} and I'''_{0t}, will each be identically placed with respect to their corresponding fundamentals.

In Fig. 2-32, V_{BC} and V_{OA} are 90° apart, with V_{OA} leading V_{BC} in accordance with the phasor diagram Fig. 2-31. It is at once evident that while I'_{0t} leads I'_{0m} by 90°, I'''_{0t} lags behind I'''_{0m} by 90° on the angular scale pertaining to the third harmonics. Consequently, from Eqs. 2-45 and 2-46,

$$\mathbf{I}'_{0m} = -j0.866\mathbf{I}'_{0t} \tag{2-47}$$
$$\mathbf{I}'''_{0m} = +j0.866\mathbf{I}'''_{0t} \tag{2-48}$$

Reference to Fig. 2-30 will show that because of symmetry any current I_{0t} in winding AO will divide equally at point O, so that the current in branch OC will be the geometrical sum of I_{0m} and $\frac{1}{2}O_{0t}$, while in branch BO the current will be the geometrical difference between I_{0m} and $\frac{1}{2}I_{0t}$. Therefore, on applying Kirchhoff's second law to terminals A, B, and C, it will be seen that so far as fundamentals are concerned

$$\begin{aligned}
\mathbf{I}'_{na} &= \mathbf{I}'_{0t} \\
\mathbf{I}'_{nb} &= \mathbf{I}'_{0m} - \tfrac{1}{2}\mathbf{I}'_{0t} \\
\mathbf{I}'_{nc} &= -\mathbf{I}'_{0m} - \tfrac{1}{2}\mathbf{I}'_{0t}
\end{aligned} \tag{2-49}$$

and that so far as the third harmonics are concerned

$$\begin{aligned}
\mathbf{I}'''_{na} &= \mathbf{I}'''_{0t} \\
\mathbf{I}'''_{nb} &= \mathbf{I}'''_{0m} - \tfrac{1}{2}\mathbf{I}'''_{0t} \\
\mathbf{I}'''_{nc} &= -\mathbf{I}'''_{0m} - \tfrac{1}{2}\mathbf{I}'''_{0t}
\end{aligned} \tag{2-50}$$

On substituting Eq. 2-47 in 2-49 and 2-48 in 2-50, the results are

$$\begin{aligned}
\mathbf{I}'_{na} &= \mathbf{I}'_{0t} \\
\mathbf{I}'_{nb} &= \mathbf{I}'_{0t}(-\tfrac{1}{2} - j0.866) = \mathbf{I}'_{0t}\underline{/240^\circ} \\
\mathbf{I}'_{nc} &= \mathbf{I}'_{0t}(-\tfrac{1}{2} + j0.866) = \mathbf{I}'_{0t}\underline{/120^\circ}
\end{aligned} \tag{2-51}$$

and

$$\begin{aligned}
\mathbf{I}'''_{na} &= \mathbf{I}'''_{0t} \\
\mathbf{I}'''_{nb} &= \mathbf{I}'''_{0t}(-\tfrac{1}{2} + j0.866) = \mathbf{I}'''_{0t}\underline{/120^\circ} \\
\mathbf{I}'''_{nc} &= \mathbf{I}'''_{0t}(-\tfrac{1}{2} - j0.866) = \mathbf{I}'''_{0t}\underline{/240^\circ}
\end{aligned} \tag{2-52}$$

Equations 2-51 and 2-52 show that the sequence of the three third harmonics in the generator windings is opposite to the sequence of the three fundamentals. In both cases, however, the sum of the instantaneous values of the three currents in each set is zero, as demanded by Kirchhoff's law applied to the junction point n.

If it be assumed that the phase relation between I'_{0t} and I'''_{0t} is as shown in Fig. 2-33, the phase relations between the other components are definitely fixed and it becomes possible to construct the wave forms of the resultant line currents. It will be seen that these wave forms are all different, though the effective (rms) value of all three currents is the same.

2-14. Two- to Six-phase Transformation, Double-T Connection. It is easy to see that two identical pairs of transformers, each connected in the manner shown in Fig. 2-29, will have identical phase relations and that the two pairs may therefore be paralleled. But if all of the secondary terminals of one pair are crisscrossed before connecting them to form the T, the result will be to reverse the phase of each secondary voltage, and the triangle of secondary voltages will then be upside down with respect to that of the other pair. Instead of using two separate pairs of transformers, let each transformer of a single pair have double-wound secondaries, as in Fig. 2-34a; after crisscrossing the terminals of one coil of each

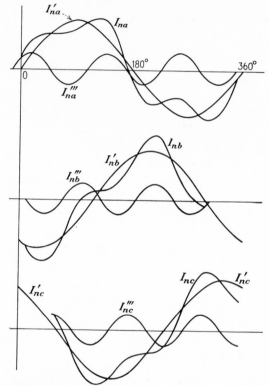

Fig. 2-33. Wave forms of line currents at no load.

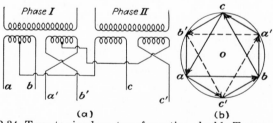

Fig. 2-34. Two- to six-phase transformation, double-T connection.

of the secondaries, the resultant leads are connected in *exactly* the same order as are those of the first set. It follows that the voltage triangle $a'b'c'$ will be reversed by 180° with respect to triangle abc, Fig. 2-34b.

If the two sets of secondary leads, abc and $a'b'c'$, are connected to independent loads, the neutral points of the two voltage triangles may be at different potentials, i.e., the two voltage Δs may float with respect to each other; but if the six leads, a, b, c, a', b', c', are connected to the correspondingly marked taps of a gramme-ring winding (illustrated diagrammatically as a circle in Fig. 2-34b), the two Δs will be fixed in position and will have the same neutral point O. Between adjacent taps of the ring, as ac', there will be a difference of potential represented by the chord ac', to the same scale used in drawing ab equal to the secondary voltage of transformer I; if this secondary voltage is V_2, the voltage between taps will be $V_2/\sqrt{3}$ and the successive tap voltages will differ in phase by 60°, thereby constituting a six-phase system.

The directions of the arrowheads of the phasors constituting the hexagon are readily determined from the consideration that the resultant of any adjacent pair of these phasors must agree in phase with that of the Δ phasor representing the voltage impressed between the end terminals of

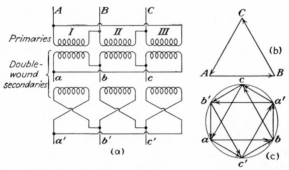

FIG. 2-35. Three- to six-phase transformation, double-Δ connection.

these adjacent sections of the ring. Thus, the arrowheads on phasors ac' and $c'b$ must point counterclockwise (for the case illustrated) in order that their resultant may be phasor ab.

Six-phase connections are commonly used in rotary converters for changing alternating to direct current, and the armature of the rotary converter is then the equivalent of the ring winding used in this discussion.

2-15. Three-phase to Six-phase Transformation. *a. Double-Δ Connection.* The principles explained in the preceding article are immediately applicable to the case of transformation from three- to six-phase by the use of three transformers. Thus, in Fig. 2-35a are shown three identical transformers, each with two independent but identical secondaries, one set connected in Δ in the usual manner, the other in reversed Δ. If the six secondary terminals are then connected to the correspondingly marked terminals of a ring winding (Fig. 2-35c), a six-phase relationship will exist between the taps of the ring.

Figure 2-35a is shown with the primary windings in Δ, in which case the line voltages will have the phases indicated in Fig. 2-35b, corresponding to the secondary phasor diagram in Fig. 2-35c.

If the primaries are connected in Y, as in Fig. 2-36a, the phasors representing primary line voltage must be as in Fig. 2-36b if the secondary phase sequence is to be the same as before.   It will be noted that Fig. 2-36b is rotated counterclockwise through 150° with respect to Fig. 2-35b; hence, if the primary line voltages have the same phase in both cases, the secondary voltages of Fig. 2-35c would have to be rotated clockwise through 150° to make them agree with those of Fig. 2-36c.

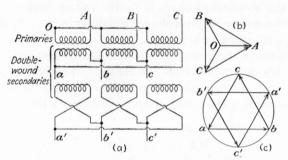

FIG. 2-36. Three- to six-phase transformation, double-Δ connection.

b. Double-Y Connection.   Instead of connecting the two sets of secondary windings in double Δ, as above, they may be connected in double star, as in Fig. 2-37a; if the line voltages have the phase relations of Fig. 2-37b, the secondary voltages will have the phase relations of Fig. 2-37c.   The neutral points O and O' will have the same potential when the secondary leads are connected to the ring winding and may therefore be connected together.   A lead brought out from this common neutral will then serve

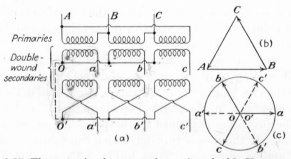

FIG. 2-37. Three- to six-phase transformation, double-Y connection.

as the neutral wire of a three-wire d-c circuit supplied from the rotary converter constituting the equivalent of the ring windings of the figure.

The diagram shows the primaries connected in Δ, but they may, of course, be connected in Y, subject to what has been said with reference to third harmonics.

c. Diametrical Connection.   Three transformers with single secondaries will produce a six-phase relationship if each of the secondary terminals is connected to the correspondingly marked tap of a ring winding, as in Fig. 2-38a and c.   It is important to observe that each set of homologous terminals, as a, b, and c, which have potentials differing in phase by 120°, must be connected to taps of the ring which are separated by an angle corresponding to this electrical displacement.   In a two-pole ring, the space angle will be 120°, in a four-pole ring, 60°, etc.   The diametrical connection, because of its simplicity is, very generally used.   If the middle

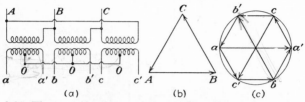

Fig. 2-38. Three- to six-phase transformation, diametrical connection.

points of the three secondaries, which have the same potential, as indicated by the line *OOO* in Fig. 2-38a, are connected together and a lead is brought out from this junction, this lead will serve as a neutral wire for the system.   It should be noted, however, that if the three middle points of the secondaries are joined together, the connection becomes identically the same as that of the double-Y connection.

2-16. Interconnected-star, or Zigzag, Connection.   Inspection of Fig. 2-37a shows that if a double-Y connection, with neutral brought out, is used to supply a rotary converter, which in turn supplies a three-wire d-c circuit, an unbalanced direct current in the neutral wire will divide in such a way that the halves of each secondary winding will carry equal currents in opposite directions.   Consequently, there will be no resultant unidirectional magnetization of the core due to this unbalanced direct current.

Suppose, however, that the rotary converter supplying the three-wire

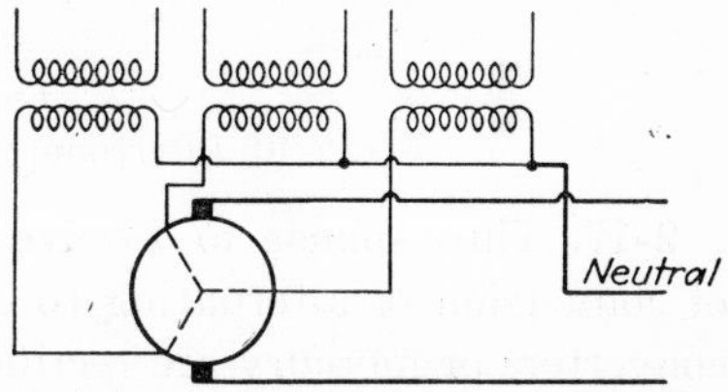

Fig. 2-39. Three-phase connection to rotary converter, with neutral.

d-c circuit is designed for three-phase instead of six-phase operation, which means that the equivalent ring winding has only three taps instead of six.   Using three transformers each with a single secondary winding, the connections would be as in Fig. 2-39.   Under these conditions, an unbalanced direct current in the neutral will divide between the three secondaries, and there will be in each of them a resultant unidirectional magnetization of the core, the effect of which will be to increase the flux density and the resultant core loss and temperature rise, as well as to distort the wave form of the exciting current.

To prevent this condition, and at the same time to continue the use of the three-tap equivalent ring winding, each of the transformer second-aries is made in two halves, and the six halves are then interconnected as shown in Fig. 2-40a.   The phasor diagram of the resultant line voltages is indicated in Fig. 2-40b.   If the voltage of each half of the transformer secondaries is V_2, the Y voltage is $\sqrt{3}\ V_2$ and the secondary line volt-age is $3V_2$.

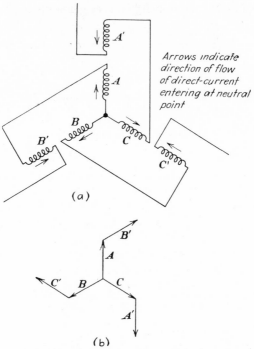

Arrows indicate direction of flow of direct-current entering at neutral point

(a)

(b)

Fig. 2-40. Interconnected star, or zigzag, connection.

2-17. Three-phase to Twelve-phase Transformation.   The efficiency of conversion of alternating to direct current by means of synchronous converters or mercury-arc rectifiers increases as the number of phases in the a-c supply circuit is increased, though not in proportion.   The gain in efficiency in going from six to twelve phases is decidedly less than in going from three to six phases, so that the use of twelve phases is justi-fied only in large units, where the saving due to increased efficiency off-sets the greater cost of the more complex wiring.   There are three prin-cipal methods for transforming from three to twelve phases, as follows:

1. Figure 2-41 represents two banks of three transformers each.   Each transformer has two identical secondary windings arranged for double-star connection to the load (represented by a ring winding).   The pri-maries of one set of transformers are Y-connected; those of the other are Δ-connected.   There is accordingly a phase shift of 30° between the sec-ondary star voltages of the two systems.

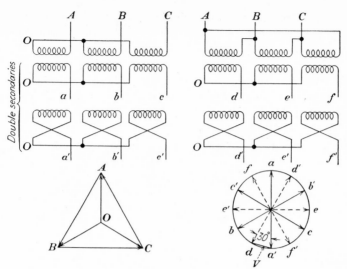

FIG. 2-41. Three- to twelve-phase transformation, Y-Δ double-star connection.

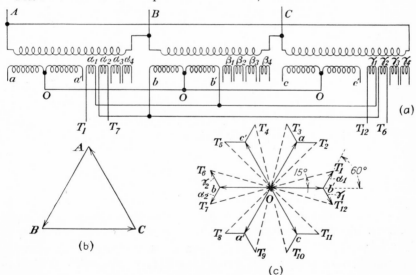

FIG. 2-42. Three- to twelve-phase transformation, double-star zigzag connection (partial drawing).

If V is the line-to-line voltage of the twelve-phase circuit, each secondary winding must be designed for $V/(2 \sin 15°) = 1.931V$ volts.   If the primary line voltage is V_1, the primary windings of the Y-connected bank must be designed for $V_1/\sqrt{3}$ volts, while the primary windings of the Δ-connected bank must be designed for V_1 volts.

2. Another method, partially indicated in Fig. 2-42, requires only three transformers, but each must have five secondaries, of which one (such as aa') may be designated as the main secondary, and the other four

(such as α_1, α_2, α_3, α_4) as teaser windings. The primary windings, connected in Δ, are supplied from a three-phase source, the phase relations of the line voltages being shown in Fig. 2-42b.

The mid-points of the three main secondaries are interconnected to form a double star, as shown in Fig. 2-42a. It will then be seen that if terminal b' is connected in the manner shown to windings γ_1 and α_1, the voltages OT_1 and OT_{12} will be 30° apart provided the ratio of each teaser voltage to that of the main secondary is $1/(2 + 2\sqrt{3})$, or 0.183. Similar considerations applied to the other terminals of the double-star show that the 12 voltages OT_1, OT_2, . . . , OT_{12}, each displaced by 30° from its adjacent neighbor, are obtainable.

If the neutral-to-line voltage of the twelve-phase system is designated as V, the voltage of each main secondary (with center taps) must be $2\sqrt{\dfrac{2}{3}}\, V = 1.634V$ and the voltage of each teaser winding must be

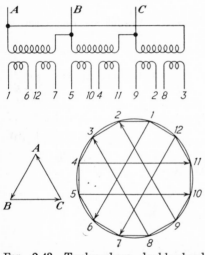

$\sqrt{2}/(3 + \sqrt{3})V = 0.299V$. The line-to-line voltage of the twelve-phase system is

$$\sqrt{2 - \sqrt{3}}\; V = 0.518V$$

3. The *double-chord* connection requires three single-phase transformers (or one three-phase transformer) with the secondary winding of each phase in two equal parts, as shown in Fig. 2-43. On connecting the secondary terminals to the correspondingly numbered taps of a gramme-ring receiver circuit (or its equivalent), the line-to-line voltages between taps will constitute a twelve-phase system.

FIG. 2-43. Twelve-phase double-chord connection.

If the voltage of each half of the transformer secondaries is V_2, the twelve-phase voltage, line to line, will be $V_2 \tan 15° = 0.268V_2$.

Inspection of Fig. 2-43 will show that, unlike the two preceding cases, the transformer connections will not of themselves yield a twelve-phase relationship. It is only when the transformer secondary terminals are properly connected to an appropriate receiver circuit that the desired twelve-phase relations are obtained.

2-18. Other Methods of Phase Transformation.* The connections described in the preceding articles cover the cases that arise in ordinary

---

* See **J. B.** Gibbs, Three-phase to Two-phase Transformation, *Elec. Jour.*, **16**:103 (1919).

practice, but occasionally it is desirable to use other methods for transforming from two- to three-phase, or vice versa.

Figure 2-44, known as the Taylor connection, requires three single-phase transformers, or one three-phase transformer. The secondary of one transformer, as bc, has a tap at its middle point, and the other two secondaries have taps at points corresponding to $V_2\sqrt{3}/2$, or 86.6 per cent. One branch of the resultant two-phase circuit, which has a voltage equal to $V_2\sqrt{3}/2$, is connected to points a and d, the other to points

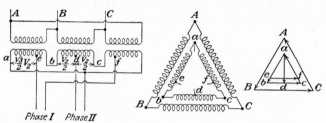

FIG. 2-44. Three- to two-phase transformation, Taylor connection.

e and f. The relationships between the primary and secondary voltage phasors are shown in the figure. The secondary circuit may be made to supply a three-phase circuit, in addition to the two-phase circuit, by connecting it to the points a, b, and c.

Figure 2-45, known as the Fortescue connection, also uses three single-phase transformers or one three-phase transformer. Two of the secondaries are provided with taps d and e, respectively, at $\sqrt{2}\, V_2/\sqrt{2 + \sqrt{3}}$,

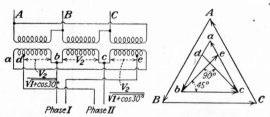

FIG. 2-45. Three- to two-phase transformation, Fortescue connection.

or 73.2 per cent. One of the two phases is connected to points b and e, the other to points c and d. The resultant two-phase voltage is

$$\sqrt{\frac{3}{2}}\,\frac{1 + \sqrt{3}}{2 + \sqrt{3}}\, V_2 = 0.897 V_2$$

In the Arnold connection (Fig. 2-46), the taps d, e, f, and g are so located that the two two-phase voltages dg and fe are symmetrical about a neutral point O, thereby making it possible to supply an interconnected two-phase system. In order to accomplish this result, tap d must be so placed that voltage ad is

$$\frac{\sqrt{3}\,V_2}{2+\sqrt{3}} = 0.464V_2$$

and taps f and g are so located that

$$bf = gc = \frac{V_2}{2+\sqrt{3}} = 0.268V_2$$

The neutral point of the two-phase system does not, however, coincide with that of the three-phase system.

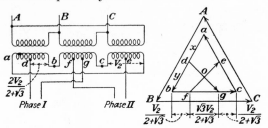

FIG. 2-46. Three- to two-phase connection, Arnold connection.

2-19. Three-phase Transformers.   Instead of using three single-phase transformers in the manner discussed in the preceding articles, it is possible to combine the windings of the three phases on a single core, using either the core or the shell type of construction, thereby effecting an appreciable saving of material and floor space.

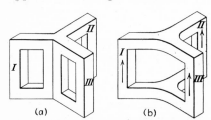

FIG. 2-47. Idealized core of three-phase transformer.

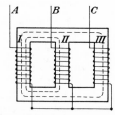

FIG. 2-48. Three-phase core-type transformer.

The three-phase core type may be thought of as evolved from three single-phase transformers lapped together as in Fig. 2-47a, with the primary and secondary windings on one leg of each core.   At the point where the three central legs come together, the yokes of the magnetic circuits are Y- or star-connected, and since the three fluxes are mutually 120° apart in time phase, their sum is zero at the junction, exactly as in the case of balanced three-phase currents meeting at a point.   Consequently, there would be no flux in the central core, and it might be omitted, as in Fig. 2-47b, without in any way altering the remaining conditions; but the difficulty and expense of constructing the core in this way preclude the use of such a design, with the result that, as usually constructed, one of the cores such as II (Fig. 2-47b) is brought in between the other two, as in Fig. 2-48. The magnetic circuits of the three phases are thus somewhat unbalanced, the central one having less reluctance than the other two, but not sufficiently to make any appreciable difference in operating characteristics; ignoring this slight unbalancing, the flux is the same in all parts of the magnetic circuit, and the cross section of cores and yokes should be the same if uniform flux density is desired throughout.

The shell type of construction is shown diagrammatically in Fig. 2-49, but with the direction of the winding the same in all three of the phases; in actual practice, the direction of the central winding is reversed with respect to the other two, as shown in Fig. 2-50, for the following reasons:

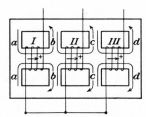

Fig. 2-49. Effect of winding direction, three-phase shell-type transformer.

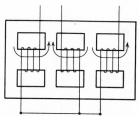

Fig. 2-50. Reversed middle coil, shell-type transformer.

Let the straight arrows on the three cores I, II, and III of Fig. 2-49 represent the positive direction through those parts of the magnetic circuit. Then in the part marked b the actual flux would be the phasor difference of the fluxes represented by the curved arrows, and since each of these is half of the main fluxes Φ_I and Φ_{II}, which differ in phase by 120°, the resultant flux would be $\Phi(\sqrt{3}/2)$; the same is true as to the flux in c, while at the same time the fluxes in parts a and d are only $\frac{1}{2}\Phi$. For the same flux density throughout, parts b and c would have to be 73 per cent wider than a or d. But if the central winding is reversed, the positive direction of the magnetic circuit through II is likewise reversed, in which case the resultant flux in parts b and c is the phasor sum of two fluxes 120° apart in phase; hence, the resultant is $\frac{1}{2}\Phi$, or the same as in a and d. This permits the width of parts b and c to be the same as a and d, thereby saving some material in the construction of the core.

It is evident from Fig. 2-50 that each phase of the shell-type transformer has an independent magnetic circuit. If one winding of the transformer is disabled and is removed from the circuit, the remaining two may therefore be operated in open Δ, but under this condition it is best to short-circuit both primary and secondary windings of the disabled phase; the effect of short-circuiting the windings of one phase is to reduce to a very small amount any stray flux that may find its way into its circuit from the other two.   In the core-type transformer, the magnetic circuits are not independent, so that one set of windings cannot be short-circuited in the manner described above; if this were done, no flux could pass through the core inside the short-circuited winding, with the result that the other two cores, being then in series, could carry only a magnetic flux having the same time phase throughout the circuit, instead of the two fluxes, differing in phase by 120°, required by the impressed voltages.

The three-phase transformer is lighter and cheaper, occupies less floor space, and is somewhat more efficient than three single-phase transformers of equivalent capacity.   These advantages are sufficient to justify its use, especially in large systems where the cost of spare units is a relatively small item.   The disadvantage, of course, is the probability that anything which injures the winding of one phase will injure the others also; but this is offset by the saving in first cost, at least in large systems, taking into account the cost of spare units.

The fact that the magnetic circuits of the three phases of a shell-type three-phase transformer are independent, just as they are in three separate single-phase units, is sufficient to show that the discussion of Art. 2-6, with respect to triple harmonics in the latter case, is also applicable to the former.   But in core-type three-phase transformers, in which the magnetic circuits are interconnected, the conditions are quite different and require further explanation.

From what has been said in Arts. 1-19 and 2-6, it would apparently be necessary, if the flux varies harmonically, to have a third-harmonic current in the exciting current of each phase of the winding.   But if this were so, and the primaries were Y-connected with the neutral point insulated, as in Fig. 2-48 (the secondaries being assumed to be open-circuited), then, since the triple-harmonic currents would all have the same phase, there would be no outlet or return circuit for them, and these apparently necessary triple-harmonic currents could not exist.   Again, supposing that the exciting currents are sinusoidal, it would be expected that the fluxes would contain triple-harmonic components all having the same time phase; if the central core of Fig. 2-47a were present, these triple-harmonic fluxes would have a return path through it, but since this central core does not exist, there is no return path for them except the air path of high reluctance that takes the place of the central core, thus ruling out the possibility of their presence.   Thus, whichever way we look at it, the relationships between flux and exciting current appear to be contradictory to the principles previously deduced.

The explanation of these apparent discrepancies is to be found in the fact that the relationships between flux and excitation discussed in Arts. 1-19 and 2-6 are based upon the condition that the flux is produced by the mmf of one winding only, whereas in the three-phase core-type transformer each of the magnetic circuits is acted upon by the mmfs of two of the phase windings, as a result of the physical interlinkage of the magnetic circuits.   Thus, referring to Fig. 2-48, the magnetic circuit through core I may be considered to be either of the closed loops indicated by the broken lines, so that in one case the circuit is acted upon by the joint mmf of phases I and II, in the other by that of phases I and III.

Let it be assumed that the flux in each of the cores varies harmonically and, for the sake of argument, that the exciting current in each of the phase windings is distorted in the manner shown in Fig. 2-51.   This distorted curve may then be resolved approximately into a fundamental A and a third harmonic B, as shown in Fig. 2-51, the upper part of which shows the assumed current and flux in phase I, the lower part the corresponding quantities of phase II, the two diagrams being 120° apart.   If

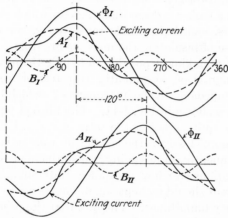

FIG. 2-51. Resolution of exciting current into fundamental and third harmonic.

the arrows in Fig. 2-47b indicate the positive directions of the magnetic circuits in the cores, then on tracing through the circuit I-II, core II is traversed in the negative direction; hence, in combining the mmfs, that of phase II must be reversed.   But since the triple-frequency harmonics of I and II are in time phase, as is clear from Fig. 2-51, then on reversing the mmf of II these triple-frequency components cancel each other, leaving as a resultant the (nearly) sinusoidal curve obtained by adding the ordinates of A_I and of A_{II} reversed.   This means that even if the triple-frequency currents were present their effects would cancel, and therefore they are not necessary in the first place and will not exist.   This conclusion is valid no matter how the windings are connected, whether Y or Δ, but it applies in full only to the construction of Fig. 2-47b, where the reluctances of all three branches of the magnetic circuit are the same. With the actual construction of Fig. 2-48, the reluctances are not all alike, so that there will be in this case a small unbalanced residual effect.

One other case remains to be considered, namely, that in which the primaries are in Y with neutral brought back to the generator. If the phase voltage of the generator contains a third harmonic, each of the cores will be traversed by fluxes of triple frequency, all of which will have the same time phase, and which therefore meet at the common junction, Fig. 2-47b. The only return path for these triple-frequency fluxes is through the air between yokes; consequently this flux constitutes a core leakage flux, linking both primary and secondary windings in the same direction through space. In this respect, it differs from the true leakage-reactance flux, for the latter links with the primary in one direction and with the secondary in the opposite direction (see Fig. 1-31).

2-20. Potential Transformers. The limited working range of voltmeters and of the potential coils of wattmeters requires the interposition of a step-down transformer when these instruments are to be used in a circuit which has a higher voltage than that for which they are designed. Such transformers, called potential transformers, serve the additional important purpose of insulating the instruments from the high potential of the line, thereby making it possible to handle them with safety.

The phasor diagram of the potential transformer, with a load corresponding to the impedance of the instruments to which it is connected, is of the general form shown in Fig. 1-11. The ratio of primary to secondary voltage is not quite equal to the ratio of turns, but approaches the latter more and more closely as the leakage impedance of the transformer is reduced; consequently, in designing transformers of this type the controlling considerations are low resistance and minimum flux leakage. The exciting current should be kept small, but its effect upon the regulation is of secondary importance. The fact that the primary and secondary terminal voltages are not quite opposite in phase is not important in voltage measurements, but in power measurements it introduces an error which must be allowed for in the manner described in the following article.

The calibration of potential transformers should be made when connected to the instruments with which they are to be used; for it is evident from Fig. 1-11 that a change in the impedance of the load, due to the use of a different instrument, or an increased number of them, will change the ratio of primary and secondary voltages. For accurate work, a separate potential transformer should be provided for each instrument.

The requirement that the leakage reactance must be small means that the primary and secondary windings must be thoroughly subdivided and interlaced, and brought as close together as possible, which in turn calls for a high grade of insulating material.

For very high voltages, the size, weight, and cost of potential transformers become considerable items.

2-21. Current Transformers. Since the ratio of primary and secondary currents of a transformer is nearly constant, alternating currents of large magnitude and at high potential can be conveniently measured by causing them to flow through one or more turns of one winding and connecting the terminals of the other winding, having a suitably larger number of turns, to an ammeter of ordinary range.   The approximate equivalent circuit of such a transformer, with the ammeter constituting the load, is shown in Fig. 2-52.

Inspection of this diagram shows plainly that under no circumstances must the ammeter circuit be opened when the system is carrying current, for this would have the effect of placing the comparatively high exciting impedance of the transformer in series with the line.   This exciting impedance, when not shunted by the low impedance of the ammeter circuit, will cause the drop of potential across the transformer terminals to rise to an abnormally high value, and the induced voltage in the secondary, or ammeter circuit, which is still higher by reason of the step-up effect, will reach a value dangerous to life.   If, therefore, it becomes necessary for any reason to remove the ammeter when the system is under load, it is essential that the secondary terminals of the transformer be first short-circuited.   The equivalent circuit of Fig. 2-52 also shows that, with a fixed secondary load represented by the ammeter (or relay coil), the voltage drop across the primary terminals will vary nearly in proportion to the magnitude of the current in the system.   In other words, the current transformer, unlike the types previously considered, operates at variable, instead of constant, impressed voltage.   It follows that the flux in the core is also variable with the load on the system and that the magnetic circuit must be designed to keep the flux density well below saturation when the primary current has its maximum permissible value.   It is also evident from the general phasor diagram of a transformer that constancy of the ratio of primary and secondary currents requires that the exciting current be kept down to a very small amount, thus again calling for low flux density in the core, this being the controlling feature fixing the design.   The leakage reactance should, of course, be kept low, but this is of secondary importance as compared with minimizing the exciting current.   Anything which produces saturation of the magnetic circuit will change the ratio of transformation; for example, if the ammeter circuit is accidentally opened under load, the high magnetization will result in more or less residual magnetism, just as though the core had been magnetized by a direct current; thereafter, the hysteresis loop, instead of being symmetrical about the origin of coordinates, will be shifted up or down, thereby increasing the exciting current and invalidating the original calibration.

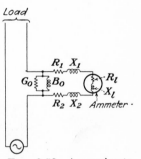

FIG. 2-52. Approximate equivalent circuit of current transformer.

The effect of the exciting current, besides altering the ratio of trans-formation, is to cause primary and secondary currents to be less than 180° apart in phase.   This is not of any particular consequence in measure-ments of current, but it becomes important when the transformer is used

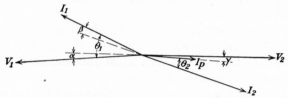

FIG. 2-53. Phase relations in power measurement.

to supply the current coil of a wattmeter.   Thus, in Fig. 2-53 are shown the relative phase positions of V_1 and V_2, the primary and secondary ter-minal voltages of the potential transformer, and I_1 and I_2, the primary and secondary currents of the current transformer.   The angle* between

FIG. 2-54. Instrument current transformer, 2,000/5 amp, 15,000-volt insulation. (*Courtesy of General Electric Company.*)

V_1 and V_2 (reversed) is α, and that between I_1 and I_2 (reversed) is β. Owing to the inductance of the potential coil of the wattmeter, the current I_p through it will lag behind V_2 by an angle γ; hence, the reading of the wattmeter will be proportional to the cosine of the angle between I_p and

---

* See Frank A. Laws, "Electrical Measurements," 2d ed., p. 609, McGraw-Hill Book Company, Inc., New York, 1938, for methods of measuring these angles.

I_2, or

$$\cos \theta_2 = \frac{\text{wattmeter reading}}{\text{volts} \times \text{amperes}}$$

The true power factor of the circuit is, however, not $\cos \theta_2$ but

$$\cos \theta_1 = \cos (\theta_2 + \alpha + \beta + \gamma)$$

Current transformers are generally designed to give a secondary current of 5 amp when the primary current has full-load value. The number of primary turns is one or more, depending upon the normal value of the line current. The equivalent of a single primary turn is secured by extending a single straight conductor through the core, as in Fig. 2-54.

2-22. The Autotransformer. If a coil ac, Fig. 2-55, is wound on a laminated core and a tap is brought out at an intermediate point b, the arrangement constitutes an autotransformer. On impressing an alternating voltage V_1 upon terminals ac, the load on the secondary ab being initially disconnected, the resultant magnetizing current will set up a flux Φ_m webers that links with all the N_1 turns between a and c, and a counter emf E_1 will be induced between these terminals such that

$$E_1 = \sqrt{2}\, \pi f N_1 \Phi_m \qquad (2\text{-}53)$$

At the same time there will be induced an emf E_2 in the N_2 turns between a and b such that

$$E_2 = \sqrt{2}\, \pi f N_2 \Phi_m \qquad (2\text{-}54)$$

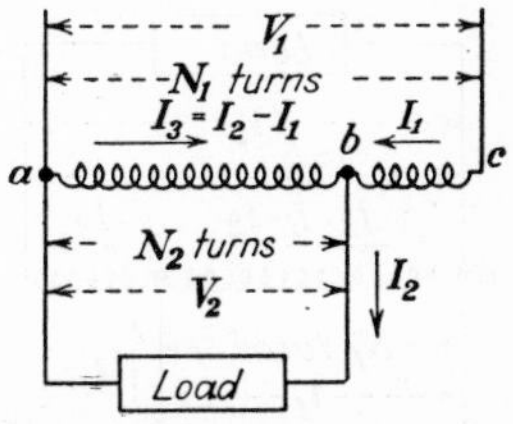

FIG. 2-55. Step-down autotransformer.

Otherwise stated, the number of volts induced per turn, E_1/N_1, or E_2/N_2, will be the same throughout the winding, just as in any ordinary transformer.

On dividing the first of these equations by the second, the result is

$$\frac{E_1}{E_2} = \frac{N_1}{N_2} = a \qquad (2\text{-}55)$$

where a is the ratio of transformation of the autotransformer. For the same reasons that obtain in a two-winding transformer, it will then be substantially correct to write

$$\frac{V_1}{V_2} = \frac{N_1}{N_2} = a \qquad (2\text{-}56)$$

where V_1 and V_2 are the terminal voltages between ac and ab, respectively. The approximation represented by Eq. 2-56 will be closer as the leakage impedances associated with the windings become smaller.

Figure 2-55 represents the case of a step-down autotransformer, and in this case $a > 1$. But if V_1 and V_2 are interchanged, as in Fig. 2-56, the result is a step-up autotransformer, and in this case $a < 1$.

If ideal conditions are assumed in both cases, namely, that core and copper losses, leakage reactance, and magnetizing current are all negligible, it would follow that

$$V_1 I_1 = V_2 I_2$$

or $\qquad \dfrac{I_2}{I_1} = \dfrac{V_1}{V_2} = a \qquad a > 1,\ \text{step-down};\ a < 1,\ \text{step-up} \qquad (2\text{-}57)$

The consequences of Eq. 2-57 with respect to the step-down and step-up autotransformer will now be considered.

a. Step-down Autotransformer. If the exciting current is negligible in comparison with the full-load current, it must be true that the mmf of current I_3 in the N_2 turns between a and b, Fig. 2-55, is equal and opposite to the mmf of current I_1 in the $N_1 - N_2$ turns between b and c; that is,

$$N_2 I_3 = (N_1 - N_2) I_1$$

or $\qquad \boldsymbol{I_3} = \dfrac{N_1 - N_2}{N_2} I_1 = (a - 1) I_1 = I_2 - I_1 \qquad (2\text{-}58)$

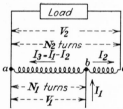

which checks with the requirements of Kirchhoff's law applied to point b.

The volt-amperes delivered to the load, $V_2 I_2$, may be written

$$P = V_2 I_2 = V_2 I_1 + V_2 (I_2 - I_1) \qquad (2\text{-}59)$$

FIG. 2-56. Step-up autotransformer.

which states that the total apparent power may be considered to consist of two parts, namely,

$P_c = V_2 I_1 \equiv$ volt-amperes *conductively* transferred to the load through bc

and

$P_i = V_2 (I_2 - I_1) \equiv$ volt-amperes *inductively* transferred to the load through ab

It follows that

$$\frac{P_i}{P} = \frac{I_2 - I_1}{I_2} = 1 - \frac{1}{a} = 1 - \frac{V_2}{V_1} = \frac{V_1 - V_2}{V_1} \qquad (2\text{-}60)$$

$$\frac{P_c}{P} = \frac{I_1}{I_2} = \frac{1}{a} = \frac{V_2}{V_1} \qquad (2\text{-}61)$$

b. Step-up Autotransformer. It is evident from Fig. 2-56 that the apparent power supplied is

$$P = V_1 I_1 = V_1 I_2 + V_1 (I_1 - I_2) \qquad (2\text{-}62)$$

which means that P consists of two parts,

$P_c = V_1 I_2 \equiv$ apparent power *conductively* transferred through bc

$P_i = V_1 (I_1 - I_2) \equiv$ apparent power *inductively* transferred through ab

whence

$$\frac{P_i}{P} = \frac{I_1 - I_2}{I_1} = 1 - a = 1 - \frac{V_1}{V_2} = \frac{V_2 - V_1}{V_2} \qquad (2\text{-}63)$$

$$\frac{P_c}{P} = \frac{I_2}{I_1} = a = \frac{V_1}{V_2} \qquad (2\text{-}64)$$

It will be noted that Eqs. 2-63 and 2-64 differ from their counterparts 2-60 and 2-61 only in that V_1 and V_2 are interchanged.   In both cases it is seen from Eqs. 2-60 and 2-63 that

$$\frac{\text{Inductively transferred power}}{\text{Total power}} = \frac{\text{high voltage} - \text{low voltage}}{\text{high voltage}}$$

Example. A 10-kva 2,300/230 volt two-winding transformer is connected as an autotransformer with the L.T. winding additively in series with the H.T. winding as in Fig. 2-57. A potential difference of 2,530 volts is impressed upon terminals ac, and a load is connected to terminals ab so that the current in winding bc is equal to the rated current of the L.T. winding.

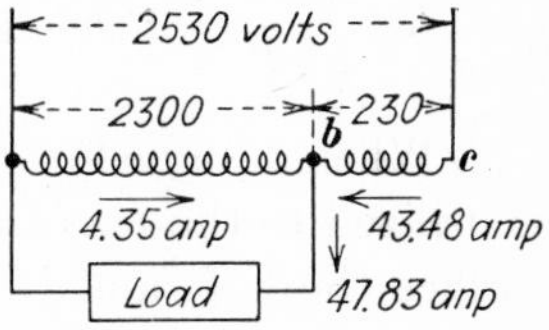

The rated current in the 230-volt winding is

$$I_1 = \frac{10,000}{230} = 43.48 \text{ amp}$$

Fig. 2-57. Ten-kva transformer connected as autotransformer.

and since there are ten times as many turns in ab as in bc, the balance of ampere-turns (ignoring the exciting current) requires that the current in the 2,300-volt winding shall be

$$I_3 = I_2 - I_1 = \frac{10,000}{2,300} = 4.35 \text{ amp}$$

which is, of course, the rated current of that winding.
   The current supplied to the load is

$$I_2 = I_1 + I_3 = \frac{10,000}{230} + \frac{10,000}{2,300} = \frac{10,000}{230} \times \frac{11}{10} = 47.83 \text{ amp}$$

This result checks Eq. 2-57, for since the ratio of transformation of the auto-transformer is

$$a = \frac{V_1}{V_2} = \frac{2,300 + 230}{2,300} = 1.1$$

it follows that

$$I_2 = aI_1 = 1.1 \times \frac{10,000}{230} = 47.83$$

The total volt-amperes supplied from the source is

$$P = V_1 I_1 = 2,530 \times \frac{10,000}{230} = 11 \times 10,000$$

while the volt-amperes supplied inductively is, by Eq. 2-60,

$$P_i = V_2(I_2 - I_1) = P\frac{a-1}{a} = P \times \frac{1}{11} = 10,000 \text{ va}$$

which is the volt-ampere rating of the original transformer.

The power supplied conductively by way of the L.T. winding bc is

$$P_c = \frac{P}{a} = 100{,}000 \text{ va}$$

The conclusion may then be drawn that a two-winding transformer connected as a step-down autotransformer will have a volt-ampere rating $a/(a-1)$ times its rating as a simple transformer. This increase becomes larger as the ratio of transformation a approaches unity; but in the limiting case when $a = 1$, the power transferred conductively is equal to the entire input, and the power transferred inductively, P_i, becomes zero, which means that there is then no need for the autotransformer.

Otherwise expressed, if an autotransformer is to be designed to have a rating P, it will consist of a two-winding transformer having a rating $P_i = \dfrac{a-1}{a} P = \dfrac{V_1 - V_2}{V_1} P$, which becomes smaller as V_2 approaches V_1. When designed in this way, the material in the autotransformer will be utilized to the maximum extent.

Since the L.T. and H.T. sides of an autotransformer are conductively connected, it does not possess the advantage inherent in a two-winding transformer, where the L.T. side is completely insulated from the H.T. side. However, when V_1 and V_2 are both large or of the same order of magnitude, as in many applications of the autotransformer, this otherwise undesirable feature is not of itself objectionable; but if an autotransformer is used to step up the voltage V_1 of a generator to a higher voltage $V_2 = aV_1$, where $a > 1$, an accidental ground on the H.T. side will subject the generator insulation to a potential stress a times its normal value.

2-23. The Phasor Diagram and Equivalent Circuit of the Autotransformer. The same considerations that lead to the phasor diagram of the two-winding transformer, as discussed in Chap. 1, are applicable without change to the case of the autotransformer. It is convenient, however, to assume first that the magnetizing current is negligible, though it is a fact that the error thus introduced is inappreciable.

In Fig. 2-58, there is reproduced the same connection diagram shown in Fig. 2-55, except that the double-subscript notation is used. If the mutual flux linking with all the N_1 turns is Φ_m webers, the emfs induced in coils ab and bc, both of which lag behind Φ_m by 90°, are

$$E_{ab} = \sqrt{2} \, \pi f N_2 \Phi_m$$

and

$$E_{bc} = \sqrt{2} \, \pi f (N_1 - N_2)\Phi_m$$

whence

$$\frac{E_{ab}}{E_{bc}} = \frac{N_2}{N_1 - N_2} = \frac{1}{a-1} \tag{2-65}$$

Since the magnetizing current is assumed to be negligible, the geometrical sum of the mmfs due to the currents in ab and cb must be zero, so that

$$N_2\mathbf{I}_{ab} + (N_1 - N_2)\mathbf{I}_{bc} = 0$$

and
$$\mathbf{I}_{ab} = -(a - 1)\mathbf{I}_{bc} \qquad (2\text{-}66)$$

Kirchhoff's second law applied to the junction point b gives

$$\mathbf{I}_{ab} = \mathbf{I}_{bc} + \mathbf{I}_{bd}$$

whence
$$\mathbf{I}_{bd} = -(a - 1)\mathbf{I}_{bc} - \mathbf{I}_{bc} = -a\mathbf{I}_{bc} \qquad (2\text{-}67)$$

The phasor diagram of Fig. 2-58 is constructed on the assumption that the secondary load is inductive; so I_{bd} will lag behind E_{ab}, and the induced emf E_{ab} must therefore be the geometrical sum of the secondary terminal

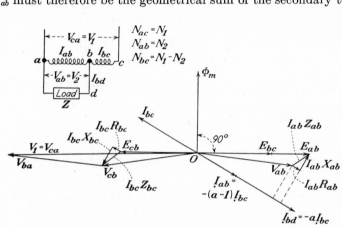

FIG. 2-58. Approximate phasor diagram of autotransformer.

voltage V_{ab} and the impedance drop due to current I_{ab} in winding ab. Therefore, as in Fig. 2-58,

$$\mathbf{E}_{ab} = \mathbf{V}_{ab} + \mathbf{I}_{ab}Z$$

But $\mathbf{V}_{ab} = \mathbf{I}_{bd}Z$, where Z is the impedance of the load, so that

$$\mathbf{E}_{ab} = \mathbf{I}_{bd}Z + \mathbf{I}_{ab}Z$$

and by Eqs. 2-66 and 2-67 this becomes

$$\mathbf{E}_{ab} = -[aZ + (a - 1)Z_{ab}]\mathbf{I}_{bc} \qquad (2\text{-}68)$$

Just as in the two-winding transformer, the voltage V_{cb} impressed upon the portion cb of the primary voltage must balance the induced emf E_{bc}, and in addition must overcome the impedance drop in winding bc. Consequently,

$$\mathbf{V}_{cb} = \mathbf{E}_{cb} + \mathbf{I}_{bc}Z \qquad (2\text{-}69)$$

as indicated in Fig. 2-58 to the left of origin O.

The connection diagram shows that the total primary impressed voltage, $V_1 = V_{ca}$, must be the sum of phasors $\mathbf{V}_{cb}$ and $\mathbf{V}_{ba}$, or

$$\mathbf{V}_{ca} = \mathbf{V}_1 = \mathbf{V}_{cb} + \mathbf{V}_{ba}$$

from which $\mathbf{V}_{cb} = \mathbf{V}_1 - \mathbf{V}_{ba} = \mathbf{V}_1 + \mathbf{V}_{ab} = \mathbf{V}_1 + \mathbf{I}_{bd}Z$ (2-70)

Substituting Eq. 2-70 in Eq. 2-69,

$$\mathbf{E}_{cb} = \mathbf{V}_1 + \mathbf{I}_{bd}Z - \mathbf{I}_{bc}Z_{bc} = \mathbf{V}_1 - \mathbf{I}_{bc}(Z_{bc} + aZ)$$

which may be rewritten in the form

$$\mathbf{E}_{bc} = -\mathbf{V}_1 + \mathbf{I}_{bc}(Z_{bc} + aZ) \qquad (2\text{-}71)$$

Dividing Eq. 2-68 by 2-71, and introducing Eq. 2-65,

$$\frac{\mathbf{E}_{ab}}{\mathbf{E}_{bc}} = \frac{1}{a-1} = \frac{[aZ + (a-1)Z_{ab}]\mathbf{I}_{bc}}{\mathbf{V}_1 - \mathbf{I}_{bc}(Z_{bc} + aZ)} \qquad (2\text{-}72)$$

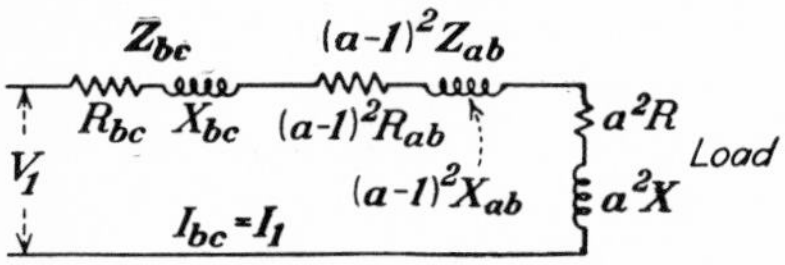

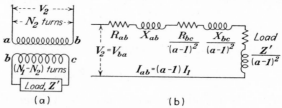

FIG. 2-59. Equivalent circuit of auto-transformer.

and from Eq. 2-72 it readily follows that

$$\mathbf{V}_1 = \mathbf{I}_{bc}[Z_{bc} + (a-1)^2 Z_{ab} + a^2 Z] \qquad (2\text{-}73)$$

The conclusion may at once be drawn from Eq. 2-73 that the equivalent circuit of the autotransformer has the form shown in Fig. 2-59, and the leakage impedance, in terms of the H.T. winding, is

$$Z_e = Z_{bc} + (a-1)^2 Z_{ab} \qquad (2\text{-}74)$$

while $a^2 Z$ is the load impedance expressed in terms of the H.T. winding.

It is both interesting and important to compare the leakage impedance of the autotransformer with that of the same structure used as a two-winding transformer, as in Fig. 2-60.   In order that the comparison may

FIG. 2-60. Equivalent circuit of corresponding two-winding transformer.

be valid, the flux must be the same in both cases, and the currents in the two parts of the windings must also be the same.   It follows that in the equivalent circuit of the two-circuit transformer, which has a ratio of transformation equal to $N_2/(N_1 - N_2) = 1/(a-1)$, the current through the winding ab must be $I_{ab} = (a-1)I_{bc}$, and the voltage

impressed upon winding ab must be $V_{ba} = V_1$. Subject to these requirements, the ratio of the leakage-impedance drop to the impressed H.T.
voltage, in the case of the autotransformer, Fig. 2-59, is

$$p_a = \frac{I_{bc}[Z_{bc} + (a-1)^2 Z_{ab}]}{V_1} \qquad (2\text{-}75)$$

while in the two-winding transformer, Fig. 2-60, the ratio is

$$p_t = \frac{I_{ab}\left[Z_{ab} + \dfrac{Z_{bc}}{(a-1)^2}\right]}{V_2} = \frac{I_{bc}\left[(a-1)Z_{ab} + \dfrac{Z_{bc}}{a-1}\right]}{V_2} \qquad (2\text{-}76)$$

so that

$$\frac{p_a}{p_t} = \frac{V_2}{V_1}\,\frac{Z_{bc} + (a-1)^2 Z_{ab}}{(a-1)Z_{ab} + \dfrac{Z_{bc}}{a-1}} = \frac{a-1}{a} \qquad (2\text{-}77)$$

Since $a > 1$, the ratio $(a-1)/a$ is less than unity, which means that the
voltage regulation of the autotransformer will be better, and its short-
circuit current larger, than that of the corresponding two-winding transformer. For example, consider a 10-kva transformer rated at 2,300/230
volts, which will have a leakage impedance of, say, 4 per cent. If it is
connected as an autotransformer, stepping down from 2,530 to 2,300 volts,
which corresponds to a transformation ratio of $a = 1.1$, the impedance
drop will be

$$4 \times \frac{0.1}{1.1} = 0.364\%$$

or only 9.1 per cent of the leakage impedance of the original two-winding
transformer. This means that if the autotransformer is short-circuited
with full primary impressed voltage, the short-circuit current will be 11
times greater than the short-circuit current of the two-winding arrangement. With 4 per cent impedance in the two-winding transformer, the
short-circuit current will be 25 times the rated current; so the short-circuit current in the windings of the autotransformer will be 275 times
rated current, thus far overtaxing the mechanical strength of the coils.
In order to protect the autotransformer against such destructive forces,
it is necessary to insert in the supply circuit a current-limiting reactor
which will hold the short-circuit current in the windings to not more than
25 times normal rated value.

The full meaning of Eq. 2-77 will be clearer if the case of the 10-kva
transformer of the preceding paragraph is examined more in detail.
Thus, if the two-winding transformer is short-circuited on the H.T. side,
the diagram of connections will be as in Fig. 2-61 and rated current will
circulate in both windings if the voltage impressed on the L.T. winding
is $0.04 \times 230 = 9.2$ volts. If the autotransformer, designed for a H.T.
voltage of $2,300 + 230 = 2,530$ volts, is short-circuited on the L.T.

(2,300-volt) side, the connections will appear as in Fig. 2-62a; but since terminals a and b are at the same potential, the diagram may be replaced by that of Fig. 2-62b, which differs from Fig. 2-61 only in that the two points marked b in Fig. 2-61 are connected.   Consequently, 9.2 volts

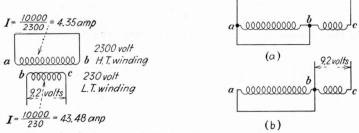

FIG. 2-61. Short-circuit test on equivalent two-winding transformer.

FIG. 2-62. Short-circuit test on auto-transformer.

impressed upon the H.T. terminals of the autotransformer will circulate full rated current in both windings, and the per cent impedance is therefore

$$\frac{9.2}{2,530} \times 100 = 0.364$$

which agrees with Eq. 2-77.

The phasor diagram of Fig. 2-58, though sufficiently accurate for practical purposes, is approximate because the no-load current I_0 has been neglected.   To take I_0 into account, it must appear, as in Fig. 2-63, slightly in advance of the mutual flux Φ_m; and since I_0 must be considered to flow through all the turns between terminals a and c, the actual

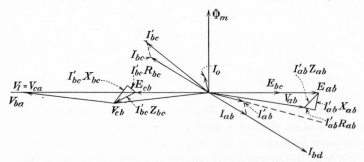

FIG. 2-63. Phasor diagram of autotransformer including no-load current.

currents in windings ab and bc are not I_{ab} and I_{bc}, as in Fig. 2-58, but are I'_{ab} and I'_{bc}, such that

$$N_2 I'_{ab} + (N_1 - N_2) I'_{bc} = N_1 I_0 = N_2 I_0 + (N_1 - N_2) I_0$$

from which

$$I'_{ab} - I_0 = -(a - 1)(I'_{bc} - I_0) \qquad (2\text{-}78)$$

Comparing Eq. 2-78 with 2-66, it is seen that $I'_{ab} - I_0$ corresponds to I_{ab} and $I'_{bc} - I_0$ to I_{bc}.   The impedance drops in windings ab and bc are therefore modified to $I'_{ab}Z_{ab}$ and $I'_{bc}Z_{bc}$, as shown in Fig. 2-63; but in that diagram I_0 is purposely exaggerated for the sake of clarity, so that the actual differences between Figs. 2-58 and 2-63 are insignificant.

2-24. The Induction Regulator.   In power plants or substations where a number of outgoing distribution circuits fed from a single source require independent voltage regulation in order to compensate for differing line drops, each of the circuits to be so regulated may be equipped with an *induction regulator.*   The latter is a transformer of special construction in which the axes of the primary and secondary windings are rotatable with respect to each other, with the primary winding connected across the supply line in the usual manner, but with the secondary winding in series with the outgoing side of the line.   It follows that the voltage induced in the secondary is either added to, or subtracted from, the supply voltage, depending upon the relative angular positions of the primary and secondary windings.

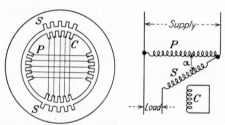

(a) Structural arrangement   (b) Connection diagram

Fig. 2-64. Induction regulator, single phase.

When induction regulators were first introduced, it was customary to wind the primary in the slots on the inner periphery of a stationary cylindrical core, and the secondary on the outer periphery of a movable core mounted concentrically inside the stator core.   This arrangement required the use of fairly large slip rings to connect the low-voltage heavy-current secondary to the outgoing line; hence, it has become present practice to place the primary winding P on the movable core, and the secondary winding S on the stationary core, as indicated in Fig. 2-64a.

The emf induced in the secondary will obviously have its maximum value when the axes of the two windings coincide.   But when the axes of the two windings are at right angles, the secondary induced emf becomes zero because there is then no mutual induction between primary and secondary, though the latter must still carry whatever current is fixed by the line load.   In the absence of corrective devices, the secondary winding would then be the equivalent of a high-reactance choke coil in series with the line, for under these conditions it plays the role of the primary of a transformer which has no secondary to reduce its exciting impedance.   For this reason, the induction regulator must be provided with a short-circuited tertiary winding, C, Fig. 2-64, the axis of which is perpendicular to that of the primary P. The result is that when S is perpendicular to P, the impedance inserted in the line is only the small leakage impedance corresponding to the short-circuited transformer represented by windings S and C.

The tertiary winding C will carry no current when windings S and P occupy the two positions corresponding to maximum boost and maximum reduction of the supply voltage. In intermediate positions, the mutual induction between S and C changes gradually from zero to a maximum and back again to zero.

The actual construction of the single-phase induction regulator is similar to that of a motor having the usual stator and rotor. The rotor is turned one way or the other, so as to vary angle α (Fig. 2-64b) by means of a small motor geared to the vertical shaft of the rotor of the regulator. The driving motor is automatically controlled by means of a voltage relay which starts, stops, or reverses the motor as the voltage of the line changes. The relay may be provided with a series coil so adjusted as to compensate for the drop in the circuit, thereby making it possible to maintain constant voltage at the center of distribution of the load on the circuit.

Induction regulators for polyphase circuits are virtually induction motors having wound primaries and secondaries, the former connected across the lines, the latter in series with the lines. Compensating coils are not required. The currents in the primary windings produce a magnetic field revolving at synchronous speed around the airgap, so that the voltages induced in the secondary windings are constant in magnitude no matter what may be the relative angular positions of stator and rotor, but the phase of the secondary voltage changes relative to that of the primary as the rotor is moved. Thus, if the line voltage is V_1 and the secondary voltage is V_2 (Fig. 2-65), the resultant voltage may be varied uniformly from $OA = V_1 + V_2$ to $OB = V_1 - V_2$ by turning the rotor through 180 electrical degrees.

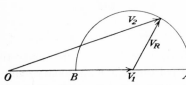

FIG. 2-65. Change in voltage effected by induction regulator.

2-25. Tap Changers. *a. No-load Type.* A commonly used method for regulating the voltage of transformers involves the use of taps which make it possible to change the number of active turns in one of the windings. The voltage changes thus obtainable are not continuous, as in the induction regulator, but occur in steps.

In small transformers thus provided with taps, the tap changing is performed manually when the transformer is completely disconnected. This process requires that the lid of the enclosing case be removed, and may require a partial draining of the oil if the transformer is of the oil-immersed type.

In order to obviate the necessity of opening the case and draining the oil, transformers of larger size are provided with some form of dial switch that can be operated from the outside by a suitable handle; but in this arrangement the tap changing must likewise be performed when the transformer is disconnected. A simple form of no-load tap-changing equipment, illustrated in Fig. 2-66, utilizes four taps (numbered 3, 4, 5, 6 in the diagram), inserted into the winding at 2.5 per cent intervals, which are connected to the correspondingly numbered stationary contacts of the dial switch; these contacts are arranged on a circle so that they may be successively bridged by the rotatable member A. When A bridges contacts 1 and 2, the entire winding is in circuit and the corresponding voltage may be designated 100 per cent; when A bridges contacts 2 and 3, the

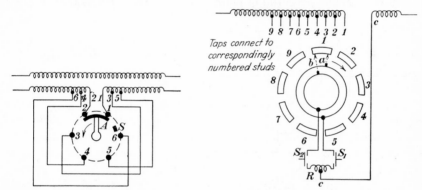

FIG. 2-66. Tap changer, no-load conditions.   FIG. 2-67. Tap changer, load conditions.

voltage becomes 97.5 per cent; and in the final position (5-6), fixed by the stop S, the voltage is 90 per cent.

As indicated in Fig. 2-66, the taps are best located adjacent to the middle of the winding, where they are not subjected to the high potentials caused by lightning and line surges. It is furthermore important to arrange the taps so that there will be a minimum displacement between the middle points of adjacent H.T. and L.T. windings as the tap position is changed (see Art. 3-16).

b. Tap Changing under Load. Figure 2-67 illustrates the basic principle that underlies all forms of tap changers designed to operate without opening the circuit, i.e., while the transformer is under load. The essential feature is the small choke coil or reactor, R, which prevents short-circuiting a section of the main winding when the movable fingers a and b are in contact with adjacent segments of the dial switch. In the position shown in Fig. 2-67, all turns of the main transformer are in service; load current from tap 1 reaches point c by way of reactor R, half of the current entering R by way of switch S_1, the other half by way of switch S_2, with the result that the mmfs of the two halves of R are in opposition, and the drop through R is insignificant because of its very small leakage reactance.

Assume now that the voltage relay which actuates the tap-changing mechanism calls for a voltage less than that represented by tap 1. The contact fingers a and b (Fig. 2-67) are rotated clockwise, but before a leaves stud 1, the switch S_1 opens, thereby preventing arcing at the dial. When a establishes contact with stud 2, the switch S_1 again closes, and the reactor R is bridged across taps 1 and 2. The potential at point c of the reactor is then midway between the potentials of taps 1 and 2.

If further reduction of voltage is necessary, the clockwise rotation of a and b continues, but just before b leaves stud 1, switch S_2 is opened, and is again closed when b reaches stud 2. The reactor R is then again short-circuited, and the potential of point c becomes the same as that of tap 2.

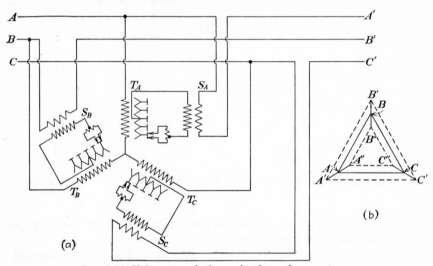

Fig. 2-68. Voltage-regulating unit, three-phase system.

2-26. Tap Changers in Three-phase Systems.

The basic principle underlying the design illustrated in Fig. 2-67 may of course be applied to three-phase transformers or to three single-phase transformers connected for three-phase operation. The tap-changing equipment may be an integral part of the transformer as a whole, or if the main three-phase transformers are not so equipped, the tap changing may be effected in a separate unit in the manner shown in Fig. 2-68a. The regulating unit consists of an assembly of exciting transformers, T_A, T_B, T_C, the secondaries of which are equipped with tap changers; and of series transformers, S_A, S_B, S_C, the secondaries of which are inserted in series with the through lines, A, B, and C, respectively. The primaries of the exciting transformers, connected in Y, are energized from the incoming lines A, B, C. The voltages induced in the secondaries of the series transformers are then either in phase with, or in opposition to, the Y voltage of the system, depending upon whether the tap connections are on one side or the other of the mid-points of the secondaries of the exciting transformers. The resultant voltages between the outgoing lines, as indicated in Fig. 2-68b by the triangles $A'B'C'$ and $A''B''C''$, may therefore be either greater or less than that between lines A, B, C.

The secondaries of the exciting transformers T_A, T_B, T_C are usually connected in Δ, and one corner of the Δ is grounded. This detail is not shown in Fig. 2-68.

Phase-angle control, in addition to voltage control under load, can be obtained by connections of the kind shown in Fig. 2-69a. The essential principle is that the voltages inserted in series with the incoming lines

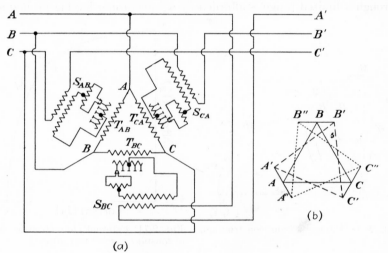

(a)

(b)

Fig. 2-69. Phase-angle control unit.

A, B, C, instead of being in phase with the Y voltage of the system (or in phase opposition thereto), must have a different phase, as indicated in Fig. 2-69b. One of the simplest ways to obtain this result is to connect the exciting transformers T_{AB}, T_{BC}, T_{CA}, in Δ across the incoming lines and the secondaries of the series transformers S_{AB}, S_{BC}, and S_{CA} in series with lines C, A, and B, respectively. The phases of the resultant voltages between the outgoing lines A', B', C' will be rotated in one direction or the other, with respect to those between lines A, B, C, depending upon the position of the taps with respect to the mid-points of the secondaries of the exciting transformers.

The need for phase-angle control arises when two transmission lines, having different impedances, but supplied from a single source, must be tied together at a distant point. Under such circumstances, the line voltages at the distant ends of the two circuits may be out of phase, so that if the connection were made directly, a circulating current would flow in the two lines thus paralleled.   By inserting a phase-angle control unit at the second junction, the division of current between the two lines can be controlled.

2-27. The Constant-current Transformer.   In street-lighting systems where incandescent lamps are connected in series, the current must be maintained at a constant value without regard to the number of lamps in use at any given moment; therefore, the voltage of the system is variable, increasing with the number of lamps in the circuit.   When the source of supply is the usual a-c generator or its equivalent, the power developed at constant potential and variable current must then be transformed into power at constant current and variable potential.

One method of obtaining an approximately constant alternating current through a limited range is afforded by a transformer having pronounced

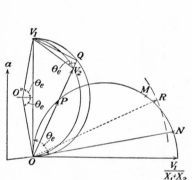

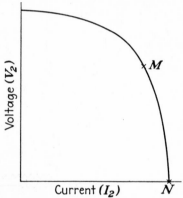

FIG. 2-70. Circle-diagram construction.   FIG. 2-71. External characteristic curve of constant-current transformer.

magnetic leakage such as results from placing the primary and secondary windings on opposite legs of the core.   Reference to the circle diagram of Fig. 1-18 will show that under this condition the diameter of the circle, or $V_1/(X_1 + X_2)$, may be so reduced that the short-circuit current of the transformer may be brought within the current-carrying capacity of the windings.   The circle diagram, of course, relates to the condition of noninductive load, but in the case of incandescent series lighting this condition will obtain.   The circle diagram is reproduced in Fig. 2-70, and it will be seen that in the range from M to N the secondary current does not depart very much from the constant value indicated by the dashed circle OR.   This diagram lends itself readily to the construction of the external characteristic curve of Fig. 2-71, which shows the relation between secondary terminal voltage and current.   Thus, if a semicircle is constructed on OV_1 as a diameter, then for any secondary current such as OP the intercepts OQ and V_1Q are, respectively,

$$OQ = I_2(R_1 + R_2 + R)$$
$$V_1Q = I_2(X_1 + X_2)$$

Drawing the line V_1V_2 so that angle V_1V_2Q is equal to the constant angle

$$\theta_e = \tan^{-1}\frac{X_1 + X_2}{R_1 + R_2}$$

the triangle V_1V_2Q will be the impedance triangle, and OV_2 will be the terminal voltage $V_2 = I_2R$ corresponding to the secondary current $I_2 = OP$. Since the angle V_1V_2O is constant and equal to $180 - \theta_e$, the locus of point V_2 will be a circle passing through points O and V_1, and with its center at point O''. This point is easily located since it lies at the intersection of a perpendicular to OV_1 through its middle point, and a line through O perpendicular to ON.

Fig. 2-72. Constant-current transformer, 20 kw, 2,400-volt primary, 6.6-amp secondary. (*Courtesy of General Electric Company.*)

A better method than that described above is embodied in the so-called "tub" type of transformer, in which the primary and secondary windings are movable with respect to each other, as indicated in Fig. 2-72. The secondary winding is suspended from a partially counterweighted arm so that the mutual repulsion between the coils when under load will cause the secondary to move away from the primary to a position of equilibrium. If the load is increased by an increase in the number of lamps in series, the current will tend to fall, the force of repulsion is reduced, and the secondary coil will approach the primary coil, thereby reducing the magnetic leakage and raising the secondary voltage. In other words, this type of transformer functions by automatically changing the leakage reactance in order to secure the desired variation in terminal voltage. The central core of the transformer is worked at a fairly high flux density in order to accentuate the leakage effect. Since the load on series incandescent circuits does not vary through a considerable range, constant-current transformers of this type are generally designed to operate between about one-half and full load.

Transformers for operating neon signs are designed for abnormally high leakage reactance, about 85 per cent, by inserting a magnetic shunt between high- and low-voltage windings. The effect of the large leakage is to produce a drooping volt-ampere characteristic, similar to Fig. 2-71, which is necessary in view of the fact that in a neon tube an increase of current is accompanied by a decreased resistance.

2-28. Three-winding Transformers. The term "two-winding transformer" conveys the idea of a single primary and a single secondary, physically insulated from each other but magnetically linked together. It is evident, however, from a consideration of construction details, such as are shown in Figs. 1-2 and 1-3, that both the primary and the secondary windings may actually consist of two or more distinct coils connected together in a variety of ways, as in Fig. 2-3. In all cases shown in that diagram, the two parts of the primary act as a single coil, and in cases *a*, *c*, *d*, and *f* the same thing is true of the two parts of the secondary; although there are actually at least four separate windings in these combinations, the connections are such that there are in effect only two independent windings. But in cases *b* and *e*, the two parts of the secondary, though electrically in series, supply the two branches of a three-wire circuit which may be unbalanced; under such circumstances, the currents in the two parts of the secondary may be quite different from each other both as to magnitude and phase, and the transformer has become a *three-winding* transformer. When such a transformer operates under load conditions, each winding will react inductively upon each of the others and there are then three mutual inductances and three self-inductances to be considered.

Cases *b* and *e* of Fig. 2-3 represent the condition of equal voltages in the two parts of the secondary circuit. It is possible, however, that in substation practice an incoming feeder line may be called upon to supply two (or more) outgoing distribution lines of different voltages. This can be accomplished by using a separate two-winding transformer for each of the separate voltages required, but when only two different secondary voltages are needed, it may be more economical or convenient to use a single three-winding transformer. The only differences between such an arrangement and those shown in the diagrams above referred to are that the secondary circuits would be physically separated throughout, instead of having a common return conductor, and the several parts of the secondary would have different numbers of turns.

Another example of the use of a tertiary winding has already been referred to in Art. 2-6 (see Fig. 2-18) for the purpose of suppressing triple-frequency secondary currents. An additional case of importance occurs in the double-cage induction motor (Chap. 8), and it will therefore be useful to analyze the theory in some detail.

Assume that in a three-winding transformer a voltage V_1 is impressed upon one winding which serves as the primary, and that the other two windings are connected to separate circuits. Let

R_{1i}, R_{2i}, R_{3i} = respective internal resistances

L_{1i}, L_{2i}, L_{3i} = respective internal inductances

$\left.\begin{matrix} M_{12} = M_{21} \\ M_{23} = M_{32} \\ M_{31} = M_{13} \end{matrix}\right\}$ = respective mutual inductances

$\left.\begin{matrix} Z_{2l} = \sqrt{R_{2l}^2 + (\omega L_{2l})^2} \\ Z_{3l} = \sqrt{R_{3l}^2 + (\omega L_{3l})^2} \end{matrix}\right\}$ = load impedances of the two secondaries

The three simultaneous differential equations which relate the instantaneous voltages and currents in the three circuits are therefore

$$v_1 = i_1 R_{1i} + L_{1i} \frac{di_1}{dt} + M_{12} \frac{di_2}{dt} + M_{13} \frac{di_3}{dt}$$

$$0 = i_2(R_{2i} + R_{2l}) + (L_{2i} + L_{2l})\frac{di_2}{dt} + M_{21}\frac{di_1}{dt} + M_{23}\frac{di_3}{dt} \quad (2\text{-}79)$$

$$0 = i_3(R_{3i} + R_{3l}) + (L_{3i} + L_{3l})\frac{di_3}{dt} + M_{31}\frac{di_1}{dt} + M_{32}\frac{di_2}{dt}$$

The complete solutions of these equations can be obtained by the usual procedure, but the work can be greatly simplified by eliminating from consideration the initial transient conditions and confining attention to steady-state operation only. It is obvious that all three steady-state currents will vary harmonically at the frequency of the impressed voltage V_1, so that the differential equations can be changed at once to the complex forms

$$\mathbf{V}_1 = \mathbf{I}_1(R_{1i} + j\omega L_{1i}) + j\omega M_{12}\mathbf{I}_2 + j\omega M_{13}\mathbf{I}_3$$
$$0 = \mathbf{I}_2(R_{2i} + j\omega L_{2i} + Z_{2l}) + j\omega M_{12}\mathbf{I}_1 + j\omega M_{23}\mathbf{I}_3 \quad (2\text{-}80)^*$$
$$0 = \mathbf{I}_3(R_{3i} + j\omega L_{3i} + Z_{3l}) + j\omega M_{13}\mathbf{I}_1 + j\omega M_{23}\mathbf{I}_2$$

As a matter of convenience, the constants that appear in Eqs. 2-80 may

---

* Z_{2l} and Z_{3l} are here to be used in the complex forms $R_{2l} + jX_{2l}$ and $R_{3l} + jX_{3l}$, respectively.

be written

$$\omega M_{12} = X_{12} \qquad \omega M_{23} = X_{23} \qquad \omega M_{13} = X_{13}$$
$$\omega L_{1i} = X_{1i} \qquad \omega L_{2i} = X_{2i} \qquad \omega L_{3i} = X_{3i}$$
$$R_{1i} + j\omega L_{1i} = R_{1i} + jX_{1i} = Z_{1i} = Z_1$$
$$R_{2i} + j\omega L_{2i} + Z_{2l} = R_{2i} + jX_{2i} + Z_{2l} = Z_2$$
$$R_{3i} + j\omega L_{3i} + Z_{3l} = R_{3i} + jX_{3i} + Z_{3l} = Z_3$$

and when these substitutions are made, the three simultaneous equations become

$$\mathbf{V}_1 = \mathbf{I}_1 Z_1 + \mathbf{I}_2 jX_{12} + \mathbf{I}_3 jX_{13}$$
$$0 = \mathbf{I}_1 jX_{12} + \mathbf{I}_2 Z_2 + \mathbf{I}_3 jX_{23} \qquad (2\text{-}81)$$
$$0 = \mathbf{I}_1 jX_{13} + \mathbf{I}_2 jX_{23} + \mathbf{I}_3 Z_3$$

These are readily solvable for $\mathbf{I}_1$, $\mathbf{I}_2$, and $\mathbf{I}_3$ in terms of V_1 and the circuit constants. The result for $\mathbf{I}_1$ is

$$\mathbf{I}_1 = \mathbf{V}_1 \frac{\begin{vmatrix} Z_2 & jX_{23} \\ jX_{23} & Z_3 \end{vmatrix}}{\begin{vmatrix} Z_1 & jX_{12} & jX_{13} \\ jX_{12} & Z_2 & jX_{23} \\ jX_{13} & jX_{23} & Z_3 \end{vmatrix}} \qquad (2\text{-}82)$$

from which it follows that the equivalent impedance of the entire transformer, regarded from the primary side, is

$$Z_e = \frac{\mathbf{V}_1}{\mathbf{I}_1} = \frac{\begin{vmatrix} Z_1 & jX_{12} & jX_{13} \\ jX_{12} & Z_2 & jX_{23} \\ jX_{13} & jX_{23} & Z_3 \end{vmatrix}}{\begin{vmatrix} Z_2 & jX_{23} \\ jX_{23} & Z_3 \end{vmatrix}} \qquad (2\text{-}83)$$

Equation (2-83) might be analyzed to determine the equivalent circuit by following somewhat the same procedure used in the analogous case discussed in Art. 1-22. But the simpler method described in what follows has the advantage that it is based directly upon simple physical considerations.

In Fig. 2-73, the three windings P_1, S_2, and S_3 represent the primary and the two secondaries which are magnetically linked together by the equivalent of a ring core. The three parts of the diagram represent the conditions

    a. P_1 and S_2 in operation, S_3 on open circuit.
    b. P_1 and S_3 in operation, S_2 on open circuit.
    c. S_2 and S_3 in operation, P_1 on open circuit.

Case a. The fluxes φ_{11} and φ_{13} represent leakage flux linked with P_1 but not with S_2; and φ_{22} and φ_{23} are leakage fluxes linked with S_2 but not with P_1. To each of these fluxes, there will correspond a leakage reactance, x_{11}, x_{13}, x_{22}, and x_{23}, respectively, all of which are expressed in terms of the primary winding P_1.

In Fig. 2-73a, there are shown as dashed lines two additional fluxes, φ_0 and φ_{12}, but these are obviously parts of the mutual flux linking P_1 and S_2, and they are set up by the magnetizing current of the two-winding transformer consisting of P_1 and S_2. Since the magnetizing current

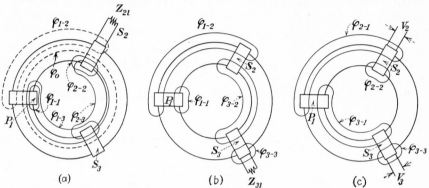

FIG. 2-73. Leakage fluxes, three-winding transformer.

is negligible in comparison with full-load current, the fluxes φ_0 and φ_{12} do not require consideration in drawing the equivalent circuit, which therefore has the form shown in Fig. 2-74a, where all quantities are expressed in terms of winding P_1.

Case b. With windings P_1 and S_3 in service, and S_2 idle, the leakage fluxes associated with P_1 are φ_{11} and φ_{12}, while those associated with S_3

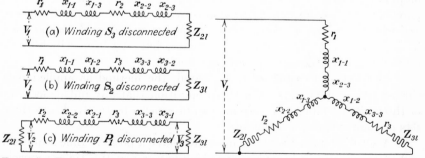

FIG. 2-74. Equivalent circuits, windings grouped in pairs.

FIG. 2-75. Equivalent circuit, three-winding transformer.

are φ_{33} and φ_{32}. The equivalent circuit for P_1 and S_3 acting alone is then represented by Fig. 2-74b.

Case c. When S_2 and S_3 are in service, with P_1 idle, the leakage fluxes linked with S_2 are φ_{22} and φ_{21}, while those linked with S_3 are φ_{33} and φ_{31}. The equivalent circuit for S_2 and S_3 acting alone is therefore represented by Fig. 2-74c.

The conclusion follows naturally that when P_1, S_2, and S_3 are simultaneously in operation, the equivalent circuit for the entire combination must have such a form that it will resolve itself successively to the arrangements shown in Fig. 2-74a, b, and c when S_3, S_2, and P_1 are disconnected, in that order. The only possible grouping that will yield this result is shown in Fig. 2-75. This diagram exhibits a cyclical regularity which makes it easy to remember; for if the branches are numbered 1, 2, and 3, corresponding to the resistances r_1, r_2, and r_3, then the star-connected reactances at the center of the diagram are so arranged that x_{23} (or x_{32}) is in series with r_1, x_{13} is in series with r_2, and x_{12} is in series with r_3; in other words, the numbers 1, 2, 3 are always associated in each branch.

The equivalent circuit of Fig. 2-75 can be redrawn in the form shown in Fig. 2-76.

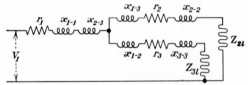

FIG. 2-76. Equivalent circuit, three-winding transformer.

2-29. Symmetrical Components in Polyphase Circuits. In Arts. 2-6 and 2-7, there have been considered some examples of unbalanced conditions which may occur in three-phase circuits, but the calculation of the currents and voltages in the several phases was based upon a straightforward application of Kirchhoff's laws. There is, however, a much more powerful method for the solution of problems involving unbalanced polyphase circuits which was developed by the late Charles L. Fortescue and which has come to be called the *method of symmetrical components;*[*] it is applicable to any number of phases, but attention will here be limited to three-phase and two-phase circuits.

a. Three-phase Circuits. Briefly stated, the method as applied to a three-phase system rests upon the proposition that any unbalanced set of three-phase voltages or currents can in general be resolved into three sets of components consisting of:

1. A set of balanced components which have a positive time sequence.

2. A set of balanced components which have a negative time sequence.

3. A set of equal components all having the same time phase, which constitute the zero-sequence components.

* C. L. Fortescue, Method of Symmetrical Coordinates Applied to the Solution of Polyphase Networks, *Trans. AIEE*, **37**(2):1027 (1918). See also C. F. Wagner and R. D. Evans, "Symmetrical Components," McGraw-Hill Book Co., Inc, 1933, and W. V. Lyon, "Applications of the Method of Symmetrical Components," McGraw-Hill Book Co., Inc., 1937.

Consider, for example, the balanced voltages V_{1p}, V_{2p}, V_{3p}, Fig. 2-77a, impressed upon a three-phase circuit.   These voltages vary harmonically with time in the cyclical order 1-2-3, and in accordance with the positive direction of rotation of the phasor diagram they may be said to have a positive sequence.   Similarly, V_{1n}, V_{2n}, and V_{3n} in Fig. 2-77b, respectively impressed upon the same parts of the circuit as are V_{1p}, V_{2p}, and V_{3p},

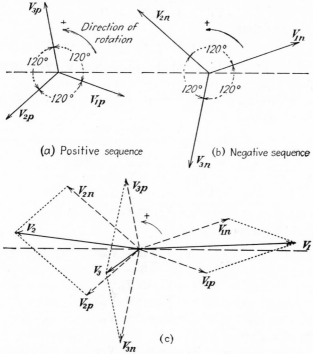

(a) Positive sequence   (b) Negative sequence

(c)

FIG. 2-77. Two balanced systems of opposite sequence and their unbalanced resultant.

constitute a negative sequence of balanced phasors because their cyclical order is 3-2-1.   The resultant voltages in the three branches of the circuit are therefore

$$\begin{aligned} \mathbf{V}_1 &= \mathbf{V}_{1p} + \mathbf{V}_{1n} \\ \mathbf{V}_2 &= \mathbf{V}_{2p} + \mathbf{V}_{2n} \\ \mathbf{V}_3 &= \mathbf{V}_{3p} + \mathbf{V}_{3n} \end{aligned} \tag{2-84}$$

and the resultant unbalanced voltages V_1, V_2, and V_3 are shown in Fig. 2-77c.

In complex notation, the two sets of balanced components may be represented by the equations

$$\begin{aligned} \mathbf{V}_{1p} &= \mathbf{V}_{1p} & \mathbf{V}_{1n} &= \mathbf{V}_{1n} \\ \mathbf{V}_{2p} &= \mathbf{V}_{1p}\underline{/-120^\circ} = \mathbf{V}_{1p}a^{-1} & \mathbf{V}_{2n} &= \mathbf{V}_{1n}\underline{/120^\circ} = \mathbf{V}_{1n}a \\ \mathbf{V}_{3p} &= \mathbf{V}_{1p}\underline{/-240^\circ} = \mathbf{V}_{1p}a^{-2} & \mathbf{V}_{3n} &= \mathbf{V}_{1n}\underline{/240^\circ} = \mathbf{V}_{1n}a^2 \end{aligned} \tag{2-85}$$

where
$$a = e^{j2\pi/3} = \cos 120° + j \sin 120° = -0.5 + j0.866$$
$$a^2 = e^{j4\pi/3} = \cos 240° + j \sin 240° = -0.5 - j0.866$$
$$a^{-1} = e^{-j2\pi/3} = \cos 120° - j \sin 120° = -0.5 - j0.866$$
$$a^{-2} = e^{-j4\pi/3} = \cos 240° - j \sin 240° = -0.5 + j0.866$$

from which it follows that

$$\mathbf{V}_{1p} + \mathbf{V}_{2p} + \mathbf{V}_{3p} = 0$$
$$\mathbf{V}_{1n} + \mathbf{V}_{2n} + \mathbf{V}_{3n} = 0$$

and from Eq. 2-84 that

$$\mathbf{V}_1 + \mathbf{V}_2 + \mathbf{V}_3 = 0 \tag{2-86}$$

If now a given set of unbalanced phasors such as $\mathbf{V}_1$, $\mathbf{V}_2$, and $\mathbf{V}_3$, which satisfy the condition that their geometric sum is zero, as in Eq. 2-86, is to be resolved into balanced positive and negative sequences, note from Eqs. 2-84 and 2-85 that

$$\mathbf{V}_1 = \mathbf{V}_{1p} + \mathbf{V}_{1n}$$
$$\mathbf{V}_2 = \mathbf{V}_{2p} + \mathbf{V}_{2n} = \mathbf{V}_{1p}a^{-1} + \mathbf{V}_{1n}a \tag{2-87}$$
$$\mathbf{V}_3 = \mathbf{V}_{3p} + \mathbf{V}_{3n} = \mathbf{V}_{1p}a^{-2} + \mathbf{V}_{1n}a^2$$

from which
$$\mathbf{V}_1 = \mathbf{V}_{1p} + \mathbf{V}_{1n}$$
$$\mathbf{V}_2a = \mathbf{V}_{1p} + \mathbf{V}_{1n}a^2$$
$$\mathbf{V}_3a^2 = \mathbf{V}_{1p} + \mathbf{V}_{1n}a^4$$

the sum of which yields the relation

$$\mathbf{V}_{1p} = \frac{\mathbf{V}_1 + \mathbf{V}_2a + \mathbf{V}_3a^2}{3} \tag{2-88}$$

Similarly,
$$\mathbf{V}_1 = \mathbf{V}_{1p} + \mathbf{V}_{1n}$$
$$\mathbf{V}_2a^{-1} = \mathbf{V}_{1p}a^{-2} + \mathbf{V}_{1n}$$
$$\mathbf{V}_3a^{-2} = \mathbf{V}_{1p}a^{-4} + \mathbf{V}_{1n}$$

the sum of which gives

$$\mathbf{V}_{1n} = \frac{\mathbf{V}_1 + \mathbf{V}_2a^{-1} + \mathbf{V}_3a^{-2}}{3} \tag{2-89}$$

Example. Let

$$\mathbf{V}_1 = 1,000 + j50$$
$$\mathbf{V}_2 = -800 + j100$$
$$\mathbf{V}_3 = -200 - j150$$

represent three unbalanced voltages which satisfy the condition that their sum is zero. Substituting in Eq. 2-88,

$$\mathbf{V}_{1p} = \frac{(1,000 + j50) + (-800 + j100)(-0.5 + j0.866) + (-200 - j150)(-0.5 - j0.866)}{3}$$
$$= 427.83 - j148.2 = 452.8\underline{/-19°6.4'}$$

and from Eq. 2-89

$$\mathbf{V}_{1n} = \frac{(1,000 + j50) + (-800 + j100)(-0.5 - j0.866) + (-200 - j150)(-0.5 + j0.866)}{3}$$
$$= 572.16 + j198.2 = 605.5\underline{/19°6.4'}$$

The preceding example, based upon the condition represented by Eq. 2-86, is clearly not the most general case, for the geometrical sum of the three phasors of an unbalanced set may differ from zero. In that case, it is possible to write

$$\mathbf{V}_1 + \mathbf{V}_2 + \mathbf{V}_3 = 3\mathbf{V}_0$$

which may be put in the equivalent form

$$(\mathbf{V}_1 - \mathbf{V}_0) + (\mathbf{V}_2 - \mathbf{V}_0) + (\mathbf{V}_3 - \mathbf{V}_0) = 0 \qquad (2\text{-}90)$$

In Eq. 2-90, the three expressions $\mathbf{V}_1 - \mathbf{V}_0$, $\mathbf{V}_2 - \mathbf{V}_0$, and $\mathbf{V}_3 - \mathbf{V}_0$ constitute a new set which satisfies the condition imposed by Eq. 2-86, and they may therefore be resolved into positive and negative sequences in the manner indicated by Eqs. 2-88 and 2-89.

In general, therefore,

$$\mathbf{V}_{1p} = \frac{(\mathbf{V}_1 - \mathbf{V}_0) + (\mathbf{V}_2 - \mathbf{V}_0)a + (\mathbf{V}_3 - \mathbf{V}_0)a^2}{3}$$

$$\mathbf{V}_{1n} = \frac{(\mathbf{V}_1 - \mathbf{V}_0) + (\mathbf{V}_2 - \mathbf{V}_0)a^{-1} + (\mathbf{V}_3 - \mathbf{V}_0)a^{-2}}{3}$$

$$\mathbf{V}_0 = \frac{\mathbf{V}_1 + \mathbf{V}_2 + \mathbf{V}_3}{3}$$

define the relations between the positive, negative, and zero sequences of the given unbalanced set. It is possible, however, to simplify the first two equations of the preceding set, for they may be written

$$\mathbf{V}_{1p} = \frac{\mathbf{V}_1 + \mathbf{V}_2 a + \mathbf{V}_3 a^2}{3} - \frac{\mathbf{V}_0}{3}(1 + a + a^2)$$

$$= \frac{\mathbf{V}_1 + \mathbf{V}_2 a + \mathbf{V}_3 a^2}{3}$$

$$\mathbf{V}_{1n} = \frac{\mathbf{V}_1 + \mathbf{V}_2 a^{-1} + \mathbf{V}_3 a^{-2}}{3} - \frac{\mathbf{V}_0}{3}(1 + a^{-1} + a^{-2})$$

$$= \frac{\mathbf{V}_1 + \mathbf{V}_2 a^{-1} + \mathbf{V}_3 a^{-2}}{3}$$

which are the same in form as Eqs. 2-88 and 2-89.

Example. Let

$$\mathbf{V}_1 = 1,000 + j50$$
$$\mathbf{V}_2 = -800 + j100$$
$$\mathbf{V}_3 = -1,100 - j270$$

From Eqs. 2-90, 2-88, and 2-89,

$$\mathbf{V}_0 = -300 - j40 = 302.6\underline{/-172°24.3'}$$

$$\mathbf{V}_{1p} = \frac{(1,000 + j50) + (-800 + j100)\underline{/120°} + (-1,100 - j270)\underline{/240°}}{3}$$

$$= 543.19 + j131.6 = 558.9\underline{/13°37.1'}$$

$$\mathbf{V}_{1n} = \frac{(1,000 + j50) + (-800 + j100)\underline{/-120°} + (-1,100 - j270)\underline{/-240°}}{3}$$

$$= 756.6 - j41.6 = 757.9\underline{/-3°8.8'}$$

The magnitudes and phase positions of V_1, V_2, and V_3 in this example are shown in Fig. 2-78, which also shows the graphical solution for V_0. In Fig. 2-79 are shown the positive- and negative-sequence components, and by way of example the manner in which V_{1p}, V_{1n}, and V_0 combine to give V_1.

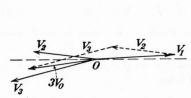

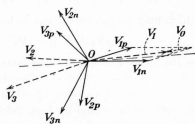

Fig. 2-78. Graphical construction of zero-sequence component.

Fig. 2-79. Resolution of unbalanced three-phase voltages.

b. *Two-phase Circuits.* A set of unbalanced two-phase voltages (or currents) can always be resolved into one or the other of two combinations: (1) a single-phase system and one balanced two-phase system; (2) two balanced two-phase systems which have opposite phase sequence.

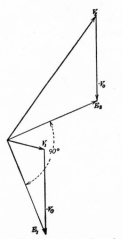

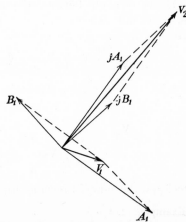

Fig. 2-80. Components of unbalanced two-phase system.

Fig. 2-81. Positive- and negative-sequence components of unbalanced two-phase system.

1. Let V_1 and V_2 in Fig. 2-80 be any pair of unbalanced two-phase voltages. It is obvious by inspection that V_1 and V_2 can each be resolved into two components such that one pair consists of components (indicated as $-V_0$) which are equal and cophasal, and another pair (indicated by E_1 and E_2) which are equal and in quadrature. Thus, let it be assumed that

$$\begin{aligned}
\mathbf{V}_1 - \mathbf{V}_0 &= \mathbf{E}_1 \\
\mathbf{V}_2 - \mathbf{V}_0 &= \mathbf{E}_2
\end{aligned} \qquad (2\text{-}91)$$

V_0 being so chosen that $E_2 = jE_1$, which in this illustration implies that E_1, E_2 have a negative-sequence relation in agreement with the original negative-sequence relation between V_1 and V_2.

Taking first the sum, and then the difference, of the expressions in Eq. 2-91,

$$V_1 + V_2 = 2V_0 + E_1(1 + j)$$
$$V_1 - V_2 = E_1(1 - j) \qquad (2\text{-}92)$$

from which, by the elimination of E_1,

$$V_0 = \frac{V_1(1 - j) + V_2(1 + j)}{2} \qquad (2\text{-}93)$$

which shows that V_0 is not half the sum of V_1 and V_2, as might have been expected by analogy with the three-phase case.

2. Let it be required to resolve the unbalanced phasors V_1 and V_2 into two balanced two-phase sets of opposite sequence, one of which is shown in Fig. 2-81 as A_1 and jA_1, the other as B_1 and $-jB_1$. It follows that

$$V_1 = A_1 + B_1$$
$$V_2 = jA_1 - jB_1$$

whence

$$A_1 = \frac{V_1 - jV_2}{2}$$
$$B_1 = \frac{V_1 + jV_2}{2} \qquad (2\text{-}94)$$

2-30. Application of Method of Symmetrical Components.   While the equations of the preceding section have been expressed in terms of voltages, it is obvious that similar expressions will give the positive-, negative-, and zero-sequence components of current in a three-phase system in which the unbalanced phase currents I_1, I_2, and I_3 take the place of V_1, V_2, and V_3. It is important to note, however, that in a Y-connected circuit which has an isolated neutral there can be no zero-sequence components; for since zero-sequence components are by definition in time phase with one another, their sum cannot be zero at the junction point as demanded by Kirchhoff's law.   It follows that there are limitations upon the phase loadings of a bank of transformers connected Y-Y unless the neutral points are connected to the source of power in such manner that the zero-sequence components of current have a return path; or unless the transformers are provided with tertiary windings as in Fig. 2-18.

Consider, for example, the case illustrated in Fig. 2-82, which represents diagrammatically three transformers 1, 2, and 3, with primaries and secondaries in Y, and with tertiary windings connected in Δ; one of the secondaries is connected to a load, while the other two are on open circuit, the combination thus presenting an extreme case of unbalance.   The conditions are similar to those of Fig. 2-15b, except that in the latter there are no tertiary windings.

It has been shown in Art. 2-6 that in the absence of tertiary windings, as in Fig. 2-15b, the current in the loaded phase is limited to the resultant of the exciting currents of the other two phases, as these may be modified by whatever unbalancing of voltage occurs on the primaries.   But in

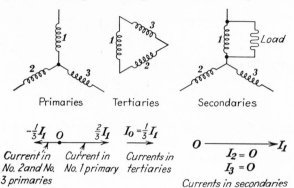

FIG. 2-82. Unbalanced loading of Y-Y transformers with tertiary windings.

Fig. 2-82 this limitation upon the loaded phase is removed by the interposition of the tertiary windings, and there may be a considerable secondary current in phase 1 while the secondary currents in phases 2 and 3 are zero.   Assuming

$$\mathbf{I}_1 = \mathbf{I}_1$$
$$\mathbf{I}_2 = 0$$
$$\mathbf{I}_3 = 0$$

it follows from the relations established in Art. 2-29 that

$$\mathbf{I}_{1p} = \mathbf{I}_{1n} = \mathbf{I}_0 = \tfrac{1}{3}\mathbf{I}_1$$

and the positive-, negative-, and zero-sequence components in each of the three phases will then be given by the following table:

Phase	Positive-sequence component	Negative-sequence component	Zero-sequence component	Sum
1	$\mathbf{I}_{1p} = \tfrac{1}{3}\mathbf{I}_1$	$\mathbf{I}_{1n} = \tfrac{1}{3}\mathbf{I}_1$	$\mathbf{I}_0 = \tfrac{1}{3}\mathbf{I}_1$	$\mathbf{I}_1$
2	$\mathbf{I}_{2p} = \tfrac{1}{3}\mathbf{I}_1 a^{-1}$	$\mathbf{I}_{2n} = \tfrac{1}{3}\mathbf{I}_1 a$	$\mathbf{I}_0 = \tfrac{1}{3}\mathbf{I}_1$	0
3	$\mathbf{I}_{3p} = \tfrac{1}{3}\mathbf{I}_1 a^{-2}$	$\mathbf{I}_{2n} = \tfrac{1}{3}\mathbf{I}_1 a^2$	$\mathbf{I}_0 = \tfrac{1}{3}\mathbf{I}_1$	0
Sum	Zero	Zero	$\mathbf{I}_1$	

At first glance, it may seem strange to speak of component currents in the secondaries of phases 2 and 3 which, since they are open-circuited, cannot carry any current; but it will be seen from the table that the resultant of the three components in phases 2 and 3 is identically zero, which means that the listed components therein are actually fictitious, but may be treated as though they had real existence.   From this point of view, the zero-sequence component of mmf in each of the three phases will be balanced by the mmf of the image current in the corresponding tertiary winding, and these image (zero-sequence) currents can flow in the closed Δ since they are all in time phase.   Similarly, the mmfs of the positive-sequence secondary currents will be balanced by the mmfs of the corresponding positive-sequence currents in the primaries; and likewise with respect to the negative-sequence components.

It will thus be seen that the effects of the zero-sequence components in the three secondary windings are screened out of the primaries by the interposition of the tertiary windings.   The currents in the three phases of the primaries are therefore (neglecting the exciting currents)

$$(\mathbf{I}_1)_{\text{prim}} = \mathbf{I}_{1p} + \mathbf{I}_{1n} = \tfrac{2}{3}\mathbf{I}_1$$
$$(\mathbf{I}_2)_{\text{prim}} = \mathbf{I}_{2p} + \mathbf{I}_{2n} = -\tfrac{1}{3}\mathbf{I}_1$$
$$(\mathbf{I}_3)_{\text{prim}} = \mathbf{I}_{3p} + \mathbf{I}_{3n} = -\tfrac{1}{3}\mathbf{I}_1$$

which add up to zero in conformity with the fact that the neutral point on the primary side is isolated.   While the primary line currents are greatly unbalanced, the degree of unbalancing is much less pronounced than on the secondary side.   The time-phase relations of the resultant currents in the primary, secondary, and tertiary windings of the three transformers are shown in the lower part of Fig. 2-82; their magnitudes are based upon the assumption that all currents are reduced to terms of the primary.

2-31. Advantages of the Method of Symmetrical Components.   The solution of problems in which balanced voltages are applied to a balanced polyphase circuit is the same as in a single-phase circuit in which the voltage is the given per-phase value and the constants are those of one of the phases of the balanced polyphase system.   If, however, the impressed voltages are not balanced, the solution of the problem by means of Kirchhoff's laws becomes complicated since it then becomes necessary to assign symbols for the current and voltage in each branch and then to set up a sufficient number of independent equations to determine all of the unknown quantities.

The method of symmetrical components permits the resolution of the given unbalanced voltages into positive-, negative-, and zero-sequence components which, when reduced to per-phase values, may be considered to act independently upon each of the balanced phases, and so set up corresponding positive-, negative-, and zero-sequence components of current.   In other words, the solution of the problem is reduced to the same considerations which apply to single-phase circuits.   The validity of this procedure was proved by Fortescue in his original paper, where it was shown that in *symmetrical* circuits the currents and voltages of different sequences do not react upon each other.   Moreover, in symmetrical circuits of static type (i.e., those which do not involve rotating machines), the constants of the circuit remain the same for the different sequence components.

In the case of *unsymmetrical* systems, the conditions are not so simple, for a current of one sequence in a given branch may give rise to voltage drops of other sequences in addition to a voltage drop of its own sequence. Such cases, which are considered in the references cited in the footnote on page 128, are beyond the scope of this book; but it may be noted that the great majority of the circuits which occur in practice are deliberately designed to maintain symmetry, thus favoring the simplification of calculations by the method of symmetrical components. This consideration is particularly important in the case of the circuits encountered in rotating machines.

Consider, for example, the case of a three-phase induction motor subjected to unbalanced impressed voltages. The positive-sequence components, which will be assumed to be dominant, will produce rotation in what may be designated the positive direction, and the resultant current, torque, slip, etc., corresponding to a particular load will be determined in terms of the normal circuit constants. But the negative-sequence voltages will set up a backwardly rotating field, which means that the circuit constants, particularly the reactances, will not be the same as in the case of the positive-sequence components, since the frequency of the rotor currents will be nearly double the line frequency. Zero-sequence currents, if present, can be disregarded because their resultant mmf is zero so far as airgap flux is concerned; this is true because these particular mmfs are in time phase, and are displaced in space by just the right amount to cause them to annul one another.

CHAPTER 3

TRANSFORMER STRUCTURE, INSULATION, HEATING, AND LOAD STRESSES

3-1. Power and Distribution Transformers. The growth of systems for the generation, transmission, and distribution of electrical energy at nominally constant potential brought into being two types of transformers which for convenience are classed as *power transformers* and *distribution transformers*. So far as fundamental principles are concerned, they are identical in kind; they differ chiefly in that high-voltage power transformers of large kva rating require more elaborate attention to insulation and to provision for cooling than is necessary in the smaller distribution transformers which operate at moderate voltage. They differ further in that power transformers are designed to have considerably greater leakage reactance than is permissible in distribution transformers; for the latter must have close voltage regulation, whereas in the case of power transformers inherent voltage regulation is less important than the current-limiting effect of relatively high leakage impedance.

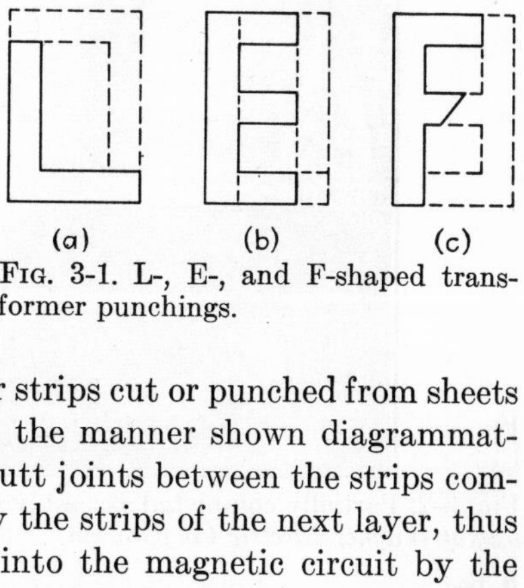

(a)   (b)   (c)

FIG. 3-1. L-, E-, and F-shaped transformer punchings.

3-2. Stacked Core Construction. The cores of power transformers of large kva rating are made of rectangular strips cut or punched from sheets of silicon steel which are assembled in the manner shown diagrammatically in Figs. 1-2, 1-3, and 1-5. The butt joints between the strips comprising any one layer are overlapped by the strips of the next layer, thus minimizing the reluctance introduced into the magnetic circuit by the joints. If the over-all dimensions of the core are not too great, the punchings may be L-shaped, as in Fig. 3-1a, or they may be E- or F-shaped for small shell-type transformers, as in Fig. 3-1b and c. Core-type transformers using rectangular punchings are assembled by stacking the strips comprising the legs and their lower connection into a U shape, after which the preformed coils and their insulating barriers are slipped into place, and the top portion of the core is then built into place. In assembling shell-type transformers, the coils with their insulating barriers are clamped with the

137

plane of the coils vertical, and the laminations, laid horizontally, are stacked layer by layer around the coils. In both cases, the laminations must be tightly clamped, but with due regard to the fact that beyond a certain point excessive pressure increases the core loss without contributing to increased rigidity. Figure 3-2 illustrates the partially completed assembly of a three-phase core-type transformer.

Fig. 3-2. Partially completed assembly of three-phase core-type transformer. (*Courtesy of Wagner Electric Corporation.*)

The silicon sheet steel used in such transformers is alloyed with 4 to 5 per cent silicon. The silicon eliminates the aging effect, namely, the gradual increase of core loss under operating conditions that was characteristic of the low-carbon (black sheet) steel formerly used. At the same time, the silicon materially reduces the core loss, the loss decreasing with increasing per cent of silicon, but at the expense of increasing hardness and brittleness of the metal.

The silicon sheet steel used in 60-cycle transformers is 14 mils thick

(No. 29, U.S. Sheet Gage); in 25-cycle transformers, the thickness usually employed is somewhat greater, 18.7 mils (No. 26) or 25 mils (No. 24). For frequencies higher than 60 cycles, the laminations must be thinner, and for this purpose sheets or strip having thicknesses of 3, 5, and 7 mils are available.   The No. 29 gage sheets for 60-cycle transformers is available in four grades, characterized by core losses, at 60 cycles and at a flux density of 10,000 gauss, of 0.72, 0.65, 0.58, and 0.52 watts per lb.

The steel itself, usually made by the open-hearth process, is poured into ingots, which are then successively rolled into slabs and strip.   The strip is then hot- or cold-rolled into sheets.   The entire process requires check tests at each stage to ensure uniformity in core loss, permeability, ductility, and thickness, as well as flatness and the presence of a thin, tightly adhering oxide coating.   The hot-rolling process orients the grain structure in the direction of rolling, with the result that when the flux is transverse to the grain the losses are 10 to 15 per cent greater than when it is in the grain direction; in the 45° direction, the loss is only slightly increased.

On the other hand, cold rolling by the high-reduction process made it possible to produce very long sheets, 100 ft or more in length, with magnetic properties that were materially improved in the direction of the grain, but with losses in the transverse direction, and in the intermediate 45° direction, from 40 to 60 per cent greater.   The strip thus produced contains silicon up to $3\frac{1}{2}$ per cent, the reduction in silicon content counteracting the embrittling effect of the cold rolling.   In order to utilize this material to the best advantage, it became necessary to design the core so that the flux is everywhere directed along the grain, thus leading to the development of the wound-strip core.

3-3. Wound and Bent-iron Cores. *a.* The General Electric Spirakore distribution transformer, in sizes up to 5 kva, has the shell-type form indicated in cross section in Fig. 3-3. The core consists of two tight spirals of steel strip, each wound through the window of the preformed coils of the winding by an ingenious machine operation that is much faster

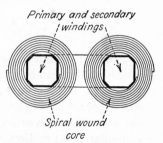

FIG. 3-3. General Electric Spirakore.

than the manual method of building up a stacked core.   It will be noted that, in addition to the advantage of having the flux everywhere directed along the grain, there are no joints to add to the reluctance of the magnetic circuit, thereby reducing the no-load current to a minimum; and the core structure is inherently rigid, thus dispensing with the auxiliary clamps that must be used with stacked cores.

The successive steps in forming each of the spiral cores are as follows:

1. The steel sheet, received from the mill in roll form, is unwound through a slitting machine which cuts the original roll to the widths

required, and the latter are rewound on mandrels of the same size and shape as the ultimate inner periphery of the completed core.

2. The core thus wound is annealed to restore the magnetic qualitities impaired by the bending of the sheet.   In cooling from the high temperature of the annealing oven, the metal tends thereafter to retain its shape.

3. The mandrel is removed, and the wound core is slipped over a roller R_1, Fig. 3-4, which is one of a pair geared to revolve in opposite directions. The outer end of the wound core is passed through the window of the winding, then back between the coiled core and roller R_2, and is then tack-welded to the adjacent inner turn at point P.   On spinning the rollers R_1 and R_2, the steel strip is thus rewound through the window of the winding in such manner that the direction of its coiling is unchanged, but the coil is left in the loose form shown in Fig. 3-4b.

4. The core is compacted to form a tight spiral by means of the rapidly spinning rollers R_3 and R_4, Fig. 3-4b, which are kept pressed against the outer layer.   The core is prevented from unrolling by spot welding the ends.

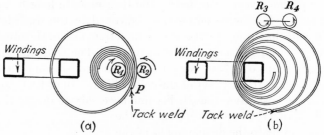

FIG. 3-4. Machine winding of spiral core.

b. *Spirally Wound Rectangular Cores.*   There are obvious limits to the size of cores that can be produced in the manner described in the preceding subsection.   In sizes larger than 5 kva, economy of material dictates the use of windings having a rectangular cross section; consequently, the steel cores must themselves be wound on mandrels having a corresponding rectangular cross section, thereby ruling out the possibility of spinning the core into its final position.

The steel strip, tightly wound on the rectangular mandrel, is annealed as before, and is then unwound and cut into lengths of approximately two turns each, but the cuts are made so that they will butt together at random when the pieces are later reassembled.   The individual pieces, which tend to maintain their shape, are nested in order, and are then sprung into position through the preformed windings, beginning with the inner section of the cut core.

c. The wound-core transformers made by the Line Material Co. are made by winding the copper coils around the legs of the preformed core, thus resulting in a core-type transformer.   The steel strip comprising the core is wound on a suitable mandrel and then annealed. The completed core is then clamped in the coil winding machine, which is so designed that the winding is applied first to one leg of the core, then to the other. Split flanges, F, Fig. 3-5, are centered around the leg of the core and are adjusted to rotate freely between idle rollers and a geared drive roller. The paper insulating tube wound on the flanges provides a winding form for the copper coils.

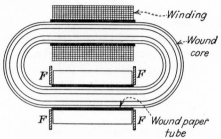

FIG. 3-5. Diagram of Line Material wound-core transformer.

d. The wound core of the Westinghouse transformer of this type is made of high-permeability silicon steel (designated by the trade name Hypersil) which is wound on a mandrel of appropriate shape and then annealed. While still at high temperature, the core is vacuum-impregnated with molten glass, which serves to insulate the steel layers and at

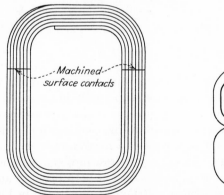

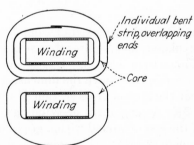

FIG. 3-6. Westinghouse wound core.

FIG. 3-7. Diagrammatic sketch, Kuhlman bent-iron core.

the same time cement them solidly together. The core is then cut as indicated in Fig. 3-6, and the cut surfaces are machined to make low-reluctance contacts when the two parts are reassembled. By thus cutting the core, the preformed coils of the winding can easily be slipped into place, and the two parts of the core are then securely clamped together.

e. The bent-iron core of the Kuhlman transformer is made in the manner indicated in Fig. 3-7. Each of the two halves of the core consists of grain-oriented steel strips that are initially formed by bending them around a suitable mandrel. The ends of the individual strips overlap to form a joint of low reluctance. When thus formed, the cores are annealed, and two of them, placed back to back as in Fig. 3-7, are opened to an H shape, the free ends being held by clamps. The double core is then mounted in a lathe and the copper coils are wound in place. After removing the clamps, the free ends of the strips are snapped back into position.

3-4. Special Cross Sections of Cores. In transformers in which the windings are circular cylinders, as in core-type transformers for very high voltage, and in wound-core transformers like Fig. 3-5, economical use of material requires that the cross section of the core shall as nearly as possible fill the circular opening inside the insulated windings. A core of circular cross section is obviously not possible when the laminations are

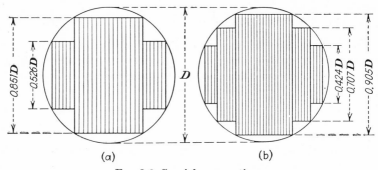

Fig. 3-8. Special core sections.

made of either stacked or wound strips; so the nearest approximation to circular section requires the use of two or three strip widths in the manner illustrated in Fig. 3-8. It is left to the student to prove that the widths of the strips must have the dimensions indicated in Fig. 3-8a and b in order that the area of cross section of the core may be a maximum.

3-5. Arrangement of Windings. In core-type transformers, each leg of the core is wound with a group of coils consisting of both primary and secondary turns, which may be *concentric cylinders* as illustrated in Fig. 1-2, where the L.T. winding is placed next to the core and the H.T. winding on the outside; but if the windings are subdivided and interlaced for the purpose of reducing leakage reactance, the L.T. and H.T. sections are arranged alternately, with a L.T. section adjacent to the core, and its mate on the outside.

In units of large capacity for very high voltages, *disk coils* are used, particularly for the H.T. winding. The conductor, made of strip copper, usually double-cotton-covered, is wound spirally on a suitable form, and two such spirals, each the mirror image of the other, are placed back to back and connected at their inner ends, as in Fig. 3-9.   In this way, the terminals of each completed pair are on the outside, thus avoiding awk-ward crossovers.   This arrangement lends itself readily to the transposition mentioned in Art. 1-15, when each con-ductor consists of two or more wires in parallel.

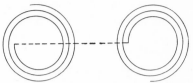

FIG. 3-9. Winding of disk coils.

In shell-type transformers, the coils may be arranged either concentrically or as a bundle of parallel pancake coils, as shown in Figs. 1-33 and 1-34.

3-6. Transformer Insulation.   The useful life of a transformer is wholly dependent upon the ability of its insulation to withstand the deteriorating effects of heat and moisture and the physical and dielectric stresses to which it is subjected under operating conditions.   Proper insulation therefore constitutes the most critical feature of transformer construction.

The American Standards* specify four types of solid insulating mate-rials, as follows:

Class O consists of cotton, silk, paper, and similar organic materials when neither impregnated nor immersed in a liquid dielectric.

Class A consists (1) of cotton, silk, paper, and similar organic materials when either impregnated or immersed in a liquid dielectric; (2) molded and laminated materials with cellulose filler, phenolic resins, and other resins of similar prop-erties; (3) films and sheets of cellulose acetate and other cellulose derivatives of similar properties; and (4) varnishes (enamel) as applied to conductors.

Class B consists of mica, asbestos, fiber glass, and similar inorganic materials in built-up form with organic binding substances.   (A small proportion of Class A materials may be used for structural purposes only.)

Class C consists entirely of mica, porcelain, glass, quartz, and similar inorganic materials.

In winding the coils, whether of the concentric-cylinder, disk, or pan-cake type, the successive layers are separated by paper strips of sufficient thickness to withstand the potential difference between them.   The coils are then dipped into a varnish compound *in vacuo* and baked, this process being repeated a sufficient number of times to give a hard finish, the end result being an impregnated winding.   The impregnating material must have good insulating qualities; it must entirely cover the fibers and render them adherent to each other and to the conductor; it must not produce interstices within itself because of evaporation of the solvent or other cause; it must not flow at the working temperature, and must not unduly deteriorate under prolonged action of heat.

In assembling the coils of a core-type transformer, the H.T. and L.T.

* See American Standards for Transformers, Regulators and Reactors, ASA C57.10.

windings are separated by cylindrical barriers of high-grade insulating material.   Annular spaces must be left for free circulation of the cooling air, if the transformer is of the dry type, or of the cooling oil, if it is of the oil-immersion type.   Shifting of the barriers due to load or short-circuit stresses must be prevented by means of spacing blocks and appropriate clamps.

In shell-type transformers, the coils are assembled with barriers between H.T. and L.T. parts made of tough paperboard impregnated with insulating oil.   Ventilating ducts in the vertical direction are formed by angles or channels made of the same material.   The entire group of coils filling the window in the core is insulated from the core by an outer housing of the same paperboard material, and is firmly anchored to resist short-circuit stresses.

The development of transformers of large size and for high voltage was made possible by immersing the entire structure in oil.   The oil served not only to increase the dielectric strength but also to facilitate the dissipation of heat by the convection currents that are set up.   Originally, mineral oil was used exclusively, but more recently (since 1932) synthetic liquids have been developed that are classed as oil.   These synthetic oils (designated Askarel in the American Standards) are chlorinated hydrocarbons, and go by such trade names as Pyranol, Inerteen, Chlorextol, and Asbestol; they have all the advantages of mineral oil as an insulating and cooling agent, and in addition have the valuable property of being nonflammable and nonexplosive; they are more expensive than mineral oil, and the varnishes, gums, and binders commonly used in oil-filled equipment, being soluble in them, cannot be used.   Mineral oil is used in most cases where its use is not prohibited by fire underwriters' regulations.

3-7. Insulation of End Turns.   Traveling waves or surges on transmission lines or distributing circuits, such as may be caused by lightning discharges, arcing grounds, or switching operations, subject the end turns of connected transformers to severe dielectric stress.   The speed of the traveling wave is suddenly checked when it strikes the high impedance of the transformer winding, and the kinetic energy of the wave is suddenly converted into potential energy which charges to a high voltage the distributed capacitance represented by the adjacent turns of the winding, as well as by the copper winding and the neighboring core and enclosing case.   These distributed capacitances are equivalent to a complicated network of capacitance, inductance, and resistance.   The capacitances at and near the end turn become charged first, followed by the others in order, but with decreasing severity as the charge penetrates.   The result is that the end turns must be more heavily insulated than those in the interior of the coil.

The effect here described is analogous to what happens when an incoming ocean wave strikes a rocky cliff.   The kinetic energy of the wave is converted into the potential energy of the column of water that surges high in the air.

3-8. Terminal Bushings. The terminals of transformers of moderate voltage can be brought out through the enclosing case by means of porcelain bushings, but with high voltages the condenser effect between the terminal lead and the rim of the opening in the case produces a concentration of dielectric flux too intense to be within the limit of dielectric strength of the insulation. This fact presented a difficult problem when very high voltages were first introduced, but it was met by two different designs which limited the dielectric flux density to safe values.

In the condenser type of bushing, Fig. 3-10, the terminal itself consists of a brass rod or tube which is wound with alternate layers of treated paper and tin foil, so proportioned as to length that the series of condensers formed by the tin-foil cylinders and the intervening insulation have equal capacitances. The dielectric stress is thereby distributed uniformly over the whole length of the terminal. To prevent tufting of dielectric flux at the sharp ends of the tin-foil cylinders, the ends are attached to foil-covered rings of sufficient cross section to hold the dielectric flux below the limit at which corona develops. The completed terminal is provided with an external enclosing cylinder of insulating material which serves as a container for a gum compound between the terminal proper and the outer tube. For outdoor service, the terminal is then surrounded with a series of petticoated porcelain disks cemented together.

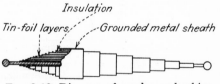

FIG. 3-10. Diagram of condenser bushing.

The other type of high-voltage terminal, called the oil-insulated terminal, consists of annular rings of porcelain or molded material cemented together around a brass rod so as to form an enclosure for oil. Cylindrical barriers surrounding the metal terminal, but inside the enclosed oil space, serve to prevent suspended particles in the oil from lining up under the influence of the electric field, which action, if not prevented, would cause a breakdown.

3-9. Insulation Tests of Transformers. The dielectric tests to which transformers must be subjected require the application for a specified time of a voltage higher than the rated voltage for the purpose of determining the adequacy of the insulating materials to withstand breakdown under normal operating conditions.

Dielectric tests are of two distinct kinds, (*a*) *impulse tests*, which as a rule are made only on transformers intended for connection to overhead lines; (*b*) applied-potential tests at low frequency.

a. Impulse Tests. Lightning discharges in the vicinity of the line terminal of a transformer produce an extremely rapid build-up of potential to a crest value.   If the potential rises high enough to cause a flashover at the terminal bushing, thereby suddenly relieving the potential stress, the resultant voltage-time curve is called a *chopped wave*, and its nature is such that the brunt of the dielectric stress is taken by the end turns only.   If on the other hand the crest voltage is insufficient to produce flashover, the voltage tails off more or less gradually, and in that case the stress on the insulation penetrates beyond the end turns into the interior of the winding; a voltage-time curve of this kind is called a *full wave*.

The purpose of impulse tests is to simulate the conditions produced by lightning.   Such tests require the use of an impulse, or surge, generator which consists of a set of capacitors and resistors so arranged that the former can be charged in parallel and discharged in series, so as to produce a single impulsive discharge of either positive or negative polarity, as desired.   The equipment* is elaborate, and requires the use of an auxiliary cathode-ray oscillograph.

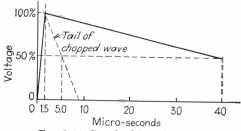

FIG. 3-11. Standard impulse wave.

The full-wave voltage-time curve accepted as standard for impulse tests is illustrated in Fig. 3-11.   It is designated as a 1.5 × 40 μsec wave, meaning that 1.5 μsec is required to reach the crest voltage, and that 40 μsec, counting from the nominal zero time, is required for the voltage to fall to half the crest value.   In practice, the steeply rising front of the wave may include oscillations, but the time from the nominal zero to the actual crest must not exceed 2.5 μsec for crest voltages up to and including 650 kv, and must not exceed 3.0 μsec for crest voltages above 650 kv.†   A chopped wave results when flashover is induced by means of a rod gap connected between the terminal under test and ground.

The impulse test, when required, is made while the transformer is excited at normal voltage, and the impulse is timed to be within 30 electrical degrees of the normal voltage of opposite polarity.   The purpose

    * P. L. Bellaschi, Characteristics of Surge Generators for Surge Testing, *Trans. AIEE*, **51**:936 (1932); The Measurement of High Surge Voltages, *Trans. AIEE*, **52**:544 (1933).   J. C. Dowell and C. M. Foust, Laboratory Measurements of Impulse Voltages, *Trans. AIEE*, **52**:537 (1933).

    † For further details, see ASA Standard C57.22, Par. 22.115.

of exciting the transformer is to allow a flow of power current into a fault if one develops.

The polarity of the impulse wave is usually negative in testing oil-immersed transformers, and positive for dry-type transformers.

The standard impulse test on a line terminal consists of one application of a reduced-voltage full wave, then two applications of a chopped

TABLE 3-1*

Insulation class, line-to-line voltage, kv rms	Low-frequency tests		Impulse tests					
			500 kva and below			Over 500 kva		
			Chopped wave		Full wave	Chopped wave		Full wave
	Oil-immersion, kv rms	Dry-type, kv rms	Kv crest	Minimum time to flashover, μsec	Kv crest	Kv crest	Minimum time to flashover, μsec	Kv crest
1.2	10	4	36	1.0	30	54	1.5	45
2.5	15	10	54	1.25	45			
5.0	19	12	69	1.5	60	88	1.6	75
8.66	26	19	88	1.6	75	110	1.8	95
15	34	31	110	1.8	95	130	2.0	110
25	50	..	175	3.0	150	175	3.0	150
34.5	70	..	230	3.0	200	230	3.0	200
46	95	..	290	3.0	250	290	3.0	250
69	140	..	400	3.0	350	400	3.0	350
92	185	..	520	3.0	450	520	3.0	450
115	230	..	630	3.0	550	630	3.0	550
138	275	..	750	3.0	650	750	3.0	650
161	325	..	865	3.0	750	865	3.0	750
196	395	..	1,035	3.0	900	1,035	3.0	900
230	460	..	1,210	3.0	1,050	1,210	3.0	1,050
287	575	..	1,500	3.0	1,300	1,500	3.0	1,300
345	690	..	1,785	3.0	1,550	1,785	3.0	1,550

* ASA C57.12, p. 8.

wave, followed by one application of a full wave. The crest voltages of the chopped and full waves are shown in Table 3-1.

b. *Potential Tests at Low Frequency.* These tests are of two types, (1) *applied-potential* tests between the windings, and between the windings and ground; (2) *induced-potential tests* that are made by impressing upon one winding a voltage that is twice the normal voltage induced in that winding.   These tests should be made at the temperature assumed under normal operating conditions.

1. *Applied-potential tests* require the use of a low-frequency step-up transformer of which one terminal of the H.T. winding is grounded and connected to the case of the transformer under test, while the other high-potential terminal is connected to the winding to be tested.   The terminals of the winding under test are short-circuited, and all other windings are grounded to the case.   The testing transformer must be so designed that its voltage can be increased uniformly from zero to the required limit in 1 min or less, and the upper limit of the test voltage must be maintained for 1 min.

2. *The induced-potential test* for transformers that are subjected to the full standard applied-potential test is made by impressing upon the terminals of one winding a voltage that is twice its normally induced voltage (unless this would result in a voltage between the terminals of any other winding in excess of the low-frequency test voltage normally required; in that case, the induced voltage between such terminals must be limited to the specified low-frequency test value for that winding).

The induced-potential test at double voltage is usually made with frequencies ranging from 120 to 400 cps, in order to keep the flux density in the core below the saturation limit.   The duration of the induced-potential test is 1 min when the frequency is not over 120 cycles, but for higher frequencies the duration is reduced in inverse proportion, so that the total number of cycles occurring in the test period shall be 7,200.

The test voltages specified by the American Standards are shown in Table 3-1.

3-10. Theoretical Heating and Cooling Curves.   The accurate calculation of the temperatures in the core and windings of a transformer is practically impossible because of the complex nature of the structure, and because it would be necessary to take into account such factors as the circulation of the oil in the ducts and in the enclosing case, and the heat exchange between coils and between coils and core.   It is, however, possible to derive equations which throw considerable light on the problem by bringing into their proper relations some of the more important factors involved.

a. Heating of a Homogeneous Body.   Let P, in watts, represent the rate at which heat energy is liberated, and let

σ = specific heat of substance, expressed in joules required to raise 1 lb through 1°C

A = radiating surface, sq in.

W = mass of body, lb

α = emissivity = watts radiated per sq in. of radiating surface per °C difference of temperature between body and surrounding medium

θ = temperature of body, °C, at any time t

θ_0 = temperature of body, °C, when $t = 0$ (assumed to be the same as the temperature of the surrounding medium)

In the time interval dt, the energy liberated amounts to $P\,dt$ joules, and the temperature will increase by $d\theta$; the body will absorb $\sigma W\,d\theta$ joules, and the amount radiated will be $\alpha A(\theta - \theta_0)\,dt$. Hence,

$$P\,dt = \sigma W\,d\theta + \alpha A(\theta - \theta_0)\,dt \qquad (3\text{-}1)$$

from which
$$\int_0^t dt = \int_{\theta_0}^\theta \frac{\sigma W\,d\theta}{P - \alpha A(\theta - \theta_0)}$$

and the rise of temperature at time t is

$$\theta - \theta_0 = \frac{P}{\alpha A}\left(1 - e^{-(\alpha A/\sigma W)t}\right) \qquad (3\text{-}2)$$

Equation 3-2 shows that after a theoretically infinite time the temperature rise is

$$\theta - \theta_0\,|_{t=\infty} = \frac{P}{\alpha A} \qquad (3\text{-}3)$$

which, when written in the form $P = \alpha A(\theta - \theta_0)$, expresses the fact that when the temperature reaches its final steady value the rate of heat production is equal to the rate at which it is dissipated. Practically, this condition is attained in a finite time, though it may be as great as 24 hr for large, self-cooled transformers if P corresponds to full-load conditions.

b. *Cooling of the Body.* In this case, no heat is developed, and Eq. 3-1 takes the form

$$0 = \sigma W\,d\theta + \alpha A(\theta - \theta_0)\,dt \qquad (3\text{-}4)$$

If the initial temperature of the hot body is θ_1 when $t = 0$,

$$\int_0^t dt = -\frac{\sigma W}{\alpha A}\int_{\theta_1}^\theta \frac{d\theta}{\theta - \theta_0}$$

from which
$$\theta - \theta_0 = (\theta_1 - \theta_0)e^{-(\alpha A/\sigma W)t} \qquad (3\text{-}5)$$

and this is the equation of the cooling curve. If it is assumed that cooling begins at a temperature equal to the final steady temperature at the end of the heating period, that is, $\theta_1 - \theta_0 = (\theta - \theta_0)_{t=\infty}$, it follows from Eq. 3-3 that the equation of the cooling curve takes the form

$$\theta - \theta_0 = \frac{P}{\alpha A}\,e^{-(\alpha A/\sigma W)t} \qquad (3\text{-}6)$$

which is the same as the variable part of Eq. 3-2, except for a change of sign. This means that under the assumed conditions the heating and cooling curves are of the same logarithmic shape, but with one of them turned upside down with respect to the other, as shown in Fig. 3-12.

On differentiating Eq. 3-2 and substituting $t = 0$ in the result, the slope of the heating curve at the origin is found to be

$$\frac{d\theta}{dt}\bigg|_{t=0} = \frac{P}{\sigma W} \qquad (3\text{-}7)$$

i.e., it is dependent upon the mass and material of the body, but not upon its radiating qualities. In fact, at the first instant, all the heat developed is absorbed, and none of it is radiated; hence, if the temperature continued to rise at this initial rate, the limiting temperature rise $P/\alpha A$ would be reached in a time

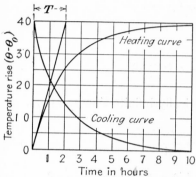

FIG. 3-12. Heating and cooling curves.

$$T = \frac{\sigma W}{\alpha A} \qquad \text{sec} \qquad (3\text{-}8)$$

which is called the *temperature time constant* of the body.

Equation 3-7 states that the initial rise of temperature, in degrees centigrade per second, is equal to the loss, in watts per pound, divided by the specific heat σ expressed in joules per pound per degree centigrade. For copper, $\sigma = 174.85$; for oil, $\sigma = 90$; for iron, $\sigma = 216$.

3-11. Cooling of Transformers. In so far as cooling methods are concerned, transformers are either of the *dry type* or of the *oil-immersed* type.

Small distributing transformers of the dry type, up to about 25 kva, are cooled by a combination of air-convection currents within the enclosing case and by natural radiation from the case itself. In larger sizes, this method is inadequate to dissipate the heat, and the *air-blast* type was developed to keep the operating temperature within bounds, though here also there are limits of size and voltage beyond which it is not possible to go. Air-blast transformers have been built in sizes up to 5,000 kva at 35,000 volts, though the upper limit is now considered to be 25,000 volts. The air supply must be filtered to prevent the accumulation of dust in the ventilating ducts. Prior to the development of nonflammable, nonexplosive insulating oil, air-blast transformers were used in indoor installations where mineral oil would have been too great a fire hazard.

In general, most transformers are now of the oil-immersed type. The oil provides better insulation than air, and at the same time it is a better conductor of heat than the air it replaces. However, the use of oil alone is insufficient to meet the problem presented by units of large rating; for as the linear dimensions are increased, the volume and weight of material, which largely determine the losses, increase as the cube of the linear dimensions, whereas the radiating surface increases only as the square. For these reasons, as the rating increases from moderate to very large values, oil-immersed equipment takes the following forms:

   a. Oil-immersed self-cooled transformers, in which the heated oil flows upward through the ducts in the core and the coils, thence down along the

Fig. 3-13. Two-hundred-kva single-phase 60-cycle 2,400/4,160Y 120/240-volt distribution transformer, showing tube cooling. (*Courtesy of Allis-Chalmers Manufacturing Company.*)

inner walls of the plain or corrugated enclosing case. A corrugated tank has about 50 per cent more radiating surface than a smooth tank. Additional radiating surface is obtained in larger sizes by welding a series of vertical tubes to the enclosing case, as in Fig. 3-13, or by bolting to the case radiators having fluted or finned surfaces.

   b. Oil-immersed forced-air-cooled transformers are similar to the self-cooled type described in paragraph *a*, but additional cooling is accomplished by motor-driven fans mounted directly on the radiators, as in Fig. 3-14.

c. Oil-immersed water-cooled transformers (Fig. 3-15) extract the heat from the oil by means of a stream of water pumped through a copper coil immersed in the oil just below the top of the tank.   The heated water is in turn cooled by means of a spray pond or by a cooling tower.

d. Oil-immersed forced-oil-cooled transformers extract the heat from the oil by pumping the oil itself upward through the windings and then back

FIG. 3-14. Oil-immersed forced-air-cooled three-phase power transformer.   (*Courtesy of General Electric Company.*)

by way of external radiators which may themselves be cooled by fans. The extra cost of the oil-pumping equipment must of course be economically justified, but it has incidentally the advantage of reducing the temperature difference between the top and bottom of the enclosing case.

While the rate at which heat is liberated is practically uniform throughout the mass of the core, the interior necessarily attains a higher temperature than the surface in order that there may be a temperature gradient to set up the outward flow of heat.   In speaking of the rise of temperature of the core, it is therefore necessary to bear in mind that this is the average rise, and that there must be some parts having a temperature higher than the average. The conduction of heat from the interior to the surface of the core takes place mostly along the laminations, the heat conductivity in this direction being 50 to 100 times greater than across them.

The thermal conductivity of fibrous insulating material is so much less than that of copper, the ratio being about 1:1,700, as to cause most of the temperature drop between coils and cooling medium to be concentrated in the insulation. In other words, while insulation of the coils from each other and from the core is extremely important, in order that disruptive

Fig. 3-15. Cooling coils for oil-immersed water-cooled transformer. (*Courtesy of Wagner Electric Corporation.*)

breakdown may be prevented, it must be remembered that the insulation operates as a barrier to the desired flow of heat. Hence, there is a conflict between electrical and thermal considerations, and it is therefore necessary to select and dispose the insulating material so as to assure safety from disruptive discharge and at the same time interfere as little as possible with the dissipation of heat.

3-12. Breathing of Transformers. In oil-cooled transformers of the ordinary type, the expansion of the oil forces out the air above it, so that, on cooling, fresh air is again drawn in, bringing with it a renewed supply of oxygen and more or less moisture. Condensation of the moisture deteriorates the insulating qualities of the oil, and the oxidation of the oil produces a deposit of sludge. These effects are particularly objectionable in large, high-voltage transformers; they are overcome by the use of an expansion tank, called a conservator, mounted on the top of the transformer case and connected thereto in such manner that the transformer case is always completely full of oil, and the upper portion of the conservator is filled with dry and chemically inert nitrogen.

3-13. Operating Temperature and Temperature Rise. Insulation of the Class A and B types, commonly used in transformers, deteriorates rapidly if exposed continuously to temperatures higher than about 100°C. Temperatures somewhat above 100°C can be withstood for limited periods, but the cumulative effect of temperature and time has not been definitely established. Accordingly, for purposes of standardization, the rating of a transformer and other inductive apparatus is based upon the *rise* of temperature above the *ambient* temperature, since the sum of these two fixes the actual temperature that must be kept within safe limits.

There are three recognized ratings, which are defined as follows:*

The *continuous rating* defines a constant load which can be carried without causing further measurable increase in temperature rise under prescribed conditions of test, and within the limitations of established standards.

The *nominal rating* defines the constant load which, having been carried without causing further measurable increase in the temperature rise, may be increased a given percentage (25 or 50 per cent) for two hours without causing limitations established for nominally rated transformers to be exceeded.

The *short-time rating* is a rating that defines the load which can be carried for a short and definitely specified time, the apparatus being approximately at room temperature at the time the temperature test is started.

The allowable temperature rise of power and distribution transformers is shown in Table 3-2.

Temperature rise of the windings is measured by the *resistance* method, and also by the *thermometer* method when so specified. The resistance method is based upon the relation indicated in Eq. 1-36, from which the rise of temperature is

$$\theta_2 - \theta_1 = \frac{R_{\theta_2} - R_{\theta_1}}{R_{\theta_1}} (\theta_1 + 234.5) \tag{3-9}$$

The thermometer method includes the use of mercury and alcohol thermometers, resistance thermometers, and thermocouples, any of these instruments being applied to the hottest part of the apparatus accessible to mercury or alcohol thermometers. (Mercury thermometers must of course not be used if the bulbs are exposed to an alternating magnetic field because eddy currents induced in the mercury will give false readings.)

The rise of temperature computed by Eq. 3-9 is the average rise throughout the winding, and allowance must be made, as in Table 3-2, for

* ASA C57.10, 1948.

the fact that some part of the winding will be the hottest spot. The hottest-spot copper temperature (which is the sum of the temperature of the cooling medium, the average temperature rise of the copper, and the hottest-spot allowance) must be below 100°C if the transformer is to have normal life expectancy; it is assumed to be 95°C for oil-immersed transformers operating at continuous rating, and with ambient temperatures limited as follows: (a) with air cooling, not over 40°C and with the average during any 24-hr period equal to 30°C; (b) with water cooling, corresponding temperatures of 30 and 25°C.

Temperature tests on self-cooled and forced-air-cooled transformers are made at ambient temperatures not less than 10°C or more than 40°C. In

TABLE 3-2. LIMITS OF TEMPERATURE RISE, DEGREES CENTIGRADE*

Type	Rating	Copper temperature rise by resistance		Hottest-spot copper temperature rise	
		Class A insulation	Class B insulation	Class A insulation	Class B insulation
Oil-immersed........	Continuous	55	..	65	Not yet established (1953)
	Nominal	60	..	75	
Dry..............	Continuous	55†	80	65	
	Nominal	60†	..	75	

The temperature rise of the insulating oil shall not exceed 50°C when measured near the exposed surface of the oil or 55°C if the transformer is equipped with an oil conservator or uses inert gas above the oil.

* From Table 11.021, ASA C57.11, 1953.

† Subject to correction if the temperature of ingoing cooling air differs from 40°C.

the case of water-cooled transformers, the ambient temperature is taken as that of the ingoing water, which should preferably be 25°C, but not less than 20°C or more than 30°C.

The accuracy of temperature-rise calculation by means of Eq. 3-9 depends upon the correctness of the initial resistance at a known (cold) temperature. Standard procedures for measuring cold temperature are:

   a. *Transformer Not Immersed in Oil.* The temperature of the windings shall be taken as the average of the readings of several thermometers inserted between the coils, with extreme care that their bulbs are as nearly as possible in actual contact with the copper of the windings. It should not be assumed that the windings are at the same temperature as the surrounding air.

   b. *Transformer Immersed in Oil.* The temperature of the windings shall be assumed to be the same as the temperature of the oil, provided the transfomer has been under oil with no excitation and with no current in its windings from three to eight hours before the cold resistance is measured, depending upon the size of the transformer.

c. The transformer must not be located in drafts or where it is in a room in which the temperature is fluctuating rapidly.

The measurement of resistance should preferably be made by the bridge method.   The drop-of-potential method is often used because of its convenience, but is not permissible if the current-carrying capacity of the winding is less than 1 amp; and if this method is used, the current through the winding must not exceed 15 per cent of the rated current of the winding in order to prevent heating that would increase the resistance being measured.

The hot-resistance measurement must of course be made as soon as possible after shutting down the transformer, but in no case more than 4 min thereafter.   Some cooling will occur in the interval between shutting down and taking the necessary readings.   If there is available a cooling curve which shows the relation between temperature and time, an appropriate correction can be made if the time interval between shutdown and the taking of readings is noted; if such a cooling curve is not available, the recommended standard correction in degrees centigrade, for oil-immersed apparatus of the usual commercial proportions in which the copper loss does not exceed 30 watts per lb, may be computed by the formula

Correction in °C = watts lost per lb of copper for each winding $\times f$

$$(3\text{-}10)$$

where f is a factor obtained by interpolation in Table 3-3.

TABLE 3-3

Elapsed time after shutdown, min	f
1	0.19
1.5	0.26
2	0.32
3	0.43
4	0.50

If the copper loss in oil-immersed apparatus does not exceed 7 watts per lb, an arbitrary correction of 1°C per min may be used, provided the elapsed time after shutdown does not exceed 4 min.   The same arbitrary correction may be used for air-blast transformers, subject to the same time limitation.   To determine the copper loss in watts per pound, the total loss in both windings, as measured by wattmeter, may be apportioned between high- and low-voltage windings in the ratio of their respective calculated I^2R losses, if the conductor I^2R and eddy losses cannot be determined conveniently.

The computed rise of temperature of dry-type, forced-air-cooled transformers (air-blast) must be corrected, when the cooling air temperature is less than 40°C, by multiplying the computed rise of temperature by the factor

$$C = \frac{274.5}{234.5 + \theta} \tag{3-11}$$

where θ is the ingoing air temperature.

A further correction of the observed (computed) temperature rise must be made in the case of standard apparatus tested at altitudes in excess of 3,300 ft (1,000 m) above sea level to make the results comparable with those obtained below the 3,300-ft level. The correction is made by reducing the high-altitude temperature by the following amounts for each 330 ft (100 m) that the altitude exceeds 3,300 ft:

Per cent

For oil-immersed, self-cooled apparatus.................. 0.4
For dry-type apparatus............................... 0.5
For oil-immersed, forced-air-cooled apparatus............. 0.6
For air-blast apparatus.............................. 1.0

3-14. Temperature Rise Due to Short Circuits.* A short circuit on a transformer is injurious because of the heating effect and the mechanical stress on the winding, both of which are proportional to the square of the current. In practice, however, the transformer must be designed to withstand these effects long enough, on the average, to allow the short circuit to burn itself clear and thus maintain continuity of service.

For purposes of standardization, the magnitude and duration of the short-circuit current are fixed by Table 3-4. Two formulas have been

TABLE 3-4

Per cent impedance	Rms symmetrical short-circuit current to be withstood	Time period, sec
4 or less	25 times rated current	2
5	20 times rated current	3
6	16.6 times rated current	4
7 or more		5

standardized for computing the temperature of the copper due to the short-circuit currents indicated in Table 3-4. One of them, Eq. 3-12, is based on the assumption that all the heat due to the current is stored in the copper; this assumption is not rigorous, but the results are sufficiently accurate for practical purposes up to 350°C. The other, Eq. 3-13, gives accurate results under any conditions. These equations are

$$\theta = Ft \left[\frac{f}{2(\theta_1 + 234.5)} + \frac{618.4K}{f} \right] + \theta_1 \tag{3-12}$$

* ASA C57.12 and C57.22.

where θ = final temperature, °C

θ_1 = initial temperature, °C

t = time, sec

K = ratio of eddy-current loss to I^2R loss at 75°C

$$F = \frac{\text{watts per lb at } \theta_1}{180}$$

$$= 4.6S^2(\theta_1 + 234.5) \times 10^{-11}$$

$$= \frac{75(\theta_1 + 234.5)}{M^2}$$

$f = 2(\theta_1 + 234.5) + Ft$

M = cir mils per amp

S = amp per sq in. of conductor

and

$$\theta = 309.5 \sqrt{\left[\left(\frac{\theta_1 + 234.5}{309.5}\right)^2 + K\right] \log_{10}^{-1} (F't) - K} - 234.5 \quad (3\text{-}13)$$

where $F' = 4.0 \times 10^{-11} \times S^2$

$$= 1.56 \times 10^{-5} \times (I^2R \text{ at } 75°C, \text{ per lb})$$

$$= 65 \ M^{-2}$$

The final temperature thus computed must not exceed 250°C in the case of Class A insulation, assuming an initial copper temperature of 95°C, or 350°C in the case of Class B insulation, assuming an initial temperature of 125°C.

3-15. Heat Runs. When a transformer is to be tested under load conditions to determine whether its temperature rise is within the pre-

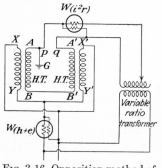

FIG. 3-16. Opposition method of testing transformers.

scribed limits, it is not practicable to apply an actual load, especially in the case of large units, for the reason that it is too expensive to supply the power and also because the rheostats required to take up the power would be too large and costly, as well as dangerous to handle in the case of high voltages. The usual method of testing, applicable to any size of single-phase transformers, is to connect two identical transformers in opposition, as shown in Fig. 3-16, for in this way both transformers may be subjected to full-load or overload conditions as to core loss and copper loss, while at the same time the power drawn from the supply circuit is only equal to the total losses in the two transformers. This opposition test, sometimes called the circulating-power or pumping-back test, was originally devised by Gisbert Kapp.

The two transformers are connected in parallel on the L.T. side to a circuit having a voltage equal to the rated L.T. voltage. The two H.T.

windings are connected in series to an auxiliary circuit having adjustable voltage, in such a way that the emfs induced in the two H.T. windings are in opposition around the series circuit.

When the adjustable voltage inserted in the series connection is zero, the two H.T. emfs balance each other, the currents in the L.T. windings will be the exciting currents, and the supply circuit will furnish the core loss of the two transformers.   On gradually increasing the auxiliary voltage in the series circuit, any desired amount of current may be made to flow in the H.T. windings; in the L.T. windings, which are short-circuited with respect to the H.T. windings, there will then flow currents greater than those in the other windings by the ratio of transformation. The power supplied by the auxiliary emf in the series circuit will be equal to the copper loss in the two transformers, and the voltage required will be double the impedance voltage of either of them.   The power taken from the L.T. supply will continue to be the combined core loss of the two transformers.

The necessary variation in the voltage of the auxiliary circuit may be obtained by means of a transformer having suitable taps, or by an induction regulator.   By grounding the H.T. circuit at point G (Fig. 3-16), the instruments in the auxiliary series circuit may be handled without danger.

On circulating full-load current through a transformer in the manner described above, the unit will reach its final temperature in 3 to 24 hr, depending upon its size, the time increasing with the size of the unit. In the case of transformers of large size, the time may be reduced very materially by running alternately for short periods first on open circuit and then on short circuit, or with reduced cooling, until the core and windings approach their final steady temperature.   In this test, the voltage for the open-circuit period and the current for the short-circuit period must be such as to give the same integrated core and copper losses as would occur under normal full-load operation.

It should be borne in mind that if the load is maintained too long at a value in excess of normal conditions, the temperature may rise too high, in which case the time required to cool off may more than offset the time saved by a temporary overloading.   In other words, the transformer has a heat inertia similar to the mechanical inertia of a flywheel.

A bank of three identical single-phase transformers may be tested simultaneously by connecting the L.T. windings in Δ to a three-phase circuit having the rated L.T. voltage and frequency; and by connecting the H.T. windings in Δ, but with the circuit opened at one corner of the Δ for the introduction of an auxiliary voltage, which can then be adjusted to circulate any desired amount of current.

A single three-phase transformer can be tested in the same manner indicated for the case of three single-phase transformers.

3-16. Mechanical Stresses.   It is well-known that parallel conductors will attract or repel each other according to whether the currents they carry are in the same or opposite directions.   In the constant-current transformer, for example, the force of repulsion between the primary and secondary coils, whose currents are opposite, is utilized to secure the desired regulation.   Similar forces exist in ordinary stationary transformers, the cause being due to the reaction between the currents in the windings and the stray magnetic field which surrounds them.   The magnitude of the force on a conductor is proportional to the product of the current in it and the intensity of the magnetic field due to the neighboring currents; and since the latter is itself proportional to the current, the force is proportional to the square of the current.   With ordinary values of current, the forces are moderate and are not sufficiently large to be noticeable, but when large transformers are subjected to short-circuit

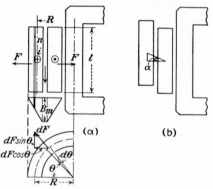

Fig. 3-17. Stresses in transformer coils.

conditions at full voltage, as may happen in power systems having very large generating capacity, the short-circuit current may reach 10 to 25 times full-load value, with stresses 100 to 625 times normal.   In such cases, the mechanical force may become so great as to wreck the transformer unless the coils are solidly braced.

To find the force on the coils of a core-type transformer, consider the outer cylindrical coil of Fig. 3-17, the directions of the current flow and leakage flux being as there indicated.   The two coils will exert a force of mutual repulsion upon each other, as shown by the arrows marked F. The field in the space between the two coils will be at any instant

$$B = \mu_0 \frac{ni}{kl}$$

where n is the number of turns in the outer coil and i is the instantaneous value of current.   The denominator kl, in meters, is the average length of path of the leakage flux, k being a factor, usually about 1.8, to take account of the spreading of the flux at the two ends of the coil.   The flux density varies uniformly from the above value at the inner surface of the coil to zero at the outer surface, the average value across the section of the coil being

$$B_{av} = \frac{\mu_0}{2} \frac{ni}{kl}$$

If the mean radius of the coil is R m, the force acting on the n elementary portions lying within the angle $d\theta$ will be

$$dF = B_{av} niR \, d\theta = \frac{\mu_0}{2} \frac{n^2 i^2 R \, d\theta}{kl} \qquad \text{newtons}$$

This force may be resolved into two components, as shown in the plan view, Fig. 3-17a, one being $dF \sin \theta$, the other $dF \cos \theta$. The latter may be neglected, since in an angle of 180° the sum of all of them will be zero. The integral of the former will be the hoop tension in the coil; it is

$$F = \frac{\mu_0}{2} \frac{Rn^2 i^2}{kl} \int_0^{\pi} \sin \theta \, d\theta = \mu_0 \frac{Rn^2 i^2}{kl} = \frac{2Tn^2 i^2}{10^7 \times kl} \qquad \text{newtons} \quad (3\text{-}14)$$

where $T = 2\pi R$ is the mean length of turn.

The instantaneous current is $i = \sqrt{2} \, I \sin (\omega t \pm \varphi)$, and

$$i^2 = 2I^2 \sin^2 (\omega t \pm \varphi)$$

where I is the effective value of the current. The average value of this expression is I^2, since the average sine squared is $\frac{1}{2}$. Hence,

$$F_{av} = \frac{2Tn^2 I^2}{10^7 \times kl} \qquad \text{newtons} \qquad (3\text{-}15)$$

If the dimensions T and l are both expressed in inches (or both in feet), Eq. 3-15 becomes

$$F_{av} = \frac{0.45}{10^7} \frac{Tn^2 I^2}{kl} \qquad \text{lb}$$

Example. In a 200-kva 11,000/2,300 volt transformer, $n = 455$, $l = 35$ in., $T = 46.3$ in., and $k = 1.8$. The equivalent impedance, in terms of the 11,000-volt winding, is 8.33 ohms. The short-circuit current at full voltage is then 1,320 amp. The radial force due to this current is thus

$$F_{av} = \frac{0.45 \times 46.3 \times 455^2 \times 1,320^2}{10^7 \times 1.8 \times 35} = 11,930 \text{ lb}$$

The above formula has been derived on the assumption that the coils are concentric and that their central points are not displaced from each other in the axial direction. Where such axial displacement exists, as in transformers whose windings are provided with taps for varying ratios of transformation, the above formula will hold approximately for the total force, but it will have both radial and axial components, as shown in Fig. 3-17b. The radial component will be $F_{av} \cos \alpha$, and the axial component $F_{av} \sin \alpha$. The latter may easily reach very large values, necessitating secure bracing to prevent motion of the coils; the bracing must be so designed as not to interfere with the free circulation of oil in the space between the coils.

In shell-type transformers having pancake coils symmetrically arranged, as in Fig. 3-18, there is a force of repulsion between the coils of each of the pairs 1-2, 3-4, 5-6, and 7-8. The force on coil 2 is opposite in direction to that acting on coil 3; likewise for coils 4-5 and 6-7. It

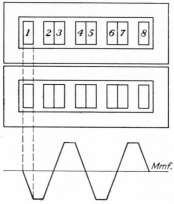

Fig. 3-18. Symmetrical arrangement of coils in shell-type transformer, and mmf diagram.

follows that there is an unbalanced force acting on the end coils, 1 and 8, which must be provided for by suitable bracing. The magnitude of the force may be computed as follows:

The average value of the leakage field across the section of the coil (in the direction l) is, in rationalized mks units,

$$B_{av} = \frac{\mu_0}{2} \frac{ni}{l}$$

and the force due to the reaction between the magnetic field and the current i in the n turns of the end coil is

$$F = B_{av} T n i \qquad \text{newtons}$$

where T is the mean length of a turn. The average value of the force, determined as in the previous case, is

$$F_{av} = \frac{\mu_0}{2} \frac{n^2 i_{av} T}{l} \qquad \text{newtons}$$

which becomes

$$F_{av} = \frac{2\pi n^2 T I^2 \times 10^5}{10^7 \times l \times 981 \times 453.6}$$

$$= \frac{1.41 n^2 T I^2}{10^7 \times l} \qquad \text{lb} \qquad (3\text{-}16)$$

where T and l are both expressed in the same unit of length.

When the coil arrangement is unsymmetrical, as illustrated in Fig. 3-19, the forces developed between the inner groups do not balance, and the excess force will be transmitted to the end coils, therefore requiring additional bracing. Thus, in the figure, 8 of the 16 coils belong to the primary and the remainder to the secondary, with directions of current as indicated.

In producing the leakage field indicated by the mmf diagram, the coils group themselves as follows: 1-2; 3-4-5-6; 7-8; 9-10; 11-12-13-14; and 15-16. The directions of the resultant forces between the two halves of

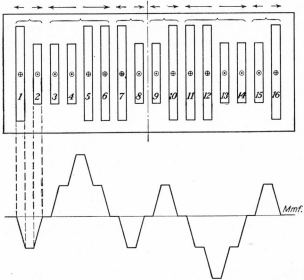

FIG. 3-19. Unsymmetrical arrangement of coils in shell-type transformer, and mmf diagram.

each group are shown by the horizontal arrows at the top of the diagram. Starting at the center line between coils 8 and 9, it is seen that the forces on these two coils balance; the forces between coils 6 and 7 likewise balance, leaving the force due to coil 5 (toward the right) to be balanced by a similar force due to coil 12. The forces due to coils 2 and 3 likewise balance, leaving unbalanced forces, acting toward the left, due to coils 1 and 4. Consequently, the bracing to be provided will correspond to the sum of these two forces, which will be more than double that due to coil 1 alone, since the average flux density across coil 4 is double that acting upon coil 1, as shown by the mmf diagram.

CHAPTER 4

FUNDAMENTAL PRINCIPLES OF ROTATING MACHINES

4-1. EMF of Elementary Alternator. The idealized elementary alternator of Figs. 4-1 and 4-2 is assumed to consist of a concentrated coil of N turns rotating at a uniform speed of n_s rps in a uniform magnetic field produced by the poles N, S. The assumption of a uniform field implies that the flux density across the diametral plane ab, Fig. 4-2, is everywhere

$$B_m = \frac{\Phi}{Dl} \tag{4-1}$$

where Φ is the total flux* crossing from N to S within the rectangular area defined by the effective coil diameter D and axial length l. At the instant

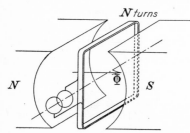

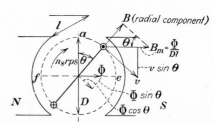

FIG. 4-1. Elementary alternator.   FIG. 4-2. Analysis of elementary alternator.

when the coil occupies the position defined by the angle θ, Fig. 4-2, the flux linked with the coil is $\varphi = \Phi \cos \theta$, and the corresponding instantaneous emf developed in the winding is

$$e = -N \frac{d\varphi}{dt} = N\Phi \sin \theta \frac{d\theta}{dt} \tag{4-2}$$

But $d\theta/dt$ is the angular velocity of the coil and may be written $\omega = 2\pi n_s$; and θ may be replaced by its equivalent, ωt, where t is the time counted from the instant when the coil lies in the plane ab. Hence, from Eq. 4-2,

$$e = 2\pi n_s N\Phi \sin \omega t \tag{4-3}$$

and the maximum and effective values of this sinusoidally varying emf

---

* Meter-kilogram-second units are implied, i.e., flux is in webers, and dimensions are in meters.

are, respectively,

$$E_m = 2\pi n_s N\Phi \tag{4-4}$$

and

$$E = \sqrt{2}\pi n_s N\Phi \tag{4-5}$$

The formula for the emf developed in the coil may also be derived from the consideration that each of the peripheral conductors, at the instant defined by the time t, is cutting across the radial component of flux density, B, at the tangential velocity $v = \pi D n_s$. Since the total number of conductors in series is $2N$, the instantaneous emf is

$$e = 2NBlv$$

and since it is evident from Fig. 4-2 that $B = B_m \sin \theta$, it follows that

$$e = (2N)(B_m \sin \theta)l(\pi D n_s)$$

and from Eq. 4-1 that

$$e = 2\pi n_s N\Phi \sin \theta$$

which is the same as Eq. 4-3.

Another way of arriving at the same result is afforded by the consideration that the coil links with the entire flux Φ when it occupies the position ab, Fig. 4-2, and that a quarter revolution later there is no flux linked with it. It follows that the total flux Φ has been cut in a time $1/4n_s$ sec; hence, the *average* emf per turn (equal to the flux cut per second) is $4n_s\Phi$, and the average emf for the N turns is $4n_sN\Phi$. Since the average value of one loop of a sine curve is $2/\pi$ times the maximum value, the maximum emf is $2\pi n_sN\Phi$, or the same as Eq. 4-4.

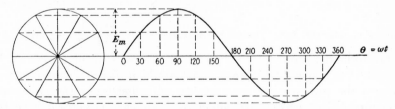

Fig. 4-3. Sinusoidal variation of emf.

Equations 4-3 to 4-5 have been derived by assuming that the coil of Figs. 4-1 and 4-2 is rotating uniformly in the clockwise direction between the stationary poles N, S; in other words, that the machine is of the *revolving-armature* type. The variation of emf as a function of θ (and therefore also as a function of time) is indicated by the sinusoidal curve of Fig. 4-3. Counterclockwise rotation of the coil would merely turn this curve upside down; or, what amounts to the same thing, the origin of coordinates would be shifted from the point $\theta = 0$ to the point $\theta = 180°$.

Since the emf is induced by relative motion between the coil and the flux, the result will be the same as if the coil were stationary and the pole pieces revolved around it, in other words, as if the machine were of the *revolving-field* type.

Finally, the emf developed in the coil remains the same as before if the coil is stationary and the flux linked with it varies harmonically with respect to time.   Thus, referring to Fig. 4-1, if the coil remains permanently in the vertical position, and if the flux from pole to pole alternates in the transverse direction in accordance with the equation $\varphi = \Phi \cos \omega t$, the resultant induced emf is represented by Eq. 4-2 and those which follow it.   As a matter of fact, this time variation of the effective flux φ is exactly the same as would result from resolving the total flux Φ, Fig. 4-2, into two components, one of which, $\varphi = \Phi \cos \theta$, is perpendicular to the plane of the coil, and the other, $\Phi \sin \theta$, lies in the plane of the coil.   The latter component can have no inductive effect since it does not link with the turns of the coil.   In effect, then, with respect to the perpendicular component $\Phi \cos \theta$, the armature winding plays the role of the secondary of

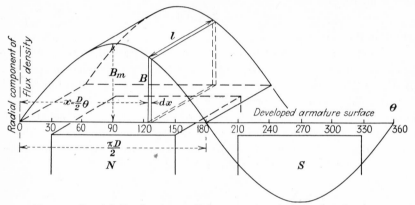

Fig. 4-4. Spatial distribution, radial component of airgap flux density.

a transformer.   From this point of view, the alternator is seen to be equivalent to a generalized transformer in which there is relative motion between the primary and secondary.   But whereas in the stationary transformer the electrical output of the secondary is derived from the electrical input to the primary, the secondary (armature) output of the alternator is derived from the mechanical input required to maintain the relative motion between the armature and the field poles.

4-2. Relation between Polar Flux and Airgap Flux Density.   The assumption of a uniform flux between poles N and S of Figs. 4-1 and 4-2 implies that the lines of induction pass straight across from pole to pole at right angles to the plane of ab; the flux density across this diametral plane is then everywhere $B_m = \Phi/Dl$, and this is likewise the radial component of flux density at points opposite the middle of the pole faces, as at e and f, Fig. 4-2.   At all other points around the cylindrical surface of the armature, the radial component of flux density follows the law $B = B_m \sin \theta$. This radial distribution of flux density is shown by the ordinates of the three-dimensional diagram, Fig. 4-4, which represents in developed form the machine of Fig. 4-2.

In the element defined by ordinate B and abscissa $x = \tfrac{1}{2}D\theta$, the radially directed flux is $d\varphi = Bl\,dx$; hence, the total effective flux per pole is

$$\Phi = \int_0^{\pi D/2} Bl\,dx = \int_0^{\pi} (B_m \sin \theta)l\,\frac{D\,d\theta}{2} = B_m\,Dl \qquad (4\text{-}6)$$

which is the same as Eq. 4-1.   The conclusion to be drawn from this result is that the *volume integral of the radial flux-density distribution is equal to the total flux per pole effective in developing the armature emf.*

Sinusoidal distribution of the radial component of flux density is never exactly realized in actual machines, though it can be closely approximated by means to be discussed later.   But in the bipolar model of Figs. 4-1 and 4-2 it is necessary to wind the armature coil on a laminated steel core in

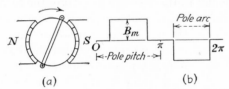

(a)   (b)

FIG. 4-5. Rectangular distribution of flux density.

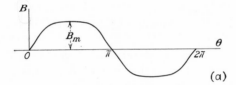

(a)

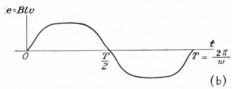

(b)

FIG. 4-6. (a) Nonsinusoidal flux density; (b) emf per conductor.

order to reduce the reluctance of the magnetic circuit to a reasonable amount, and in that case the flux in the airgap tends to distribute itself in the manner indicated in Fig. 4-5a.   In developed form, this distribution is rectangular, as shown in Fig. 4-5b, but the fringing of the flux at the pole tips yields the distribution indicated in Fig. 4-6a, which is similar to Fig. 4-5b except that the sharp corners have been rounded off.   Whatever the shape of the flux-density curve may be, provided successive half loops are symmetrical, the area under one loop of the curve is proportional to the useful flux per pole, as may be seen from the form of the integral in Eq. 4-6.

It is important to realize that whatever the *space distribution* of the flux density may be, as in Fig. 4-6a, the *time variation of the emf per conductor* has the same form, as shown in Fig. 4-6b.   The flux density is plotted as a function of the space angle θ, whereas the emf is plotted as a function of the time t, the time scale being so chosen that the space angle $\theta = 2\pi$ is equivalent to the time T required to make one revolution, so that $T = 2\pi/\omega$.

4-3. EMF of Elementary Multipolar Alternator. The multipolar machine of Fig. 4-7 embodies an extension of the principles underlying the simple bipolar machine of Fig. 4-2. Structurally, the two differ principally in that the relative motion between the armature inductors and the magnetic field is obtained in the case of Fig. 4-7 by arranging the winding on the stationary armature core, and rotating the crown of radially projecting poles. In both cases, the wires of the armature winding are all in series, and they are disposed in slots separated from each other by an angular distance equal to the pole pitch. All of the pole pieces are identical in form and construction, and all have the same exciting winding, to the end that the resultant flux may be the same in magnitude and distribution in each of the parallel magnetic circuits. But whereas the induced emf in the case of the bipolar machine passes through one complete cycle in one revolution, it will be evident that a corresponding cycle is completed in the case of the multipolar machine when the field structure rotates through the angle subtended by a double pole pitch; in other words, the number of *cycles per second* is equal to the number of revolutions per second in the case of a bipolar generator, but it is equal to the number of revolutions per second multiplied by the number of pairs of poles in a multipolar machine. The number of cycles per second is called the *frequency*, f, so that

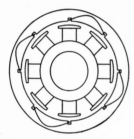

Fig. 4-7. Multipolar revolving-field alternator.

$$f = \frac{pn_s}{2} = \frac{pn}{120} \tag{4-7}$$

where p = number of poles

n = revolutions per minute

It follows, therefore, that if in a multipolar alternator the flux is Φ lines per pole, distributed sinusoidally around the airgap, and if the total number of armature turns in series is N, all turns being concentrated in a single set of slots as in Fig. 4-7, the generated emf will be simply $p/2$ times as great as that given by Eq. 4-3, or it is .

$$e = 2\pi \frac{p}{2} n_s N\Phi \sin \theta$$

$$= 2\pi f N\Phi \sin \omega t \tag{4-8}$$

It is to be noted, however, that the angle $\theta = \omega t$ in Eq. 4-8 is not the actual space angle as measured around the periphery of the armature, since the complete cycle indicated by the angle 2π in Fig. 4-6a now corresponds to the angle subtended by the double pole pitch, namely, $2\pi/(p/2)$ radians.   In other words, each degree of actual angular space displacement is now equivalent to $p/2$ *electrical degrees.*

The angular velocity of a bipolar machine is $\omega = 2\pi n_s$, and in that case the frequency f is equal to n_s.   The angular velocity of a multipolar machine must accordingly be taken as $\omega = 2\pi n_s \times (p/2) = 2\pi f$, so that in general $\omega = 2\pi f$ without regard to the number of poles.

4-4. Frequency of Alternation.   Standard frequencies in the United States are 25 and 60 cps.   Other frequencies are used occasionally, there being some systems in which a frequency of 50 cps is used, and for railway work, especially abroad, frequencies as low as $12\frac{1}{2}$ cps are employed. In the early days of the electrical industry, a common frequency was $133\frac{1}{3}$ cps, or, as it was then commonly expressed, 16,000 alternations per minute.   This frequency was found to be too high, especially when the transmission and distribution lines became longer, for the inductive effect of the circuit at this relatively high frequency then became very pronounced.   The frequency of 60 cps was determined to a large extent by the circumstance that below this frequency the filaments of incandescent lamps showed an appreciable flicker.   The lower frequency* of 25 cps came into extensive use, especially for long-distance transmission, in order still further to reduce the inductive effect of the transmission line, though later developments of the art have made it possible to neutralize many of the difficulties caused by line inductance.

Equation 4-7 is useful in determining the speed at which an alternator must run in order to develop a given frequency when the number of poles is known; for example, in 60-cycle circuits the product of p and the rpm is 7,200, while in 25-cycle circuits this product is 3,000.   The following table shows the speeds corresponding to different numbers of poles for both 25- and 60-cycle circuits:

p	Rpm	
	25 cycles	60 cycles
2	1,500	3,600
4	750	1,800
6	500	1,200
8	375	900
10	300	720
12	250	600
14	214.3	514.3
16	187.5	450
18	166.7	400
20	150	360

* See B. G. Lamme, The Technical Story of the Frequencies, *Trans. AIEE*, **37**:65 (1918).

It will be noted that the 60-cycle frequency provides a much wider and better distributed range of speeds than is possible with 25 cycles.   This is especially important in the case of motors for industrial applications.

4-5. Factors Affecting the Induced EMF.   It has been shown in Art. 4-2 that the emf induced in a single conductor of the armature winding varies with respect to time in the same manner as the field intensity in the airgap is distributed in space.   The total emf due to all the conductors in series between terminals is, at any instant, the algebraic sum of the corresponding instantaneous emfs in the conductors so connected. This sum, as well as the resultant effective value of the emf, will obviously depend upon (a) the distribution of the field intensity in the airgap; (b) the number of the conductors in series and the manner in which they are disposed on the armature; and upon the relative velocity with which the conductors move through the flux.

The windings of the elementary machines represented by Figs. 4-1 and 4-7 utilize only a fraction of the available space.   In order to improve the weight efficiency, it is therefore necessary to insert additional windings in the space that would otherwise be wasted.   When this is done, the emfs of neighboring conductors are displaced in time phase, and it is therefore necessary to connect them in such manner that the emfs of those which are in series will be mainly additive.

The nonsinusoidal distributions of field intensity indicated by Figs. 4-5b and 4-6a are periodic, single-valued functions that do not include infinite discontinuities; in accordance with Fourier's theorem, they can therefore be resolved into a fundamental sine wave and a series of higher space harmonics.   The emf developed in any single conductor therefore consists of a sine wave of fundamental frequency upon which are superposed time harmonics which have frequencies that are integral multiples of the fundamental frequency.   In most cases that arise in a-c machines, only the odd harmonics are present because of the fact that the flux-density curves like Fig. 4-6a are symmetrical in successive half loops; if these successive half loops are not symmetrical, even harmonics are present.

On connecting in series a number of conductors which are spaced at intervals around the armature, the individual emfs of fundamental frequency combine to give a resultant emf which is likewise of fundamental frequency; each set of harmonic emfs of a given frequency combine to produce a resultant harmonic emf of the same frequency.   But the manner in which these individual components combine is not the same for all the frequencies, and the end result is that the final wave form of emf (plotted as a function of time) is in general not the same as the space wave form of flux density upon which all these emfs depend.

These considerations indicate that the derivation of a general formula for the emf of a rotating machine must rest upon (1) the nature of the field form, i.e., the curve showing the space distribution of field intensity around the airgap; (2) the type of winding, which determines the order in which the individual conductors are connected.

4-6. Fourier Analysis of Airgap Flux Density and MMF Distribution. In a machine of the salient-pole type having a uniform airgap (iron to iron) and a smooth-core armature, the pole faces and the surface of the armature opposite them will be equipotential surfaces provided that possible saturation of the iron is neglected.   Neglecting the effect of fringing of the flux at the tips of the poles, the field intensity in the airgap due to the field excitation acting alone would then have the rectangular distribution indicated in Fig. 4-5b.   The effect of fringing is to give to the field form the shape shown in Fig. 4-6a, in other words, the sharp corners are rounded off.   If the pole faces are so shaped, as by chamfering the tips or by making the curvature of the pole faces eccentric with respect to the armature surface, as to make the airgap progressively larger from the center to the tips of the poles, the flux distribution can be made to have a form approaching the ideal sinusoidal form of Fig. 4-4.

Under no-load conditions, the flux in the airgap produced by the field excitation will distribute in the manner indicated in Fig. 4-8.   Each of the tubes of induction will include a flux that may be computed by multiplying the difference of magnetic potential between its ends by the permeance of the tube.   If the reluctance of the iron is neglected, the armature surface and the pole face may as a first approximation be regarded as equipotential surfaces, and the permeance of each tube will be proportional to the ratio of its mean cross section to its mean length.   Where the tubes diverge considerably, as in the vicinity of the pole tips, additional lines of induction can be drawn to facilitate the estimation of mean dimensions.   A guide for sketching the lines of induction is afforded by the criterion that the

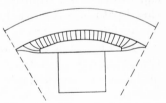

Fig. 4-8. Map of airgap flux distribution.

lines of induction enter and leave the iron substantially at right angles to the surface.   Since with a given difference of magnetic potential the field distributes itself in such a manner that the total flux is a maximum, the calculations can be checked by laying out two or three maps of the flux and selecting the one that yields the largest total flux.

The essential feature of this discussion is that the field intensity at any point may be considered to be proportional to the product of the mmf and the permeance at that point.   It is therefore a matter of great importance to know the point-by-point distribution of both mmf and permeance if accurate determinations of field distribution are to be made.

In all cases that arise in practice, the curves showing the point-by-point variation of these quantities are periodic and single-valued and may therefore be resolved into a fundamental and higher harmonics. In the general case with which we are here concerned, the dependent variable y can be expressed as a function of the independent variable α, between the limits 0 and π, by the equation

$$y = f(\alpha) = A_1 \sin \alpha + A_2 \sin 2\alpha + A_3 \sin 3\alpha + \cdots$$
$$+ A_r \sin r\alpha + \cdots + B_1 \cos \alpha + B_2 \cos 2\alpha + B_3 \cos 3\alpha + \cdots$$
$$+ B_r \cos r\alpha + \cdots \quad (4\text{-}9)$$

where the coefficients are given by

$$A_r = \frac{2}{\pi} \int_0^\pi f(\alpha) \sin r\alpha \, d\alpha \quad (4\text{-}10)$$

$$B_r = \frac{2}{\pi} \int_0^\pi f(\alpha) \cos r\alpha \, d\alpha \quad (4\text{-}11)$$

Two special cases that are frequently encountered are concerned with the space distribution of mmf of a single coil of the armature winding. In one of these cases, the coil is of full pitch, i.e., its throw (or spread) is from center to center of adjacent poles, as in Figs. 4-1 and 4-2; in the other case, the coil has fractional pitch, its throw being less than the pole pitch. In both cases, it is customary to assume that when the coil is carrying current the point-by-point distribution of its mmf (in ampere-turns) is represented by a straight line, as in Figs. 4-9 and 4-10. The justification of this assumption is that the mmf of a coil is by definition equal to the work required to carry a unit magnet pole once around any closed path linking with the coil, and since the iron part of such a path has negligible reluctance in comparison with that of the airgap, the effective mmf acting on the airgap remains substantially constant throughout the coil spread. If this constant mmf is designated as A, it follows that in the case of the full-pitch coil, Fig. 4-9,

$$y = f(\alpha) \Big|_0^\pi = A$$

and by Eq. 4-10 the coefficients of the sine series of Eq. 4-9 are given by

$$A_r = \frac{2}{\pi} \int_0^\pi A \sin r\alpha \, d\alpha = \frac{4}{\pi} \frac{A}{r} \quad (4\text{-}12)$$

where the odd harmonics only need be considered, since the mmf curve is symmetrical in successive half loops; and for this reason it follows from Eq. 4-11 that the coefficients of the cosine series are all zero. Consequently, a rectangular wave form such as that of Fig. 4-8 can be represented by the series

$$y = \frac{4}{\pi} A \left(\sin \alpha + \frac{1}{3} \sin 3\alpha + \frac{1}{5} \sin 5\alpha + \cdots + \frac{1}{r} \sin r\alpha + \cdots \right)$$
$$(4\text{-}13)$$

The fundamental and the third and fifth harmonics have been drawn to scale in Fig. 4-9.

The fractional-pitch coil of Fig. 4-10 represents a function y in which

$$y = 0 \qquad \text{between } \alpha = 0 \text{ and } \alpha = \gamma$$
$$y = A \qquad \text{between } \alpha = \gamma \text{ and } \alpha = \pi - \gamma$$
$$y = 0 \qquad \text{between } \alpha = \pi - \gamma \text{ and } \alpha = \pi$$

Applying Eq. 4-10,

$$A_r = \frac{2}{\pi}\left(\int_0^{\gamma} 0 \sin r\alpha \, d\alpha + \int_{\gamma}^{\pi-\gamma} A \sin r\alpha \, d\alpha + \int_{\pi-\gamma}^{\pi} 0 \sin r\alpha \, d\alpha \right)$$
$$= \frac{4}{\pi}\frac{A}{r} \cos r\gamma$$

and from Eq. 4-11 the coefficients of the cosine series are all zero.   Hence

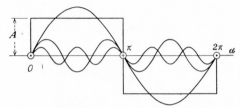

FIG. 4-9. Full-pitch rectangular distribution of mmf.

the fractional-pitch, rectangular distribution of Fig. 4-10 can be represented by the series

$$y = \frac{4}{\pi} A \left(\cos \gamma \sin \alpha + \frac{1}{3} \cos 3\gamma \sin 3\alpha + \frac{1}{5} \cos 5\gamma \sin 5\alpha + \cdots \right.$$
$$\left. + \frac{1}{r} \cos r\gamma \sin r\alpha + \cdots \right) \quad (4\text{-}14)$$

The fundamental and the third and fifth harmonics are drawn to scale in Fig. 4-10 for the case where $\gamma = 36°$, corresponding to a pole arc which embraces 60 per cent of the pole pitch.

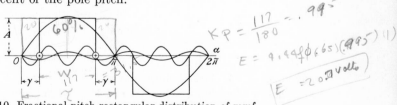

FIG. 4-10. Fractional-pitch rectangular distribution of mmf.

It is important to note that if the coil pitch is greater than the pole pitch the mmf distribution will not be symmetrical in successive half loops, and in that case even harmonics will be present.

4-7. Armature Windings.   Direct-current machines are always constructed with armature windings of the closed type, such as the gramme-ring winding or the lap- or wave-wound drum winding. Such windings may also be used in a-c machines, as when such a closed winding is provided with taps and slip rings for single-phase or polyphase operation. In general, however, the windings of a-c machines are of the open type, as exemplified by the simple case shown in Fig. 4-1. Three such windings, spaced 120 electrical degrees apart and connected in Y, constitute an open-type winding, and this is the arrangement generally used; but if the three coils were connected in Δ, the winding would be of the closed type.

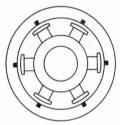

FIG. 4-11. Single-phase concentrated winding.

The chief characteristics of a-c windings are defined by such features as (1) the number of phases; (2) the number of circuits in parallel per phase, which may be one or more; (3) the connections between phases, which may be star or mesh (Y or Δ in three-phase machines); (4) the number of coil layers per slot, which may be either one or two, but with the two-layer type predominating; (5) the angular spread of the consecutive conductors belonging to a given phase belt; (6) the pitch of the individual coils comprising the winding; and (7) the arrangement of the end connections.

Consider first the single-phase concentrated winding of the six-pole machine of Fig. 4-11, in which the conductors, all in series, are placed in equally spaced slots equal in number to the number of poles. All of the conductors will at every instant be the seat of emfs equal to and in phase with each other in the direction through the winding, and the time wave form of the resultant emf will obviously be the same as that of the space distribution of field intensity. The end connections for the series grouping of the active conductors can be arranged in either of the two ways shown in the developed diagrams of Fig. 4-12. These are clearly electrically identical, the arrangement of Fig. 4-12a being known

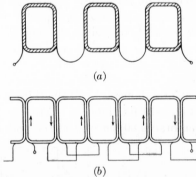

(a)

(b)

FIG. 4-12. (a) Half- and (b) whole-coiled windings.

as a *half-coiled* winding, while that of Fig. 4-12b is a *whole-coiled* winding. In the case of the half-coiled winding the number of coils (per phase) is equal to half the number of poles, while in the whole-coiled winding the number of coils (per phase) is equal to the number of poles.

Several important advantages follow from the use of *distributed* windings, which differ from the concentrated type in that the conductors simultaneously subjected to the inductive action of a single pole occupy two or more adjacent slots in the manner indicated in Fig. 4-13.   The emfs generated in the conductors occupying adjacent slots are displaced from each other in time phase, so that the total emf of the entire winding is less than in the case of a concentrated winding having the same total number of conductors; but the wave form is in general better, the armature reaction is less, as will be shown later, and the greater superficial

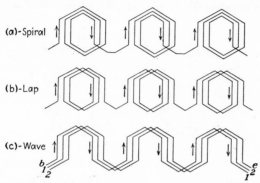

FIG. 4-13. Three types of end connections, half-coiled windings.

area of the coils contributes to a better dissipation of the heat developed by ohmic losses.

The end connections of a distributed winding may be arranged in several ways, all electrically identical, as shown in Fig. 4-13*a, b, c*; all these diagrams are of the half-coiled type.   The order of grouping and the resultant shape of the coils give rise to the respective designations of *spiral*, *lap*, and *wave* windings. The windings of Figs. 4-12 and 4-13 are all of the single-layer type, but it is possible to arrange them as two-layer windings, as shown in Fig. 4-14, lap windings being commonly used in this case.   The two-layer lap winding of Fig. 4-14 be-

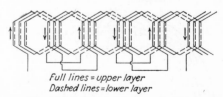

Full lines = upper layer
Dashed lines = lower layer

FIG. 4-14. Two-layer lap winding.

longs to the whole-coiled type, and analogous arrangements are, of course, possible in the case of spiral and wave windings, though these are not illustrated.

All of the windings thus far shown are single-phase windings, and have *full pitch* in the sense that the span from center to center of adjacent belts of conductors is equal to the pole pitch.   The fact that some of the individual coils, as in Fig. 4-13*a*, have greater or less pitch than the average does not alter the conclusion as to the pitch of the winding as a whole.

The extension to the case of polyphase machines of the ideas embodied in the foregoing single-phase windings follows naturally from the fact that additional independent windings can be placed in the vacant space

between the slots of the original winding.   Thus, Fig. 4-15a and b shows
the machine of Fig. 4-11 arranged for two- and three-phase windings,
respectively; in the former, a winding identical with the original one is
placed in slots midway between those of the first set, so that the emfs of
the two windings have a relative phase displacement of 90°; in the latter,
two additional windings B and C, each like the original A, are placed in
two sets of slots symmetrically placed with respect to the first set.   It is

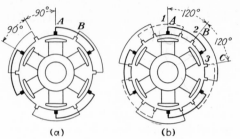

Fig. 4-15. Two- and three-phase windings, half-coiled.

important to note that if point 1 of phase A in Fig. 4-15b is designated as
the beginning of that winding, then the points marked 2 and 3, respectively 120 and 240° from point 1, are correspondingly the beginnings of
phases B and C, and must be so treated in connecting the windings for
Y or Δ operation.

Inspection of Fig. 4-15 shows that the use of single-layer polyphase
windings makes it necessary to provide for the crossing of the end connections of the several phases.   This is done by bending the coil ends in

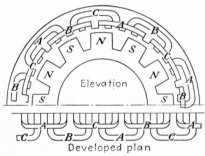

Fig. 4-16. Two-range half-coiled three-
phase winding (single layer).

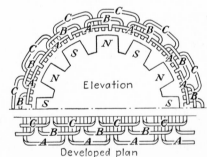

Fig. 4-17. Three-range whole-coiled three-
phase winding (single layer.)

the manner indicated in Fig. 4-16, which shows a *two-range* half-coiled
winding, or, as in Fig. 4-17, which shows a *three-range* whole-coiled winding.   The general appearance of windings of this kind gives rise to the
designation *chain* windings.

4-8. Fractional-pitch Windings.   When the span from center to center
of the coil sides comprising a phase belt is less than the pole pitch, the
winding as a whole is said to be a *fractional-pitch* winding.   Such windings

are extensively used for the reason that the wave form is more nearly sinusoidal than with full-pitch windings, and because of the saving in copper and the greater stiffness of the coils due to the shorter end connections. The latter reason is especially important in the case of two-pole high-speed turbo-alternators, because of the bending stresses produced in the end connections under short-circuit conditions.

Fractional-pitch windings are ordinarily of the two-layer lap-wound type, though single-layer lap windings are also used occasionally. The use of fractional pitch makes it possible to use a number of slots which is not an exact multiple of the number of poles, thus tending to suppress pulsations of flux as the teeth move relative to the pole faces and so largely eliminating tooth ripples in the wave form of the generated emf (see Art. 4-13).

Figure 4-18 illustrates a two-layer lap winding for a three-phase machine having six slots per pole, and a coil pitch equal to two-thirds of the pole pitch. It will be noted that each slot contains coil sides belonging to different phases, which has an effect upon the leakage reactance of the winding and upon the resultant mmf of the winding.

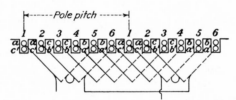

Fig. 4-18. Two-layer fractional-pitch lap winding for three-phase machine.

All of the windings that have here been discussed are characterized by the condition that the number of slots per pole is an integer. It will be noted that the number of slots per pole and per phase is also an integer, being equal to unity in Figs. 4-11 and 4-15 and to two in Fig. 4-18. Windings in which the number of slots per pole is an integer may be called *integral-slot* windings; otherwise stated, an integral-slot winding is one in which the total number of slots is a multiple of the number of poles. It is possible, however, to design windings in which the number of slots is not a multiple of the number of poles, and such windings are called *fractional-slot* windings; they are widely used because of certain inherent advantages which are discussed in Art. 4-9.

4-9. Fractional-slot Windings. Assume that the armature of a three-phase alternator is designed with nine slots per pole and that the pole arc embraces 60 per cent of the pole pitch. The angular span of each pole is then 108 electrical degrees, and the angle from center to center of adjacent slots is 20 electrical degrees. As the poles move relative to the armature, the number of slots under each pole face will be alternately five and six, with the result that the reluctance of the main magnetic circuit will pulsate and thereby set up a high-frequency harmonic in the induced voltage. Cases may arise where this harmonic has such amplitude as to cause interference with telephone circuits in the vicinity of the lines supplied by the generator; hence, this effect is very objectionable.   The obvious remedy is to select a number of slots that is not a multiple of the number of poles, for in that case the disposition of the slots with respect to the poles is different in successive pole pitches, thus giving rise to a kind of vernier action that annuls any tendency toward flux pulsation.

Although the number of slots in fractional-slot machines is not a multiple of the number of poles, it is obvious that considerations of symmetry require that *the number of slots must be a multiple of the number of phases.* Windings of this type may be arranged for any number of phases, but since three-phase machines are much more usual than any other polyphase arrangement, the following discussion of their properties will be restricted to the three-phase case.   These windings may be constructed either as single-layer or as double-layer arrangements, though the latter type is much the more common.   In fact, the use of the two-layer barrel type of winding is now so general in all polyphase machinery that the single-layer type has become practically obsolete.   It is considered here mainly because a study of its properties leads most simply to an understanding of the two-layer arrangement.

Single-layer Winding.   Consider, for example, a three-phase winding for a 10-pole machine distributed in $3 \times 14 = 42$ slots, corresponding to $14\!/\!10 = 7\!/\!5$ slots per pole per phase.   The circumstance that there is here a common factor of 2 between the 14 slots per phase and the 10 poles means that the slot arrangement relative to any set of 5 consecutive poles is exactly duplicated in the next set of 5 consecutive poles.   The characteristic ratio of $7:5$ will then define the slot positions not only for the 10-pole machine that has been assumed but also for a 20-pole machine having 28 slots per phase, or 84 slots in all, or for a 40-pole machine having a total of 168 slots.   In general, if

S = total number of slots (a multiple of 3)
p = number of poles

then for a three-phase winding the number of slots per pole per phase is $(S/3)/p$; and if there is a common factor, say, k, between $S/3$ and p, the characteristic ratio is s_k/p_k, where

$$s_k = \frac{\frac{1}{3}S}{k}$$

$$p_k = \frac{p}{k}$$

and k, the common factor, expresses the number of times the slot arrangement repeats itself in one complete traverse of the armature periphery.

In order that the winding may be disposed in the slots so as to fulfill the requirement of complete symmetry, it is necessary that successive arcs of 60 electrical degrees, measured along the armature surface, shall include conductors belonging to successive phases of the winding. Thus, in Fig. 4-19 are shown five successive pole pitches for the machine under consideration, together with the 21 slots in which the (three) phase windings are to be placed. The angle between adjacent slots is (in electrical degrees)

$$\beta = \frac{p \times 180}{S} = \frac{p_k}{s_k} \times 60$$

and in the particular case under discussion, $\beta = 42\frac{6}{7}°$. If the first slot of the group of 21 is placed directly under the middle of one of the poles, the successive slots, fixed with respect to this point as origin, will be displaced by angles successively equal to β, 2β, 3β, . . . , that is, $42\frac{6}{7}°$,

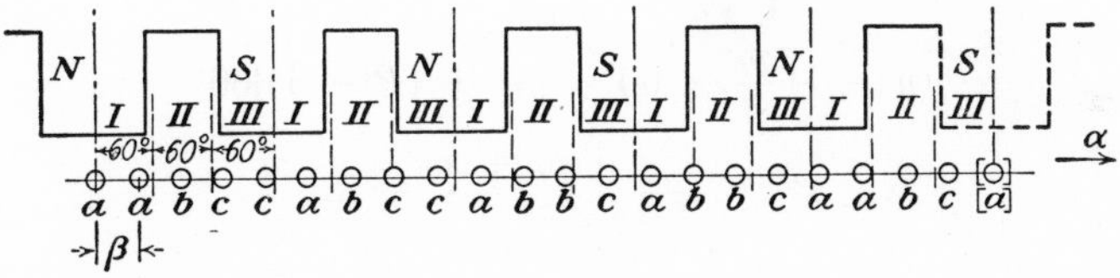

FIG. 4-19. Single-layer fractional-slot winding, $\frac{7}{5}$ slots per pole per phase.

$85\frac{5}{7}°$, $128\frac{4}{7}°$, etc., as shown in the diagram. If it is now agreed that phase I shall occupy the arc defined by $0° \gtreqless \alpha < 60°$, and that phases II and III shall occupy the spans defined by $60° \gtreqless \alpha < 120°$ and $120° \gtreqless \alpha < 180°$, repeating this sequence for values of α greater than 180°, the order of conductors becomes

$$aabccabccabbcabbcaabc$$

which can be arranged in three groups of seven conductors each thus,

$$aabccab$$
$$ccabbca$$
$$bbcaabc$$

where a, b, and c indicate conductors belonging to phases I, II, and III, respectively. (Note the cyclical interchange of the letters in these three groups, in the order a, c, b, a, c, b.) It will be observed that in each of the three groups there are first two conductors belonging to one phase, then one conductor of the next, two of the next, and then one each of the next two; these numbers may be written

$$21211$$

and these may be called the index numbers of the winding, since they indicate the order of arrangement over the entire periphery.

This method becomes somewhat cumbersome when the slot angle β, as in this case, is fractional. It will, however, be evident from Fig. 4-19 that if the slots, beginning at the left, are numbered 1, 2, 3, 4, 5, . . . , the corresponding values of α are 0, β, 2β, 3β, 4β, . . . , or in general the angle α corresponding to the nth slot is

$$\alpha_n = (n - 1)\beta = (n - 1)\frac{p_k}{s_k} \times 60$$

Now it is to be remembered that a conductor in such a slot belongs to

Phase I   if $\alpha \gtreqless$ 0, 180, 360, . . . , or in general $(3\nu)60$
Phase II if $\alpha \gtreqless$ 60, 240, 420, . . . , or in general $(3\nu + 1)60$
Phase III if $\alpha \gtreqless$ 120, 300, 480, . . . , or in general $(3\nu + 2)60$

where ν is an integer taking the successive values 0, 1, 2. Hence, if P indicates the number of the phase corresponding to any slot (where P must be either 1, 2, or 3)

$$(n - 1)\frac{p_k}{s_k} \times 60 \gtreqless [3\nu + (P - 1)]60$$

or $$P \gtreqless \frac{(n - 1)p_k + s_k}{s_k} - 3\nu$$

To use this formula, it is only necessary to assign to ν the smallest integral value which will make P numerically *less than* 4. For example, in the thirteenth slot ($n = 13$)

$$P \gtreqless \frac{12 \times 5 + 7}{7} - 3\nu = 9\tfrac{4}{7} - 3 \times 2 = 3\tfrac{4}{7}$$

Hence, the conductor in this slot belongs to phase III, checking with Fig. 4-19.

Inspection of Fig. 4-19 shows that the conductors of phase I (those marked a) are displaced from the center lines of the north and south poles by the successive angles:

North poles: 0, β, $9\beta - 360$, $17\beta - 720$, $18\beta - 720$
South poles: $5\beta - 180$, $13\beta - 540$

But if the diagram is completed so as to show all of the 10 poles, the displacements of the a conductors with respect to the center lines of the second set of north poles will duplicate the displacements with respect to the south poles of the first set; and the displacements with respect to the south poles of the second set will duplicate the displacements with respect to the north poles of the first set. The complete table of displacements relative to either set of poles, but rearranged as to order, is therefore

0, β, $5\beta - 180$, $9\beta - 360$, $13\beta - 540$, $17\beta - 720$, $18\beta - 720$

Substituting the value of $\beta(= 42\tfrac{6}{7}°)$, these correspond to

0, $42\tfrac{6}{7}$, $34\tfrac{2}{7}$, $25\tfrac{5}{7}$, $17\tfrac{1}{7}$, $8\tfrac{4}{7}$, $51\tfrac{3}{7}$

which, when written in order of increasing magnitude, are

$$0,\ 8\tfrac{4}{7},\ 17\tfrac{1}{7},\ 25\tfrac{5}{7},\ 34\tfrac{2}{7},\ 42\tfrac{6}{7},\ 51\tfrac{3}{7}$$

which are seen to be the successive integral multiples of $8\tfrac{4}{7}°$.   Since all the conductors of any one phase are connected in series, the actual irregularly scattered positions are therefore equivalent to a perfectly regular distribution with respect to a single pair of equivalent poles, as in Fig. 4-20; and from this diagram it is clear that the particular winding under discussion is equivalent to a distributed winding having *full pitch and seven slots per pole per phase.*

In general, a fractional-slot winding characterized by the ratio s_k/p_k slots per pole per phase, where s_k and p_k are prime to each other, will be

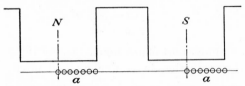

FIG. 4-20. Phase distribution equivalent to that of Fig. 4-19.

equivalent to a full-pitch distributed winding having $q = s_k$ slots per pole per phase, the angle between these equivalent slots being

$$\gamma = \beta/p_k = 60/s_k$$

Two-layer Windings.   Fractional-slot windings arranged in two layers follow as a natural development of the single-layer arrangement just described.   Since each coil side in the top layer must be connected to one in the bottom layer so that the spread of the coil is approximately 1-pole pitch, it follows that in the 10-pole 42-slot winding that has been used as an example the coil pitch (expressed in terms of slots) must be

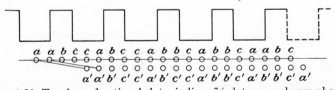

FIG. 4-21. Two-layer fractional-slot winding, $\tfrac{7}{5}$ slots per pole per phase.

approximately $\tfrac{42}{10} = 4.2$.   The coil must therefore span either four or three slots, and in Fig. 4-21 this coil span is shown as four slots.   The arrangement of the phase conductors in both layers then follows the same order as in the single-layer winding of Fig. 4-19.   It will be noted that, in the particular case shown in Fig. 4-21, most of the slots, though not all of them, are occupied by conductors belonging to the same phase.   If a coil pitch of three slots had been used, the conductors in a slot would in general not belong to the same phase.   This overlapping of the phase windings has an effect upon the leakage reactance which will be considered later.

Since all of the conductors belonging to one phase of the winding are in series, the order of their connection is immaterial so far as the resultant emf is concerned. It is therefore possible to consider the entire winding as made up of a full-pitch distributed winding that includes all conductors in the top layer, in series with another full-pitch distributed winding that includes all conductors in the bottom layer. Each of these two component windings is similar in all respects to the single-layer winding previously considered, but their separate emfs are not in phase with each other because of the fractional pitch of the individual coils. In Fig. 4-21, for example, the coil span is

$$\frac{4}{42\frac{2}{10}} = \frac{20}{21}$$

of full pitch, thus falling short of an angular span of $180°$ by $180\frac{2}{21} = 8\frac{4}{7}°$. The effect of this reduction in equivalent coil pitch is considered in Art. 4-11.

It will be observed that the fractional-slot winding bears to the integral-slot winding somewhat the same relation as a wave winding for a d-c armature bears to a lap winding. For in a fractional-slot winding the coil sides of any one phase are distributed in wave fashion over all of the poles, thus obtaining with comparatively few coils and slots the same advantages of a distributed winding which in the integral-slot winding call for decidedly more numerous coils and slots. Other advantages of a distributed fractional-pitch winding are the smoothing of the wave form of emf and the reduction or elimination of the effect of harmonics upon armature reaction. The possibility of securing these electrical and magnetic advantages, while at the same time realizing the mechanical advantage of fewer coils and slots, accounts for the practical usefulness of the fractional-slot type of winding.

4-10. Induced EMF in Full-pitch Distributed Windings. Breadth Factor. *a. Field Intensity Sinusoidal.* Assuming for the present that the radial component of the field intensity in the airgap is represented by a sinusoidal curve as in Fig. 4-4, it has been shown that the instantaneous emf developed in a concentrated winding of full pitch is (see Eq. 4-8)

$$e = 2\pi fN\Phi \sin \omega t$$

where f = frequency, cps
Φ = flux per pole, webers
N = number of turns in series

and from this it follows that the effective (rms) value of the fundamental emf of a concentrated winding is

$$E = \sqrt{2}\,\pi fN\Phi = 4.44fN\Phi \tag{4-15}$$

When the coils comprising a phase of the winding are distributed in two or more slots per pole, in the manner shown in Fig. 4-13, the emfs in the adjacent coils will be out of phase with respect to one another, and their resultant will be less than their algebraic sum.   In other words, when the N turns of a concentrated winding are spread out, the resultant emf will be less than that given by Eq. 4-15, and the factor (less than unity) by which the latter must be multiplied in order to obtain the actual emf is called the *breadth factor*.

Let the N turns of the original concentrated winding be distributed in q slots per pole, and let γ be the angle (in electrical degrees) between the adjacent slots of a group, as indicated in Fig. 4-22.   If E is the emf that would be generated by the entire group of N turns if they were concentrated in a single slot, the emf due to the N/q turns per slot will be $E/q = E'$.   If the emf due to the coils in the first slot of the successive groups is represented in complex notation by $\mathbf{E}'$, that of the second will be out of phase with it by angle γ, and can therefore be represented by $\mathbf{E}'e^{j\gamma}$; the remaining emfs will then be represented by $\mathbf{E}'e^{j2\gamma}$, $\mathbf{E}'e^{j3\gamma}$, . . . , $\mathbf{E}'e^{j(q-1)\gamma}$, and the resultant emf will be

$$\mathbf{E}_1 = \mathbf{E}'(1 + e^{j\gamma} + e^{j2\gamma} + \cdots + e^{j(q-1)\gamma})$$

The terms in the parentheses constitute a geometrical series whose sum is given by the well-known formula

$$\text{Sum} = \frac{ar^n - a}{r - 1}$$

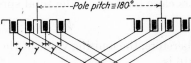

FIG. 4-22. Distribution of full-pitch coils.

where a = first term = 1
    r = ratio = $e^{j\gamma}$
    n = number of terms = q

Hence, $\mathbf{E}_1 = \mathbf{E}' \dfrac{e^{jq\gamma} - 1}{e^{j\gamma} - 1} = \mathbf{E}' \dfrac{(\cos q\gamma - 1) + j \sin q\gamma}{(\cos \gamma - 1) + j \sin \gamma}$

The real value of E_1 is therefore

$$E_1 = E' \sqrt{\frac{(\cos q\gamma - 1)^2 + \sin^2 q\gamma}{(\cos \gamma - 1)^2 + \sin^2 \gamma}} = \frac{E}{q} \frac{\sin (q\gamma/2)}{\sin (\gamma/2)} \qquad (4\text{-}16)$$

and the breadth factor for the emf of fundamental frequency is therefore

$$k_{b_1} = \frac{\sin (q\gamma/2)}{q \sin (\gamma/2)} \qquad (4\text{-}17)$$

For example, in a three-phase machine having four slots per pole per phase, as in Fig. 4-22, $q = 4$ and $\gamma = 180°/(3 \times 4) = 15°$, whence

$$k_{b_1} = \frac{\sin \dfrac{4 \times 15°}{2}}{4 \sin (15°/2)} = 0.9576$$

The geometrical significance of Eqs. 4-16 and 4-17 is clearly seen in Fig.

4-23, where the successive emfs of the several coils, each numerically equal to $E' = E/q$ and displaced in phase from its neighbor by angle γ, are shown in their relative phase positions. The successive phasors may be looked upon as chords of a circle of radius R, such that

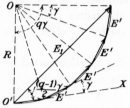

$$R \sin \frac{\gamma}{2} = \frac{E'}{2} = \frac{1}{2} \frac{E}{q}$$

and their resultant E_1 is

$$E_1 = 2R \sin \frac{q\gamma}{2}$$

Substituting for R, there results

FIG. 4-23. Component emfs of distributed winding.

$$E_1 = E \frac{\sin (q\gamma/2)}{q \sin (\gamma/2)}$$

from which the breadth factor k_{b_1} is seen to be the same as that given by Eq. 4-17.*

A special case arises when q, the number of coils in the phase belt, is indefinitely increased, at the same time that the angle γ correspondingly approaches zero, subject to the condition that the total spread of the phase belt remains the same as before. This condition is sensibly approached in the case of a smooth-core winding with successive conductors close together. The total spread of the phase belt is (see Fig. 4-24)

$$\psi = (q - 1)\gamma$$

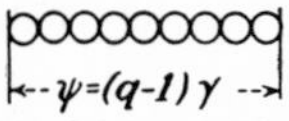

Therefore, the limiting value of the term $\sin (q\gamma/2)$ in Eq. 4-16 is

FIG. 4-24. Uniformly distributed winding belt.

$$\lim_{\substack{q \to \infty \\ \gamma \to 0}} \sin \frac{q\gamma}{2} = \sin \frac{\psi + \gamma}{2} = \sin \frac{\psi}{2}$$

---

* Two formulas of importance in subsequent work follow quite simply from Eq. 4-16 and Fig. 4-23. They are those which give the sums of the two series

$$1 + \cos \gamma + \cos 2\gamma + \cos 3\gamma + \cdots + \cos (q - 1)\gamma$$

and $(\sin 0) + \sin \gamma + \sin 2\gamma + \sin 3\gamma + \cdots + \sin (q - 1)\gamma$

If the cosine series is multiplied through by $E' = E/q$, the terms are represented to scale by the projections upon an axis $O'X$ of the successive chords of Fig. 4-23. Their sum is therefore the projection upon $O'X$ of the geometrical sum of the chords themselves, i.e., of E_1; hence,

$$E'[1 + \cos \gamma + \cos 2\gamma + \cdots + \cos (q - 1)\gamma] = E_1 \cos \frac{(q - 1)\gamma}{2}$$

and by Eq. 4-16

$$1 + \cos \gamma + \cos 2\gamma + \cdots + \cos (q - 1)\gamma = \frac{\sin (q\gamma/2)}{\sin (\gamma/2)} \cos \frac{(q - 1)\gamma}{2}$$

Similarly, the sum of the sine series (if multiplied through by E') represents the projection of E_1 upon an axis perpendicular to $O'X$, whence

$$\sin \gamma + \sin 2\gamma + \cdots + \sin (q - 1)\gamma = \frac{\sin (q\gamma/2)}{\sin (\gamma/2)} \sin \frac{(q - 1)\gamma}{2}$$

and the limiting value of the term $q \sin (\gamma/2)$, which may be written

$$\frac{\sin (\gamma/2)}{1/q} = \frac{\sin (\gamma/2)}{\gamma/(\psi + \gamma)}$$

may be found by separately differentiating the numerator and denominator. Hence,

$$\lim_{\gamma \to 0} \frac{\sin (\gamma/2)}{\gamma/(\psi + \gamma)} = \left\{ \frac{\frac{1}{2} \cos (\gamma/2)}{[(\psi + \gamma) - \gamma]/(\psi + \gamma)^2} \right\}_{\gamma \to 0} = \frac{\psi}{2}$$

and the value of the breadth factor for the fundamental emf of a uniformly distributed winding is therefore

$$k_{b_1} = \frac{\sin (\psi/2)}{\psi/2} \tag{4-18}$$

Reference to Fig. 4-23 shows that, under the conditions specified in this special case, the successive chords E' approach more and more nearly the arcs which they subtend, and their algebraic sum approaches the arc $Rq\gamma$, while their geometrical sum is the chord $E_1 = 2R \sin (q\gamma/2)$. The breadth factor is the ratio of these two expressions, i.e., it is the ratio

$$\frac{\text{Chord}}{\text{Arc}} = \frac{\sin (q\gamma/2)}{q\gamma/2}$$

and as γ approaches zero, this becomes the same as Eq. 4-18.

b. *Field Distribution Including Harmonics.*   Let the field form contain any number of odd space harmonics in addition to the fundamental of amplitude B_1, and let their amplitudes be B_3, B_5, . . . , etc.   For the sake of simplicity, assume that all these harmonics have the same origin of coordinates as the fundamental, in other words, that each loop of the resultant field form is symmetrical about its middle point.   Any component space harmonic of the field form, say the rth, is then of the form

$$b = B_r \sin r\alpha$$

and its space distribution is shown in Fig. 4-25 for the particular case $r = 3$.

Each loop of the harmonic represents a flux Φ_r (webers) which may be considered to be produced by a fictitious pole, there being r of these fictitious poles in each pole pitch; it is therefore at once evident that the frequency of the emf induced in the full-pitch coil will be r times the fundamental frequency.   It is furthermore evident from Fig. 4-25 that since r is an odd number the emf developed in the full-pitch coil will be due to the flux Φ_r from only one of the fictitious poles; for the fluxes from the remaining $r - 1$ poles form oppositely directed pairs that annul each other.   The conclusion follows that the effective (rms) value of the harmonic emf induced in a concentrated full-pitch coil of N turns is, by analogy with Eq. 4-15,

$$E_r = \sqrt{2}\ \pi f_r N \Phi_r = \sqrt{2}\ \pi f r N \Phi_r \tag{4-19}$$

The magnitude of Φ_r can be found from the fact that the average value of the harmonic field intensity in one loop is $(2/\pi)B_r$, so that

$$\Phi_r = \frac{2}{\pi}\ B_r\ \frac{\pi D}{pr}\ l \tag{4-20}$$

The effect upon the amplitudes of the voltage harmonics due to distributing the winding is of the same nature as in the case of the fundamental, except that the reduction in the magnitude of the resultant is in most

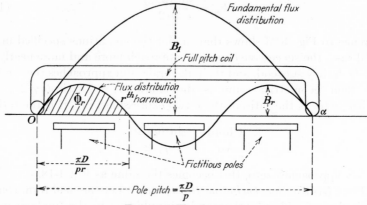

FIG. 4-25. Flux harmonic.

cases relatively much greater. Thus, referring to Fig. 4-22, if the angle between adjacent slots is γ electrical degrees, it is equivalent to $r\gamma°$ for the rth harmonic, and the breadth factor accordingly becomes

$$k_{b_r} = \frac{\sin\ (qr\gamma/2)}{q\ \sin\ (r\gamma/2)} \tag{4-21}$$

If the winding is uniformly distributed ($q = \infty$), it follows similarly from Eq. 4-18 that

$$k_{b_r} = \frac{\sin\ (r\psi/2)}{r\ \sin\ (\psi/2)} \tag{4-22}$$

Table 4-1 shows the breadth factors for the fundamental and the harmonics, up to and including the 19th, for three-phase machines having two to six slots per pole per phase and also for uniformly distributed windings where $q = \infty$.

The negative sign of some of the tabulated factors means that the emf harmonic is reversed in phase with respect to the fundamental. It will be noted that in nearly all cases the effect of distributing the winding is to

TABLE 4-1. BREADTH FACTOR, THREE-PHASE MACHINES

r	q = slots per pole per phase					
	2	3	4	5	6	∞
1	0.9659	0.9598	0.9577	0.9567	0.9561	0.9549
3	0.7071	0.6667	0.6533	0.6472	0.6440	0.6366
5	0.2588	0.2176	0.2053	0.2000	0.1972	0.1910
7	−0.2588	−0.1774	−0.1576	−0.1494	−0.1453	−0.1364
9	−0.7071	−0.3333	−0.2706	−0.2472	−0.2357	−0.2122
11	−0.9659	−0.1774	−0.1261	−0.1095	−0.1017	−0.0868
13	−0.9659	0.2176	0.1261	0.1022	0.0920	0.0735
15	−0.7071	0.6667	0.2706	0.2000	0.1726	0.1273
17	−0.2588	0.9598	0.1576	0.1022	0.0837	0.0562
19	0.2588	0.9598	−0.2053	−0.1095	−0.0837	−0.0503

reduce the effect of the harmonics very materially, though, with two slots per pole per phase, the 11th and 13th harmonics retain their effect to the same extent as the fundamental, and the same is true of the 17th and 19th harmonics in the case of three slots per pole per phase.

In general, the orders of the harmonics of a distributed three-phase winding which thus retain their effect to the same extent as the fundamental are defined by the formula

$$r = 2mkq \pm 1 \Big|_{m=3} = 6kq \pm 1$$

where k may have the integral values 1, 2, 3, ... When k is greater than unity, the harmonics are usually of such a high order as to be of minor consequence, but when $k = 1$, these particular harmonics, called the *slot harmonics*, may be large enough to give serious trouble. A particular case of a three-phase machine in which q was equal to 6, and for which the slot harmonics were accordingly the 35th and 37th, is described in Art. 4-13.

4-11. Induced EMF in Fractional-pitch Windings. Pitch Factor. In the full-pitch distributed winding of Fig. 4-22, the resultant emf induced in the left-hand belt of conductors will at every instant be equal in magnitude to the resultant emf induced in the right-hand belt. These two emfs are in phase opposition with respect to the direction from front to back of the winding, but they are directly in phase with respect to the positive direction around the coil as a whole.

In the fractional-pitch winding of Fig. 4-26, each of the two belts of conductors will develop an effective emf equal to $\frac{1}{2}E_1$, where E_1 is given by Eq. 4-16; but since the spread of the coil is less than a pole pitch by a factor $x < 1$, these two emfs are not in phase. Thus, if the instantaneous fundamental emf of the left-hand belt in Fig. 4-26 is $\sqrt{2}(E_1/2) \sin \theta$, that of the right-hand belt will at the same instant be $(E_1/\sqrt{2}) \sin (\theta + x\pi)$; at the same instant, the rth harmonic of emf in the left-hand belt will be $(E_r/\sqrt{2}) \sin r\theta$, and that of the right-hand belt will be

$$\frac{E_r}{\sqrt{2}} \sin r(\theta + x\pi)$$

The instantaneous emf of the entire coil is therefore in general

$$e = \frac{E_r}{\sqrt{2}} [\sin r\theta - \sin r(\theta + x\pi)] = \sqrt{2} \, E_r \sin \frac{rx\pi}{2} \sin (r\theta - \varphi) \qquad (4\text{-}23)$$

where

$$\tan \varphi = \cot \frac{rx\pi}{2} \qquad (4\text{-}24)$$

Equations 4-23 and 4-24 lead to the conclusion that the effective emf of the coil is $E_r \sin (rx\pi/2)$, whereas it would be E_r if the coil were of full

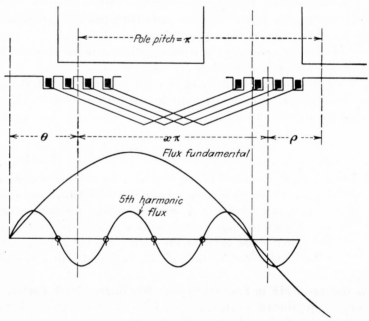

Fig. 4-26. Fractional-pitch winding.

pitch. Accordingly, the use of the fractional pitch decreases the emf by a factor

$$k_{p_r} = \sin \frac{rx\pi}{2} \qquad (4\text{-}25)$$

and k_{p_r} is therefore called the *pitch factor*. Another expression for the pitch factor may be derived by noting (see Fig. 4-26) that $x\pi = \pi - \rho$, where ρ is the angle by which the coil fails to span a full pole pitch. It follows that

$$k_{p_r} = \sin \frac{rx\pi}{2} = \sin r \frac{\pi}{2} \cos \frac{r\rho}{2} \tag{4-26}$$

and if r is assigned the values 1, 3, 5, 7, . . . , the pitch factor will take the values shown in the following table:

r	k_{p_r}
1	$+ \cos (\rho/2)$
3	$- \cos (3\rho/2)$
5	$+ \cos (5\rho/2)$
7	$- \cos (7\rho/2)$

An additional conclusion deducible from Eq. 4-23 is that the emf of a fractional-pitch winding differs in phase from that of an otherwise equivalent full-pitch winding by an angle $\varphi = \tan^{-1}[\cot (rx\pi/2)]$. Thus, if $r = 1$ and $x = \frac{2}{3}$, $\varphi = 30°$ is an angle of lag; but if $r = 5$ and $x = \frac{2}{3}$, $\varphi = -30°$, which is equivalent to an angle of lead of 30°.

Finally, then, the general equations for the effective values of the fundamental and harmonic emfs are, respectively,

$$E = 4.44k_{b_1}k_{p_1}fN\Phi \tag{4-27}$$

and
$$E_r = 4.44k_{b_r}k_{p_r}frN\Phi_r \tag{4-28}$$

where in each case Φ and Φ_r are sinusoidally distributed.

4-12. Wave Form of EMF, Nonsinusoidal Field Distribution. The discussion of Art. 4-11 was based upon the assumption that each loop of the flux-distribution curve is symmetrical about its mid-point, which is equivalent to the assumption that only the sine terms in Eq. 4-9 are present, and therefore that the fundamental and all the harmonics have a common origin. In the general case, however, the curve of flux distribution may be asymmetrical, and its equation may be written

$$B = B'_1 \sin \alpha + B'_3 \sin 3\alpha + B'_5 \sin 5\alpha + \cdots + B'_r \sin r\alpha + \cdots$$
$$+ B''_1 \cos \alpha + B''_3 \cos 3\alpha + B''_5 \cos 5\alpha + \cdots + B''_r \cos r\alpha + \cdots \tag{4-29}$$

where the coefficients $B'_1, B'_3, \ldots , B''_1, B''_3, \ldots$ may be either positive or negative.

On combining the terms of Eq. 4-29 in pairs, it becomes

$$B = B_1 \sin (\alpha + \varphi_1) + B_3 \sin (3\alpha + \varphi_3)$$
$$+ \cdots + B_r \sin (r\alpha + \varphi_r) + \cdots \tag{4-30}$$

where
$$B_r = \sqrt{(B'_r)^2 + (B''_r)^2}$$
$$\varphi_r = \tan^{-1}\frac{B''_r}{B'_r} \tag{4-31}$$

In Fig. 4-27, for example, the fundamental, third, and fifth harmonics are drawn to represent the arbitrary values $\varphi_1 = +15°$, $\varphi_3 = -45°$, $\varphi_5 = +45°$. The resultant asymmetrical curve of field distribution is then constructed by adding corresponding ordinates of the three components.

If the armature is wound with a concentrated winding, the two sides of a coil are at a given instant moving through fields of equal intensity but of opposite sign, this being true not only with respect to the resultant field but also with respect to each of its components. The oppositely directed emfs induced in the active sides of the coil then add directly, and the effect is to produce a time wave of emf identical in shape with the space distribution of flux density.

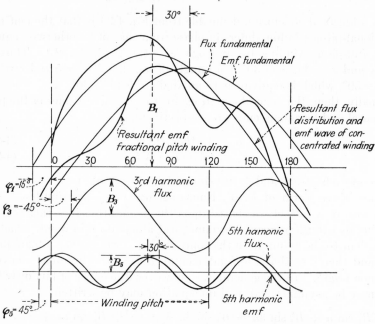

FIG. 4-27. Change of emf wave form due to fractional pitch.

The effect of using a winding of fractional pitch is to make the time wave form of emf differ in shape from the space wave form of flux distribution. Thus, in Fig. 4-27, where the winding has two-thirds pitch (that is, $x = \frac{2}{3}$ and $\rho = 60°$), the effect of the third harmonic of flux is eliminated, since $k_{p_r} = \cos[(3 \times 60)/2] = 0$. The resultant wave form of emf therefore contains only the fundamental and a fifth harmonic, hence cannot be the same as the wave form of field distribution. Furthermore, in accordance with Eqs. 4-23 and 4-24, the emf fundamental has a pitch factor $k_{p_1} = \cos{}^{60}\!/_2 = 0.866$, and a phase displacement (lagging) of $\tan^{-1}[\cot \frac{2}{3}(\pi/2)] = 30°$ with respect to the flux fundamental; the fifth emf harmonic has a pitch factor $k_{p_5} = \cos[(5 \times 60)/2] = -0.866$ and a phase displacement, with respect to the fifth harmonic of flux, of $\tan^{-1}[\cot {}^{1}\!/_3(\pi/2)] = -30°$, therefore leading by 30°.

The fact that the pitch factor is represented by the equation

$$k_{p_r} = \cos \frac{r\rho}{2}$$

makes it possible to eliminate any harmonic of order r by making $r\rho/2$ equal to $\pi/2$ or to some odd multiple of $\pi/2$. Thus, there is no 3d harmonic of emf in the case illustrated in Fig. 4-27 where $\rho = 60°$; furthermore, with this particular coil pitch, namely, $x = \frac{2}{3}$, all odd multiples of the 3d harmonic, such as the 9th, 15th, 21st, etc., will also be suppressed.

A pitch of $\frac{2}{3}$ is used in the case of Y-connected three-phase generators which are to be operated with grounded neutral in order to eliminate any internal source of the triple-harmonic currents that are likely to flow through the neutral. But in Y-connected generators, whether the neutral is grounded or not, there can be no third harmonic in the line voltage, since the phases are so connected that the phase voltages combine at an angle of 60° referred to the fundamental; this means that any triple harmonics present in the phase voltages combine at an angle of $3 \times 60 = 180°$, that is, they are in phase opposition and therefore are neutralized so far as the line voltage is concerned; for the same reason, all harmonics which are multiples of the 3rd are neutralized. Consequently, in Y-connected machines which are to be operated with insulated neutral, it is desirable to select a winding pitch which will minimize the 5th and 7th harmonics, since the 11th and higher harmonics are usually small enough to be insignificant. The 5th harmonic can be eliminated entirely by making $5\rho/2 = 90°$, or $\rho = 36°$, which is equivalent to a winding pitch of $(180 - 36)/180 = \frac{4}{5}$; similarly, the 7th harmonic can be eliminated by making $7\rho/2 = 90°$, which is equivalent to the use of a winding pitch $(180 - 18\frac{0}{7})/180 = \frac{6}{7}$. The average of these two pitches is very nearly $\frac{5}{6}$ for which the corresponding pitch factors of the 5th and 7th harmonics are, respectively, 0.2588 and -0.2588. In other words, a $\frac{5}{6}$ pitch reduces the amplitudes of these two harmonics in the voltage wave to about one-fourth of the magnitude they would have in a full-pitch winding having a slot distribution otherwise the same.

When an emf wave form is composed of a fundamental and harmonics the rms values of which are E_1, E_3, E_5 . . . , the effective value of the resultant wave is

$$E = \sqrt{E_1^2 + E_3^2 + E_5^2 + \cdots}$$

without regard to the phase positions of the components. For example, consider the case of an alternator which has a concentrated winding (one slot per pole per phase), so that $k_{b_r} = k_{p_r} = 1$ and which has a field distribution of the type indicated in Fig. 4-10. This represents the idealized field distribution produced by salient poles which have a pole arc 60 per cent of the pole pitch, and where the airgap is uniform. The angle $\gamma = 0.2\pi = 36°$. If the maximum ordinate of the rectangle in Fig.

4-10 is designated B_m, it follows from Eq. 4-14 that the field distribution is represented by

$$B = \frac{4}{\pi} B_m(0.809 \sin \alpha - 0.103 \sin 3\alpha - 0.200 \sin 5\alpha$$
$$- 0.044 \sin 7\alpha + \cdot \cdot \cdot)$$

It follows that B_1, B_3, B_5, and B_7 are equal to $(4/\pi)B_m$ multiplied, respectively, by 0.809, -0.103, -0.200, and -0.044; and by Eqs. 4-27 and 4-28 the effective values of the corresponding emfs are respectively equal to a constant times these numerical factors. The effective value of the resultant emf is therefore proportional to

$$\sqrt{0.809^2 + 0.103^2 + 0.200^2 + 0.044^2} = 0.841$$

If the third and higher harmonics of the space distribution of flux were neglected, the effective emf of the fundamental would be proportional to 0.809, which amounts to slightly more than 96 per cent of the emf computed by taking into account all the significant harmonics. The difference would be considerably reduced if the winding were distributed, and still more if fractional pitch were used. It follows from these facts that in most practical cases the induced emf of a machine is determined almost entirely by the fundamental of the space distribution of flux density.

4-13. Tooth Ripples. Skewing of Slots. In the preceding discussion of field forms, the effect of the slots in the armature surface has been ignored. It is clear, of course, that the tufting of the flux at the tooth tips will cause the field form to contain ripples, which, if they remained stationary with respect to the pole faces, could be taken into account as an additional harmonic in the field form; but since the tufts of flux follow the teeth in their passage across the pole face, this procedure is not applicable. In reality, the effect is the same as though there were superposed upon the main flux an additional flux, ϕ, which pulsates at the frequency with which the teeth pass the pole tips; thus, referring to Fig. 4-28, a complete cycle of this tooth frequency takes place in the time required for the pole to move through an angle equivalent to one tooth pitch. If there are q slots per pole per phase and m phases, there will be $2mq$ cycles of tooth frequency for each complete cycle of fundamental frequency; in other words,

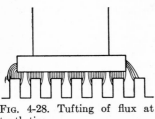

Fig. 4-28. Tufting of flux at tooth tips.

f_s = tooth frequency = fundamental frequency
$\times$ number of slots per pair of poles

If the flux per pole due to the fundamental of the field form is Φ, then, ignoring possible additional components, the flux linked with the turns of the armature winding is at a time t

$$\varphi = (\Phi + \phi \sin 2\pi f_s t) \cos 2\pi ft$$

$$= \Phi \cos 2\pi ft + \frac{\phi}{2} [\sin 2\pi (f_s - f)t + \sin 2\pi (f_s + f)t]$$

and the emf due to this flux is

$$e = - N \frac{d\varphi}{dt} = 2\pi f N \Phi \sin 2\pi ft - \frac{\phi N}{2} [2\pi (f_s - f) \cos 2\pi (f_s - f)t$$

$$+ 2\pi (f_s + f) \cos 2\pi (f_s + f)t] \quad (4\text{-}32)$$

The first term on the right-hand side of Eq. 4-32 is the emf of fundamental frequency, while the remaining term is the emf due to the tooth ripples. It will be noted that this is made up of two frequencies $f_s - f$ and $f_s + f$; and because

$$f_s = f s_p$$

where s_p is the number of slots per pair of poles, it follows that the teeth and slots give rise to two harmonics whose frequencies are $s_p - 1$ and $s_p + 1$ times that of the fundamental. Thus, if there are six slots per pole, the harmonics due to the tooth ripple will be the 11th and 13th.

An unusual case of trouble due to the tooth ripple occurred in the case of a 2,000-kva 25-cycle 1,500-rpm turbo-alternator, which, as originally installed, had a stator with 36 slots, and a two-pole cylindrical rotor with an exciting winding distributed in 36 slots. It is clear that in this case the reluctance of the main magnetic circuit is appreciably greater when teeth are opposite slots than when teeth are opposite teeth, thereby aggravating the pulsation to be expected in any case. With 36 teeth per pair of poles, the 35th and 37th harmonics will be present,* and an oscillogram of this particular machine taken under no-load conditions showed such a pronounced harmonic compounded of these frequencies that the curve had a saw-tooth form. The actual frequency of the 35th harmonic is $25 \times 35 = 875$ cps, and whenever this machine was in operation, it induced this frequency in telephone circuits paralleling the power lines; a frequency of 875 cps in the telephones produced a shrill note, approximately high A in the musical scale, with the result that the generator when running put the telephone lines out of commission. A temporary remedy was effected by removing the bronze wedges which held the rotor coils in place, using steel wedges instead; but ultimately the entire rotor was replaced by a new one having a different number of slots.

Since the primary cause of tooth ripples is the variable reluctance of the magnetic circuit due to the passage of the teeth and slots across the pole face, it follows that if the extra reluctance due to the slot openings is small compared with that of the airgap (iron to iron) the tooth ripples will likewise be small enough to be inappreciable; this may in some cases

---

* These are the slot harmonics as defined in Art. 4-10.

be brought about by using numerous small slots with small openings, and an airgap that is long in comparison with the width of the openings. Where this design is rendered impracticable as, for instance, when the slots become too narrow to accommodate the conductors and their insulation, and the teeth too narrow to carry the magnetic flux without excessive saturation, the tooth ripples can be largely eliminated by selecting a number of slots which is not a multiple of the number of poles. The winding is then of the fractional-slot type described in Art. 4-9. The fact that the number of slots is not a multiple of the number of poles results in a vernier relation between the teeth and slots under successive poles; that is to say, the space relation between the teeth and slots opposite a given pole face is not the same as is the simultaneous space relation between the teeth and slots opposite the next and succeeding poles. It follows that the pulsations of flux and emf produced in the coils under one of the poles are more or less neutralized by other out-of-phase pulsations in the remaining coils of the winding.

Another method for preventing undesirable pulsations of reluctance is to *skew* the slots relative to the pole faces. In induction motors, this is accomplished by spiraling the slots of the rotor in the manner indicated in Fig. 4-29a, where the dashed lines represent the boundaries of the polar flux of the stator. This method

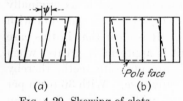

(a)   (b)

FIG. 4-29. Skewing of slots.

is not practical in large alternators, but an equivalent effect can be obtained, if necessary, by skewing the edges of the pole faces, as in Fig. 4-29b. It is to be noted that the effect of skewing is to introduce a breadth factor; for if the emf induced in a single conductor by the main flux of full pole pitch is E when there is no skewing, it becomes $E[\sin (\psi/2)/(\psi/2)]$ when the angle of skew, in electrical degrees, is ψ; and in the case of a harmonic flux of the rth order the reduction factor becomes $\sin (r\psi/2)/(r\psi/2)$.

4-14. Armature Reaction. Let it be assumed for the present that when a machine, wound in the manner discussed in the preceding articles, is under load both the induced emf and the current are sinusoidal. The effect of harmonics, if present, will be reserved for later analysis.

In general, the induced emf and the current will not be in phase, but whatever the actual conditions may be, the current can always be resolved into two components, one of which is in phase with the emf in the case of a generator, or in phase opposition to the emf in the case of a motor; and the other is in quadrature with the emf. Thus, in the simple *generator* shown diagrammatically in Fig. 4-30, the coil sides AB will be directly under the middle of the pole faces when the emf has its maximum value, and the in-phase component of current will also have maximum value in

this position, indicated by (a).   If the quadrature component of current
is lagging by 90° behind the emf, this component of current will reach its
maximum value when the coil has moved 90 electrical degrees from position (a) to position (b); but if the quadrature component is leading, it
reaches its maximum 90 electrical degrees prior to position (a), as shown
at (c).   The dots and crosses indicating the direction of current flow can
be determined by Fleming's right-hand rule or in any other preferred

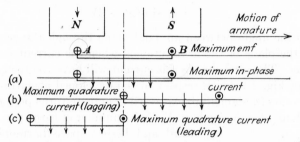

Fig. 4-30. Magnetizing effect of in-phase and quadrature current components
(generator).

manner.   The point is that the in-phase current magnetizes along an
axis midway between the main poles in such manner that the main flux
tends to increase at the trailing pole tips, and to decrease at the leading
pole tips; in other words, there is a cross-magnetizing action exactly as
in a d-c generator.   On the other hand, the lagging quadrature component of current magnetizes in direct opposition to the main poles; and
the leading quadrature component aids the magnetizing action of the
main poles.

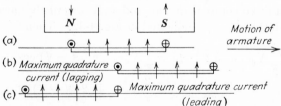

Fig. 4-31. Magnetizing effect of in-phase and quadrature current components (motor).

Figure 4-31 represents similarly the conditions in a synchronous motor.
The position of maximum induced emf is the same in both Figs. 4-31 and
4-30, but since in a motor the induced emf plays the role of counter emf,
the in-phase current must be in opposition.   It will be seen that the
in-phase current is again cross-magnetizing, but the trailing tips of the
poles are now weakened, and the leading tips are strengthened, just as
in d-c motors; also that the lagging quadrature current strengthens the
main poles, while the leading quadrature current weakens them.

4-15. MMF of Armature Reaction.   *Concentrated Winding.*   Consider
first the elementary single-phase alternator of Fig. 4-32.   Assume that

the airgap flux is sinusoidally distributed and that its axis coincides with that of the poles N, S. The emf generated in the armature winding will then be sinusoidal, in accordance with the equation

$$e = E_m \sin \theta = E_m \sin \omega t$$

and on completing the circuit through a load of constant impedance the current will be given by

$$i = I_m \sin (\omega t - \psi)$$

where ψ is the angle between an axial plane through the centers of the poles and the plane of the armature coil when the current has its maximum value. The mmf due to this current will have the rectangular distribution of Fig. 4-9 (with respect to the developed armature), and the amplitude of its fundamental, expressed in ampere-turns per pole, will be, from Eq. 4-13, $(4/\pi)N_p i$, where N_p is the number of turns per pole. The third and higher space harmonics will be ignored for the present, and consideration of their effect will be reserved until later.

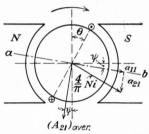

FIG. 4-32. Elementary single-phase alternator.

The mmf due to the armature coil is directed along an axis perpendicular to the plane of the coil; in other words, it moves with the coil as the latter rotates, but changes in magnitude from instant to instant as the angle $\theta = \omega t$ changes. Select as an axis of reference a line ab making an angle ψ with the axis of the poles, and resolve the armature mmf into two components, a_{11} and a_{21}, respectively parallel and perpendicular to this axis, as indicated in Fig. 4-32. Then

$$a_{11} = \frac{4}{\pi} N_p i \cos (\omega t - \psi) = \frac{4}{\pi} N_p I_m \sin (\omega t - \psi) \cos (\omega t - \psi)$$

$$= \frac{2}{\pi} N_p I_m \sin 2(\omega t - \psi) \qquad (4\text{-}33)$$

$$a_{21} = \frac{4}{\pi} N_p i \sin (\omega t - \psi) = \frac{4}{\pi} N_p I_m \sin^2 (\omega t - \psi)$$

$$= \frac{2}{\pi} N_p I_m [1 - \cos 2(\omega t - \psi)] \qquad (4\text{-}34)$$

It will be noted that both components a_{11} and a_{21} vary with time at a frequency double that of the fundamental; but since the average value of a sine or cosine function is zero when taken over a complete cycle, it follows that the average values of a_{11} and a_{21} are

$$(A_{11})_{av} = 0 \qquad (4\text{-}35)$$

$$(A_{21})_{av} = \frac{2}{\pi} N_p I_m \qquad (4\text{-}36)$$

Equation 4-36 has the physical meaning that the unvarying *average* value of the component perpendicular to axis *ab* is fixed in position with respect to the poles. Its instantaneous value pulsates at double frequency, as shown by Eq. 4-34.

Considering the average values only, as given by Eqs. 4-35 and 4-36, it is evident that the component $(A_{21})_{av}$ may be resolved into two components, $(A_{21})_{av} \sin \psi$ and $(A_{21})_{av} \cos \psi$, of which the former is a *demagnetizing* component when ψ is an angle of lag, since it is directed in opposition to the field mmf, and the latter is a *transverse*, or *cross-magnetizing*, component, since it is directed at right angles to the field mmf and tends to skew the resultant field in the direction of rotation of the armature.

The double-frequency pulsations of the single-phase armature, while having zero average value, cannot be ignored, since their effect is to induce double-frequency emfs and currents in the pole pieces and in the field windings; but this effect will be deferred for later consideration.

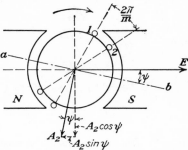

Consider now the same machine wound for m phases, two of which are indicated in Fig. 4-33. The first phase will produce component mmfs, parallel to and perpendicular to axis *ab*, of the magnitudes given by Eqs. 4-33 and 4-34; the second phase, which, with the direction of rotation indicated,

FIG. 4-33. Elementary m-phase alternator.

cated, develops a current ahead of that of the first by angle $2\pi/m$, will by analogy have components

$$a_{12} = \frac{2}{\pi} N_p I_m \sin 2\left(\omega t - \psi + \frac{2\pi}{m}\right)$$

and

$$a_{22} = \frac{2}{\pi} N_p I_m \left[1 - \cos 2\left(\omega t - \psi + \frac{2\pi}{m}\right)\right]$$

where N_p is the number of armature turns per phase per pole. Similar expressions will hold for each of the other phases, the angles entering into them increasing successively by steps equal to $2\pi/m$. Thus, the expressions for the last phase are

$$a_{1m} = \frac{2}{\pi} N_p I_m \sin 2\left[\omega t - \psi + (m - 1)\frac{2\pi}{m}\right]$$

$$a_{2m} = \frac{2}{\pi} N_p I_m \left\{1 - \cos 2\left[\omega t - \psi + (m - 1)\frac{2\pi}{m}\right]\right\}$$

Adding together all of the terms representing the parallel components, the sum is

$$A_1 = a_{11} + \cdots + a_{1m} = \frac{2}{\pi} N_p I_m \sum_{r=0}^{r=m-1} \sin 2\left(\omega t - \psi + r\frac{2\pi}{m}\right) \quad (4\text{-}37)$$

while the corresponding sum of the perpendicular components is

$$A_2 = \frac{2}{\pi} m N_p I_m - \frac{2}{\pi} N_p I_m \sum_{r=0}^{r=m-1} \cos 2\left(\omega t - \psi + r\frac{2\pi}{m}\right) \quad (4\text{-}38)$$

The sum of the sine and of the cosine series in Eqs. 4-37 and 4-38 is readily shown to be zero in both cases; for any of the angles concerned is $2(\omega t - \psi) + r(4\pi/m)$, each differing from the next by $4\pi/m$; these angles are indicated in Fig. 4-34, and by making the phasors OA, AB, BC, etc., each equal to unity, their projections on the vertical axis OY are the sines, and their projections on the horizontal axis OX are the cosines, appearing in expressions 4-37 and 4-38. No matter what the value of m (the number of phases) may be, except for the case when $m = 2$, the resultant diagram is a closed, regular polygon; hence, the sum of the pro-

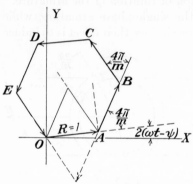

FIG. 4-34. Phasor relations in balanced m-phase circuit.

jections of its sides on any axis is zero. It follows, therefore, that Eqs. 4-37 and 4-38 reduce to

$$A_1 = 0 \quad (4\text{-}39)$$

$$A_2 = \frac{2}{\pi} m N_p I_m \quad (4\text{-}40)$$

which mean (1) that the component of armature mmf A_1 parallel to the axis ab is identically zero at all times, since the result is independent of ωt; and (2) that the remaining component of armature mmf, A_2, perpendicular to axis ab, is *unvarying in magnitude for a given armature current, and it is stationary with respect to the poles*.

Although the geometrical proof inherent in Fig. 4-34 fails for the case when $m = 2$ for the reason that a closed polygon does not result, the results embodied in Eqs. 4-39 and 4-40 are still valid. For if the two components of armature mmf represented by Eqs. 4-33 and 4-34 hold for the first phase, the corresponding equations for the second phase are

$$a_{12} = \frac{2}{\pi} N_p I_m \sin 2\left(\omega t - \psi + \frac{\pi}{2}\right)$$

$$a_{22} = \frac{2}{\pi} N_p I_m \left[1 - \cos 2\left(\omega t - \psi + \frac{\pi}{2}\right)\right]$$

from which
$$A_1 = a_{11} + a_{12} = 0$$
$$A_2 = a_{21} + a_{22} = \frac{2}{\pi} \times 2 \times N_p I_m$$

thus agreeing with Eq. 4-40 when $m = 2$.

It follows from Eq. 4-40 and from Fig. 4-33 that the resultant steady armature mmf A_2 may be resolved into two components, one in the direction of the field mmf and the other transverse to the field excitation.   The former will be *demagnetizing* if ψ is an angle of lag (i.e., armature current lagging behind the emf), and *magnetizing* if ψ is an angle of lead; it alters the magnitude of the flux per pole, but does not distort its distribution. The cross-magnetizing component is always so directed, in the case of generator action, as to skew the field in the direction of rotation of the armature with respect to the field structure, increasing the field intensity under the trailing pole tips, and decreasing it under the leading pole tips, but without altering its magnitude as a whole (neglecting the effect of saturation).   The direct or demagnetizing (or magnetizing) effect is therefore

$$A_d = \frac{2}{\pi} m N_p I_m \sin \psi \qquad \text{amp-turns per pole} \qquad (4\text{-}41)$$

and the quadrature or cross-magnetizing effect is

$$A_q = \frac{2}{\pi} m N_p I_m \cos \psi \qquad \text{amp-turns per pole} \qquad (4\text{-}42)$$

It will be noted that these expressions for polyphase machines include as a special case those already derived for a single-phase machine, for if m is placed equal to unity, the original relations result; they do not, however, show that pulsations of mmf occur in the single-phase machine.

It follows further from Eqs. 4-41 and 4-42 that if the current is in phase with the generated emf ($\psi = 0$), there is no demagnetizing or magnetizing effect, but the cross-magnetizing action is at its maximum; if, on the other hand, the current differs in phase from the emf by 90°, the cross-magnetizing effect vanishes, and the entire armature mmf is demagnetizing if ψ is an angle of lag, or magnetizing if it is an angle of lead.   These effects are similar to those which take place in a d-c generator when the brushes are shifted, the phase angle in the case of the alternator being the analogue of the angle of brush shift.

While the above relations have been derived with reference to a bipolar machine, it is easy to see that they hold equally well for multipolar machines provided that N_p is interpreted to mean the number of armature turns per phase per pole.

4-16. The Rotating Magnetic Field.   The final deduction drawn from Eq. 4-40 in the preceding article is equivalent to the statement that *the armature mmf due to a system of balanced polyphase currents is constant in* *magnitude and that it rotates at synchronous speed with respect to the arma-ture.* This conclusion, which can be verified in other ways, three of which are described below, is of great importance, not only in the analysis of generator characteristics, but in connection with all types of a-c motors. It must be remembered, however, that this conclusion holds only for the fundamental of armature mmf and that the effect of the higher harmonics remains to be analyzed.

a. The following graphical method furnishes a convincing proof of the synchronous rotation of the magnetic field produced by a three-phase winding, which is shown in developed form in Fig. 4-35. A simple con-centrated winding of full pitch has been chosen to avoid complicating the diagram.

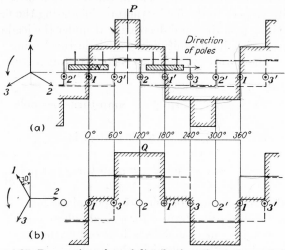

FIG. 4-35. Progression of mmf distribution, three-phase winding.

Assume that at a definite time the phasors representing the three cur-rents have the time-phase positions shown at the left of Fig. 4-35*a*, so that current i_1 is passing through its positive maximum while i_2 and i_3 are simultaneously negative and numerically equal to half their maximum values. Let the armature be stationary, and let the poles move to the right as indicated in the drawing; then, assuming for the sake of simplicity that the current is in phase with the emf, the various conductors will carry currents in the directions indicated by the conventional dots and crosses, and the mmf distributions due to the three windings will have the rec-tangular forms shown; that due to phase 1 is shown in full light lines; that due to phase 2 in dot-and-dash lines; and that due to phase 3 in broken lines. The rectangles corresponding to phases 2 and 3 should coincide in part, but to avoid confusion they have been drawn with slightly different altitudes. The resultant of the three sets is found by adding correspond-ing ordinates of the several rectangles, thus giving the stepped distribution shown in hatched lines.   The center of this resultant distribution is at point P, which is seen to be halfway between the poles, therefore conforming with the fact that when ψ is zero, the resultant armature reaction is purely cross-magnetizing.

One-twelfth of a period later ($\omega t = 30°$), the phasors representing the currents will have assumed the position shown at the left of Fig. 4-35b, showing that $i_1 = +(\sqrt{3}/2)I_m$, $i_2 = 0$, and $i_3 = -(\sqrt{3}/2)I_m$.   The rectangular distributions of mmf due to phases 1 and 3 therefore have equal altitudes, while that of phase 2 is zero.   The resultant, shown in hatched lines, now has its center at Q, which is clearly 30° from the original center at P, but is still halfway between the poles since the latter have moved 30 electrical degrees in synchronism with the rotation of the phasor diagram.

On repeating this process for other values of ωt, it will be found that for every advance in the time phase of the currents there is an equal advance in the angular position of the resultant mmf, thus checking the previous conclusion as to the synchronous rotation of the magnetic field of the armature.*   The change in shape of the resultant distribution, evident in Fig. 4-35a and b, is caused by the harmonics in the rectangular mmf waves, as will be explained later.

b. Another way of dealing with the magnetic field of the armature which is very useful in analyzing the behavior of many types of a-c machines is based upon the fact† that any harmonically varying quantity may be considered to be the resultant of two *oppositely rotating* components, each having an unvarying magnitude equal to half the maximum value of the original alternating quantity and rotating with the periodicity of the latter.   Thus, referring to Fig. 4-36, let Ni represent the instantaneous value of a harmonically varying mmf

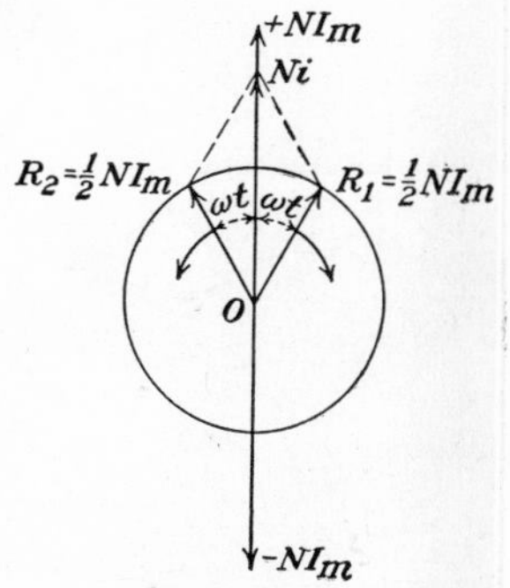

Fig. 4-36. Resolution of harmonically varying phasor into two rotating components.

which is *stationary in space* with respect to the coil producing it but which *alternates with respect to time* in accordance with the equation

$$Ni = NI_m \cos \omega t$$

The extreme space positions of the mmf will then be $+NI_m$ and $-NI_m$, as shown, and all intermediate values will be represented by points on the line joining these extremes.   Let R_1 and R_2, each equal to $\frac{1}{2}NI_m$, represent two mmfs unvarying in magitude, but rotating in opposite direc-

---

* It will be observed that whenever any one of the currents passes through its positive maximum value the axis of the resultant mmf distribution coincides with the center line of that winding.

† Originally enunciated by Fresnel in his analysis of polarized light.

tions at angular velocity ω, in such manner that both are directed vertically upward when $\omega t = 0$. It follows from the geometry of the figure that their resultant is at any instant t

$$2 \times \frac{NI_m}{2} \cos \omega t$$

which is the same as the expression for Ni above, thus justifying the proposition. The importance of this device depends upon the fact that a flux or mmf *varying with time, but fixed in space*, is thereby converted into two components *unvarying in time but rotating oppositely in space*.

Fig. 4-37. Rotor with damping grids in pole faces.   (*Courtesy of Allis-Chalmers Manufacturing Company.*)

Applying this principle to the single-phase machine of Fig. 4-32, the varying mmf of the armature may be resolved into two components, one rotating clockwise, the other counterclockwise, at synchronous speed with respect to the armature. Since the armature is itself rotating at synchronous speed in the clockwise direction, one component is fixed in position with respect to the field structure, while the other is rotating with respect to the field structure at twice synchronous speed, thus accounting for the double-frequency effect mentioned in Art. 4-15. The component of armature mmf which is stationary with respect to the poles will combine with the mmf of the latter to produce a resultant flux per pole Φ, fixed in position relative to the field structure; the double-frequency component of armature flux will have a maximum value ϕ and may be assumed to vary harmonically.   The resultant flux linked with the armature winding at any instant will therefore be

$$\varphi = [\Phi + \phi \sin (2\omega t - \delta)] \cos \omega t$$

and, by the same process exemplified in Eq. 4-32, there will be induced in the armature winding, in addition to the main emf of fundamental frequency, additional components, of fundamental and triple frequencies, respectively.   The pulsations of flux due to the double-frequency armature reaction are undesirable for obvious reasons.   Consequently, single-phase alternators are always provided with a damping grid, or cage, in

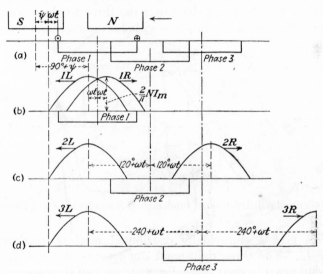

Fig. 4-38. Resolution of polyphase mmf into rotating components.

the pole faces; this consists of a series of copper bars arranged parallel to the axis of the armature in slots or holes punched in the laminations of the pole faces, and short-circuited at both ends by copper bands brazed to the bars, as in Fig. 4-37.   The current induced in these short-circuited grids by the double-frequency armature field will be so directed, in accordance with Lenz's law, as to damp out the greater part of the pulsation.

c. In polyphase machines carrying balanced currents, the resolution of the alternating mmf of each phase into two oppositely rotating components of constant (half) magnitude leads to the same results previously deduced.   For example, consider the three-phase winding shown in Fig. 4-38, where the field poles are moving to the left relative to the armature. Assume that the emf in each of the phases reaches its maximum value when the active conductors are opposite the middle of the pole faces, and assume also that the current lags behind the emf by angle ψ. Under the assumed conditions, the emfs and currents of phases 2 and 3 will lead those of phase 1 by 120° and 240°, respectively. Resolve the fundamental of the mmf of phase 1, having the maximum value $(4/\pi)N_pI_m$, into two equal rotating components each equal to $(2/\pi)N_pI_m$, and consider the conditions at a time t after the current in phase 1 has passed its maximum value; it is clear that each of the two rotating components of phase 1 must have moved through an angle ωt, one to the right, the other to the left, of the middle point of the coils of phase 1, as in Fig. 4-38b. In the same way, as shown in Fig. 4-38c, the two rotating components due to phase 2 will each have moved 120 $+ \omega t$ electrical degrees from the mid-point of that winding; similarly, in Fig. 4-38d, the two components of phase 3 will each have moved 240 $+ \omega t$ electrical degrees from the mid-point of phase 3. Inspection of Fig. 4-38 will show that the three left-hand components, $1L$, $2L$, and $3L$, are exactly in phase with one another, and therefore add

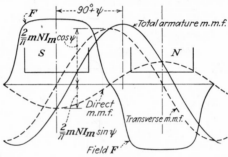

Fig. 4-39. Sinusoidal distribution of fundamental armature mmf and its components, full-pitch winding.

directly to give a sinusoidally distributed mmf of maximum value $(2/\pi)mN_pI_m$. The three right-hand components, $1R$, $2R$, and $3R$, are exactly 240° apart in their space distributions, and their sum is therefore identically zero at every instant. The three left-hand components of armature mmf travel synchronously in the same direction as the field structure, hence are stationary with respect to the latter. It will be seen from Fig. 4-38 that the axis of the resultant armature mmf is displaced from the axis of pole S by an angle 90 $+ \psi$, and this fact is also represented in Fig. 4-39. In the latter figure, there are also shown the two sinusoidally distributed fundamental components of armature mmf for the case of a full-pitch winding; one component, the quadrature, or cross-magnetizing, mmf, has a maximum value of $(2/\pi)mN_pI_m \cos \psi$, while the other, the direct (magnetizing, or demagnetizing) component, has a maximum value of $(2/\pi)mN_pI_m \sin \psi$. The diagram also shows the field distribution F due to the exciting winding acting alone.

4-17. Effect of Distributed and Fractional-pitch Windings on Armature Reaction. The preceding analysis of armature reaction has been based for the sake of simplicity upon the assumption of a concentrated winding of full pitch. It is therefore necessary to determine what modifications are introduced when the winding is distributed or is of fractional pitch, or both.

a. Effect of Distributing the Winding. A full-pitch distributed winding like that of Fig. 4-22 is equivalent to q concentrated coils, each of full pitch, and each displaced from its neighbor by an angle γ. The rectangular mmf due to each individual coil may then be resolved into a fundamental and odd harmonics in accordance with Eqs. 4-12 and 4-13. On adding the q fundamentals, which differ in phase from one another by steps of $\gamma°$, the resultant will be less than their algebraic sum in exactly the same manner as the resultant fundamental emf of a distributed winding is less than that of a concentrated winding having the same number of turns; the same thing is true of the higher harmonics of the mmf distribution. It follows, therefore, that the breadth factor previously derived in connection with the formula for emf is directly applicable to the formula for armature reaction. Consequently, the amplitude of the fundamental of the armature mmf becomes (from Eq. 4-40)

$$A = \frac{2}{\pi} k_{b_1} m N_p I_m = \frac{2\sqrt{2}}{\pi} k_{b_1} m N_p I \qquad \text{amp-turns per pole} \quad (4\text{-}43)$$

b. Effect of Fractional Pitch. It has been shown in Eq. 4-14 that the amplitude of the fundamental of a short-pitch rectangle (Fig. 4-10) is less than that of a full-pitch rectangle by the factor $\cos \gamma$. Comparison of Figs. 4-10 and 4-26 will show that angle γ in the former is the same as $\rho/2$ in the latter. But $\cos (\rho/2)$ is the pitch factor for the fundamental of the induced emf; hence, it applies also to the space fundamental of the mmf. The complete expression for the amplitude of the space fundamental of armature mmf is therefore

$$A = \frac{2}{\pi} k_{b_1} k_{p_1} m N_p I_m = \frac{2\sqrt{2}}{\pi} k_{b_1} k_{p_1} m N_p I \qquad \text{amp-turns per pole} \quad (4\text{-}44)$$

4-18. Space Harmonics of MMF. Up to this point, the discussion of armature reaction has been concerned only with the fundamental sinusoidal component of the rectangularly distributed armature mmf; and the current producing the mmf has been assumed to vary harmonically at fundamental frequency. In other words, there have been neglected the *space harmonics* in the mmf wave and the *time harmonics* in the wave form of current. Cases may arise, unless precautions are taken to avoid them, in which the interaction of the two kinds of harmonics may produce undesirable results; consequently, an analysis of the effects of both sets of harmonics is necessary. The conclusions have a direct application not only to synchronous generators and motors but also to induction motors.

a. Concentrated Coils, Full and Fractional Pitch. Two types of windings of basic importance have already been considered in connection with Figs. 4-9 and 4-10. They are the concentrated windings of full pitch and of fractional pitch, and by assembling these units in various combinations all practicable types of distributed windings can be built up. It has been shown in Eq. 4-13 that the mmf distribution of a full-pitch concentrated winding can be expressed as

$$a = \frac{4}{\pi} A \left(\sin \alpha + \frac{1}{3} \sin 3\alpha + \cdots + \frac{1}{r} \sin r\alpha + \cdots \right) \quad (4\text{-}45)$$

It has been similarly shown in Eq. 4-14 that the mmf distribution of a fractional-pitch winding (Fig. 4-10) can be expressed as

$$a = \frac{4}{\pi} A \left(\cos \gamma \sin \alpha + \frac{\cos 3\gamma}{3} \sin 3\alpha + \cdots + \frac{\cos r\gamma}{r} \sin r\alpha + \cdots \right) \quad (4\text{-}46)$$

The magnetizing effect of a single coil of fractional pitch can be regarded as due to two full-pitch coils displaced laterally with respect to each other by an angle 2γ, as in Fig. 4-40, each rectangle having half the altitude of the resultant. Each of the full-pitch rectangular components

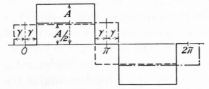

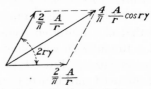

FIG. 4-40. Resolution of fractional-pitch distribution into two full-pitch components.

FIG. 4-41. Amplitude of rth harmonic of fractional-pitch distribution.

can in turn be resolved into a fundamental and odd higher harmonics having half the amplitudes of Eq. 4-46, the two fundamentals being displaced by angle 2γ and the corresponding rth harmonics by angle $2r\gamma$. In general, therefore, the amplitude of the rth harmonics of the resultant fractional pitch distribution will be given by the construction of Fig. 4-41, from which

$$A_r = 2 \times \frac{2}{\pi} \frac{A}{r} \cos \frac{1}{2} (2r\gamma) = \frac{4}{\pi} \frac{A}{r} \cos r\gamma$$

which agrees with Eq. 4-46.

The relative magnitudes of the fundamental and harmonics as determined by the coefficients of Eqs. 4-45 and 4-46 are shown in Figs. 4-42 and 4-43. In Fig. 4-42, the ordinates represent the numerical factor by which the altitude of the rectangle must be multiplied in order to obtain

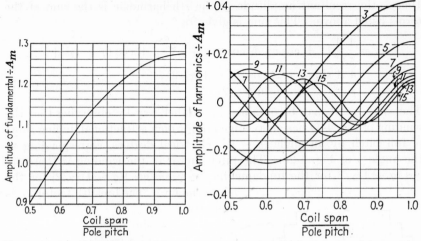

FIG. 4-42. Amplitude factors of fundamental, coil of fractional pitch.

FIG. 4-43. Amplitude factors of harmonics, coil of fractional pitch.

the amplitude of the fundamental, while abscissas represent the ratio pole arc to pole pitch, or, more strictly, the base of the rectangle in per cent of the pole pitch. In Fig. 4-43, the ordinates represent the factors by which the altitude of the rectangle must be multiplied in order to obtain the amplitudes of harmonics from the 3d to the 15th.

b. Stepped Distribution. CASE 1. If the winding is distributed in slots in the manner indicated in the lower part of Fig. 4-44, each of the individual coils will contribute a rectangularly distributed mmf of the types discussed in (*a*). If the outer full-pitch coil is assumed to have the same number of turns as the inner fractional-pitch coils, the maximum mmf of all the component rectangular distributions will be the same, namely, A_m/q, where q is the number of the coils in the group.

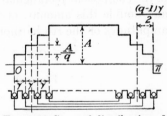

FIG. 4-44. Stepped distribution of mmf, case 1.

Referring to Eqs. 4-45 and 4-46, the amplitudes of the rth harmonics of the successive coils, beginning with the outer full-pitch coil, are, respectively,

Coil	Amplitude
1 (outer)	$\dfrac{4}{\pi}\dfrac{A}{q}\dfrac{1}{r}$
2	$\dfrac{4}{\pi}\dfrac{A}{q}\dfrac{\cos r\gamma}{r}$
3	$\dfrac{4}{\pi}\dfrac{A}{q}\dfrac{\cos 2r\gamma}{r}$
· · · · · ·	· · · · · · · · · ·
q (inner)	$\dfrac{4}{\pi}\dfrac{A}{q}\dfrac{\cos (q-1)r\gamma}{r}$

Hence, the resultant amplitude of the rth harmonic is the sum of the terms listed above. This sum is given by*

$$A_r = \frac{4}{\pi} \frac{A}{qr} [1 + \cos r\gamma + \cos 2r\gamma + \cdots + \cos (q - 1)r\gamma]$$

$$= \frac{4}{\pi} \frac{A}{r} \frac{\sin (qr\gamma/2) \cos [(q - 1)r\gamma/2]}{q \sin (r\gamma/2)} \tag{4-47}$$

The same result may be obtained in another way by observing that the winding of Fig. 4-44 has an average pitch which is fractional, falling short of full pitch by an angle $(q - 1)\gamma$ electrical degrees, corresponding to the angle ρ^- of Fig. 4-26. The pitch factor of the winding is therefore $\cos (q - 1)\gamma/2$ for the fundamental, or $k_{p_r} = \cos [(q - 1)r\gamma/2]$ for the rth harmonic. The breadth factor k_{b_r} is similarly

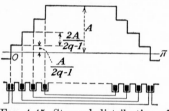

$$\frac{\sin (rq\gamma/2)}{q \sin (r\gamma/2)}$$

FIG. 4-45. Stepped distribution of mmf, case 2.

so that the product $k_{b_r} \cdot k_{p_r}$ gives the result in Eq. 4-47.

CASE 2. If, instead of making the outer coil of Fig. 4-44 with the same number of turns as the inner ones, it has only half this number, the distribution of mmf will take the form of Fig. 4-45. If the maximum ordinate of the resultant stepped curve is A, the altitudes of the component rectangular curves will be $A/(2q - 1)$ for the outer coil, and double this amount, or $2A/(2q - 1)$, for each of the others. The amplitudes of the rth harmonic due to each of these coils will be

Coil	Amplitude
1 (outer)	$\dfrac{4}{\pi} \dfrac{A}{2q - 1} \dfrac{1}{r}$
2	$\dfrac{4}{\pi} \dfrac{2A}{2q - 1} \dfrac{\cos r\gamma}{r}$
3	$\dfrac{4}{\pi} \dfrac{2A}{2q - 1} \dfrac{\cos 2r\gamma}{r}$
$\cdots\cdots$	$\cdots\cdots\cdots\cdots\cdots$
q (inner)	$\dfrac{4}{\pi} \dfrac{2A}{2q - 1} \dfrac{\cos (q - 1)r\gamma}{r}$

The resultant amplitude of the rth harmonic is the sum of these terms, or

$$\frac{4}{\pi} \frac{2A}{2q - 1} \frac{1}{r} \left[\frac{1}{2} + \cos r\gamma + \cos 2r\gamma + \cdots + \cos (q - 1)r\gamma \right]$$

The cosine series in this expression differs from that of Eq. 4-47 only in the first term; hence, its sum differs from that of Eq. 4-47 by the quantity $\frac{1}{2}$; consequently, the resultant amplitude of the rth harmonic for

* See footnote, page 184.

the case considered is

$$
\begin{aligned}
A_r &= \frac{4}{\pi}\frac{2A}{2q-1}\frac{1}{r}\left[\frac{\sin\dfrac{qr\gamma}{2}\cos\dfrac{(q-1)r\gamma}{2}}{\sin(r\gamma/2)}-\frac{1}{2}\right] \\
&= \frac{4}{\pi}\frac{A}{2q-1}\frac{1}{r}\frac{\sin(2q-1)(r\gamma/2)}{\sin(r\gamma/2)}
\end{aligned}
\tag{4-48}
$$

CASE 3.   Figure 4-46 illustrates a distributed winding, arranged in slots, with the outer coil of less than full pitch, but with all coils having the same number of turns.   This case occurs in the rotor windings of turbo-alternators and in the stator windings of generators and motors.   It follows from Eq. 4-14 that the amplitudes of the rth harmonic of the several coils are given by the following table:

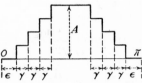

FIG. 4-46. Stepped distribution, fractional pitch.

Coil	Amplitude
1 (outer)	$\dfrac{4}{\pi}\dfrac{A}{q}\dfrac{\cos r\epsilon}{r}$
2	$\dfrac{4}{\pi}\dfrac{A}{q}\dfrac{\cos r(\epsilon+\gamma)}{r}$
3	$\dfrac{4}{\pi}\dfrac{A}{q}\dfrac{\cos r(\epsilon+2\gamma)}{r}$
. . . . . .	. . . .
q	$\dfrac{4}{\pi}\dfrac{A}{q}\dfrac{\cos r[\epsilon+(q-1)\gamma]}{r}$

The amplitude of the rth harmonic of the composite curve of Fig. 4-46 is then the sum of the above terms, or

$$
\begin{aligned}
A_r = \frac{4}{\pi}\frac{A}{qr}\{&\cos r\epsilon[1+\cos r\gamma+\cos 2r\gamma+\cdots+\cos(q-1)r\gamma] \\
&-\sin r\epsilon[\sin r\gamma+\sin 2r\gamma+\cdots+\sin(q-1)r\gamma]\}
\end{aligned}
\tag{4-49}
$$

The sum of the cosine series in Eq. 4-49 is the same as that of Eq. 4-47, and the sum of the sine series is*

$$
\frac{\sin(qr\gamma/2)\sin[(q-1)r\gamma/2]}{\sin(r\gamma/2)}
\tag{4-50}
$$

Substituting these values in Eq. 4-49, we have

$$
\begin{aligned}
A_r &= \frac{4}{\pi}\frac{A}{qr}\frac{\sin(qr\gamma/2)}{\sin(r\gamma/2)}\left[\cos r\epsilon\cos\frac{(q-1)r\gamma}{2}-\sin r\epsilon\sin\frac{(q-1)r\gamma}{2}\right] \\
&= \frac{4}{\pi}\frac{A}{r}\frac{\sin(qr\gamma/2)}{q\sin(r\gamma/2)}\cos r\left[\epsilon+\frac{(q-1)\gamma}{2}\right]
\end{aligned}
\tag{4-51}
$$

* See footnote, page 184.

c. Trapezoidal Distribution. CASE 1. FULL-PITCH TYPE. If the winding of Fig. 4-44 is subdivided more and more by indefinitely increasing the number of coils and slots in the belt having angular width $\beta = (q - 1)\gamma$,

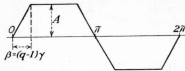

FIG. 4-47. Trapezoidal distribution, full pitch.

the stepped diagram will approach as a limit the trapezoidal form of Fig. 4-47. The amplitude of any harmonic of this distribution may then be found from Eq. 4-47 by determining the limiting value of the latter when q approaches infinity and γ approaches zero, subject to the condition that $(q - 1)\gamma = \beta = \text{constant}$. The result is

$$A_r = \frac{4}{\pi} \frac{A}{r} \frac{\sin (r\beta/2) \cos (r\beta/2)}{r\beta/2} = \frac{4}{\pi} \frac{A}{\beta r^2} \sin r\beta \qquad (4\text{-}52)$$

and the complete equation for the full-pitch trapezoidal distribution is, therefore,

$$a = \frac{4}{\pi} \frac{A}{\beta} \left(\sin \beta \sin \alpha + \frac{\sin 3\beta}{9} \sin 3\alpha + \frac{\sin 5\beta}{25} \sin 5\alpha + \cdots \right) \qquad (4\text{-}53)$$

CASE 2. FRACTIONAL-PITCH TYPE. The case shown in Fig. 4-48 is that of a uniformily distributed winding of less than full-pitch spread. It is clearly a special case of the stepped distribution of Fig. 4-46, since it may be derived from the latter by indefinitely increasing the number of steps q, subject to the

FIG. 4-48. Trapezoidal distribution, fractional pitch.

condition that $(q - 1)\gamma = \beta$. The limiting form of Eq. 4-51 becomes

$$A_r = \frac{4}{\pi} \frac{A}{r} \frac{\sin \dfrac{r\beta}{2} \cos r\left(\epsilon + \dfrac{\beta}{2}\right)}{r\beta/2} = \frac{8}{\pi} \frac{A}{\beta r^2} \sin \frac{r\beta}{2} \cos r\left(\epsilon + \frac{\beta}{2}\right) \qquad (4\text{-}54)$$

which represents, therefore, the amplitude of the rth harmonic of the fractional-pitch trapezoidal distribution.

d. Triangular Distribution. Uniformly distributed windings of the type represented in Fig. 4-49 are perhaps most common in the case of d-c armatures. Two cases may be distinguished, namely, that of the full-pitch distribution of Fig. 4-49, and that of the fractional-pitch arrangement of Fig. 4-50.

CASE 1. FULL PITCH. The triangular form of Fig. 4-49 is a special case of Fig. 4-47, since it follows from the latter when the angle β becomes $\pi/2$. On making this substitution in Eq. 4-52, we have

$$A_r = \frac{8}{\pi^2} \frac{A}{r^2} \sin \frac{r\pi}{2} = -(-1)^{(r+1)/2} \frac{8}{\pi^2} \frac{A}{r^2} \qquad (4\text{-}55)$$

where the amplitudes of the successive harmonics are alternately positive and negative, as is shown on substituting for r the successive odd values 1, 3, 5, 7, etc.

CASE 2. FRACTIONAL PITCH.   Figure 4-50 is clearly the special case of Fig. 4-48 obtained when $\epsilon + \beta = \pi/2$.   Substituting this relation in Eq. 4-54, there results

$$A_r = \frac{8}{\pi}\frac{A}{\beta r^2} \sin r\left(\frac{\pi}{4} - \frac{\epsilon}{2}\right) \cos r\left(\frac{\pi}{4} + \frac{\epsilon}{2}\right) \tag{4-56}$$

The formulas thus derived for a number of different types of windings may be quite simply summarized.   Thus, if a winding consists of N_p turns per pole with all the turns concentrated in slots separated by a full pole pitch, the coil produces mmf of $A_m = N_p I_m$ amp-turns per pole.

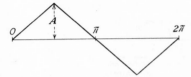

FIG. 4-49. Triangular distribution, full pitch.   FIG. 4-50. Triangular distribution, fractional pitch.

This may be resolved into a fundamental sinusoidal distribution of amplitude $(4/\pi)A_m$, and a series of odd harmonics of which the rth has the amplitude $(4/\pi r)A$.   If the same winding is now spread out so that each side of the coil forms a belt occupying two or more consecutive slots, and if at the same time the pitch of the coil is shortened, the amplitude of the fundamental space harmonic becomes

$$A_1 = \frac{4}{\pi} k_{b_1} k_{p_1} N_p I_m = \frac{4}{\pi} k_1 N_p I_m$$

and that of the rth harmonic becomes

$$A_r = \frac{4}{\pi}\frac{1}{r} k_{b_r} k_{p_r} N_p I_m = \frac{4}{\pi r} k_r N_p I_m$$

The various values of $k_1 = k_{b_1} k_{p_1}$ and $k_r = k_{b_r} k_{p_r}$ for any type of winding follow readily from formulas 4-47 to 4-56.

4-19. Traveling Waves of MMF Due to Time Harmonics.   Each of the diagrams in Figs. 4-44 to 4-50 shows the space distribution of mmf due to some particular (fixed) value of current in one phase of a winding.   It has been shown that each distribution may then be resolved into space harmonics, beginning with a fundamental of full span (one pole pitch) and the higher odd harmonics.   For example, Fig. 4-51 represents the fundamental and the third and fifth space harmonics of a winding in which

$q = 4$, $\gamma = 15°$, and $\epsilon = 0$ and in which the current has an instantaneous value i.   In the case shown, the two harmonics have positive amplitudes, but in general some of them may be positive, others negative.

If point O in Fig. 4-51 is any arbitrary reference point *on the armature surface*, the space distribution of any one of the mmf harmonics due to current i_1 in phase 1 may be represented by

$$a_1 = (A_r)_i \sin r(\alpha - \delta)$$

where δ defines the position of the phase belt with respect to the origin O; and the coefficient $(A_r)_i$ indicates the amplitude (maximum value) of the distributed mmf due to the instantaneous current i_1.   The current itself

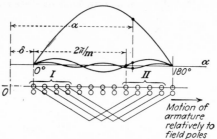

FIG. 4-51. Harmonics of mmf of phase belt.

may be alternating at a frequency which is any odd multiple (s) of the fundamental frequency in accordance with the relation

$$i_1 = I_m \cos\ s(\omega t - \zeta) = I_m \cos s(\theta - \zeta)$$

Here ζ is an arbitrary time-phase angle such that when $\theta = \omega t = \zeta$ the current is passing through its positive maximum.   As the current changes from instant to instant, the ordinates of the mmf distribution curve will change proportionately; hence, we may write

$$a_1 = A_{rs} \sin r(\alpha - \delta) \cos s(\theta - \zeta) \tag{4-57}$$

where A_{rs} is the maximum amplitude of the rth space harmonic of mmf produced by the sth time harmonic of current in phase 1 and is given by the equation

$$A_{rs} = \frac{4}{\pi} \frac{1}{r} k_r N_p (I_m)_s$$

If the machine has m phases, the next phase to the right of the one shown in Fig. 4-51 will produce a space distribution of the same form as the first, but when referred to the same origin of coordinates the angle $\alpha - \delta$ must be replaced by $\alpha - \delta - (2\pi/m)$.   At the same time, the fundamental of the current in phase 2 leads that of phase 1 by $2\pi/m$; hence, $\theta - \zeta$ must be replaced by $\theta - \zeta + (2\pi/m)$.   Accordingly, the mmf distribution of the second phase is given by

$$a_2 = A_{rs} \sin r \left(\alpha - \delta - \frac{2\pi}{m} \right) \cos s \left(\theta - \zeta + \frac{2\pi}{m} \right) \qquad (4\text{-}58)$$

and that of the kth phase is

$$a_k = A_{rs} \sin r \left[\alpha - \delta - (k - 1)\frac{2\pi}{m} \right] \cos s \left[\theta - \zeta + (k - 1)\frac{2\pi}{m} \right]$$

$$(4\text{-}59)$$

Adding together the expressions for all of the m phases, the sum will give the resultant distribution due to the entire winding. It will be noted that each term in this summation contains a product of the form $\sin x \cos y$, which can be written

$$\sin x \cos y = \tfrac{1}{2}[\sin (x + y) + \sin (x - y)]$$

Hence, the resultant distribution of the rth harmonic is

$$a = \frac{A_{rs}}{2} \sum_{k=1}^{k=m} \sin \left[r(\alpha - \delta) + s(\theta - \zeta) - (k - 1)(r - s)\frac{2\pi}{m} \right]$$

$$+ \sin \left[r(\alpha - \delta) - s(\theta - \zeta) - (k - 1)(r + s)\frac{2\pi}{m} \right]$$

$$= \frac{A_{rs}}{2} \sum_{k=1}^{k=m} \sin \left[P - (k - 1)(r - s)\frac{2\pi}{m} \right]$$

$$+ \sin \left[Q - (k - 1)(r + s)\frac{2\pi}{m} \right] \qquad (4\text{-}60)$$

where
$$P = r(\alpha - \delta) + s(\theta - \zeta)$$
$$Q = r(\alpha - \delta) - s(\theta - \zeta) \qquad (4\text{-}61)$$

When the quantity k in Eq. 4-60 takes all the possible values 1, 2, 3 . . . , m, the two sine series assume the forms

$$\sin P + \sin (P - \varphi_1) + \sin (P - 2\varphi_1) + \cdots + \sin [P - (m - 1)\varphi_1]$$

and

$$\sin Q + \sin (Q - \varphi_2) + \sin (Q - 2\varphi_2) + \cdots + \sin [Q - (m - 1)\varphi_2]$$

$$(4\text{-}62)$$

where $\varphi_1 = (r - s)(2\pi/m)$ and $\varphi_2 = (r + s)(2\pi/m)$. Expanding the first series of Eq. 4-62 and collecting terms, it becomes

$$\sin P[1 + \cos \varphi_1 + \cos 2\varphi_1 + \cdots + \cos (m - 1)\varphi_1]$$
$$- \cos P[\sin \varphi_1 + \sin 2\varphi_1 + \cdots + \sin (m - 1)\varphi_1] \qquad (4\text{-}63)$$

Substituting for the cosine series* the value given in Eq. 4-47 and for the

* See footnote, page 184.

sine series that given by Eq. 4-50, expression 4-63 becomes

$$\frac{\sin (m\varphi_1/2)}{\sin (\varphi_1/2)} \sin \left[P - \frac{(m-1)\varphi_1}{2} \right]$$

and the corresponding sum of the second series in Eq. 4-62 is by analogy

$$\frac{\sin (m\varphi_2/2)}{\sin (\varphi_2/2)} \sin \left[Q - \frac{(m-1)\varphi_2}{2} \right]$$

When these results are inserted in Eq. 4-60 and the values of φ_1 and φ_2 are substituted, the result is

$$a = \frac{A_{rs}}{2} \left[\frac{\sin (r-s)\pi}{\sin [(r-s)\pi/m]} \sin \left(P - \frac{(m-1)(r-s)\pi}{m} \right) \right.$$
$$\left. + \frac{\sin (r+s)\pi}{\sin [(r+s)\pi/m]} \sin \left(Q - \frac{(m-1)(r+s)\pi}{m} \right) \right] \quad (4\text{-}64)$$

This equation is sufficiently general to permit the determination of the magnitude and distribution of any *space harmonic of mmf* produced by any *time harmonic in the current wave*, except in the particular case when $m = 2$, which requires modifications considered later in this article. Remembering that both r and s are odd numbers, the quantities $r - s$ and $r + s$ are both even numbers, and since $\sin (r-s)\pi$ and $\sin (r+s)\pi$ are therefore zero, it would appear at first glance that the entire expression reduces to zero; but if $r - s$ is a multiple of m,

$$\frac{\sin (r-s)\pi}{\sin [(r-s)\pi/m]} = \frac{0}{0} = m$$

and if $r + s$ is a multiple of m,

$$\frac{\sin (r+s)\pi}{\sin [(r+s)\pi/m]} = \frac{0}{0} = m$$

as may be proved by separately differentiating the numerators and denominators of these fractions, in which cases the corresponding terms in the brackets of 4-64 do not vanish.

As an example, consider the conditions determined by Eq. 4-64 when $m - 3, r = 1, s = 1$; this set of values defines the fundamental space harmonic produced by the fundamental time harmonic in a three-phase machine.   We have then

$$a = \tfrac{3}{2} A_{11} \sin P = \tfrac{3}{2} A_{11} \sin (\alpha + \theta - \delta - \zeta) \quad (4\text{-}65)$$

which means that if the point defined by the abscissa α moves along the armature surface so that

$$\sin (\alpha + \theta - \delta - \zeta) = 1$$

or
$$\alpha = -\theta + \delta + \zeta + \frac{\pi}{2} = -\omega t + \delta + \zeta + \frac{\pi}{2} \quad (4\text{-}66)$$

the ordinate a at that point will have the constant magnitude $a = \frac{3}{2}A_{11}$. The negative sign of $\theta = \omega t$ in Eq. 4-66 means that the armature mmf of Fig. 4-51 is moving to the left at synchronous speed (with respect to the winding itself) and is therefore stationary with respect to the poles. This checks the conclusions derived in Art. 4-16 and constitutes an analytical proof of the synchronous rotation of the fundamental armature mmf though it adds nothing to what is already known.

A more general method of determining the speed at which the mmf wave of Eq. 4-65 is rotating is to impose the condition that α is to change in such a way that a remains constant at the moving point defined by α. This means that $\sin(\alpha + \theta - \delta - \zeta)$ is constant, or

$$\alpha + \theta - \delta - \zeta = \text{constant}$$

Differentiating both sides of this equation with respect to t,

$$\frac{d\alpha}{dt} + \omega = 0$$

or

$$\frac{d\alpha}{dt} = -\omega$$

Consider now the combination $m = 3$, $r = 3$, $s = 1$, which defines the third space harmonic of mmf due to the time fundamental of current. It will be found that A_{31} vanishes, i.e., in a three-phase machine there is no third space harmonic of mmf due to the fundamental current. The same thing is true of all the odd multiples of the third space harmonic, namely, the 9th, 15th, etc.

When $m = 3$, $r = 5$, $s = 1$, defining the fifth space harmonic of mmf produced by the fundamental current in a three-phase machine,

$$a = \frac{3}{2}A_{51}\sin Q = \frac{3}{2}A_{51}\sin[5(\alpha - \delta) - (\theta - \zeta)]$$

This represents a traveling (rotating) wave whose speed may be found as before by differentiating the term in the brackets; accordingly

$$\frac{d\alpha}{dt} = \frac{\omega}{5}$$

which means that the wave is moving toward the *right* in Fig. 4-51 (relative to the armature winding) at a speed one-fifth of synchronous speed. The fundamental, it will be recalled, moves with the poles toward the left. In other words, the fifth space harmonic of armature mmf rotates at $\frac{6}{5}$ of synchronous speed with respect to the poles. It is this motion of the fifth harmonic which is chiefly responsible for the successive changes of form of the stepped diagram of armature mmf shown in Fig. 4-35.

Proceeding in a similar manner for larger values of r, but retaining $m = 3$, and $s = 1$, it will be found that if synchronous speed is represented by unity, and if the direction of rotation of the field structure relative to the armature is taken as positive, the 1st, 5th, 7th, 11th, 13th, . . . space harmonics rotate with respect to the armature winding at speeds of $+1$, $-\frac{1}{5}$, $+\frac{1}{7}$, $-\frac{1}{11}$, $+\frac{1}{13}$, . . . , that is, alternately in opposite directions.

Investigating in like manner the components of the armature mmf produced by the 3rd time harmonic of current, i.e., substituting $m = 3$, $s = 3$, it is found that the space fundamental $r = 1$ is suppressed. But when $r = 3$, it follows from Eq. 4-64 that

$$a = \tfrac{3}{2}A_{33}(\sin P + \sin Q)$$
$$= \tfrac{3}{2}A_{33} \sin [3(\alpha - \delta) + 3(\theta - \zeta)] + \tfrac{3}{2}A_{33} \sin [3(\alpha - \delta) - 3(\theta - \zeta)]$$

which means that there are now two components, of equal amplitude, rotating in opposite directions and at synchronous speed with respect to the armature winding. One of them is therefore stationary with respect to the field structure, the other moving at twice synchronous speed in the backward direction. The higher space harmonics due to $s = 3$ are all suppressed, except those which are odd multiples of the 3d; and these, such as the 9th and 15th, are of the same double type as the 3d, rotating in both directions, but with respect to the armature at speeds of one-third and one-fifth of synchronous speed.

TABLE 4-2. SPEEDS AND DIRECTIONS OF ROTATION OF COMPONENTS OF ARMATURE MMF OF THREE-PHASE WINDINGS

Order of space harmonic r	Order of time harmonic s						
	1	3	5	7	9	11	13
1	$+1$	....	-5	$+7$	....	-11	$+13$
3	.....	± 1	.....	.....	± 3		
5	$-\frac{1}{5}$	....	$+1$	$-\frac{7}{5}$	....	$+\frac{11}{5}$	$-\frac{13}{5}$
7	$+\frac{1}{7}$	....	$-\frac{5}{7}$	$+1$	....	$-\frac{11}{7}$	$+\frac{13}{7}$
9	.....	$\pm \frac{1}{3}$	.....	.....	± 1		
11	$-\frac{1}{11}$	....	$+\frac{5}{11}$	$-\frac{7}{11}$	....	$+1$	$-\frac{13}{11}$
13	$+\frac{1}{13}$	....	$-\frac{5}{13}$	$+\frac{7}{13}$	....	$-\frac{11}{13}$	$+1$
15	.....	$\pm \frac{1}{5}$	.....	.....	$\pm \frac{3}{5}$		
17	$-\frac{1}{17}$	....	$+\frac{5}{17}$	$-\frac{7}{17}$	....	$+\frac{11}{17}$	$-\frac{13}{17}$
19	$+\frac{1}{19}$	....	$-\frac{5}{19}$	$+\frac{7}{19}$	....	$-\frac{11}{19}$	$+\frac{13}{19}$

All of these facts are summarized in Table 4-2, the numbers indicating the speed at which the armature field moves relative to the armature winding, and the signs indicating the direction, in accordance with the conventions described above.

Equation 4-64 may be used to determine the nature of the resultant space harmonics when m is equal to, or greater than, 3, but it requires modification for the special case where $m = 2$.   For the special case of a two-phase winding ($m = 2$), Eq. 4-57 holds for the first phase, but for the second phase it becomes

$$a_2 = A_{rs} \sin r \left(\alpha - \delta - \frac{\pi}{2} \right) \cos \left(\theta - \zeta + \frac{\pi}{2} \right)$$

$$= \frac{A_{rs}}{2} \sin \left[r(\alpha - \delta) + s(\theta - \zeta) - \frac{r - s}{2} \pi \right]$$

$$+ \frac{A_{rs}}{2} \sin \left[r(\alpha - \delta) - s(\theta - \zeta) - \frac{r + s}{2} \pi \right] \quad (4\text{-}67)$$

Since r and s are both odd numbers, it follows that when $(r - s)/2$ is zero or even, $(r + s)/2$ will be odd; hence, Eq. 4-67 becomes

$$a_2 = + \frac{A_{rs}}{2} \sin [r(\alpha - \delta) + s(\theta - \zeta)] - \frac{A_{rs}}{2} \sin [r(\alpha - \delta) - s(\theta - \zeta)]$$

when $(r - s)/2$ is zero or even, or

$$a_2 = - \frac{A_{rs}}{2} \sin [r(\alpha - \delta) + s(\theta - \zeta)] + \frac{A_{rs}}{2} \sin [r(\alpha - \delta) - s(\theta - \zeta)]$$

when $(r - s)/2$ is odd.

Since Eq. 4-57 may be written

$$a_1 = \frac{A_{rs}}{2} \sin [r(\alpha - \delta) + s(\theta - \zeta)] + \frac{A_{rs}}{2} \sin [r(\alpha - \delta) - s(\theta - \zeta)]$$

it follows that the resultant field is

$$a = A_{rs} \sin [r(\alpha - \delta) + s(\theta - \zeta)] \qquad \text{when } \frac{r - s}{2} \text{ is zero or even}$$

$$\qquad\qquad\qquad\qquad\qquad\qquad\qquad\qquad\qquad\qquad\qquad\qquad (4\text{-}68)$$

$$a = A_{rs} \sin [r(\alpha - \delta) - s(\theta - \zeta)] \qquad \text{when } \frac{r - s}{2} \text{ is odd}$$

On substituting any pair of values for r and s in these equations, it will be found that the results are the same as for the quarter-phase winding ($m = 4$); hence, Table 4-3, computed by means of Eq. 4-64 for $m = 4$, holds for the case where $m = 2$.   The distinctive differences between Tables 4-2 and 4-3 are readily apparent.

4-20. Resolution of Traveling Waves into Standing Waves.   There is one aspect of Eq. 4-57 which is sufficiently important to warrant special mention.   In the form

$$a = A_{rs} \sin r(\alpha - \delta) \cos s(\theta - \zeta)$$

there is embodied the analytical expression of the fact that the quantity a is sinusoidally distributed along the axis α, and that the ordinates of this space distribution are each moving up and down between a positive and negative value as $\theta = \omega t$ changes with time.   In other words, the

TABLE 4-3. SPEEDS AND DIRECTION OF ROTATION OF COMPONENTS OF ARMATURE MMF FOR QUARTER- AND TWO-PHASE WINDINGS

Order of space harmonic r	Order of time harmonic, s						
	1	3	5	7	9	11	13
1	$+1$	-3	$+5$	-7	$+9$	-11	$+13$
3	$-\frac{1}{3}$	$+1$	$-\frac{5}{3}$	$+\frac{7}{3}$	-3	$+\frac{11}{3}$	$-\frac{13}{3}$
5	$+\frac{1}{5}$	$-\frac{3}{5}$	$+1$	$-\frac{7}{5}$	$+\frac{9}{5}$	$-\frac{11}{5}$	$+\frac{13}{5}$
7	$-\frac{1}{7}$	$+\frac{3}{7}$	$-\frac{5}{7}$	$+1$	$-\frac{9}{7}$	$+\frac{11}{7}$	$-\frac{13}{7}$
9	$+\frac{1}{9}$	$-\frac{1}{3}$	$+\frac{5}{9}$	$-\frac{7}{9}$	$+1$	$-\frac{11}{9}$	$+\frac{13}{9}$
11	$-\frac{1}{11}$	$+\frac{3}{11}$	$-\frac{5}{11}$	$+\frac{7}{11}$	$-\frac{9}{11}$	$+1$	$-\frac{13}{11}$
13	$+\frac{1}{13}$	$-\frac{3}{13}$	$+\frac{5}{13}$	$-\frac{7}{13}$	$+\frac{9}{13}$	$-\frac{11}{13}$	$+1$
15	$-\frac{1}{15}$	$+\frac{1}{5}$	$-\frac{1}{3}$	$+\frac{7}{15}$	$-\frac{3}{5}$	$+\frac{11}{15}$	$-\frac{13}{15}$
17	$+\frac{1}{17}$	$-\frac{3}{17}$	$+\frac{5}{17}$	$-\frac{7}{17}$	$+\frac{9}{17}$	$-\frac{11}{17}$	$+\frac{13}{17}$
19	$-\frac{1}{19}$	$+\frac{3}{19}$	$-\frac{5}{19}$	$+\frac{7}{19}$	$-\frac{9}{19}$	$+\frac{11}{19}$	$-\frac{13}{19}$

expression represents the physical fact that the mmf distribution due to a single coil or group of coils carrying the same alternating current is a standing wave, i.e., one with fixed nodal points; it is stationary with respect to the coil which gives rise to it but is pulsating with time. By making use of the fact that

$$\sin x \cos y = \tfrac{1}{2}[\sin (x + y) + \sin (x - y)]$$

as has been done in developing Eq. 4-60, this standing wave becomes

$$a = \tfrac{1}{2}A_{rs}[\sin (r\alpha + s\theta - r\delta - s\zeta) + \sin (r\alpha - s\theta - r\delta + s\zeta)] \quad (4\text{-}69)$$

which represents two waves traveling relative to the winding in opposite directions. This is the same result that has been discussed in connection with Fig. 4-38. But this circumstance admits of an additional deduction, for on expanding the two sine terms in the above expression it becomes

$$a = \tfrac{1}{2}A_{rs}[\sin r(\alpha - \delta) \cos s(\theta - \zeta) + \cos r(\alpha - \delta) \sin s(\theta - \zeta)$$
$$+ \sin r(\alpha - \delta) \cos s(\theta - \zeta) - \cos r(\alpha - \delta) \sin s(\theta - \zeta)] \quad (4\text{-}70)$$

While this expression reduces at once to the original equation 4-57, it tells the story that each of the two oppositely traveling waves represented by Eq. 4-69 is made up of two equal waves which are in quadrature in time and in space and each stationary with respect to the winding. In other words, the original, single, stationary but alternating mmf can by this device be resolved either into (1) a pair of equal and oppositely rotating mmfs (each having half the amplitude of the original) or into (2) two pairs of alternating mmfs (stationary with respect to the winding) in which the components of each pair are in time and space quadrature, but with time-phase sequences that are opposite.

CHAPTER 5

FUNDAMENTAL PRINCIPLES OF
ASYNCHRONOUS MACHINES

5-1. General. * The synchronous machines that have been briefly discussed in Chap. 4 are characterized by a fixed relation between speed, frequency, and number of poles in accordance with the formula $f = pn/2$. Asynchronous machines, as the name implies, are not subject to this fixed relationship. There is a wide variety of asynchronous generators and motors, single-phase and polyphase, some with commutators and some without, presenting an equally wide variety of operating characteristics. It is very helpful in approaching the study of these types to consider first certain basic principles, based upon physical considerations which are common to many or all of them, rather than to take up the several types of machines one at a time as though each belonged in a separate, self-contained category independent of all the others.

In the treatment of the ordinary stationary transformer, consisting of two separate electric circuits linked together by a common magnetic circuit, it was shown that the energy supplied to the primary is inductively transferred to the secondary except for the losses due to primary resistance and to hysteresis and eddy currents in the core. The secondary current and voltage are in a sense the mirror images of the corresponding primary quantities, the analogy being particularly obvious in a transformer having a 1:1 ratio, and being more and more complete as the magnetic circuit approaches perfection. Two major considerations govern the entire analysis:

a. Kirchhoff's second law, when applied to the primary, demands that the impressed voltage shall at every instant equal the sum of the counter emf and the leakage-impedance drop.

b. Primary and secondary mmfs combine to produce a resultant just sufficient to maintain the flux, which in turn induces the counter emf in the primary, and the working emf in the secondary.

In applying these principles to the stationary transformer, the analysis proceeded on the tacit understanding that the two electric circuits were

---

* It is recommended that students read an article entitled The Theory, Design and Working of Alternate-current Motors, by L. B. Atkinson, *Proc. Inst. Civil Engrs.* (*London*), **133**:113 (1898).

at rest relative to each other, so that the frequency was the same in both primary and secondary. But the principles themselves are sufficiently universal to apply to the more general case of relative motion between primary and secondary circuits; consideration (*a*) indicated above is obviously true without restriction; and (*b*) is subject only to the limitation that the primary and secondary mmfs must continue to act upon the same magnetic circuit if there is relative motion between the electric circuits. It will be found, as the analysis of asynchronous machines develops, that these simple principles are of fundamental importance.

Practically all of the asynchronous types of commercial importance have much the same reversible properties that are characteristic of d-c machines, i.e., they are capable of operating both as generators and motors; but with few exceptions they are used as motors, and it is therefore important to realize at the outset that the identical principles which control the operation of d-c motors are here again fully applicable.

5-2. EMF Induced in a Rotating Commutated Winding. Consider an elementary bipolar machine (Fig. 5-1) assumed to be so constructed that the flux per pole, ϕ, in webers, is sinusoidally distributed; in other words, that the radial component of field intensity in the airgap, if plotted along the developed armature surface, would define a sinusoid. The armature winding, though indicated in the drawing as a simple gramme ring, may be a lap- or wave-wound drum winding of usual type. The brushes are assumed to be placed in the geometrical neutral axis. When the armature is rotated at a speed of n rps, the rotational or speed emf will be given by the equation

$$E_r = \frac{p}{a} \phi Z n \qquad (5\text{-}1)$$

where p = number of poles

a = number of parallel armature circuits

Z = number of armature conductors

So long as the flux ϕ remains fixed in magnitude, the emf E_r will be unidirectional in the circuit connected to the brushes, without regard to the magnitude of the speed; the machine is, in fact, the familiar d-c generator; an unvarying (zero-frequency) field flux generates an emf of zero frequency no matter what the speed may be, the only effect of change of speed being to influence the magnitude of the emf proportionally.

But suppose that the exciting current is varied by means of the reversing field rheostat shown in Fig. 5-1; then, assuming that the speed remains constant in magnitude and direction, the emf will rise and fall as the flux ϕ rises and falls, and will reverse when ϕ is reversed, all in strict compliance with the proportionality between E_r and ϕ as demanded by Eq. 5-1. It follows quite naturally that if the field excitation in Fig. 5-1 is supplied from an a-c source, the emf developed in the armature circuit will alternate with a frequency equal to that of the field excitation, independent of the speed. A change in speed affects only the amplitude of the generated emf, though a reversal of speed would, of course, reverse the phase of the armature emf.

In deriving Eq. 5-1, the flux was assumed to be fixed in magnitude; if it is now to be regarded as an alternating quantity, and in particular one which varies harmonically with respect to time, such that

$$\phi = \Phi \sin \omega t = \Phi \sin 2\pi f t$$

Eq. 5-1 becomes

$$e_r = \frac{p}{a} \Phi Z n \sin \omega t = E_{r_{\max}} \sin \omega t \quad (5\text{-}2)$$

where

$$E_{r_{\max}} = \frac{p}{a} \Phi Z n \quad (5\text{-}3)$$

and the effective value of the generated armature emf becomes

$$E_r = \frac{E_{r_{\max}}}{\sqrt{2}} = \frac{\sqrt{2}}{2} \frac{p}{a} \Phi Z n$$

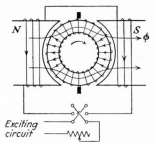

FIG. 5-1. Emf in elementary bipolar machine.

But $pn/2 = f_r$ is the frequency corresponding to the speed of rotation, and as this is not necessarily the same as the line frequency f with which the field is supplied, the speed frequency will be represented by f_r; therefore,

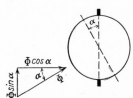

$$E_r = \sqrt{2} f_r \Phi \frac{Z}{a} \quad (5\text{-}4)$$

The frequency of E_r, being the same as that of the exciting field, is

$$f = \frac{\omega}{2\pi}$$

FIG. 5-2. Effect of brush displacement.

While these conclusions have been based upon the bipolar diagram of Fig. 5-1, the equations themselves are quite general and are applicable without modification to multipolar machines which satisfy the assumed conditions, namely, that the airgap flux is sinusoidally distributed and that the flux as a whole varies harmonically with time.

5-3. Effect of Brush Position upon Generated EMF. In the preceding analysis, it was assumed that the brush axis coincided with the geometrical neutral; but if the brush axis is displaced from the geometrical neutral by an angle α, as in Fig. 5-2, the emf generated in the displaced brush axis will be reduced, and when α becomes $\pi/2$ electrical degrees, the brush emf will be zero. To determine in what manner the brush emf depends upon α, it is possible to proceed as follows:

Since the flux Φ (maximum value) is sinusoidally distributed in space, it can be resolved into two *space* components, one of which, having maximum value $\Phi \sin \alpha$, has its axis in line with the brush axis, and the other, having maximum value $\Phi \cos \alpha$, is perpendicular thereto. Since the brush axis coincides with the axis of the flux $\Phi \sin \alpha$, there can be no emf due to rotation of the armature through it, and the rotational brush emf will depend wholly upon the flux component $\Phi \cos \alpha$. Consequently, the brush emf given by Eq. 5-4 becomes

$$E_r = \sqrt{2}\, f_r \Phi \frac{Z}{a} \cos \alpha \tag{5-5}$$

5-4. EMF Induced by Transformer Action in a Commutated Winding.

In the machine illustrated in Fig. 5-1, there is obviously no inductive coupling between the armature winding on the one hand and the field winding on the other, since their axes are at right angles. Alternation of the field flux will therefore not induce any emf in the brush axis by transformer action, and the only emf that can appear in the brush axis under the conditions shown in the figure is that which is generated by rotation.

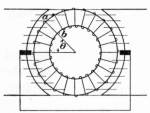

FIG. 5-3. Transformer, or induced, emf.

But if the brush axis coincides in direction with the field axis, as in Fig. 5-3, it is clear that regardless of the speed with which the armature is rotating the armature winding always presents the same aspect to the field; consequently, the field flux which crosses from pole to pole by way of the armature core links with the armature circuit through the brush axis with the result that there will appear in this axis an induced or transformer emf of line frequency quite independent of the speed of rotation. Under the conditions shown in Fig. 5-3, there can be no rotational emf in the brush axis.

In order to determine the magnitude of the transformer emf, it must be noted that not all of the flux issuing from the north pole of Fig. 5-3 links with all of the turns comprising an armature circuit; for the assumption of sinusoidal distribution of field intensity in the airgap is equivalent to the assumption that in the airgap the lines of force pass straight across from pole to pole (in the two-pole model shown). The coil marked ab in Fig. 5-3 links with a flux $\frac{1}{2}\Phi \sin \theta$, and in accordance with the transformer equation 1-3 the emf induced in this particular turn is

$$(E_t)_{ab} = \sqrt{2}\, \pi f \frac{\Phi}{2} \sin \theta \tag{5-6}$$

The emf per turn therefore varies from coil to coil in traversing a circuit from brush to brush, the variation following a sine law with zero values at the two terminal points of the curve. The average emf per turn will then be determined by replacing $\sin \theta$ by its average value $2/\pi$, and the emf induced in the entire circuit of Z/a turns (still referring to the ring-wound armature of Fig. 5-3) will be

$$E_t = \sqrt{2}\,\pi f\,\frac{\Phi}{2}\frac{2}{\pi}\frac{Z}{a} = \sqrt{2}\,f\Phi\,\frac{Z}{a} \qquad (5\text{-}7)$$

Comparison of Eqs. 5-4 and 5-7 shows that the rotational or speed emf differs from the induced or transformer emf only in that f_r replaces f. This means that at synchronous speed the rotational emf in the brush axis of Fig. 5-1 is the same as the induced emf in the brush axis of Fig. 5-3.

While the derivation of Eq. 5-7 was based upon the ring winding of Fig. 5-3, the result is valid for lap- or wave-wound drum armatures; for in the latter case the maximum flux linked with a single turn is Φ instead of $\Phi/2$, and the number of turns in series per circuit is $Z/2a$ instead of Z/a.

5-5. Rotational and Transformer EMFs in General. Let Fig. 5-4 represent diagrammatically an armature rotating in a sinusoidally distributed field which has maximum flux Φ and which varies harmonically

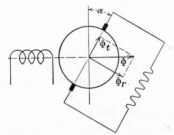

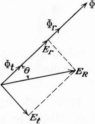

FIG. 5-4. Components of field flux.   FIG. 5-5. Phase relations between flux components and emfs.

with time; the brushes are displaced from the neutral axis by an angle α. The speed of rotation is arbitrary, corresponding to a frequency f_r, which is in general different from the frequency f of the field flux. The flux Φ may then be resolved into two components, one of which is $\Phi_r = \Phi \cos \alpha$, perpendicular to the brush axis, the other being $\Phi_t = \Phi \sin \alpha$ in line with the brush axis. The former will develop in the brush axis a speed emf E_r in accordance with Eq. 5-5,

$$E_r = \sqrt{2}\,f_r\Phi\,\frac{Z}{a}\cos\alpha$$

which will alternate with frequency f and which will be either in time phase with $\Phi \cos \alpha$ (and therefore also with Φ) or in time phase opposition thereto, depending upon the direction of rotation. In Fig. 5-5, the phasor Φ is drawn in an arbitrary position, and E_r in phase with it.

On the other hand, the flux component Φ_t, which is in time phase with Φ and Φ_r, induces by transformer action an emf E_t in the brush axis, and by Eq. 5-7 this is given by

$$E_t = \sqrt{2}\,f\Phi\,\frac{Z}{a}\sin\alpha \qquad (5\text{-}8)$$

This emf has frequency f, and is in time quadrature with Φ_t, as shown in Fig. 5-5. The resultant emf E_R in the brush axis is the geometrical sum of E_r and E_t; hence,

$$E_R = \sqrt{E_r^2 + E_t^2} = \sqrt{2}\,\frac{\phi Z}{a}\,\sqrt{f_r^2\cos^2\alpha + f^2\sin^2\alpha} \qquad (5\text{-}9)$$

If the armature runs at synchronous speed, so that $f_r = f$, this becomes

$$E_R = \sqrt{2}\,\frac{f\Phi Z}{a}$$

which means that at synchronous speed the resultant emf in the brush axis, being independent of α, is the same for all positions of the brushes; but the phase of E_R under the condition of synchronous speed changes with the brush position, as may be seen from Fig. 5-5, since it lags behind Φ by an angle θ whose tangent is E_t/E_r; that is,

$$\tan\theta = \frac{f}{f_r}\tan\alpha$$

and at synchronism the time-phase angle by which E_R lags behind Φ is the same as the space angle through which the brushes are displaced from the neutral axis. A machine operated in this way serves as a *phase shifter*.

5-6. Development of Torque in Commutated Rotor. Assume an arrangement of armature and field as indicated in Fig. 5-6, entirely similar to that of an ordinary d-c machine except that both the field flux and the armature current are alternating with frequency f. The flux, assumed as before to be sinusoidally distributed, may be resolved into components $\Phi\cos\alpha$ and $\Phi\sin\alpha$, respectively perpendicular to, and in line with, the brush axis. Of these two components, only the former can react with the armature current to produce torque;

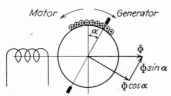

Fig. 5-6. Development of torque.

and at a general time t when this component of flux is equal to $\phi\cos\alpha = \Phi\sin\omega t\cos\alpha$ and the corresponding armature current is given by $i = \sqrt{2}\,I\sin(\omega t \pm \varphi)$, the instantaneous torque is proportional to $\phi i\cos\alpha$.

At the moment defined by time t, the instantaneous armature emf is, by Eq. 5-2,

$$e = \frac{p}{a}\,(\Phi\cos\alpha)Zn\sin\omega t$$

so that the instantaneous power developed is

$$ei = \sqrt{2}\left(\frac{p}{a}\,\Phi Zn\right)I\cos\alpha\sin\omega t\sin(\omega t \pm \varphi) \qquad \text{watts}$$

and if the corresponding torque, in kilogram-meters, is T_i, it follows that

$$2\pi n T_i \times \frac{980}{10^2} = \sqrt{2}\,\frac{p}{a}\,\Phi Z n I \cos \alpha\,[\sin \omega t \sin (\omega t \pm \varphi)]$$

$$= \frac{\sqrt{2}}{2}\,\frac{p}{a}\,\Phi Z n I \cos \alpha\,[\cos \varphi - \cos (2\omega t \pm \varphi)] \quad (5\text{-}10)$$

The torque is seen to be represented by an expression one term of which is constant, the other of which alternates at double frequency but with an average value of zero. The constant or steady torque is therefore

$$T = 0.0115\,\frac{p}{a}\,\Phi Z I \cos \alpha \cos \varphi \qquad \text{kg-m}$$

$$\equiv 0.083\,\frac{p}{a}\,\Phi Z I \cos \alpha \cos \varphi \qquad \text{lb-ft} \quad (5\text{-}11)$$

It will be seen from Eq. 5-11 that the torque has maximum value when the flux and current are in time phase, and is zero when they are in time quadrature. It is likewise evident that if the torque is to have its largest value the flux and armature current must be in space quadrature (that is, $\cos \alpha = 1$, or $\alpha = 0°$).

5-7. Speed of A-C Motors. The speed of a d-c motor is determined by the condition that the counter emf E_a developed in the armature winding must satisfy the relation

$$E_a = V - I_a R_a \quad (5\text{-}12)$$

where V = voltage impressed upon armature terminals

$I_a R_a$ = ohmic drop in armature circuit

From this relation, it follows, on substituting for E_a its value $\Phi Z'n$ [where $Z' = (p/a)Z$], that

$$n = \frac{V - I_a R_a}{\Phi Z'} \quad (5\text{-}13)$$

Both Eqs. 5-12 and 5-13 are necessary consequences of Kirchhoff's second law, which of course holds for a-c circuits provided that instantaneous values of current and voltage are inserted in the equations. It follows, therefore, that in an a-c motor relations similar to those of Eqs. 5-12 and 5-13 must hold except that phasor quantities must replace simple numerical quantities, and impedances must take the place of ordinary resistances.

An apparent exception occurs in the case of the synchronous motor, which can run at one definite speed or not at all; but Eq. 5-13 is still satisfied in such machines, and constancy of speed merely requires that any change in the numerator must be compensated by a proportional change in the denominator.

In a machine like that of Fig 5-1, where there is only one field flux Φ, and where the brush axis is perpendicular to the axis of flux, the counter emf E_r (due to the speed) is the only active emf developed in the armature winding; hence, in that case, by Eq. 5-4,

$$\mathbf{E}_r = \mathbf{V} - \mathbf{I}_a Z_a = \sqrt{2}\, f_r \Phi\, \frac{Z}{a} = 0.707\, \frac{p}{a}\, \Phi Z n \qquad (5\text{-}14)$$

from which the speed n is determined. Since the impedance drop $I_a Z_a$ is generally small in comparison with V, it follows, just as in the case of d-c motors, that a constant* flux calls for substantially constant speed, and a variable flux for variable speed.

But in general the conditions obtaining in an a-c motor are not so simple as in the case just discussed, for the speed emf is not necessarily the only active emf to be considered in the armature winding. Thus, referring to Fig. 5-7, which is substantially the same as Fig. 5-4 and subject to the conclusions applicable to the latter diagram, there exists in the armature circuit not only the speed emf E_r, due to rotation through $\Phi \cos \alpha$, but also the transformer emf E_t induced by $\Phi \sin \alpha$. In such a case, Kirchhoff's law requires that

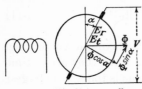

Fig. 5-7. Conditions affecting motor speed.

$$\mathbf{V} = \mathbf{E}_r + \mathbf{E}_t + \mathbf{I}_a Z_a \qquad (5\text{-}15)$$

The speed of rotation is involved in the term $\mathbf{E}_r$ in accordance with Eq. 5-5; hence, the speed is affected by the term $\mathbf{E}_t$ in addition to the other factors already considered.

5-8. Connections of Electric Circuits. In the preceding discussion of fundamental features, nothing was said about the connections of the armature and field windings to each other or to the external circuit or circuits; the relations that have been presented are in fact quite independent of these connections. But it is plain that the characteristics of the machine as a whole, whether it be used as generator or as motor, must depend upon the manner of connecting the various circuits. It is not intended at this point to discuss in detail the effect of various connections upon characteristic performance, but only to outline principles which may be applied to particular cases as they arise.

The outstanding difference between d-c and a-c machines is that whereas in the former case current can be supplied (or delivered) only by *conductive* connections, in the latter the same result can be obtained by *inductive*, in addition to conductive, connections. Consider, for example, the simple armature indicated in Fig. 5-8a supplied with current by conductive connection from a suitable external source; the same current can be induced in the armature by the device indicated in Fig.

---

* In the case of an alternating flux, the term "constant flux" means that its effective value remains constant.

5-8*b*, where the armature, with brushes either directly short-circuited or connected through an impedance, becomes the secondary of a transformer which receives energy from the primary winding on the stator. The equivalent circuit corresponding to Fig. 5-8*b* is indicated in Fig. 5-9; it is the same as that of the ordinary transformer, the only material differences arising from the fact that here the exciting admittance is large because of the airgap between stator and rotor, and the leakage reactances X_1 and X_2 are likewise larger than is usual in the stationary transformer having a completely closed magnetic circuit. On transferring the exciting admittance to the line side of the primary impedance (as indicated by the dotted lines in Fig. 5-9), thereby obtaining the approximate equivalent circuit, it is seen that the principal effect, so far as the supply circuit is concerned, is to add to the secondary leakage impedance, which alone exists in Fig. 5-8*a*, the leakage impedance of the primary. Of course, it will be evident that the magnitude of the armature current in Fig. 5-8*b* will depend upon the ratio of transformation between primary and secondary windings, but by suitable choice of primary winding the current in Fig. 5-8*b* can be made to be equal in magnitude to that in Fig.

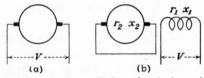

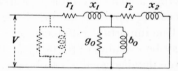

FIG. 5-8. Emf supplied conductively and inductively.

FIG. 5-9. Circuit equivalent to Fig. 5-8*b*.

5-8*a* (the line voltage being the same in both); but the phase of the armature current with respect to that of V cannot be identically the same in both cases.

a. Series Connections. As a further example of these fundamental considerations, take the case of an a-c motor connected in simple series fashion, as in Fig. 5-10. It is well-known that a d-c motor of this type will continue to run in the same direction on reversing the polarity of the supply circuit; so it may be expected to do the same thing when supplied from an a-c source. The use of alternating current introduces certain complications not present in the d-c motor (as, for example, the necessity of laminating the field structure), but these will be reserved for later consideration; for the time being, the point of interest is that the armature is conductively supplied with current identical in magnitude and phase with that which excites the main magnetic field. If there are now invoked the conclusions of the previous paragraph, the connections of Fig. 5-10 can be changed to those of Fig. 5-11 without greatly modifying the original characteristics, except as noted in the following paragraph. The stator winding C, which is wound in slots in the same cylindrical stator which carries winding F, serves as the primary of a series (current) transformer to transfer the line current to the armature, and the latter is then capable of reacting with the field due to winding F to develop torque.   The two stator windings are wound in space quadrature, in the manner of a two-phase winding, though in this case the two windings are not identical as to number of turns.   But when two windings in space quadrature, acting on the same magnetic circuit, like F and C, carry the same current, their mmfs combine to produce a resultant flux whose axis

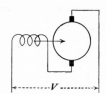

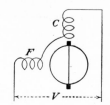

FIG. 5-10. Series motor, conductively supplied.

FIG. 5-11. Series motor, inductively supplied

FIG. 5-12. Connections equivalent to those of Fig. 5-11.

lies between those of F and C, and the machine is then equivalent to one having a connection diagram like Fig. 5-12; this type is usually referred to as the repulsion motor, though the name is not appropriate.

One important difference between the machines of Figs. 5-10 and 5-11 may be examined profitably at this point without unduly anticipating a more detailed analysis to be given in a later chapter.   Figure 5-13 indicates in outline form the physical relations between stator and rotor corresponding to the connection diagram of Fig. 5-10, the stator winding

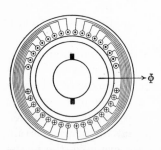

FIG. 5-13. Stator and rotor axes at right angles.

being embedded in slots on the inner face of the stator.   Since the two windings, stator and rotor, have their axes at right angles, there can be no inductive relation between them, and each of them, with respect to the common magnetic circuit, is like the primary of a transformer which has either no secondary at all, or a secondary on open circuit. For a given voltage at the terminals of either winding, the current is therefore limited to what corresponds to the exciting current of a transformer, and with correspondingly low power factor.   To overcome this difficulty, the diagram of Fig. 5-10 may be modified to the form of Fig. 5-14, where coil C, magnetizing along the brush axis, partially or wholly annuls the armature flux as in a compensated d-c machine.   Here F and C are conductively connected to the armature; but by using the connections of Fig. 5-15, where C is inductively associated with the armature, the same result may be obtained. In Fig. 5-15, the armature is the primary, and winding C the secondary, whereas in Fig. 5-11 the conditions are just reversed. Electrically the two diagrams (Figs. 5-11 and 5-15) are identical, and all of the arrangements shown in Figs. 5-10 to 5-15 will have the familiar characteristics of series-wound machines; and of these characteristics the feature of variable field flux is the important one.

b. *Shunt Connections.* Since a series motor, suitably designed to adapt it to the use of alternating current, will develop a considerable unidirectional torque for the reason that the field flux and armature current

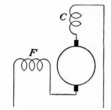
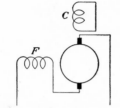
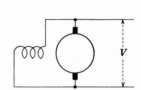

FIG. 5-14. Conductively compensated series motor. FIG. 5-15. Inductively compensated series motor. FIG. 5-16. Shunt motor.

reverse simultaneously, it might be expected that the same result will ensue in the case of the shunt connection of Fig. 5-16; but although the reversals will necessarily occur with the same frequency, the flux and armature current are not in time phase as they are in the series motor, and the torque is therefore small in accordance with Eq. 5-11; for the field winding is like the primary of an open-circuited transformer, and the flux Φ will lag behind the impressed voltage V by nearly 90°, as in Fig. 5-17; and the armature current I_a, if reasonably in phase with V, as it should be in order that the power delivered to the motor may be of practical magnitude, will then be so nearly in time quadrature with Φ as to reduce the torque to a small value. It will be observed from Fig. 5-16 that the armature circuit, like the field circuit, is in the condition of the primary of a transformer which has no secondary, and that this circumstance will tend to make I_a lag heavily behind V and so come more

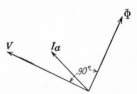

FIG. 5-17. Approximate phase relations in shunt motor.

nearly into phase with Φ; but though such a result would of itself improve the torque, the high armature inductance which brings the armature current into better phase agreement with Φ also reduces the magnitude of I_a and thus counteracts the apparent gain due to phase shift. Moreover, the power factor of the machine as a whole would thus be seriously impaired. Improvement of the power factor could be effected by compensating the armature, either conductively as in Fig. 5-18a or inductively as in Fig. 5-18b, but as this would still leave the armature current and field flux nearly in time quadrature, nothing would be gained.

The modification that is obviously required to overcome these difficulties is to bring the time phases of Φ and I_a into substantial coincidence at the same time that their space orientation remains in quadrature. Since it is desired that I_a shall be as nearly as possible in phase with V, and that Φ shall also be in phase with I_a, one way to accomplish this result would be to excite the field by a voltage that is in quadrature with the voltage V of Fig. 5-17. Thus, in Fig. 5-19a, the armature (conductively compensated) is supplied from one phase of a two-phase supply

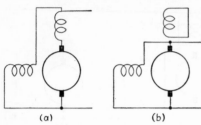

(a)   (b)

Fig. 5-18. Conductively and inductively compensated shunt motor.

circuit, while the field is supplied from the other phase; in Fig. 5-19b, the working current is supplied to the armature by induction from one phase, while the field is supplied from the second phase. But while the desired result is accomplished in this manner, it has been done at the expense of departing from a single-phase to a polyphase supply circuit; and in the particular case here discussed the two phases are unbalanced as to load, since one of them supplies the full working current to the armature, while the other furnishes only the small exciting current to the field. The unbalancing of the two-phase supply can be overcome by methods to be treated later, but it is relevant to state now that the simple considerations thus far discussed constitute a useful introduction to the theory of the polyphase induction motor.

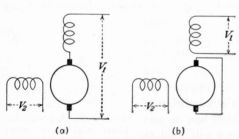

(a)   (b)

Fig. 5-19. Conductive and inductive armature connection, separate phase excitation.

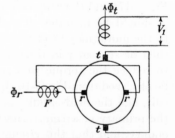

Fig. 5-20. Self-excited induction motor; double armature winding.

For present purposes, it is simplest to confine attention to the single-phase connections with which the analysis was originally concerned, and in particular to find whether it is possible to excite the field of Fig. 5-19b without resorting to separate excitation from an independent source of supply. Consider Fig. 5-20, which is derived from Fig. 5-19b by adding to the latter a second commutated armature winding with brushes r, r at right angles to the original pair t, t. Rotation of the armature through the transformer flux Φ_t will generate a speed emf E_r in the speed axis

r, r, and E_r will be in time phase (or time-phase opposition) with Φ_t. But Φ_t, being a transformer flux, is very nearly in quadrature with V_1, as shown in the phasor diagram in Fig. 5-21; consequently, the field winding F is excited by an emf substantially in quadrature with V_1, just as in Fig. 5-19b. The speed emf E_r will produce a current in the winding F which will then develop a flux Φ_r in the speed axis r, r, and the reaction of the armature current induced (by transformer action) in the t, t axis with the flux Φ_r will yield torque. It should be noted that when the rotor is originally at rest there can be no flux in the speed axis r, r, hence such a machine when used as a motor has no starting torque; but it will be shown later that if the rotor is given an initial impulse in either direction the field Φ_r will be so directed as to build up the torque in the same direction.

The double rotor winding of Fig. 5-20 is not essential, since the same result can be accomplished with the original single winding by providing two sets of brushes on one and the same commutator, as in Fig. 5-22.

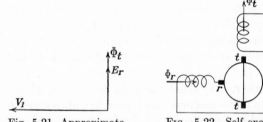

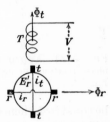

Fig. 5-21. Approximate phase relations, motor of Fig. 5-20.

FIG. 5-22. Self-excited induction motor, single armature winding.

FIG. 5-23. Self-excited induction motor.

One set of brushes t, t, in the transformer axis, serves to convey the line current into the armature winding by induction; the other set r, r, in the speed axis, excites the field winding. Each individual conductor in the armature winding will then carry a current which is the resultant of the two separate component currents, one of them being the induced current I_t flowing in the transformer axis t, t, the other the generated or speed current I_r flowing in the speed axis r, r. But a little reflection will show that the field winding F is not really required, for if brushes r, r are directly connected, as in Fig. 5-23, the current I_r flowing through the armature winding will itself excite the flux Φ_r.

The original scheme of connections shown in Fig. 5-16 has thus been evolved into that of Fig. 5-23 by a step-by-step process, and the end result is a single-phase induction motor with self-excitation. The complete determination of the characteristics of such a machine requires considerable additional analysis, which will be taken up in a subsequent chapter. At this stage, it will suffice to mention one point to clinch the argument that the motor of Fig. 5-23 has the typical shunt characteristic of nearly constant speed: In the transformer axis t, t (Fig. 5-23) the voltage V impressed upon the stator winding T is equivalent to a nearly equal voltage (assuming a 1:1 ratio of transformation between primary and secondary) transferred into the armature winding by induction; since in any motor whatever there must be a counter emf substantially equal and opposite to the impressed voltage (unless there are other active emfs induced or otherwise supplied from another source, not present in the case here considered), it is essential that rotation of the winding through Φ_r should generate a speed emf E'_r in the t, t axis which shall be substantially equal and opposite to V.   But Φ_r is due to current in the r, r axis set up by E_r, and E_r may be taken to be in phase with the flux Φ_t which developed it; and since conditions in the speed axis r, r are those inherent in a transformer on open circuit, E_r and Φ_r must be substantially in quadrature, as indicated in Fig. 5-24.   Rotation of the armature through Φ_r will

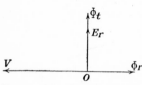

FIG. 5-24. Approximate phase relations in motor of Fig. 5-23.

then develop a speed emf E'_r in the t, t axis, and E'_r will be in phase with Φ_r, consequently in phase opposition to V.   Now, reference to Eqs. 5-4 and 5-7 shows that substantial equality of induced and generated emfs requires corresponding equality of the products $f\Phi_t$ and $f_r\Phi_r$.   At standstill, both f_r and Φ_r are zero, and as the speed increases, f_r and Φ_r increase together.   At synchronism, when $f_r = f$, Φ_r will be equal to Φ_t; hence, it follows that a motor of this type, when once started, will tend to run at nearly synchronous speed, and the flux Φ_r, which corresponds to the field flux of an ordinary d-c motor, also tends to be constant.

5-9. The Revolving Field in Asynchronous Machines.   The conclusions of the preceding article lead to the interesting result that the single-phase induction motor of the type shown in Fig. 5-23 has two component magnetic fields, Φ_t and Φ_r, in space quadrature with respect to each other. The flux Φ_t, being a transformer flux in the axis t, t, must have such magnitude that its alternation induces in the primary winding T (Fig. 5-23) an emf nearly equal and opposite to the constant impressed voltage V, and Φ_t must therefore be nearly a quarter period (90°) behind V, as indicated in Figs. 5-21 and 5-24; rotation through the flux Φ_t generates the emf E_r which appears in the speed axis r, r, and E_r will be either in phase with, or in phase opposition to, Φ_t, depending upon the direction of rotation.   In Fig. 5-21, E_r was arbitrarily taken in phase with Φ_t.   But E_r will produce current I_r in the speed axis, and this in turn will produce the flux Φ_r; and since the armature winding in the axis r, r does not link inductively with any other winding that could serve as a secondary, it is equivalent to the primary winding of a transformer on open circuit.   The flux Φ_r must therefore be nearly in time quadrature with E_r, and lagging behind E_r, just as Φ_t lags behind V by nearly a quarter period.   These relations are shown in Fig. 5-24. It thus appears that the two fluxes Φ_t and Φ_r, in addition to being in space quadrature because of the disposition of the two sets of brushes, are also in time quadrature (nearly). At synchronism, when Φ_t and Φ_r are equal in magnitude, their resultant is therefore a magnetic field of constant magnitude rotating at synchronous speed around the airgap, as has been proved in Chap. 4. At speeds other than synchronous, their resultant is an elliptically rotating field whose magnitude changes from point to point as the rotation continues. A simple physical conception of the meaning of an elliptically rotating field may be obtained from the following consideration: In Fig. 5-24, let it be assumed that Φ_r is smaller than Φ_t, corresponding to the condition of subsynchronous speed; then Φ_t can be divided into two parts, one of which, Φ_t', is numerically equal to Φ_r, the other, Φ_t'', equal to the remainder, or $\Phi_t - \Phi_r$.

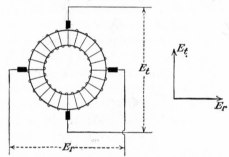

FIG. 5-25. Balanced two-phase winding.

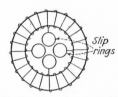

FIG. 5-26. Quarter-phase winding with slip rings.

Then Φ_r and Φ_t' may be combined to form a single rotating field of constant magnitude, and upon this rotating field there is superposed the magnetic field Φ_t'', which is stationary in space but varying harmonically in time.

The validity of the conclusion that at synchronism there exists in the machine of Fig. 5-23 a uniformly rotating magnetic field of constant magnitude is easily checked in terms of considerations developed in Chap. 4. For since at synchronism E_t and E_r are equal (they are, of course, in time quadrature), the effect is the same as though the armature winding of Fig. 5-23 were supplied in the manner indicated in Fig. 5-25. This will be recognized as quite similar to the case of a quarter-phase (or two-phase) ring-wound generator (Fig. 5-26) equipped with two pairs of slip rings, each pair being connected to a circuit across which there is a voltage equal to, but in quadrature with, the other. It has been proved (in Chap. 4) that a winding like Fig. 5-26 will produce a magnetic field which rotates at uniform (synchronous) speed with respect to the winding; since Fig. 5-25 is identical with Fig. 5-26 for the particular position of the latter, it must follow that the resultant field in Fig. 5-25 is likewise rotating. But there is an interesting and important difference between the two cases.

The magnetic field in Fig. 5-26 rotates synchronously with respect to the winding, so that if the winding were itself to rotate, the resultant motion of the magnetic field in the surrounding fixed space would be compounded of the two rotations; thus, if the winding is rotating at synchronous speed in a direction opposite to that in which the field rotates relative to the winding, the resultant magnetic field stands still in space. But in Fig. 5-25, because of the commutator and brushes, the winding and its taps always present the same aspect to an external observer; hence, the resultant magnetic field in Fig. 5-25 always rotates at synchronous speed in space without regard to the magnitude or direction of the speed of the rotor itself.

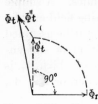

Fig. 5-27. Components of elliptical rotating field.

In case the two component fluxes Φ_t and Φ_r are unequal in magnitude, and differ in time phase by an angle not 90°, as in Fig. 5-27, it is still possible to resolve the greater flux (such as Φ_t) into two components Φ_t' and Φ_t'', such that Φ_t' is equal to Φ_r and in quadrature therewith, these two then combining to form a circularly rotating field, leaving a residual alternating field in the axis of Φ_t but with the time phase of Φ_t''. The actual resultant is still an elliptical rotating field.

5-10. EMF and Current Relations Due to Revolving Field. Let it be assumed that the armature of Fig. 5-23 is rotating at any arbitrary speed in a magnetic field whose components Φ_t and Φ_r are numerically equal and in quadrature both in time and in space. This assumption could not be exactly complied with in the case of an actual motor arranged like Fig. 5-23, though it is closely approximated as synchronism is approached. The joint effect of Φ_t and Φ_r under the assumed conditions is then to produce a magnetic field of constant magnitude $\Phi = \Phi_t = \Phi_r$ rotating synchronously around the armature periphery (which is itself supposed to be rotating, either in the same direction as the magnetic field or opposite thereto). The effect, so far as the armature winding is concerned, is the same as though the armature were surrounded by a crown of synchronously rotating magnets, two being indicated in Fig. 5-28 to conform to the prior assumption of a bipolar model, though a multipolar field is equally possible provided suitable modifications are made in the disposition of armature windings and brushes; these magnets may be either permanent magnets or electromagnets excited by direct current; or the armature may be surrounded by a slotted stator, as in Fig. 5-13, wound with a suitable balanced polyphase winding and supplied with corresponding balanced polyphase current.

The conditions thus defined are represented in detail in Fig. 5-29 for the special case of a bipolar model, taken for the sake of simplicity. The rotating poles, only one of which is shown, carrying the sinusoidally distributed flux Φ, rotate at synchronous speed corresponding to the frequency f, and the ring-wound rotor rotates at a speed corresponding to some different frequency f_r. Brushes occupy an axis perpendicular to an arbitrarily assumed axis of reference OX. At any arbitrarily selected moment, an individual turn ab of the armature winding occupies a position displaced from the reference axis by angle θ, and at the same instant

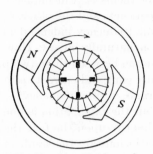

FIG. 5-28. Rotating field produced by moving magnets.

FIG. 5-29. Emf in moving coil due to rotating field.

the axis of the flux Φ is displaced by angle φ. The flux linked with the coil ab (assumed to have one turn) is then

$$\phi = \frac{\Phi}{2} \sin (\varphi - \theta) \qquad (5\text{-}16)$$

and the instantaneous emf in coil ab is

$$e = -\frac{d\phi}{dt} = -\frac{\Phi}{2}\left[\cos (\varphi - \theta)\frac{d\varphi}{dt} - \cos (\varphi - \theta)\frac{d\theta}{dt}\right] \qquad (5\text{-}17)$$

But since
$$\varphi = 2\pi f t$$
$$\theta = 2\pi f_r t$$

we have
$$\frac{d\varphi}{dt} = 2\pi f$$
$$\frac{d\theta}{dt} = 2\pi f_r$$

and on substituting these relations in Eq. 5-17

$$e = -\pi\Phi(f - f_r) \cos 2\pi(f - f_r)t \qquad (5\text{-}18)$$

Equation 5-18 brings into prominence the important fact that the emf in coil ab alternates with the *slip frequency*

$$f_s = f - f_r \qquad (5\text{-}19)$$

so named because it is a measure of the speed with which the armature winding slips relative to the axis of the flux; obviously, this conclusion is true of all the armature coils, since ab was any arbitrarily selected coil.

The current in the armature winding therefore also alternates at slip frequency.

At first sight, this result seems to be completely at variance with all that has preceded in this chapter. For if the uniformly rotating field Φ of Fig. 5-29 is resolved into the equal component fields Φ_t and Φ_r with which we have previously been concerned, one of them, Φ_t, will induce in the brush axis an emf of line (synchronous) frequency, and the other, Φ_r, will generate a rotational emf E_r likewise of line frequency independently of the rotational frequency f_r. The question naturally arises: How is it possible to reconcile the apparent contradiction between these two points of view, one of which says that the armature emfs and currents alternate at slip frequency, the other that they alternate at line frequency? Such a reconciliation is in reality quite simple, but the explanation is none the less interesting and important; it rests primarily upon the fact that the apparently different and contradictory conclusions are the result of considering the physical phenomena from quite different points of view which cause them to assume different aspects.

It will be noted, for example, that in deriving Eq. 5-18 the emf induced in coil ab was considered from the point of view of an observer moving with the rotor. Such an observer would see the stator slide past him at a speed proportional to the slip frequency, and to him there could be no question concerning the frequency of the emf developed in the (relatively) moving armature winding.

On the other hand, the report that would be given by an observer stationed at a fixed point in the surrounding space, say, on one of the brushes in Fig. 5-29, would be quite different. He would see the armature winding moving past him at the rotational frequency f_r, and alternations of slip frequency f_s taking place in or on the rotor itself would to him appear to have the frequency

$$f_r + f_s = f$$

This is all there is to the apparent contradiction; it is an example of relativity.

It is, however, possible to verify the argument in another way. Thus, Eq. 5-18, which represents the emf in a single turn of the armature winding, may be written

$$e = -\pi\Phi(f - f_r)(\cos\theta\cos\varphi + \sin\theta\sin\varphi) \qquad (5\text{-}20)$$

At the same moment of time that the coil ab of Fig. 5-29 is displaced from the reference axis by angle θ, each of the other coils in series with it from brush to brush will be displaced by angles ranging from $-\pi/2$ to $+\pi/2$, and by steps which are integral multiples of the small angle $\Delta\theta$ between adjacent coils. The total emf between brushes t, t is therefore the sum of a series of terms like Eq. 5-20, and the trigonometric terms of the summation may be arranged in two parts, thus:

$$\cos \varphi \left[\cos\left(-\frac{\pi}{2}\right) + \cos\left(-\frac{\pi}{2} + \Delta\theta\right) + \cos\left(-\frac{\pi}{2} + 2\,\Delta\theta\right) \right.$$
$$\left. + \cdots + \cos 0° + \cdots + \cos\left(\frac{\pi}{2} - 2\,\Delta\theta\right) + \cos\left(\frac{\pi}{2} - \Delta\theta\right) + \cos\frac{\pi}{2} \right]$$

and

$$\sin \varphi \left[\sin\left(-\frac{\pi}{2}\right) + \sin\left(-\frac{\pi}{2} + \Delta\theta\right) + \cdots + \sin 0° \right.$$
$$\left. + \cdots + \sin\left(\frac{\pi}{2} - \Delta\theta\right) + \sin\frac{\pi}{2} \right]$$

It is evident that the term in brackets in the first expression will plot as a cosine curve (Fig. 5-30), while that in the second expression will plot as a sine curve within the same limits. The average value of the cosine curve between the given limits is $2/\pi$, while that of the sine curve is zero. Since the number of terms in each of these brackets is $Z/2$ in the simple bipolar ring winding here under consideration, the total

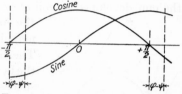

FIG. 5-30. Variation of sine and cosine between $-\pi/2$ and $+\pi/2$.

emf between brushes t, t at the instant represented by Fig. 5-29 is

$$\sum e = \frac{Z}{2}\,\pi\Phi(f - f_r)\,\frac{2}{\pi}\cos\varphi = \Phi Z(f - f_r)\cos 2\pi f t \qquad (5\text{-}21)$$

In other words, the emf between brushes is alternating with frequency f, with respect to the brushes, thus agreeing with the previous conclusions.

Moreover, Eq. 5-21 states that the maximum emf between brushes t, t is

$$E_{max} = \Phi Z f - \Phi Z f_r$$

from which the effective emf is

$$E = \frac{\sqrt{2}}{2}\,\Phi Z f - \frac{\sqrt{2}}{2}\,\Phi Z f_r \qquad (5\text{-}22)$$

But on comparing this result with Eqs. 5-4 and 5-7, it is seen (remembering that in the bipolar model $a = 2$) that the resultant brush voltage is

$$E = E_t - E_r$$

In other words, if the component flux Φ_t induces in the axis t, t an emf E_t which is equivalent to the voltage conductively impressed upon the armature of a d-c machine, then rotation through the component flux Φ_r develops the counter emf E_r. At synchronism, when $f_r = f$, $E_r = E_t$, and the resultant brush voltage is zero. This checks with the consideration that a winding which is rotating at synchronous speed through a magnetic field that is itself rotating at the same speed in the same direction cannot develop any emf because there is no relative motion between armature conductors and magnetic lines of force.

5-11. The Squirrel-cage Winding. The analysis developed in the preceding article provides means for studying the effect of types of rotor windings other than the simple ring winding thus far used. There is no difficulty in extending the ideas to drum-wound rotors having either lap or wave windings, for it is merely necessary to replace the factor a (the number of parallel circuits in the armature winding), which appeared in Eqs. 5-4 and 5-7. But suppose that the closed-ring winding of Fig. 5-29 is replaced by the type of winding indicated in Fig. 5-31, where each coil is separate and distinct from each of the others. It is quite clear that the emf developed in coil ab of Fig. 5-31 differs in no way from that of

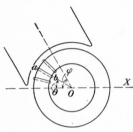

FIG. 5-31. Emf in closed moving coil due to rotating field.

the corresponding coil of Fig. 5-29, and that its magnitude is represented by Eq. 5-18 or 5-20. The difference between the two cases arises from the fact that whereas in Fig. 5-29 the emfs in the successive coils add together to produce a single resultant, which then sets up a current that is the same in all the turns from brush to brush, in Fig. 5-31 the emf in each coil sets up its own individual current, and there are no brushes to be considered. It is both interesting and important to investigate the properties of a winding like Fig. 5-31, for it will shortly be shown that it is a step in the evolution from a commutated winding like Fig. 5-29 to the familiar squirrel-cage winding.

Each coil of Fig. 5-31, such as ab, will have induced or generated in it a current i such that at any instant

$$i = \frac{e_{max}}{z} \cos (\varphi - \theta - \psi) \qquad (5\text{-}23)$$

where, by Eq. 5-18,

$$|e_{max}| = \pi\Phi(f - f_r)$$

and z = impedance of coil

ψ = angle by which current lags behind emf

It is here assumed that the impedance of all the individual coils is the same and that it does not vary as the coil moves from point to point; this is substantially true if the rotor is surrounded by a cylindrical stator of the kind indicated in Fig. 5-13, though the presence of teeth and slots does introduce a variation of leakage reactance and of effective resistance which will be neglected. The phase angle ψ is then fixed by the usual relation

$$\tan \psi = \frac{x}{r}$$

where x = leakage reactance of coil

r = effective resistance of coil

It must be noted that we are here dealing with emfs and currents of slip frequency, so that

$$x = 2\pi f_s L$$

where L is the inductance of the coil, expressed in henrys.

If we confine attention to the particular moment depicted in Fig. 5-31 when the rotating flux Φ is displaced from the reference axis by angle φ, it will be seen that the phase of the emf (and therefore of the current as well) will change from coil to coil by an electrical angle $\Delta\theta$ corresponding to the space displacement between coils.
So far as the emf is concerned, this is the same effect noted in the preceding article, with the exception that these successive out-of-phase emfs are no longer in series. The currents are likewise not in series, but their mmfs are additive around the ring of the armature core within the span of the pole pitch in which all these currents are similarly directed.   The entire set of currents thus distributed around the armature constitutes a polyphase arrangement such that each coil within a pole pitch is a separate phase winding; in the bipolar model

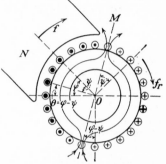

Fig. 5-32. Distribution of current in face conductors of Fig. 5-31.

of Fig. 5-31, there will be $Z/2$ phases in all, if Z is the total number of peripheral conductors.   At the moment under consideration, when the physical conditions are as represented in Fig. 5-31, the emf will be a maximum in the particular coil which then occupies the flux axis; for in that position the conductor is in a field of maximum intensity, and the rate of cutting lines of force is greatest; moreover, it is seen from Eq. 5-18 that e has its maximum (absolute) value when $\theta = \varphi$.   At the same instant, the current will be at its maximum in that particular coil for which the expression $\varphi - \theta - \psi$ in Eq. 5-23 is zero, i.e., when $\theta = \varphi - \psi$.   On either side of the position of maximum current, the individual coils carry currents which shade off to zero within a range of 90 electrical degrees, as indicated in Fig. 5-32.   On the left-hand side of the rotor, the current flows out of the plane of the diagram as may easily be checked by using Fleming's right-hand rule in accordance with the assumed polarity and direction of relative motion.   On the other (right-hand) side of the armature, the current obviously flows in the reverse direction and with a similar distribution.

The joint effect of all the individual armature currents is to produce maximum mmf along an axis OM (Fig. 5-32) perpendicular to the plane of the coil in which the current is then at its maximum value. As Fig. 5-32 shows, the direction of OM is inclined at angle ψ to a line perpendicular to the flux axis, indicating that the rotor mmf has a demagnetizing component when ψ is an angle of lag. Quantitatively, the rotor mmf due to the coils on each half of the rotor may be determined by adding their individual mmfs. Since each coil is assumed to have one turn, the mmf of any general coil, expressed in ampere-turns, is by Eq. 5-23

$$\text{Amp-turns per coil} = I_{\max} \cos (\varphi - \theta - \psi)$$
$$= I_{\max} [\cos (\varphi - \psi) \cos \theta + \sin (\varphi - \psi) \sin \theta] \quad (5\text{-}24)$$

The successive terms differ in phase since θ changes by increments of $\Delta\theta$, and the summation is to be extended from $\theta = -[(\pi/2) - (\varphi - \psi)]$ to $\theta = (\pi/2) + (\varphi - \psi)$, as is seen from Fig. 5-32. The average value of $\cos \theta$ within this range is, in accordance with Fig. 5-33,

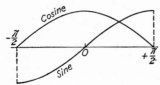

$$\frac{1}{\pi} \int_{-[(\pi/2)-(\varphi-\psi)]}^{(\pi/2)+\varphi-\psi} \cos \theta \, d\theta = \frac{2}{\pi} \cos (\varphi - \psi)$$

and the average value of $\sin \theta$ within the same range is

FIG. 5-33. Variation of sine and cosine between $-[(\pi/2) - (\varphi - \psi)]$ and $(\pi/2) + (\varphi - \psi)$.

$$\frac{1}{\pi} \int_{-[(\pi/2)-(\varphi-\psi)]}^{(\pi/2)+\varphi-\psi} \sin \theta \, d\theta = \frac{2}{\pi} \sin (\varphi - \psi)$$

On substituting these averages in Eq. 5-24 and multiplying the result by $Z/2$, the total mmf in axis OM is found to be

$$A = \frac{2}{\pi} \frac{Z}{2} I_{\max} = \frac{\sqrt{2}}{\pi} ZI \quad \text{amp-turns} \quad (5\text{-}25)$$

where I is the effective current per turn. The fact that A turns out to be a constant indicates that the rotor mmf rotates at synchronous speed around the airgap, therefore retaining a fixed angular position with respect to the axis of flux Φ so long as ψ remains unaltered.

This result is strictly in accordance with the fact that the polyphase rotor winding, carrying current of slip frequency f_s, produces a constant mmf rotating with respect to the winding at a speed corresponding to f_s; and since the rotor is itself rotating at a speed equivalent to frequency f_r, the resultant speed of the rotor mmf in space is $f = f_r + f_s$.

If the special type of winding indicated in Fig. 5-31 is provided with the closed conductor C shown in Fig. 5-34a, so that all of the original independent loops are now metallically connected, there will be no change in any of the conclusions concerning the emfs and currents in the individual coils; the only effect of the ring C is to make all of the points to which it is connected have the same potential. Exactly the same condition represented in Fig. 5-34a is brought about in a commutated ring winding (or in a lap- or wave-wound drum winding) by short-circuiting the segments of the commutator by the ring R (Fig. 5-34b).

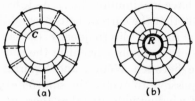

FIG. 5-34. Equivalent forms of loop windings.

If in Fig. 5-34a attention is fixed upon the two diametrically opposite loops shown in Fig. 5-35a, it will be noted that the currents in the two interior conductors flow in opposite directions. If these two loops are imagined to be stretched until they meet at the center, as in Fig. 5-35b, the two oppositely directed currents will annul each other, and these

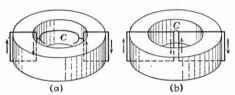

FIG. 5-35. Evolution from half to full loops.

interior connectors may therefore be omitted, thus leaving a single turn around the diametral section. If all the other loops are similarly paired, the result is a cage winding like Fig. 5-36a, with all the central crossing points insulated from one another; but since all of these points may be

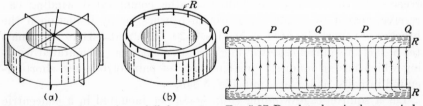

FIG. 5-36. Evolution from full loops to squirrel-cage winding.

FIG. 5-37. Developed squirrel-cage winding showing distribution of current.

at the same potential without affecting conditions in the loops themselves, they may be joined at the common crossing point, and the effect is then the same as though the peripheral face conductors were connected at each end to the conducting end ring R, Fig. 5-36b. This is the familiar squirrel-cage winding commonly used in induction motors.

Figure 5-37 is a development of the squirrel-cage winding of Fig. 5-36b. It serves to show how the end rings R act as return paths for the currents in the face conductors, the latter being grouped in pairs.   The end rings must have sufficient cross section to carry the resultant current at points like Q, where it is greatest; these points are obviously midway between points P, where the end-ring current is zero, but where the currents in the face conductors have maximum value.   As it has been shown in connection with Fig. 5-32 that the current belts around the armature periphery travel around the rotor at slip frequency, the same thing is true with regard to the points of maximum current in the end rings.

5-12. Equivalence between Wound and Squirrel-cage Rotors.   The fact that it is thus possible to evolve the squirrel-cage winding from the commutated type of winding indicates that there must be a close resemblance or equivalence between their properties.   Such an equivalence does indeed exist, though exact identity naturally calls for very definite quantitative relations between number, size, and disposition of the conductors comprising the two kinds of winding, since it is upon these that the resistance and inductance must depend.   The chief difference

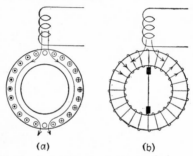

(a)   (b)

FIG. 5-38. Equivalent squirrel-cage and ring windings.

between the two types is that whereas the squirrel-cage winding can receive its current only by induction, the commutated winding can receive current by conduction through brushes, or by induction if the brushes are short-circuited as in Figs. 5-20, 5-22, and 5-34b.   As a matter of fact, a squirrel-cage winding is equivalent to a commutated winding which has an infinitely great number of pairs of brushes, short-circuited in pairs, as is clear from Fig. 5-34b.

Let a squirrel-cage winding (Fig. 5-38a) be mounted in a concentric cylindrical stator of the type shown in Fig. 5-13, the stator having a winding which magnetizes along a single axis.   The lines of induction will take the general path indicated in Fig. 5-38, and since the rotor winding is short-circuited in this as in all other directions, there will be induced in the rotor conductors currents so directed as to oppose the flux in accordance with Lenz's law.   The rotor and stator together constitute a short-circuited transformer, and the current will be limited only by the leakage impedance of the two windings.   No torque will result since the axis of the rotor current coincides with that of the main field.   If the rotor is now replaced by another having a commutated ring (or drum) winding with brushes short-circuited in the axis of the stator winding as in Fig. 5-38b, exactly the same conditions prevail.

Now let the squirrel-cage rotor be placed in a stator excited by two windings in series, as in Fig. 5-39a. The flux due to the winding with vertical axis will induce in the rotor a vertically distributed set of currents exactly as in Fig. 5-38a; and at the same time the stator winding with horizontal axis will induce a rotor distribution of similar kind, but horizontally distributed. The vertically distributed rotor current cannot react with its own inducing flux to produce torque, nor can the horizontally distributed rotor react with its inducing flux. The vertically

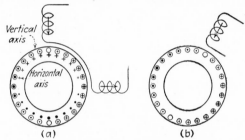

FIG. 5-39. Superposition of component cophasal currents.

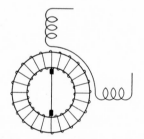

FIG. 5-40. Commutated winding, not equivalent to Fig. 5-39a.

FIG. 5-41. Commutated winding, equivalent to Fig. 5-39a.

distributed rotor current can, however, react with the horizontal flux to produce torque, but this torque is equal and opposite to that produced by the interaction between the vertical flux and the horizontal rotor current. The arrangement is in fact equivalent to a single stator winding (Fig. 5-39b) magnetizing along an axis that is in line with the resultant of the two stator mmfs of Fig. 5-39a; and the rotor then serves as a short-circuited secondary in the same inclined axis. On comparing Fig. 5-39 with Fig. 5-40, it is seen that the conditions are materially different, for with the single short-circuited rotor axis the machine becomes a motor having series characteristics; but in Fig. 5-41 there are two short-circuited axes in the rotor, each in line with its own stator winding, and there can then be no torque.

The essential conclusion to be drawn from these considerations is that a squirrel-cage winding serves as a short-circuited secondary with axis in line with the axis of any stator winding that may surround it. It is then equivalent to a commutated winding with brushes short-circuited in the axis of the stator winding.

5-13. Summary. Most of the considerations that have been treated in this chapter are perfectly general, capable of adaptation to the numerous combinations of circuits that arise in connection with particular types of machines. A clear understanding of the physical principles that have been discussed opens the way to a detailed study of particular machines without digressions to establish these basic principles as the need for them arises. In most presentations of the theory of asynchronous machines, it has been customary to start with the polyphase induction motor because from some points of view it is simpler than other types; but the student who has mastered the ideas in this chapter will find it possible to take up any of the other types in any order whatever.

CHAPTER 6

BASIC THEORY OF POLYPHASE INDUCTION MOTORS

6-1. Historical. As early as 1885, Galileo Ferraris, then professor of physics at the University of Turin, constructed a small motor in the manner illustrated in Fig. 6-1. It consisted of two pairs of radially disposed electromagnets attached to a common yoke, and a concentrically mounted cylinder of copper which was set into rotation when the electromagnets were excited, in pairs, by two alternating emfs displaced in phase from each other. This arrangement was the outgrowth of a theory deduced from the known fact that two beams of plane-polarized light, in space and time quadrature, will combine to form a beam of circularly polarized light. Reasoning by analogy, Ferraris concluded that two alternating magnetic fields, at right angles in space and differing in time phase by a quarter period, would similarly combine to produce a rotating magnetic field.   In

the actual model incorporating this idea, the resultant rotating field induced currents in the copper cylinder which by their reaction with the field produced sufficient torque to cause rotation.   The motor was, of course, nothing more than a toy, notwithstanding its embodiment of an important new principle, for the large airgaps prevented the development of appreciable flux and torque; it must be remembered, though, that at that time the laws of the magnetic circuit were just beginning to be understood.   In any case, Ferraris did not fully realize the technical and commercial importance of his idea.

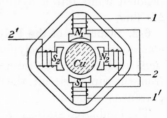

Fig. 6-1. Ferraris motor.

Almost simultaneously, but independently, in 1886, Nikola Tesla, at that time connected with the Westinghouse Electric and Manufacturing Company, conceived the idea of the rotating magnetic field as a means for driving an armature not provided with the commutator and brushes hitherto regarded as necessary structural features; instead, he utilized an armature provided with a closed winding in which the working current could be set up by induction, rather than by conduction.   The original Tesla motor, as revealed in the famous United States patent issued May 1, 1888, had the form illustrated in Fig. 6-2, and the wording of this patent showed clearly that Tesla realized from the beginning the technical use-

245

fulness and commercial importance of the idea of the rotating field.   Ferraris' first disclosure of his ideas appeared in a publication dated Mar. 18, 1888, but the Tesla patent, though issued a little later, was uniformly sustained in ensuing litigation which continued for many years.   The chief reason for upholding the Tesla patent was that Tesla had been the first to realize the importance of the principles involved and to reduce these principles to practicable form.   The record of this long-continued litigation is incorporated in a voluminous mass of expert testimony, attorney's briefs, and judicial decisions.   Much of it is of great interest

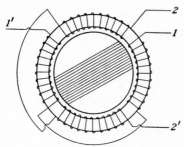

FIG. 6-2. Tesla motor.

to students of electrical engineering, for it covers a period of intense technical and commercial development during which the basic theory was itself being evolved and perfected.   Running through a great deal of the expert testimony was the theory that each of the several windings produced its own flux, which then combined with the other fluxes to produce the resultant flux.   It is known now, of course, that this theory of superposition has serious limitations in magnetic circuits subject to saturation, and that it is more correct to combine the several independent mmfs into a resultant which is then responsible for the resultant flux.

6-2. Structure of the Polyphase Induction Motor.   In the form most commonly used, the polyphase induction motor consists essentially of a *stator* and a *rotor*, the former supporting windings which receive energy from the supply circuit, the latter carrying windings in which the working current is induced.

The laminated stator core, made of sheet-steel punchings 14 to 25 mils thick, is slotted on its inner cylindrical surface, and the winding consists of embedded coils disposed in exactly the same manner as those of a revolving-field synchronous alternator designed for the same number of poles.   In motors of large rating, the stator slots are of the open type, i.e., the side walls of the slots are parallel, to facilitate the insertion of form-wound coils which are completely insulated before they are slipped into place; but in smaller sizes, the slots are partially closed in order to reduce the effective length of the airgap between stator and rotor, in which case the coils, though externally form-wound, are introduced through the narrow slot openings one wire at a time, the slot lining having been previously inserted from the side (see Fig. 6-3).

The frame of the motor, which with the associated end shields serves to carry the bearings, to transmit the torque to the base frame, and to support and protect the core and the coil ends, takes various forms depending upon the operating conditions to which the motor is to be subjected, as follows:*

The *open* type presents the minimum obstruction to the flow of ventilating air consistent with the requirements of mechanical strength.

The *dripproof* type incorporates a cast-iron frame completely enclosing the top half of the motor, but with openings below the center line for the admission

Fig. 6-3. Partially wound stator core.   (*Courtesy of Wagner Electric Corporation.*)

and discharge of air impelled by fan blades on the rotor.   The ventilating openings are so arranged as to protect against the entry of drops of liquid or solid particles falling at an angle not greater than 15 deg. from the vertical, or which strike and run along a surface.

The *splash-proof* motor has ventilating openings so disposed that drops of liquid or solid particles approaching at an angle not greater than 100 deg. from the vertical cannot enter either directly or by running along a surface.

* "Standard Handbook for Electrical Engineers," 8th ed., p. 738, McGraw-Hill Book Company, Inc., New York, 1949.

The *totally enclosed* type, while not air-tight, prevents the exchange of air between the inside and outside of the enclosing case.

Totally enclosed fan-cooled motors provide cooling by one or more external fans which are integral parts of the machine.

Enclosed self-ventilated motors have openings for the admission and discharge of air through ducts sufficiently long to insure an air supply free from objectionable impurities. Circulation of air is effected by fans integral with the rotor.

Enclosed separately ventilated motors are similar to the self-ventilated type except that the air is circulated by fans or blowers which are separate from the motor itself. In large motors of this kind the ventilating system may be of the closed type in which case the heat is extracted by circulating water in surface air coolers.

Fig. 6-4. Squirrel-cage rotor. (*Courtesy of Allis-Chalmers Manufacturing Company.*)

The rotor winding is generally of the squirrel-cage type, which in machines of large size consists of copper bars occupying nearly closed slots on the outer periphery of the rotor core; these bars are solidly brazed to end rings (Fig. 6-4). In early motors of this type, the bars were bolted to the end rings; but this construction was found to be faulty because the expansion and contraction caused by temperature changes under load tended to loosen the bolts and thereby alter the contact resistance, which, though small in itself, was considerable in comparison with the small resistance of the winding as a whole. This consideration led to the construction, illustrated in Fig. 6-5, which is now common in motors of small

FIG. 6-5. Cutaway section of squirrel-cage motor, with cast-aluminum rotor winding. (*Courtesy of Wagner Electric Corporation.*)

and moderate size, where the entire cage winding, bars and end rings together, is made of aluminum cast in place as an integral unit.   This construction has the advantage of economy in manufacture in addition to eliminating contact resistance.

Squirrel-cage induction motors, when supplied with constant voltage at the primary (stator) terminals, tend to run at nearly synchronous speed, but with the speed falling slightly with increasing load, exactly as in the case of the d-c shunt motor; however, the starting torque of an ordinary squirrel-cage motor is limited to approximately double the full-load torque when full voltage is impressed upon the stator winding, and under these conditions the starting current is five to eight times its full-load value.   It follows that in cases where high starting torque is required, a different type of rotor is necessary.   One way of securing large

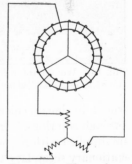

FIG. 6-6. Three-phase wound rotor with starting rheostat.

starting torque is to provide the rotor with a winding shown diagrammatically in Fig. 6-6, and in finished form in Fig. 6-7.   It is, of course, obvious that the coils of a wound rotor must be so proportioned and connected as to produce the same number of poles as the stator winding.

The terminals of the rotor winding are brought out through slip rings to a suitably controlled and balanced rheostat.

In both the types that have been described, the stator carries the primary winding and the rotor the secondary. In the general case, the primary may be defined as the winding to which energy is supplied from the line source and the secondary as the winding in which the working current is produced by induction. Cases arise where it is desirable to have the primary on the rotor and the secondary on the stator; for example, if in Fig. 6-6 the line voltage is high and the secondary current large, it

FIG. 6-7. Wound rotor for 5,500-hp 660-volt three-phase 25-cycle 370-rpm motor. (*Courtesy of Allis-Chalmers Manufacturing Company.*)

would be inconvenient to conduct this large current to the rheostat through slip rings. In such a case, the primary, wound on the rotor, can be supplied with its relatively small current through slip rings, while the stationary secondary terminals can be connected directly to the rheostat. In either case, the revolving magnetic field will travel at synchronous speed with respect to the primary winding. In the first case, it will move at synchronous speed in space, since the primary itself is stationary; in the second case, it will move in space at a speed corresponding to slip frequency.

There are definite restrictions upon the number of rotor slots as compared with the number of stator slots, the principal one being that these two numbers shall not be equal; for if they were, the reluctance of the magnetic circuit as a whole would vary from a maximum when teeth are opposite slots to a minimum when teeth are opposite teeth. The frequency of the resulting flux pulsation would be high, since the time of a complete period would be only the brief interval required for a point on the rotor to travel a distance equal to the tooth pitch. Such a pulsation would introduce objectionable extra core losses; but, even more important, the rotor would tend to lock with the stator, especially at starting, with teeth opposite teeth. The best preventive is to make the number of stator and rotor teeth prime to each other, thereby providing a sort of vernier action between the two sets of teeth; and if conditions are such

Fig. 6-8. Squirrel-cage rotor showing skewing of slots. *(Courtesy of General Electric Company.)*

that prime numbers are not convenient, then their greatest common factor should be as small as possible.

It is customary to build the stator laminations so that the teeth and slots are parallel to the axis of the shaft; but in the case of the rotor the laminations are slightly skewed (Fig. 6-8). The chief reason for skewing the rotor teeth is to eliminate the locking action, which is most pronounced if the airgap flux is radially disposed along the whole length of the opposite teeth; the skewing introduces a tangential component into the pull between opposite teeth, and so tends to minimize the locking action. Incidentally, the skewing reduces the tendency of the teeth to vibrate as reeds, which might be the cause of noise. It should be noted, however, that the chief cause of magnetic noise is the rhythmic vibration of the motor frame produced by the radial pull of the magnetic flux in the airgap. Another cause of noise, which can be avoided by careful design and construction, is mechanical irregularities capable of setting up high-frequency flutterings of the air, in and around the moving parts, which may create sound waves.

The airgap, or, more accurately, the clearance between the tips of the stator and rotor teeth, must be made as small as possible in order to reduce to a minimum the primary and secondary leakage flux; for since the secondary (rotor) current, upon which the torque and power depend, is supplied inductively from the primary (stator), it is essential that the magnetic linkage between primary and secondary be as complete as possible. From this point of view, the induction motor has the properties of a transformer, and any airgap, however small, will cause the leakage reactance and the magnetizing current to be greater than in an equivalent stationary transformer having a closed magnetic circuit. The effect of the airgap is to reduce the power factor, especially at light loads. The length of the airgap is therefore determined mainly by such mechanical considerations as freedom from vibration of the shaft and the wearing quality of the bearings and may be smaller in low-speed than in high-speed machines. In small fractional-horsepower motors, the gap is as small as 0.02 in., increasing to 0.04 or 0.05 in. in machines of higher rating and speed.

6-3. Theories of Operation. The analysis of the operating characteristics of polyphase induction motors may be approached by more than one avenue. The original or classical method, which is in many respects also the most realistic, employs the revolving magnetic field as the central feature. It is also possible, as has been indicated in Art. 5-8, to resolve the actual rotating field into two components, each varying harmonically in time but remaining stationary in space, and differing from each other, both in time and in space, by 90 electrical degrees. There are distinct advantages in each of these methods, and both should be mastered if all aspects of the machine are to be thoroughly comprehended.

The late Dr. Charles P. Steinmetz* pointed out that from one point of view the induction motor may be regarded as a direct evolution from the d-c shunt motor; that from another it is closely akin to the static transformer; that from still another it resembles a generator feeding a fictitious resistance; and that all these points of view are useful in understanding the physical behavior of the machine.

The evolution from the d-c shunt motor has been indicated in part in Art. 5-8, particularly in connection with Fig. 5-19b, where it was shown that in order to develop adequate torque the armature of a shunt-type motor had to be supplied inductively or conductively from one phase of a two-phase supply, the field from the other. It was pointed out that

---

* "Theory and Calculation of Alternating-current Phenomena," 5th ed., pp. 208, 222, 237, McGraw-Hill Book Company, Inc., New York, 1916.

such a disposition of the two phases would result in unbalancing, since one phase supplies the full working current, while the other supplies only the field-exciting current.   To overcome this objection, suppose that two such motors, identical in all respects, are mechanically coupled, as in Fig. 6-9, so that phase 1 supplies the armature of the first machine and the field of the second, while phase 2 supplies the armature of the second and the field of the first.   Each phase is then equally loaded with half of the entire input to the complete unit.   But it will be evident that such an arrangement is exactly equivalent to the single machine of Fig. 6-10, where the single armature winding, short-circuited along two perpendicular axes, carries simultaneously two sets of superposed working currents, each of them reacting to produce torque with the flux in the other axis.   Since it has been shown in Art. 5-12 that a squirrel-cage rotor, suitably proportioned, is the equivalent of a wound rotor short-circuited

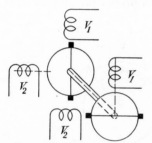

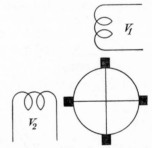

FIG. 6-9. Two unbalanced two-phase induction motors mechanically coupled.

FIG. 6-10. Balanced two-phase induction motor.

in the two axes of Fig. 6-10, this substitution can be made without altering conditions in the primary; and finally, since the two primary windings combine to produce a rotating magnetic field, the two-phase arrangement of Fig. 6-10 can be replaced by any polyphase stator winding that yields an equivalent rotating field, or it can be replaced by an appropriate set of salient revolving poles excited by direct current.   The evolution from the shunt motor to the fully developed polyphase induction motor is thus complete.

It is this chain of reasoning which brings out clearly not only the close resemblance of the polyphase induction motor to the ordinary shunt motor, but also the transformer features which give rise to the working currents in the rotor of Fig. 6-10.   Nevertheless, the step-by-step development has in the end led to a structure quite different in appearance from the d-c shunt motor that is its prototype.   Such a structure, made up of a stator and a rotor like those of Figs. 6-3 and 6-4, may now be looked upon as equivalent to the synchronously revolving set of poles, shown in Fig. 6-11 (for the case of a four-pole machine), surrounding either a squirrel-cage rotor or a rotor carrying a polyphase winding such as is indicated in Figs. 6-6 and 6-7.

Let us now consider somewhat more in detail than has yet been done the conditions in the structure of Fig. 6-11 when the rotor is initially stationary but with the external field rotating at synchronous speed. The revolving flux sweeps across the rotor conductors, and emfs are developed in them in precisely the same way as though the flux were stationary and the rotor conductors were moving backward (counterclockwise in Fig. 6-11) across the lines of induction, just as in any generator. If the rotor conductors had no reactance, the current would be in phase with the emf in each individual bar, but because of reactance each current lags in phase behind its emf and may be thought of as resolved into two components, one in phase with the corresponding emf, the other lagging by a quarter period. These component currents will then have the distribution shown in Fig. 6-12a and b. Applying Fleming's left-hand rule for motor action, it will be noted that the in-phase component of current is distributed in belts in such manner that each of them is in proper position to react with

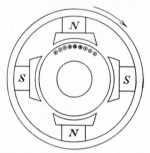

Fig. 6-11. Rotating field produced by revolving salient poles.

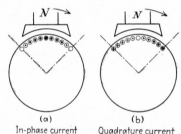

(a)   (b)

In-phase current   Quadrature current

Fig. 6-12. Distribution of in-phase and quadrature-current belts.

the flux to produce torque in the direction of rotation of the original revolving field. The quadrature component of current is on the other hand so distributed that no torque results. The net torque is therefore proportional to the in-phase component of the rotor current, in other words, to the power factor of the rotor circuit, so that, other things being equal, the initial torque of such a motor decreases with increasing reactance. At standstill, that is, with the rotor blocked, the frequency of the rotor current is line frequency, but with increasing speed the rotor frequency becomes less and less, becoming zero at synchronism. The rotor reactance, being proportional to its frequency, therefore decreases as the speed increases.

It will thus be observed that the rotor current is due in the first place to true generator action, and that the reaction of the current with the flux then gives rise to motor torque. It is for this reason that the induction motor presents features resembling those of a generator, and the development of power thus leads to the concept that the rotor currents are being supplied to a fictitious resistance equivalent to the actual motor load.

Whichever point of view is adopted, whether based on the cross-field theory of Fig. 6-10 or on the rotating-field theory of Figs. 6-11 and 6-12, it is possible to develop the complete working characteristics of the machine. Both will be examined, but the latter method, based on the rotating magnetic field, will be considered first.

6-4. EMF and Current Relations. General Phasor Diagram. In order to simplify the analysis, it will be assumed (*a*) that the voltage V_1 impressed upon each phase of the primary winding is purely sinusoidal and alternating at frequency f_1; (*b*) that the flux per pole Φ is sinusoidally distributed in space around the airgap and that it is rotating at synchronous speed. Actually, the impressed voltage may include time harmonics, and the flux may be distorted by the presence of space harmonics, but the consideration of their effects is best deferred for the present.

Likewise, for the sake of simplicity (combined with generality), it will be assumed that the rotor is equipped with a coil winding arranged for the same number of poles as the primary, but with m_2 phases instead of the m_1 phases of the primary. This is indicated diagrammatically in Fig. 6-13.

If p represents the number of poles for which the stator and rotor windings are designed, the flux will rotate at a speed n_1 rpm, such that

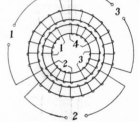

$$\frac{p}{2}\frac{n_1}{60} = \frac{pn_1}{120} = f_1$$

So far as the stationary primary winding is concerned, the effect of the synchronously rotating magnetic field is the same as though each phase were linked with a stationary flux of magnitude

Φ alternating at line frequency; but the rotor, running at n_2 rpm, corresponding to a frequency f_2, such that $pn_2/120 = f_2$, is slipping with respect to the rotating field at frequency

$$f_s = f_1 - f_2 = sf_1$$

where $s = (f_1 - f_2)/f_1 = 1 - (n_2/n_1)$ is the *slip* expressed as a fraction of synchronous speed, and the effect is therefore the same as though each phase of the secondary were linked with a stationary flux of magnitude Φ alternating at slip frequency sf_1.

It follows, therefore, from Eq. 5-27 that under standstill conditions the emf developed in each phase of the primary and the secondary will be given, respectively, by

$$E_1 = 4.44k_{b_1}k_{p_1}f_1N_1\Phi \tag{6-1}$$

and

$$E_2 = 4.44k_{b_2}k_{p_2}f_1N_2\Phi \tag{6-2}$$

while under running conditions, when the slip is s, the secondary emf will be

$$sE_2 = 4.44 k_{b_2} k_{p_2} s f_1 N_2 \Phi \qquad (6\text{-}3)$$

where k_{b_1}, k_{b_2} = breadth factors
k_{p_1}, k_{p_2} = pitch factors
N_1, N_2 = turns in series per phase
Φ = flux per pole, webers

Each of these two emfs will lag behind Φ by 90 electrical degrees, and since the secondary winding constitutes a closed circuit, a current will be produced in it given by

$$I_2 = \frac{sE_2}{\sqrt{R_2^2 + s^2 X_2^2}} = \frac{E_2}{\sqrt{(R_2/s)^2 + X_2^2}} \qquad (6\text{-}4)$$

where X_2 is the reactance of the secondary winding per phase, measured at line frequency. The two equivalent forms of Eq. 6-4 admit of two interpretations: The first form states that the active emf is of slip frequency and of correspondingly reduced magnitude, and that it acts upon a circuit of constant resistance and variable reactance; this is in strict accord with the actual physical facts. The second form states that the effect, so far as the magnitude of the secondary current is concerned, is the same as though the rotor were stationary and its resistance were variable, the emf and current being then of line frequency.

It is obvious that, in the case of the second of these two alternative views, the mmf of the secondary may be combined with that of the primary just as in any stationary transformer. The same thing is true in the case of the first alternative, for the following reasons: The m_2 phases of the secondary, each carrying current I_2 (of slip frequency) successively differing in phase from one another by an angle $2\pi/m_2$, will combine to produce a resultant mmf rotating at slip speed with respect to the secondary winding, and in the same direction in space as the original rotating magnetic field. The truth of this statement can easily be verified by referring to Fig. 6-11; for if the rotor is turning clockwise at less than synchronous speed, it is slipping counterclockwise relative to the field poles, and the conditions are therefore the same as in the armature of an alternator which is running at slip speed in a stationary field; i.e., the armature mmf, rotating with respect to its own winding, is stationary with respect to the field. It follows from this consideration that the secondary mmf due to the rotor current, while rotating relative to the rotor at slip speed, is itself carried forward by the rotor so that for given load conditions it preserves a fixed position relative to the rotating field. The net result is that the primary and secondary mmfs are stationary with respect to each other, and are therefore capable of combining to yield the resultant mmf, which in turn sets up the flux. The geometrical combination of primary and secondary mmfs is in this case fully justified by the fact that the magnetic circuit has the same reluctance in all positions of the axis of the flux, as indicated in Fig. 6-14, because of the cylindrical forms of the concentric stator and rotor.

In accordance with Eq. 4-44, the primary and secondary mmfs, expressed in ampere-turns per pole, are

$$A_1 = \frac{2\sqrt{2}}{\pi} k_{b_1} k_{p_1} m_1 N_{p_1} I_1 = N_1' I_1 \qquad (6\text{-}5)$$

and

$$A_2 = \frac{2\sqrt{2}}{\pi} k_{b_2} k_{p_2} m_2 N_{p_2} I_2 = N_2' I_2 \qquad (6\text{-}6)$$

(where N_{p_1} and N_{p_2} represent the number of turns per pole per phase in the primary and secondary, respectively) and the resultant of these two mmfs must be just sufficient to maintain the flux Φ through the magnetic circuit. The similarity to the static transformer is obvious. If the secondary current were zero, corresponding to the condition of synchronous

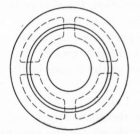

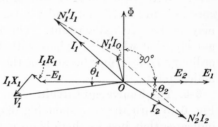

FIG. 6-14. Magnetic circuit, four-pole frame.

FIG. 6-15. General phasor diagram.

speed or to the condition of open-circuited secondary, the primary winding would necessarily take from the line a magnetizing (or, more correctly, a no-load) current of I_0 amp per phase in order to provide the mmf needed to maintain the flux Φ. It follows, therefore, that under load conditions it is necessary that

$$N_1' \mathbf{I}_1 + N_2' \mathbf{I}_2 = N_1' \mathbf{I}_0 \qquad (6\text{-}7)$$

or, dividing through by N_1'

$$\mathbf{I}_1 + \frac{N_2'}{N_1'} \mathbf{I}_2 = \mathbf{I}_0 \qquad (6\text{-}8)$$

Referring now to Fig. 6-15, let the flux Φ be represented by a phasor in any arbitrary position. The emfs E_1 and E_2 will then lag behind Φ by 90°, and E_2 will set up current I_2 lagging behind E_2 by an angle θ_2 such that

$$\tan \theta_2 = \frac{X_2}{R_2/s}$$

The secondary mmf $N_2' I_2$, in time phase with I_2, will then call for a primary current I_1 such that Eq. 6-7 is satisfied, which means that $N_1' I_1$

and $N_2'I_2$ must be the sides of a parallelogram which has $N_1'I_0$ as its diagonal. Just as in any magnetic circuit containing iron, the phase of I_0 must lead that of Φ by a small hysteretic angle of advance. The primary impressed voltage per phase, V_1, must then include components to balance E_1 and to supply the primary leakage-impedance drop, $I_1(R_1 + jX_1)$. The construction of this general phasor diagram is seen to be identical with that of the ordinary transformer.

There is one point, however, wherein the conditions in the induction motor differ somewhat from those in the static transformer. The no-load current I_0 leads the flux Φ because of the presence of a component to supply the friction and windage losses in addition to the core loss; in the stator, the flux is substantially constant in magnitude, and it alternates at line frequency; but in the rotor core, while the flux is also substantially constant, it alternates at slip frequency, which varies with the rotor speed and with the load, so that at synchronism the rotor core loss would be zero. Within the limits of normal motor operation, the change in rotor core loss and in friction and windage is quite small; hence, these losses may be treated as constant. The true magnetizing component of I_0, namely, that which is in phase with Φ, is considerably greater than in an ordinary transformer because of the presence of the airgap in the magnetic circuit.

6-5. The Equivalent Circuit. The practical identity of the diagram of Fig. 6-15 with the corresponding diagram of the stationary transformer indicates that just as there is an equivalent circuit for the transformer there should be a similar one for the induction motor. The two equivalent circuits cannot be expected to be identical in all their implications, for in the case of the motor the primary and secondary circuits are movable with respect to each other at a speed which varies with the load, and they do not necessarily have the same number of phases. In short, the polyphase induction motor is a transformer of much more general type than the ordinary two-circuit static transformer thus far considered; nevertheless, as is plain from Fig. 6-15, primary and secondary quantities such as emfs, currents, resistances, and reactances are intimately related, and it is possible to reduce secondary quantities to terms of the primary, or vice versa, just as was done in the case of the transformer.

Thus, from Eqs. 6-1 and 6-2 it is seen that at standstill the ratio of primary to secondary emf per phase is

$$\frac{E_1}{E_2} = \frac{k_{b_1}k_{p_1}N_1}{k_{b_2}k_{p_2}N_2} = a \tag{6-9}$$

Consequently, secondary emfs reduced to equivalent standstill values, if multiplied by this ratio of voltage transformation, will be reduced to equivalent primary terms.

In the same way, Eq. 6-8 shows that the corresponding ratio of current transformation, which will convert actual secondary current per phase to the equivalent primary current, is

$$\frac{N_2'}{N_1'} = \frac{m_2 k_{b_2} k_{p_2} N_{p_2}}{m_1 k_{b_1} k_{p_1} N_{p_1}} = \frac{m_2 k_{b_2} k_{p_2} N_2}{m_1 k_{b_1} k_{p_1} N_1} = \frac{m_2}{m_1} \frac{1}{a} \tag{6-10}$$

It follows that the factor by which secondary resistance, reactance, and impedance must be multiplied to convert them to equivalent primary terms is $m_1 a^2 / m_2$. For convenience in developing the analysis, it is desirable to deal with secondary quantities reduced to terms of the primary; but to distinguish such equivalent values from the actual values, the equivalent quantities will be designated by a subscript e; thus, E_{2e} will represent the secondary emf reduced to primary terms, and E_{2e} is accordingly equal to E_1.

On changing secondary quantities to terms of the primary, Fig. 6-15 takes the form shown in Fig. 6-16, and it is then possible to convert the relations between the

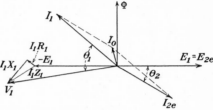

FIG. 6-16. Phasor diagram reduced to terms of primary.

phasors of this diagram into corresponding analytical expressions. Thus, using Eqs. 6-4 and 6-8,

$$\mathbf{I}_{2e} = \frac{s\mathbf{E}_{2e}}{R_{2e} + jsX_{2e}} = \frac{\mathbf{E}_2}{R_{2e}/s + jX_{2e}} \tag{6-11}$$

and
$$\mathbf{I}_1 + \mathbf{I}_{2e} = \mathbf{I}_0 \tag{6-12}$$

Applying the same reasoning as in the case of the static transformer (Art. 1-4), it is possible to write

$$\mathbf{I}_0 = \frac{-\mathbf{E}_1}{R_0 + jX_0} = -\mathbf{E}_1(G_0 - jB_0) \tag{6-13}$$

where $R_0 + jX_0$ is the exciting impedance, and $G_0 - jB_0$ is the exciting admittance; and finally, in accordance with Fig. 6-16,

$$\mathbf{V}_1 = -\mathbf{E}_1 + \mathbf{I}_1(R_1 + jX_1) \tag{6-14}$$

On combining Eqs. 6-11 to 6-14, eliminating successively E_1, I_{2e}, and I_0, it is found that

$$\mathbf{V}_1 = \mathbf{I}_1 \left(R_1 + jX_1 + \cfrac{1}{G_0 - jB_0 + \cfrac{1}{R_{2e}/s + jX_{2e}}} \right) \tag{6-15}$$

Equation 6-15 shows that so far as the primary is concerned, the impressed voltage per phase is equal to the current per phase multiplied by an impedance represented by the term in parentheses. The form of this expression shows that the equivalent circuit (per phase) is as indicated in Fig. 6-17; it is similar to the equivalent circuit of the transformer, but it will be noted that there is no clearly defined separate load impedance such as is shown in Fig. 1-13. On the other hand, it is seen that the effect of varying load on the actual motor is taken into account by the variable resistance R_{2e}/s. In other words, the operation of the motor under load is the same as though the primary were feeding into a variable, noninductive rheostat which is itself part of a circuit connected as in Fig. 6-17. It will be noted that when $s = 1$ (standstill), the conditions are identical with those of a short-circuited static transformer; and that when $s = 0$ (synchronism), the conditions are identical with those in a transformer having open-circuited secondary. These facts reflect the transformer features of the induction motor.

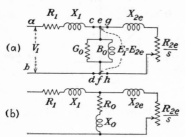

FIG. 6-17. Alternative forms of exact equivalent circuit of polyphase induction motor.

In general, the impedance drop in the primary, I_1Z_1, is a small percentage of the impressed voltage V_1; so there is little error involved in treating E_1 (Fig. 6-16) as substantially equal to V_1. This is equivalent to transferring the exciting admittance from the position shown in Fig. 6-17 to that shown in Fig. 6-18, which is then the approximate equivalent circuit of the polyphase induction motor. The analytical representation of this change, derived from inspection of Fig. 6-18, is accordingly

$$I_1 = V_1\left[(G_0 - jB_0) + \frac{1}{(R_1 + R_{2e}/s) + j(X_1 + X_{2e})}\right] \quad (6\text{-}16)$$

which means that the primary current I_1 is the resultant of two components, one of which is approximately equal to

$$I_0 = V_1(G_0 - jB_0) \quad (6\text{-}17)$$

and the other, equivalent to I_{2e}, is

$$I_{2e} = \frac{V_1}{(R_1 + R_{2e}/s) + j(X_1 + X_{2e})} \quad (6\text{-}18)$$

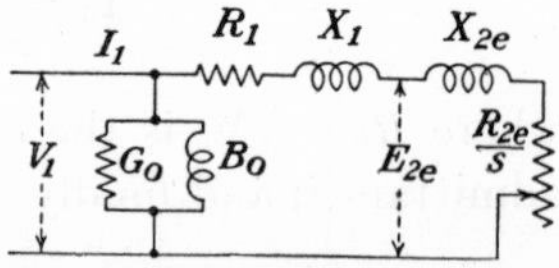

FIG. 6-18. Approximate equivalent circuit.

In the equivalent circuit of Fig. 6-18, the whole effect of the motor load is included in the variable resistance R_{2e}/s, but since

$$\frac{R_{2e}}{s} = R_{2e} + R_{2e}\frac{1 - s}{s}$$

the approximate equivalent circuit can be redrawn as in Fig. 6-19. Here the resistance R_{2e} is an inherent part of the internal impedance of the machine, but the *variable resistance $R_{2e}(1 - s)/s$ is the electrical analogue* *of the mechanical load.* It is this fact which accounts for the concept, referred to in Art. 6-3, that the induction motor can be thought of as a generator feeding a fictitious resistance.

6-6. Mechanical Power Developed. It will be seen from Fig. 6-19 that the power (per phase) supplied to the motor from the line is

$$P_1 = V_1 I_1 \cos \theta_1 \qquad \text{watts} \qquad (6\text{-}19)$$

where the meaning of the symbols is indicated in the phasor diagram, Fig. 6-20, constructed to agree with the circuit of Fig. 6-19. A part of this power, amounting to $I_{2e}^2(R_1 + R_{2e})$ watts per phase, is consumed as ohmic loss in the primary and secondary windings, and the remainder is converted into mechanical power. Not all the mechanical power thus

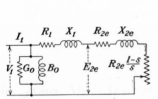

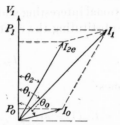

FIG. 6-19. Approximate equivalent cir- FIG. 6-20. Power components of current.
cuit.

developed is available at the shaft, for there is a further loss due to friction, windage, and hysteresis and eddy currents in the core. The loss due to these causes is taken into account by the exciting admittance in Fig. 6-19, and it is seen from Fig. 6-20 that it amounts to $V_1 I_0 \cos \theta_0$ watts per phase; it is equivalent in its nature to a friction drag applied to the shaft. The *net mechanical output* per phase is therefore

$$P = V_1 I_1 \cos \theta_1 - I_{2e}^2(R_1 + R_{2e}) - V_1 I_0 \cos \theta_0 \qquad (6\text{-}20)$$

But from Fig. 6-20 it is seen that

$$I_1 \cos \theta_1 = I_{2e} \cos \theta_2 + I_0 \cos \theta_0$$

and since it follows from the circuit of Fig. 6-19 that

$$I_{2e} = \frac{V_1}{\sqrt{\left(R_1 + R_{2e} + R_{2e}\dfrac{1-s}{s}\right)^2 + (X_1 + X_{2e})^2}} = \frac{V_1}{Z_e}$$

and

$$\cos \theta_2 = \frac{R_1 + R_{2e} + R_{2e}\dfrac{1-s}{s}}{Z_e}$$

substitution of these relations in Eq. 6-20 gives

$$P = \frac{V_1^2 R_{2e}}{(R_1 + R_{2e}/s)^2 + (X_1 + X_{2e})^2} \frac{1-s}{s} \qquad (6\text{-}21)$$

which gives the mechanical power per phase in terms of the slip s, all other terms in the expression being constants. Further, since

$$\frac{V_1^2}{(R_1 + R_{2e}/s)^2 + (X_1 + X_{2e})^2} = I_{2e}^2$$

it follows from Eq. 6-21 that

$$P = I_{2e}^2 R_{2e} \frac{1 - s}{s} \tag{6-22}$$

which means that *the mechanical power developed per phase may be regarded as the ohmic loss in a fictitious secondary resistance of $R_{2e}(1 - s)/s$ ohms per phase.*

Additional interesting and important facts are deducible from Eq. 6-22, for on substituting the relation

$$I_{2e} = \frac{E_{2e}}{\sqrt{(R_{2e}/s)^2 + X_{2e}^2}}$$

it becomes

$$P = E_{2e}(1 - s)I_{2e} \frac{R_{2e}/s}{\sqrt{(R_{2e}/s)^2 + X_{2e}^2}} = E_{2e}(1 - s)I_{2e} \cos \theta_2 \tag{6-23}$$

This shows that the emf, which, together with the secondary current, is responsible for the mechanical output, is equal to $E_{2e}(1 - s)$; but sE_{2e} is the voltage actually consumed in the secondary impedance, and E_{2e}, induced by transformer action, is equivalent to the voltage impressed upon the armature terminals of an ordinary d-c motor. The difference between them, or $E_{2e}(1 - s)$, is therefore analogous to the counter emf in a d-c motor.

Moreover, since

$$sE_{2e}I_{2e} \cos \theta_2 = I_{2e}^2 R_{2e} = \text{secondary copper loss per phase}$$

it follows that

$$P + I_{2e}^2 R_{2e} = E_{2e}I_{2e} \cos \theta_2 = \text{electrical input to the secondary per phase}$$

a fact which will be found useful in later applications.

Again, the expression $E_{2e}I_{2e} \cos \theta_2$ may be written

$$\frac{sE_{2e}I_{2e} \cos \theta_2}{s} = \frac{I_{2e}^2 R_{2e}}{s}$$

from which it follows that

$$\text{Electrical input to the secondary per phase} = P + I_{2e}^2 R_{2e} = \frac{I_{2e}^2 R_{2e}}{s}$$

$$= \frac{\text{secondary copper loss per phase}}{\text{slip}} \tag{6-24}$$

On multiplying numerator and denominator of Eq. 6-21 by s, it becomes

$$P = \frac{V_1^2 R_{2e} s (1 - s)}{(sR_1 + R_{2e})^2 + s^2(X_1 + X_{2e})^2} \qquad (6\text{-}25)$$

which shows that $P = 0$ when $s = 0$ (synchronism) and also when $s = 1$ (standstill). Furthermore, the sign of P depends upon the magnitude and sign of s in accordance with the following tabulation:

Item	Value of s	Sign of P
1	$0 < s < 1$	Positive
2	$s < 0$	Negative
3	$s > 1$	Negative

The physical meaning of these three items is readily interpreted as follows:

1. When the slip is between zero and unity, the motor speed is between standstill and synchronism, and the direction of rotation is the same as that of the rotating magnetic field. The positive sign of P therefore indicates motor action.

2. When the slip is less than zero, i.e., is negative as to sign, the rotor is being driven forward, in the same direction as the rotating field, and the actual speed is greater than synchronous speed. The relative direction of rotation between the rotor and the magnetic field has therefore been reversed, and the rotor emfs and currents are likewise reversed, indicating that the machine has changed from motor to generator action. The negative sign of P is in accord with this reversal of function.

3. When s is greater than unity, the motor is being driven backward through the forwardly rotating magnetic field. The rotor emf continues to have the same direction as at standstill (or as at any speed between synchronism and standstill) but becomes greater in magnitude because of the high relative speed of cutting the lines of induction. The machine has become an electric brake, hence the negative sign of P.

6-7. Torque. The mechanical power per phase represented by Eq. 6-25 determines the magnitude of the torque. If the torque, in pound-feet, is indicated by T and the rotor speed is n_2 rpm, it follows that

$$m_1 P = 2\pi n_2 T \times \frac{746}{33{,}000}$$

and since $n_2 = n_1(1 - s)$,

$$T = \frac{33{,}000}{2\pi n_1 \times 746} \frac{m_1 V_1^2 R_{2e} s}{(sR_1 + R_{2e})^2 + s^2(X_1 + X_{2e})^2} \qquad (6\text{-}26)$$

Referring to the discussion immediately following Eq. 6-21, it will be noted that

$$T = \frac{33,000}{2\pi n_1 \times 746} \frac{m_1(I_{2e}^2 R_{2e})}{s} \qquad (6\text{-}27)$$

and in accordance with Eq. 6-24 this is equivalent to

$$T = \frac{33,000}{2\pi n_1 \times 746} \times \text{total electrical input to the secondary} \qquad (6\text{-}28)$$

Equation 6-27 states that *the product of torque and slip is proportional to the total secondary copper loss.* This means that, at standstill ($s = 1$), the torque is directly proportional to the secondary resistance, and indicates that large starting torque demands correspondingly large rotor resistance.

The maximum torque that the motor can develop is determined by the condition that $dT/ds = 0$. On differentiating Eq. 6-26, it is found that the condition for maximum torque is

$$s = \pm \frac{R_{2e}}{\sqrt{R_1^2 + (X_1 + X_{2e})^2}} \qquad (6\text{-}29)$$

The positive sign corresponds to motor action, the negative to generator action. Considering only the case of motor action, the maximum torque, found by substituting this value of s in Eq. 6-26, is

$$T_{\max} = \frac{33,000}{2\pi n_1 \times 746} \frac{m_1 V_1^2}{2[R_1 + \sqrt{R_1^2 + (X_1 + X_{2e})^2}]} \qquad (6\text{-}30)$$

The maximum torque, called the *breakdown,* or *pull-out,* torque, characterizes the load which will cause the motor to stall. In accordance with Eq. 6-29, the maximum torque occurs at a slip which is directly proportional to the secondary resistance, though Eq. 6-30 shows that the maximum torque is itself independent of the secondary resistance. In case it is desired to have the maximum torque occur at starting, Eq. 6-29 shows that the rotor resistance would have to be equal to $\sqrt{R_1^2 + (X_1 + X_{2e})^2}$. In general, the primary resistance R_1 is sufficiently small in comparison with the reactance to justify the omission of the term R_1^2 in this expression; *hence, for maximum torque at starting,* $R_{2e} \cong X_1 + X_{2e}$, or, approximately, *the rotor resistance should be equal to the total leakage reactance,* all quantities being expressed in terms of the primary. Subject to this condition, the current will lag approximately 45° behind the impressed voltage, which means that the corresponding power factor will be in the neighborhood of 70 per cent.

Variation of R_{2e} is usually accomplished by a three-phase Y-connected rotor winding with slip rings, of the type shown in Fig. 6-7, thus permitting the use of a rheostat, which may be externally mounted. In some designs, the variable resistance is mounted internally, i.e., on the rotor spider inside the core, in which case no slip rings are required; the rheostat is then manipulated by links actuated by a rod which is concentrically mounted in the hollow shaft, and which projects beyond the end of the shaft.   It is, of course, possible to design the rotor to obtain any starting torque up to the possible maximum, but unless special measures are adopted, a high starting torque obtained by correspondingly large fixed rotor resistance will entail a sacrifice of efficiency and speed regulation under normal running conditions.

The nature of the variation of torque with slip is shown in Fig. 6-21, which has been constructed by assuming $R_1 = 0.2$ and $X_1 = X_{2e} = 1.0$ and then assigning various values to R_{2e}.   It will be noted that positive values of s have been laid off to the left, and negative values to the right, of the point $s = 0$; in this way, the abscissas may be made to correspond with the speed, expressed in per cent of synchronous speed, reading in

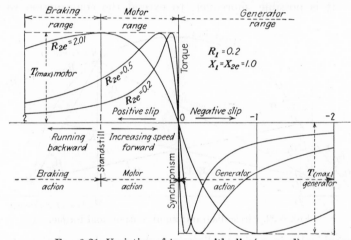

Fig. 6-21. Variation of torque with slip (or speed).

the usual manner from left to right.   When the speed is greater than synchronous, corresponding to negative values of s, the torque also becomes negative, in accordance with Eq. 6-26, and the machine then operates as a generator.   Under these conditions, the determination of maximum torque calls for the use of the negative sign in Eq. 6-29, and the maximum torque for the case of generator action becomes

$$T_{\max,\,gen} = \frac{33,000}{2\pi n_1 \times 746} \frac{m_1 V_1^2}{2[\sqrt{R_1^2 + (X_1 + X_{2e})^2} - R_1]} \tag{6-31}$$

which is somewhat greater than the corresponding maximum for motor action.

Figure 6-21 shows that in the range of motor action between standstill and the speed at which maximum torque is developed, the torque increases more than proportionately to the speed.   This means that within this range there is a condition of instability, in the sense that if the torque developed is greater than the resisting torque the speed will continue to rise until the point of maximum torque has been passed; beyond the point of maximum torque, and up to synchronism, the conditions become stable, for here any increase of load torque causes the motor to slow down and therefore automatically to develop greater torque to meet the load requirement. Conversely, if the load torque becomes greater than the breakdown torque of the motor, the slowing down of the speed is accompanied by a decreased motor torque and the speed promptly falls to zero.

6-8. The Circle Diagram. Because the equivalent circuit of the polyphase induction motor is identical with that of the static transformer supplying noninductive load, it follows that the circle diagram derived for that case (see Art. 1-11 and Fig. 1-18) is immediately applicable to the motor. It is possible, moreover, to extend the construction so as to

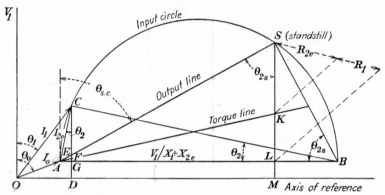

FIG. 6-22. Circle diagram: input, output, and torque.

show graphically in a single diagram* the complete relations between emfs, currents, power input and output, torque, speed, power factor, and efficiency with an accuracy sufficient for most practical purposes.

Thus, referring to Fig. 6-22, the locus of the primary current phasor $OC = I_1$ is a circle which has a diameter $AB = V_1/(X_1 + X_{2e})$ amp. Point A defines the magnitude and phase position of the no-load current $OA = I_0$, and corresponds to synchronous speed ($s = 0$) when the fictitious load resistance $R_{2e}(1 - s)/s$ is infinite (see **Fig. 6-19**). Point S is the standstill point ($s = 1$), and corresponds to short-circuit conditions with full voltage impressed upon the primary.

When the load is such that the primary current has some general value such as OC, the input to the motor, per phase, is proportional to the·

---

* The circle diagram, in the form originally published, is usually attributed to Alexander Heyland [see *Elektrotech. Z*, **41**:561 (1894)]. B. A. Behrend claimed priority on the basis of an article in the same journal published in January, 1896. See introduction to Behrend's "The Induction Motor," 2d ed., McGraw Hill Book Company, Inc., New York, 1921, for a full account of the history of this interesting development.

in-phase component of current CD, and by an appropriate choice of scale CD can be read in watts or horsepower.

In the same way, it is evident that GD, the in-phase component of the no-load current OA, is proportional to the nearly constant loss made up of core loss, friction, and windage. It follows that the difference CG between the input CD and the constant loss GD represents the power output plus the copper losses in the stator and rotor windings.

Under standstill conditions at full voltage, the input per phase, represented by SM, is consumed in core loss and copper loss only, since friction and windage loss is absent. However, the portion of the standstill input represented by $LM = GD$ may be considered to represent the standstill core loss with reasonable accuracy, since the absence of friction and windage is practically offset by the increased rotor core loss under standstill conditions. It follows from this approximation that the portion of the blocked-rotor input represented by SL is the standstill copper loss.

From the similar triangles AEG and ASL (Fig. 6-22), it follows that

$$\frac{EG}{SL} = \frac{AG}{AL} = \frac{AC \sin \theta_2}{AS \sin \theta_{2s}}$$

and it is also seen that

$$AC = AB \sin \theta_2$$
$$AS = AB \sin \theta_{2s}$$

from which

$$\frac{\sin \theta_2}{\sin \theta_{2s}} = \frac{AC}{AS}$$

whence

$$\frac{EG}{SL} = \frac{(AC)^2}{(AS)^2} = \frac{I_{2e}^2}{I_{sc}^2} = \frac{I_{2e}^2(R_1 + R_{2e})}{I_{sc}^2(R_1 + R_{2e})}$$

The conclusion follows that if SL, to the scale of power, is the copper loss at standstill when the current is AS, the intercept EG is the copper loss when the current is AC.

If now the line SL is divided at point K into two parts, SK and KL, respectively proportional to R_{2e} and R_1 (using, for example, the construction indicated by the dashed lines at the right-hand side of Fig. 6-22), it must necessarily follow that for any general current such as $I_{2e} = AC$ the secondary copper loss $I_{2e}^2 R_{2e}$ is represented by EF, and the primary copper loss $I_{2e}^2 R_1$ by FG.

Accordingly, of the total input per phase CD, the portion EG represents primary and secondary copper loss per phase, GD represents core loss, friction, and windage per phase, and the remainder CE must represent the mechanical output per phase. The line AS, which is the locus of all such points as E, is therefore called the *output line*.

Reference to Eq. 6-28 shows that the torque is proportional to the electrical input to the secondary, and by Eq. 6-24 this input is $P + I_{2e}^2 R_{2e}$, which in Fig. 6-22 is represented by the intercept CF. The locus of points F, as C moves around the circle, is the line AK, which is accordingly called the *torque line*.

Figure 6-23, which is in part a reproduction of Fig. 6-22, serves to determine by graphical construction the slip, efficiency, and power factor. The vertical lines AQ and $O'Y$ are drawn, the former through the no-load point A, the latter through the point O' where the output line AS (extended backward) intersects the axis of reference. From any convenient point P on the output line, PQ is drawn parallel to the torque line, and PY is drawn parallel to the axis of reference; both PQ and PY are then divided into 100 equal parts, as indicated in the diagram. The line AC, which represents the secondary current corresponding to the

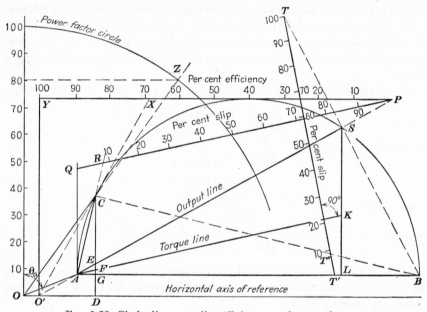

Fig. 6-23. Circle diagram: slip, efficiency, and power factor.

load point C, is then extended until it intersects QP at point R. Similarly, the line $O'C$ is extended until it intersects PY at point X. It then remains to prove that, for the load conditions defined by point C, QR is the per cent slip, and PX the per cent efficiency, to the scales fixed by $QP = 100$ and $PY = 100$.

To show that QR is a measure of the slip, note that triangles CFA and AQR are similar, so that

$$\frac{CF}{FA} = \frac{AQ}{QR}$$

and that triangles EFA and AQP are likewise similar, so that

$$\frac{EF}{FA} = \frac{AQ}{PQ}$$

Dividing the second equation by the first,

$$\frac{EF}{CF} = \frac{QR}{QP}$$

But it has been proved that the slip is proportional to the secondary copper loss EF divided by the torque CF; hence, QR is the slip in terms of QP as unity or 100 per cent.

There is another graphical method for determining the slip which is in some respects better than the one just described. Thus, let the line BS be extended to any convenient point T, such that the line TT', drawn perpendicular to the torque line AK, is made equal to 100 on any convenient scale. Then the line CB will intersect TT' at a point T''', and the intercept $T'T''$ will then be the per cent slip to the same scale to which TT' represents 100. The proof of this statement follows easily from the fact that triangles AQP and $BT'T$ are similar, since their corresponding sides are mutually perpendicular; and the same thing is true with regard to triangles AQR and $BT'T''$.

The efficiency is given by the ratio

$$\frac{\text{Output}}{\text{Input}} = \frac{CE}{CD} = \frac{CD - ED}{CD} = 1 - \frac{ED}{CD}$$

From the similar triangles EDO' and $O'YP$,

$$\frac{ED}{O'D} = \frac{OY'}{PY}$$

and from the similar triangles CDO' and $O'YX$,

$$\frac{CD}{O'D} = \frac{O'Y}{XY}$$

from which, by division,

$$\frac{ED}{CD} = \frac{XY}{PY}$$

or

$$\text{Efficiency} = \frac{CE}{CD} = \frac{PX}{PY}$$

The power factor is easily found by drawing a quadrant of a circle with center at O and a radius equal to 100 arbitrary units. On extending the primary current phasor OC until it intersects this quadrant at point Z, and projecting Z upon the vertical scale, the power factor is determined.

It is to be noted that the proportions of Figs. 6-22 and 6-23 have been purposely exaggerated for the sake of clarity. The actual diagram approaches the proportions shown in Fig. 6-27.

6-9. Determination of Circle Diagram by No-load Tests. Although the circle diagram as illustrated in Figs. 6-22 and 6-23 is based upon simplifying assumptions, it serves to predict the principal operating characteristics of the motor with satisfactory accuracy. The data required for its construction are easily obtained from the two no-load tests described below; they are similar in nature to the open-circuit and short-circuit tests explained in Chap. 1 for the case of static transformers.

a. *The Running-light Test.* If the motor is run at no load with rated voltage (at normal frequency) impressed upon its stator winding, the magnitude and phase of the observed primary current will very nearly define the position of point A in Figs. 6-22 and 6-23, provided the phase voltages are balanced and have sine wave forms. Thus, if the no-load readings of voltage, current, and power, all reduced to per-phase values, are V_1, I_0, and P_0, respectively, the phase position of I_0 will be fixed by the relation $\cos \theta_0 = P_0/V_1 I_0$. But since point A corresponds to the condition of synchronous speed ($s = 0$), the point defined by the no-load readings of current and power lies slightly above A because there must be just enough slip to develop sufficient rotor current to produce the necessary no-load torque. The theoretically correct way to fix the position of point A would require that the rotor be driven at synchronous speed by an auxiliary machine at the time V_1, I_0, and P_0 are measured.

The total power input ($m_1 P_0$) when the motor is running light is consumed in supplying the following losses:

1. The copper loss in the stator winding.

2. The core loss in the stator iron.

3. The core loss in the rotor, consisting almost entirely of hysteresis since the slip is so small that eddy currents are negligible.

4. High-frequency losses in the teeth of both stator and rotor, due mainly to eddy currents caused by rapid flux pulsations as the teeth and slots change their relative positions.

5. Bearing friction and windage.

Theoretically, there is an additional copper loss in the rotor, but the rotor current at no load is so small that this item may be neglected.

If, when the motor is running without load, the impressed voltage is varied through a range from a small fraction of its rated value to somewhat more than normal, these losses, with the exception of friction, windage, and the stator copper loss, will vary almost in proportion to the square of the voltage. The friction and windage loss will remain practically constant since the speed will not change appreciably. The stator copper loss, $I_0^2 R_1$ watts per phase, can easily be calculated by measuring the primary resistance at the temperature at which the tests are made. Accordingly, it is possible to write

Total no-load power input − total stator copper loss = P_t
$$= \text{constant} \times (\text{voltage})^2 + \text{friction and windage}$$

So if P_t is plotted against the square of voltage, the graph will be a straight line which intersects the axis of power coordinates at the constant value of friction and windage.*

If P_r represents the portion of the total running-light power input (P_0 times the number of phases) which remains after deducting the total copper and core loss in the stator, we have

P_r = rotor hysteresis loss + high-frequency tooth losses

+ friction and windage

and it follows from Eq. 6-22 that

$$P_r = m_1 I_{2e}^2 R_{2e} \frac{1 - s}{s}$$

From Fig. 6-17, it is seen that

$$I_{2e}^2 = \frac{E_1^2}{(R_{2e}/s)^2 + X_{2e}^2}$$

whence

$$P_r = \frac{m_1 E_1^2 R_{2e} s(1 - s)}{R_{2e}^2 + s^2 X_{2e}^2}$$

But at no load the slip s is so small that $s^2 X_{2e}^2$ is negligible in comparison with R_{2e}^2, and $1 - s$ is substantially equal to unity; hence,

$$P_r \cong \frac{m_1 E_1^2 s}{R_{2e}} \tag{6-32}†$$

In this formula, E_1 is the emf induced in the stator, and differs from V_1 by the impedance drop $I_0(R_1 + jX_1)$. The slip s should be measured directly by a stroboscope or its equivalent, not by taking the difference between synchronous speed and the observed no-load speed. The values of X_1 and R_{2e} can be found by means of the blocked-rotor test described under the heading b below. There is no simple way by which the rotor hysteresis loss can be directly measured; so it is usual to compute it from the known values of flux density, rotor core dimensions, and slip frequency. It may be noted, however, that if the rotor is driven at synchronous speed by a cradle-mounted synchronous motor, so that the mechanical input may be measured directly, rotor hysteresis disappears, and the mechanical power supplied to the rotor shaft will then include only the tooth losses and friction and windage, thus providing means for separating all the component losses.

In general, it is sufficiently accurate to assume that in making the running-light test at rated voltage and frequency the observed values of V_1, I_0, and P_0 will fix the position of point A in the circle diagram.

* P. L. Alger, "The Nature of Polyphase Induction Machines," p. 105, John Wiley & Sons, Inc., New York 1951.

† This formula was originally published by P. L. Alger and R. Eksergian, *Jour. AIEE*, October, 1920.

b. The Standstill or Blocked-rotor Test. It has been pointed out in Art. 6-5 that at standstill ($s = 1$) the conditions are the same as in a short-circuited transformer, so that if the rotor is blocked to prevent rotation it is possible to circulate full-load or even larger current in both stator and rotor by impressing reduced voltage on the stator. By varying the impressed voltage over a sufficient range, and taking simultaneous readings of primary current and power input, the relation between current and voltage on the one hand, and between power input and voltage on the other, can be plotted as curves which by extrapolation will give the magnitude and phase position of the primary current at full voltage, and so fix the position of point S in Figs. 6-22 and 6-23.

Since it is known that the center of the circle lies on the line AB drawn perpendicular to phasor V_1, it is only necessary to extend the bisector of the chord AS until it intersects the line AB, thereby fixing the position of the center of the circle.

In making the blocked-rotor test, it is desirable to obtain readings at the largest value of current which can be used without overheating the windings. It is therefore necessary to take the readings quickly and to observe the copper temperature before and after the test in order to avoid errors due to changed resistance. Theoretically, the graph showing the relation between the short-circuit current and the impressed voltage (both expressed per phase) should be a straight line through the origin of coordinates, but it will usually show a slight curvature because of the effect of magnetic saturation in altering the leakage reactance, and of skin effect in altering the effective resistance, of the windings. These effects are particularly accentuated in the case of deep-bar rotors and in double squirrel-cage machines, where at standstill the leakage reactance is materially lower than at full speed; in such machines, the standstill test should be made at the lowest obtainable frequency; the observed low-frequency value of reactance must then be multiplied by the ratio of the rated frequency to the test frequency to give the reactance to be used in computing performance characteristics.

In the case of a general-purpose motor, if the standstill test is made with a sufficiently low value of impressed voltage, the flux will be correspondingly small and the core loss will be negligible. Since there is no friction and windage loss, the entire input may be considered to be consumed in copper loss. Therefore, if the simultaneous readings of impressed voltage, current, and power input, all reduced to per phase values, are V_s, I_s, and P_s, respectively, if follows from the approximate equivalent circuit that

$$P_s = I_s^2(R_1 + R_{2e}) \qquad (6\text{-}33)$$

from which R_{2e} can be computed since R_1 can be measured by direct current.

A check upon the value of R_{2e} is afforded by measuring the standstill torque by means of a lever arm and spring balance; for by Eq. 6-27 the torque at standstill is

$$T_{s=1} = \frac{33,000}{2\pi n_1 \times 746} \, m_1 I_s^2 R_{2e} \qquad \text{lb-ft}$$

though according to Alger* the right-hand side of this equation should be multiplied by an empirical factor, usually about 0.9, to allow for nonfundamental secondary losses.

Again, since the magnetizing current is negligible at the reduced voltage used in this test,

$$V_s = I_s \sqrt{(R_1 + R_{2e})^2 + (X_1 + X_{2e})^2}$$

or $\qquad X_1 + X_{2e} = \sqrt{\left(\dfrac{V_s}{I_s}\right)^2 - (R_1 + R_{2e})^2}$ \qquad (6-34)

from which the diameter of the circle, $V_1/(X_1 + X_{2e})$, may be computed; and the slope of the line AS in Fig. 6-22 is then

$$\tan \theta_{2s} = \frac{X_1 + X_{2e}}{R_1 + R_{2e}}$$

Since there is no simple way by which X_1 and X_{2e} can be separately measured, it is standard practice to assume that their sum, $X_1 + X_{2e}$, may be split in accordance with the following table:

Class	Description	$\dfrac{X_1}{X_1 + X_{2e}}$	$\dfrac{X_{2e}}{X_1 + X_{2e}}$
Squirrel-cage:			
A............	Normal starting torque, normal starting current (general-purpose motor)	0.5	0.5
B............	Normal starting torque, low starting current	0.4	0.6
C............	High starting torque, low starting current	0.3	0.7
D............	High slip, high resistance	0.5	0.5
Wound rotor....	....	0.5	0.5

6-10. Operating Characteristics from the Circle Diagram. Reference to the circle diagrams of Figs. 6-22 and 6-23 will show that as the point C moves clockwise around the circle the motor output increases from zero at point A to a maximum value and then again falls to zero at point S. For each intermediate value of the output between these two zero limits, there will be two values of each of the dependent variables, namely, the primary and secondary current, power factor, torque, slip, and efficiency. On plotting these quantities as ordinates and the corresponding output as

* *Op. cit.,* p. 108.

abscissas, the characteristic curves of Fig. 6-24 are obtained.   The portions of the curves shown in broken lines lie beyond the point of maximum power output, and indicate a region of instability.*   The normal working range of the motor, i.e., between no load and rated load, lies well within the point of maximum output, and on the circle diagram the working range is represented by a relatively small arc in the neighborhood of point A. If the load were to equal or exceed the maximum output, the motor would stall on reaching the critical point, but in practice the fuses or circuit breaker would interrupt the supply before this point is reached in order to prevent serious overheating.

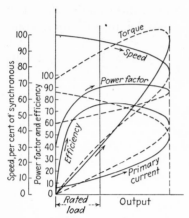

FIG. 6-24. Characteristic curves of polyphase induction motor.   (Maximum output $2\frac{1}{2}$ times normal; $i_s = 5.85 \times$ full-load current.)

Referring to Fig. 6-25, it is plain that maximum power output occurs when the load point C is at C_p, where the radius of the circle is perpendicular to the output line AS; and that the maximum torque corresponds to the load point C_t located on a radius perpendicular to the torque line AT.   It will be seen that maximum power output occurs at a slip somewhat less than the slip which corresponds to maximum torque; in other words, as the load on the motor is increased from an initial zero value, maximum output is reached sooner than maximum torque.

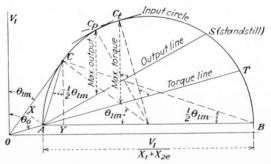

FIG. 6-25. Maximum power factor, torque, and output.

Maximum power factor obviously occurs when the load point C, Fig. 6-25, is so located that θ_1 has the minimum value θ_{1m}, that is, when OC is

---

* The only way by which readings can be made in the region of instability is to connect the induction motor mechanically to an adjustable-speed motor which will hold the speed at any desired value.

tangent to the circle ACB. Figure 6-25 shows that for this condition $AX = AY$, from which

$$I_0 \sin (\theta_0 - \theta_{1m}) = \frac{V_1}{2(X_1 + X_{2e})} (1 - \cos \theta_{1m})$$

thereby fixing the maximum power factor in terms of quantities all of which are known. If θ_0 is so nearly 90° that the difference is inappreciable, this equation reduces to

$$\text{Maximum power factor} = \frac{\frac{1}{2}V_1/(X_1 + X_{2e})}{I_0 + \frac{1}{2}V_1/(X_1 + X_{2e})}$$

which has the geometrical significance shown in Fig. 6-26.

The circle diagram brings out clearly certain over-all relations which are of importance to designers and users of induction motors. For since the diameter of the circle is $AB = V_1/(X_1 + X_{2e})$, which expression has the dimensions of current, it follows that all other linear dimensions in the diagram are expressible in amperes to the same scale selected for the diameter AB. The intercept CE in Fig. 6-22, which represents power output, can then be converted to equivalent watts by multiplying the scaled number of amperes by the factor m_1V_1 (that is, the number of primary phases times the impressed volts per phase). Similarly, the scaled ampere value of CF in Fig. 6-26, if multiplied by m_1V_1, becomes the total

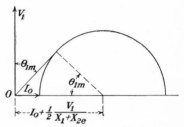

FIG. 6-26. Approximate condition for maximum power factor.

electrical input to the secondary, in watts, and this result is called the *torque in synchronous watts;* in accordance with Eq. 6-28, the torque in synchronous watts can be converted into pound-feet by multiplying it by the factor $33{,}000/(2\pi n_1 \times 746)$.

With these considerations in mind it will be seen that in high-efficiency machines (i.e., those in which the total resistance is small) the starting current at full voltage approaches the diameter of the circle, while the breakdown torque approaches the radius. Hence the per-unit maximum torque will be less than half the per-unit starting current; otherwise stated, the maximum torque in synchronous watts will be less than half the starting volt-amperes, and the maximum output in watts will be still smaller than half the starting volt-amperes.

The breakdown torque of induction motors at full voltage is fixed by American Standards Association (ASA) rules at not less than 200 per cent of the torque at rated load. To provide for the effect of an allowable 10 per cent reduction in voltage (which would reduce the 200 per cent maximum torque to $200 \times 0.90^2 = 162$ per cent of rated value), it is customary to design for a breakdown torque approximating 250 per cent, which means a starting current of not less than 500 per cent, or 5.0 on a per-unit basis.   In practice, the ASA regulations prescribe that the starting current of 220-volt three-phase motors rated at more than 15 hp shall not exceed 14.5 amp per rated horsepower; which means, since the rated current per horsepower is

$$\frac{746}{\sqrt{3} \times 220 \times 0.8} = 2.45 \text{ amp}$$

(assuming that the product of efficiency and power factor is about 0.8) that the starting current is $14.5/2.45 = 6.0$ times the rated full-load current.   The starting torque for the condition $s = 1$ can then be computed from Eq. 6-27 if the secondary resistance is known; or if it is desired that the per-unit starting torque shall be 1.5, it follows that the per-unit resistance must be $1.5/6^2 = 0.042$, or somewhat more than 4 per cent.

6-11. The Exact Circle Diagram.   The derivation of the circle diagram given in Art. 6-8 was based upon the approximate equivalent circuit of Figs. 6-18 and 6-19.   One might therefore be tempted to believe that the simple circular form of the current locus is a consequence of this approximation; nevertheless, it is a fact that the more exact equivalent circuit of Fig. 6-17 also yields a circular current locus.   But before entering upon a proof of this fact, it is desirable to point out certain limitations of the so-called "exact" equivalent circuit which make it at best only a close approach to the truth, and not a mathematically exact representation of physical reality.

One of these limitations has already been mentioned; it arises from the fact that the exciting admittance, made up of the exciting conductance G_0 and the exciting susceptance B_0, is not strictly constant, but changes somewhat with the load because of varying friction, windage, and core loss.   In addition, it must be remembered that R_1, X_1, R_2, and X_2 are themselves subject to variation with the load.   The resistances, for example, that must be used in the computations are not the pure ohmic resistances that would be measured by a Wheatstone bridge or by the drop-of-potential method, but they are the effective resistances, which are always greater than the simple ohmic resistances because of the actual nonuniform distribution of the current in the cross section of the conductor.   The nonuniform current distribution is a manifestation of skin effect, and is caused by the crowding of the current toward the surface layers due to the magnetic field; this effect is especially pronounced in the rotor under standstill conditions, i.e., at starting, for the secondary is then subject to the inductive effect of a magnetic field alternating at line frequency, as contrasted with conditions near synchronism when the secondary frequency is greatly reduced.   As a matter of fact, the change of effective secondary resistance between standstill and full speed can be so exaggerated by appropriate design as to make the starting torque considerably greater than it would otherwise be, without at the same time impairing efficiency and speed regulation under normal running conditions.

In like manner, the primary and secondary leakage reactances are functions of the magnitude and distribution of the leakage flux, and these in turn depend upon the permeance of the leakage paths. Changing load conditions cause changes in the current and therefore of the permeability of the teeth and neighboring iron, thus affecting the reactances.

In spite of all these disturbing effects, the assumption that the so-called "constants" of the equivalent circuit (G_0, B_0, R_1, X_1, R_2, X_2) remain invariant yields remarkably accurate results—accurate, that is, when compared with actual measurements. This close agreement is due to several reasons: In the first place, the variations in the "constants" are of the second order of magnitude, and those which change the most (as R_2) are themselves so small in comparison with others that the effect is largely masked under normal running conditions; in the second place, normal running conditions comprise such a small part of the entire range between standstill and synchronism as still further to reduce the discrepancies; and, in the third place, actual observations must be made with instruments which are themselves not absolutely accurate, and the readings are in addition subject to personal errors of observation. In short, the difference between absolute truth (if there is such a thing) and observed facts is not sharply defined, and the more or less hazy zone of uncertainty between them includes the effect of simplifying assumptions and of errors of observation.

It must not be assumed, therefore, that an analysis based upon the so-called exact equivalent circuit is rigorous in the mathematical sense; the word "exact" is really a misnomer, but it has been generally used to distinguish this case from that of the confessedly approximate circuit. It is to be expected that it will yield results very nearly the same as those already derived from the approximate circuit. The chief value of the more complete analysis therefore derives not from increased accuracy but from certain principles and procedures that have wide application and intrinsic importance of their own.

6-12. Analytical Derivation of the Exact Circle Diagram. In the equivalent circuit of Fig. 6-17, the admittance measured between terminals ab is $\sqrt{G^2 + B^2}$, and this is equivalent to a total resistance of $G/(G^2 + B^2)$ ohms in series with a total reactance of $B/(G^2 + B^2)$ ohms. Between the points cd, this total resistance is reduced by R_1 ohms, and the total reactance is reduced by X_1 ohms. Proceeding in this way through the circuit, the results may be arranged in the following tabular form:*

* K. J. Laurel, The Exact Circular Current Locus of the Induction Motor, *Elec. World,* **52**:78 (1908).

Part of circuit	Resistance or conductance		Reactance or susceptance		Unit
ab	G		B		mho
cd	$\dfrac{G}{G^2 + B^2} - R_1 = \alpha$	(6-35)	$\dfrac{B}{G^2 + B^2} - X_1 = \beta$	(6-36)	ohm
ef	$\dfrac{\alpha}{\alpha^2 + \beta^2} - G_0 = \gamma$	(6-37)	$\dfrac{\beta}{\alpha^2 + \beta^2} - B_0 = \delta$	(6-38)	mho
gh	$\dfrac{\gamma}{\gamma^2 + \delta^2} = \dfrac{R_{2e}}{s}$	(6-39)	$\dfrac{\delta}{\gamma^2 + \delta^2} = X_{2e}$	(6-40)	ohm

Starting with Eq. 6-40, and eliminating successively α, β, γ, and δ, the result is

$$\left(G - \frac{N}{M}\right)^2 + \left(B - \frac{P}{M}\right)^2 = \left(\frac{1}{2M}\right)^2 \tag{6-41}$$

where
$$N = R_1 X_{2e} Y_0^2 + R_1 B_0 + X_{2e} G_0$$
$$P = X_1 X_{2e} Y_0^2 + B_0(X_1 + X_{2e}) + \tfrac{1}{2} \tag{6-41a}$$
$$M = X_1 + X_{2e}[1 + Z_1^2 Y_0^2 + 2(R_1 G_0 + X_1 B_0)] + Z_1^2 B_0$$

Equation 6-41 shows that the locus of the variables G and B is a circle of radius $1/2M$, the coordinates of the center being N/M and P/M. If G and B are multiplied by V_1, the products become, respectively, equal to the in-phase and quadrature components of the primary current. Just as in all the circle diagrams thus far encountered, the position and size of the circle are independent of the secondary resistance, the role of the latter (more precisely that of R_{2e}/s) being to fix the positions of particular points on the locus. Two of these points are of special interest, namely, those corresponding to synchronism ($s = 0$) and standstill ($s = 1$). It is therefore desirable to consider the relative positions of these points in greater detail, and at the same time to consider the relations between the approximate and the exact circle diagrams for the purpose of evaluating the error introduced by the use of the approximate diagram.

As the first step, it is necessary to obtain a general idea of the relative magnitudes of the resistances and reactances that are characteristic of the usual commercial motors. Selecting the squirrel-cage type for general power purposes which do not require large starting torque, the following specifications may be taken as typical:

a. Maximum torque = 2.5 × full-load torque.

b. Slip at full load, 3 per cent.

c. Power factor at full load, 90 per cent.

d. Efficiency at full load, 90 per cent.

It should be noted that performance specifications cannot be laid down wholly at random, for all of the operating characteristics are functions of the geometry of the circle diagram and are therefore interrelated. The circle is completely fixed when any three points on it are determined;

hence, the specifications must fix three points, and only three. The impo-
sition of one or more additional requirements chosen at random would
naturally lead to inconsistencies.

Applying the given specifications to the approximate diagram (such as
Fig. 6-24), we have from Eqs. 6-26 and 6-30 and specification a

$$\frac{T_{\max}}{T} = \frac{(R_1 + R_{2e}/s)^2 + (X_1 + X_{2e})^2}{2\,\dfrac{R_{2e}}{s}\,[R_1 + \sqrt{R_1{}^2 + (X_1 + X_{2e})^2}]} = 2.5 \qquad (6\text{-}42)$$

For practical purposes, it is sufficiently accurate to assume $R_1 = R_{2e}$ and
$X_1 = X_{2e}$; on substituting these relations in Eq. 6-42, together with the
specification that at full load $s = 0.03$, it is found that

$$X_1 = 3.12 R_1$$

whence $\qquad\qquad \tan \theta_{2s} = \dfrac{X_1 + X_{2e}}{R_1 + R_{2e}} = \dfrac{X_1}{R_1} = 3.12 \qquad\qquad (6\text{-}43)$

If a semicircle is drawn on any arbitrarily selected diameter AB (Fig.
6-27) which then represents $V_1/(X_1 + X_{2e}) = V_1/2X_1$, the standstill

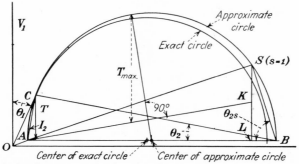

FIG. 6-27. Relation between approximate and exact circle diagrams for typical motor.

point is found by drawing BS at an angle θ_{2s} with AB. Bisecting the
perpendicular dropped from S to AB, and drawing the lines AS and AK,
the output and torque lines are fixed. The full-load point C is then
located by drawing BC at an angle θ_2 with BA such that

$$\tan \theta_2 = \frac{X_1 + X_{2e}}{R_1 + R_{2e}/s} = \frac{2X_1}{R_1(1 + 1/0.3)} = \frac{0.06 X_1}{1.03 R_1} = 0.181 \quad (6\text{-}44)$$

The secondary current I_2 is then represented by AC, and

$$I_2 = \frac{V_1}{2X_1} \sin \theta_2 = 0.089 \frac{V_1}{X_1} \qquad (6\text{-}45)$$

The in-phase and quadrature components of I_2 are $I_2 \cos \theta_2 = 0.087 V_1/X_1$
and $I_2 \sin \theta_2 = 0.0158 V_1/X_1$, respectively, and if to these are added
the in-phase and quadrature components of I_0, which are, respectively,

$V_1 G_0$ and $V_1 B_0$, the results are the in-phase and quadrature components of the primary current I_1. Since the phase angle of I_1 is specified by the requirement c that $\cos \theta_1 = 0.90$, it follows that

$$\tan \theta_1 = \frac{V_1 B_0 + 0.0158 V_1 / X_1}{V_1 G_0 + 0.087 V_1 / X_1} = 0.484 \tag{6-46}$$

Since the efficiency at full load is specified to be 90 per cent, the output is $0.9 V_1 I_1 \cos \theta_1$; hence, from the relation

$$\text{Input} = \text{output} + \text{losses}$$

we have $V_1 I_1 \cos \theta_1 = 0.9 V_1 I_1 \cos \theta_1 + V_1 (V_1 G_0) + I_2^2 (R_1 + R_{2e})$

or, since $\cos \theta_1 = 0.9$,

$$0.09 V_1 I_1 = V_1^2 G_0 + 2 R_1 \left(\frac{0.089 V_1}{X_1} \right)^2 \tag{6-47}$$

Substituting in Eq. 6-47 the relation

$$I_1 = V_1 \left[\left(B_0 + \frac{0.0158}{X_1} \right)^2 + \left(G_0 + \frac{0.087}{X_1} \right)^2 \right]^{\frac{1}{2}} \tag{6-48}$$

the result is

$$0.0081 \left[\left(B_0 + \frac{0.0158}{X_1} \right)^2 + \left(G_0 + \frac{0.087}{X_1} \right)^2 \right] = \left(G_0 + \frac{0.00508}{X_1} \right)^2 \tag{6-49}$$

Equations 6-46 and 6-49 now provide means for solving for G_0 and B_0, the result being

$$G_0 = \frac{0.00966}{X_1}$$
$$B_0 = \frac{0.03098}{X_1} \tag{6-50}$$

The coordinates of the center of the approximate circle are

$$V_1 \left[B_0 + \frac{1}{2(X_1 + X_{2e})} \right]$$

and $V_1 G_0$, and the radius is $\dfrac{\frac{1}{2} V_1}{X_1 + X_{2e}}$; taking $X_1 = X_{2e}$, substituting for G_0 and B_0 from Eqs. 6-50, and dropping the common factor V_1, the coordinates of the center, and the radius, both expressed in terms of equivalent admittance, take the values shown in the table below. Computing the corresponding coordinates and radius of the exact circle by means of Eqs. 6-41a, 6-42, and 6-49, they take the values also shown in the table. It will be seen that the differences are very small. The two circles, constructed from the dimensions given in the table, are shown in Fig. 6-27;

this is a reproduction of the original drawing, which was drawn to a large scale in order to obtain accuracy. Within the working range from no load to full load, it is practically impossible to distinguish between the two circles. Beyond full load, the departure between them increases, but with the constants used in this example it is at no point very great.

Dimension	Approximate circle	Exact circle
Horizontal (quadrature) coordinate of center............	$\dfrac{0.281}{X_1}$	$\dfrac{0.268}{X_1}$
Vertical (in-phase) coordinate of center................	$\dfrac{0.0097}{X_1}$	$\dfrac{0.0095}{X_1}$
Radius...	$\dfrac{0.25}{X_1}$	$\dfrac{0.238}{X_1}$

It is apparent, therefore, that the error due to the use of the approximate equivalent circuit and the circle diagram corresponding thereto is within the tolerance limit required for practical purposes; so the approximate circuit may be used as sufficiently accurate.

6-13. The Exact Circle Diagram by the Method of Inversion. Equation 6-41 of the preceding article embodies the analytical proof of the fact that the locus of the primary current phasor is a circle notwithstanding the apparent complications of the relations expressed in Eq. 6-15. The derivation of Eq. 6-41, which requires the algebraic manipulation of the six immediately preceding equations, is rather long and tedious; so it is very interesting that the same conclusions follow very quickly and easily from the geometrical interpretation of Eq. 6-15, which may be rewritten in the form

$$\mathbf{I}_1 = \mathbf{V}_1 \left(\frac{1}{R_1 + jX_1 + \dfrac{1}{G_0 - jB_0 + \dfrac{1}{R_{2e}/s + jX_{2e}}}} \right) \qquad (6\text{-}51)$$

The expression in the parentheses obviously represents the equivalent admittance of the machine as a whole; i.e., it is equal to $G - jB$, which when multiplied by $\mathbf{V}_1$ gives the primary current $\mathbf{I}_1$ in the form of two components, one of which, $\mathbf{V}_1G$, is in phase with $\mathbf{V}_1$, the other, $\mathbf{V}_1B$, in quadrature with $\mathbf{V}_1$. To prove that the current locus is a circle, it is therefore only necessary to show that the equivalent admittance of the entire machine defines a circle when the single variable entering into its magnitude, namely, the slip s, takes all possible values. But before analyzing the geometrical meaning of the parentheses in Eq. 6-51, it is first necessary to consider the two geometrical propositions presented below.

As a starting point, let $\mathbf{v}$ be a complex number represented by the correspondingly labeled phasor in Fig. 6-28, and let it be defined by the relation

$$\mathbf{v} = \mathbf{v}_1 + \lambda\mathbf{v}_2$$

where $\mathbf{v}_1$ and $\mathbf{v}_2$ are complex numbers and λ is a simple numeric which may take all real values between plus and minus infinity. It is plain that as λ takes all possible values the locus of the terminal point of $\mathbf{v}$ lies on the straight line AB extended to infinity in both directions.

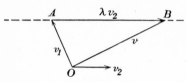

FIG. 6-28. Variable phasor with straight-line locus of terminal point.

Proposition 1. If the locus of the terminal point of a phasor is a straight line, the locus of the terminal point of its reciprocal is a circle.

In Fig. 6-29 the phasor $\mathbf{v}$, instead of being shown as the resultant of $\mathbf{v}_1$ and $\lambda\mathbf{v}_2$, has the equivalent form

$$\mathbf{v} = \mathbf{v}_0 + \mu\mathbf{v}_2$$

where $\mathbf{v}_0$ is perpendicular to the straight-line locus AB, and μ is again a numeric which may have any real value, positive or negative.

If $\mathbf{v}$ is referred to the line OX (parallel to AB) as an axis of reference, it may be represented by

$$\mathbf{v} = ve^{j\theta}$$

where v is the actual magnitude of OP and θ may have any value from zero to $180°$. The reciprocal of $\mathbf{v}$ is therefore

$$\frac{1}{\mathbf{v}} = \frac{1}{v} e^{-j\theta}$$

which is clearly a phasor, such as OP', lying as much below axis OX as OP is above it, but the length of which is as yet undefined.

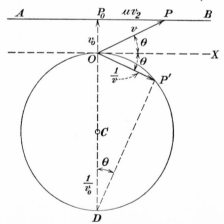

FIG. 6-29. Locus of reciprocal of phasor of Fig. 6-28.

When angle θ takes the special value $\pi/2$, phasor $\mathbf{v}$ becomes equal to $\mathbf{v}_0$, and $1/v$ is numerically equal to $1/v_0$. But since

$$\mathbf{v}\Big|_{\theta=\pi/2} = \mathbf{v}_0 = v_0 e^{j(\pi/2)}$$

we have

$$\frac{1}{\mathbf{v}}\Big|_{\theta=\pi/2} = \frac{1}{v_0} e^{-j(\pi/2)}$$

which means that the reciprocal of OP_0 is $OD = 1/v_0$. The scale to which OD is drawn is immaterial, and any convenient length may be used; but the length $OD = 1/v_0$ having been arbitrarily selected, let a circle be drawn upon it as a diameter, and let the phasor OP', drawn below axis OX at angle θ, be extended until it intersects the circle at P'. On drawing the chord DP', it is seen that

$$OP' = OD \sin \theta = \frac{1}{v_0} \sin \theta$$

But it is also evident from triangle OP_0P that $\sin \theta = v_0/v$; hence,

$$OP' = \frac{1}{v_0}\frac{v_0}{v} = \frac{1}{v}$$

thereby proving that as point P moves along the straight line AB the terminal point of the reciprocal phasor moves around the circle.

In some of the cases where this proposition finds application, the chief concern is with the magnitude of the reciprocal length, and in that event its angular position is immaterial. It is therefore possible to change the form of Fig. 6-29 to that shown in Fig. 6-30, which makes it easier to see the relative magnitudes of the phasor $\mathbf{v} = OP$ and its reciprocal, $OP' = 1/v$.

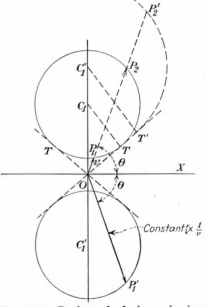

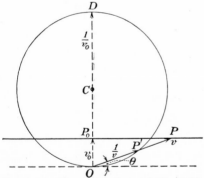

FIG. 6-30. Alternative form of Fig. 6-29.   FIG. 6-31. Reciprocal of phasor having circular locus.

Proposition 2.   If the locus of the terminal point of a phasor is a circle which does not pass through the origin of the phasor, the locus of the terminal point of its reciprocal is also a circle.

In Fig. 6-31 let OP_1 be a phasor $\mathbf{v}$ which varies in such manner that its terminal point lies on a circle which does not pass through the origin O, and which has its center at a point C_1. When $\mathbf{v} = OP_1$ is referred to an axis OX drawn perpendicular to OC_1, its equation is

$$\mathbf{v} = ve^{j\theta}$$

though here there are in general two values of $\mathbf{v}$, namely, OP_1 and OP_2, for each possible value of θ. But without regard to the magnitude of $\mathbf{v}$, whether it be OP_1 or OP_2, its reciprocal is

$$\frac{1}{\mathbf{v}} = \frac{1}{v} e^{-j\theta}$$

which represents a phasor which lies below axis OX by the same angle that $\mathbf{v}$ is above it.

It is well-known from plane geometry that the product of the two intercepts OP_1 and OP_2 is constant and equal to $(OT)^2$, where OT is the length of the tangent drawn from O to the circle C_1; that is,

$$(OP_1)(OP_2) = (OT)^2 = \text{constant}$$

from which it follows that

$$OP_2 = \text{constant} \times \frac{1}{OP_1}$$

which means that OP_2 is directly proportional to the reciprocal of $OP_1 = \mathbf{v}$, and, by an appropriate choice of scale, OP_2 may be made equal to $1/\mathbf{v}$. The proper position of this reciprocal is, however, below the axis of reference at an angle θ, as indicated by the line OP_1', and the point P_1' lies on a circle C_1' which is the mirror image of circle C_1 reflected below the axis of reference. If, however, the angular position of the reciprocal is not in question, but only its magnitude, the latter is sufficiently defined by the length OP_2, thereby eliminating the need for the auxiliary circle below the axis of reference. Furthermore, if the scale to which $1/\mathbf{v}$ is represented by OP_2 is not convenient, it is only necessary to draw another circle, with its center at, say, C_1'', and with a radius such that the new circle is tangent to the line OT (prolonged if necessary). The reciprocal of $\mathbf{v} = OP_1$ is then represented by OP_2' to the modified scale.

It is to be noted that since $(OP_1)(OP_2) = (OT)^2$ the magnitudes of $\mathbf{v} = OP_1$ and its reciprocal $1/\mathbf{v} = OP_2$ will both be represented to a scale in accordance with which the length of the tangent OT is equal to unity.

Application to Eq. 6-51. In Fig. 6-32 the length $OL = Z_2$ represents the variable impedance $R_{2e}/s + jX_{2e}$, which appears in the final sub-denominator of Eq. 6-51. The component $OK = X_{2e}$ is the fixed secondary leakage reactance, and $KL = R_{2e}/s$ is the variable resistance, which takes into account the varying load. The locus of the terminal point of Z_2 is the line AB; so in accordance with Proposition 1 the reciprocal of Z_2 is represented by the chord OP of a circle having its center C on a line through O perpendicular to AB. If the radius of circle C is so chosen that the chord OM is equal to unity to the scale of both ohms and mhos, then $OP = 1/Z_2$.

Equation 6-51 requires that the admittance $G_0 - jB_0$ must be added geometrically to $1/Z_2$. This can be done by laying off G_0 to the left of origin O, and B_0 vertically upward to point O'; hence, the length $O'P$ correctly represents the quantity $G_0 - jB_0 + 1/Z_2$ both as to magnitude and position.

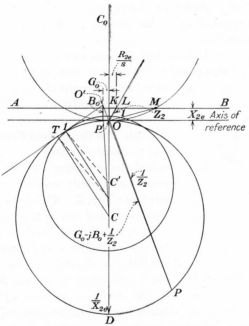

FIG. 6-32. Change of scale of reciprocal.

The line $O'P$ intersects circle C at a point P', and the length $O'P'$ is therefore proportional to the reciprocal of $O'P$. However, since

$$(O'P)(O'P') = (O'T)^2 \neq 1$$

where $O'T$ is the length of the tangent drawn from O' to circle C, it follows that $O'P'$ is not *equal* to the reciprocal of $O'P$ to the original scale of ohms, which was fixed by making $OM = 1$. It is therefore necessary to construct a new circle, with its center at C' on line $O'C$, so that all dimensions of the new circle will be related to those of the original circle C by the ratio $1/(O'T)^2$. This can be done by the simple geometrical construction indicated to the left of line OD in Fig. 6-32.

Circle C' is reproduced in Fig. 6-33, together with the reference points O and O' which appear in Fig. 6-32. Lengths such as $O'Q$ drawn from point O' to the circle C' then represent to scale the impedance expressed by $1/(G_0 - jB_0 + 1/Z_2)$; but by Eq. 6-51 there must be added to this impedance the primary leakage impedance $R_1 + jX_1$, which can be done graphically by shifting the origin from O' to O''. Hence, if $O''Q$ is equal to $R_1 + jX_1 + \dfrac{1}{G_0 - jB_0 + 1/Z_2}$, its reciprocal is *proportional* to $O''Q'$.

The product of $O''Q$ and $O''Q'$ is $(O''T'')^2$, whereas it should be unity if the final admittance is to be shown to the original scale. It is therefore again necessary to change circle C' to a new circle C'' by the construction indicated. Finally, therefore, the resultant admittance of the machine as a whole, corresponding to the arbitrary value of Z_2 used in Fig. 6-32, is $O''Q''$ in Fig. 6-33.

The conclusion is obvious that the final locus of the primary current is a circle, and that this result will hold true without regard to the number of terms in the expression, such as that of Eq. 6-51, which defines the resultant admittance of the machine.

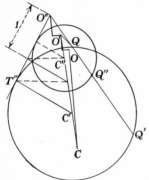

FIG. 6-33. Final stage of inversion.

6-14. The Cross-field Theory.   The physical concepts underlying this theory (also called the component-field theory) have already been briefly outlined in Art. 6-3 and in parts of Chap. 5.   The stator winding, which may consist of two or more phases, produces a single rotating field which may be imagined to be resolved into equal component alternating fluxes, each stationary in space and differing from each other in time and space phase by 90 electrical degrees.   The effect is the same as though the stator winding consisted of two phases, each independently producing an alternating flux, stationary in space, in the manner indicated in Fig. 6-10.   The rotor may be of the squirrel-cage type, or it may have a commutated winding short-circuited by two sets of brushes, one in each of the two flux axes; for it has been shown in Chap. 5 that these two types of rotor windings are exactly equivalent to each other.

In order to distinguish between the two axes, one of them will be designated by the symbol t, the other by the symbol r, as in Fig. 6-34a, though it is plain from the symmetry of the structure that there is no real difference between them.   In each axis, the relation between primary (stator) and secondary (rotor) current must necessarily be the same as in an ordinary stationary transformer, i.e., the resultant of their respective mmfs must be just sufficient to maintain the flux through the magnetic circuit coinciding with their axis.   The flux in either axis induces in the corresponding primary winding an emf which must be balanced by a component of the impressed voltage; and the impressed voltage must contain, in addition, a component to balance the primary leakage-impedance drop.

In the rotor circuits, however, the conditions involve more than ordi-

nary transformer relations.   For while in the t axis, for example, there is
an emf induced by Φ_t in accordance with usual transformer action, there
is also an emf developed by rotation through Φ_r, and the latter emf is
opposite in phase to the former; it corresponds to the counter emf in an
ordinary d-c motor.   The induced transformer emf corresponds to the
voltage impressed on the terminals of an ordinary motor, though here it is
inductively, instead of conductively, supplied.   In addition to these two
main emfs in each axis, which, by opposing each other, limit the working
current, there must also be considered the leakage-impedance drops.

   In order that the phase relations between currents and voltages in the
two axes may be analyzed with due regard to consistency, it is necessary
to adopt certain conventions.   Thus, in Fig. 6-34b, let it be considered
that in the t axis the upward vertical direction is to be taken as positive;
and that in the r axis the positive direction is to the right, conforming to
the usual cartesian notation.   Let it be considered further that a current

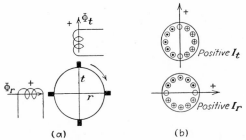

(a)   (b)

FIG. 6-34. Conventional system of notation.

flowing in either axis (or the emf which produces the current) is positive
if it is so directed as to produce a positively directed mmf and negative if
it produces a negatively directed mmf; thus, Fig. 6-34b shows positively
directed current distributions in the two axes.

   Assume that the two equal components of flux Φ_t and Φ_r have the time-
phase relation indicated in Fig. 6-35 and that the corresponding rotation
of the rotor is clockwise, as in Fig. 6-34a.   Considering the physical hap-
penings in the t axis, it is apparent that the effect of Φ_t will be to induce
an emf E_{tt} lagging behind Φ_t by 90°.   At the same time, clockwise rotation
through positive Φ_r will develop a negatively directed emf E_{rr} in the t axis,
hence opposite in phase to Φ_r, as may easily be verified by applying
Fleming's right-hand rule, or any equivalent method, to Fig. 6-36a.
Consequently, E_{tt} and E_{rr} are opposite in phase, as shown in Fig. 6-35a.*
The difference between these two emfs, indicated by E_T, is then consumed
in driving the current I_t through the rotor leakage impedance.

   * The double subscripts defining the emfs have been so chosen that the first subscript
indicates the flux to which the emf is due; the second, whether the emf is caused by
transformer action (t), or by rotational effect (r).

Considering next the axis r, the effect of Φ_r is to induce by transformer action an emf E_{rt} lagging 90° behind Φ_r as in Fig. 6-35b.* But in this case clockwise rotation through positive Φ_t will generate a positively directed speed emf E_{tr} in the r axis, as shown in Fig. 6-36b; that is, E_{tr} is in phase with Φ_t, hence in phase opposition with E_{rt}. The resultant voltage E_R in the r axis is then the difference between E_{rt} and E_{tr}, and it is consumed in driving the current I_r through the rotor leakage impedance.

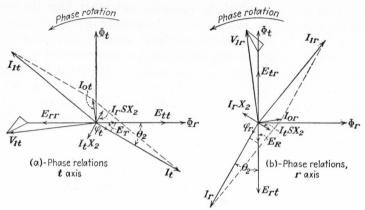

FIG. 6-35. Phasor diagram, cross-field theory.

In each axis, the magnetizing current I_0 will be the resultant of the corresponding stator and rotor currents provided that the actual values of secondary current are first reduced to terms of the primary. Assuming that this has been done, the remainder of the phasor diagram is completed in the now familiar manner. In Fig. 6-35, the primary currents have been designated as I_{1t} and I_{1r}, and the primary voltages as V_{1t} and V_{1r}. It is plain that conditions are the same in the two circuits and that each contributes half of the total power developed.

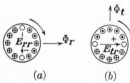

FIG. 6-36. Showing signs of E_{rr} and E_{tr}.

The torque is chiefly due to the reaction between Φ_t and I_r on the one hand, and between Φ_r and I_t on the other. It will be observed that I_t lags behind Φ_r by angle θ_2, which is the phase displacement between resultant emf and current in each of the two rotor axes; on the other hand, current I_r lags behind Φ_t by $180 + \theta_2$, which at first glance might lead to the conclusion that the two torques are in opposition and so annul each other. To resolve this apparent difficulty, observe that the component of I_t in time quadrature with Φ_r is not effective in producing torque, leaving for consideration only the component of I_t in phase with Φ_r. It will be seen from Fig. 6-34b that a positive I_t will react

* The two parts of Fig. 6-35, though shown separately for convenience, constitute in reality a single diagram.

with a positive Φ_r to produce torque in the clockwise direction. In like manner, the component of I_r in time-phase opposition with Φ_t means that a negative I_r reacts with a positive Φ_t, and Fig. 6-34b shows that such a combination also produces clockwise torque.

6-15. Analytic Theory of Cross Fields. In Eqs. 5-4 and 5-7, it was shown that the ratio of the speed emf to the transformer emf is equal to the ratio of the speed frequency to the line frequency. If the actual speed, in terms of synchronous speed as unity, is designated as S, it follows that

$$\frac{E_{rr}}{E_{tt}} = \frac{E_{tr}}{E_{rt}} = S$$

and
$$E_T = E_{tt} - E_{rr} = E_{tt}(1 - S)$$
$$E_R = E_{rt} - E_{tr} = E_{rt}(1 - S)$$

(6-52)

Since the slip s is equal to $1 - S$,

$$E_T = sE_{tt}$$
$$E_R = sE_{rt}$$

Furthermore, E_{tt} and E_{rt} are numerically equal to each other since they are due to the equal flux components Φ_t and Φ_r, respectively, and, provided secondary quantities are reduced to terms of the primary, they are also equal to the emfs induced in the primary. In other words, $E_{tt} = E_{rt} = E_1 = E_2$, and the actual emf in the secondary is

$$E_T = E_R = sE_{2e}$$

which is the same in form as the expression for the secondary emf deduced by the rotating-field method; but whereas the secondary emf sE_{2e} in the rotating-field theory is of slip frequency, it is here of line frequency, and so also are the secondary currents $I_t = I_r = I_{2e}$. The leakage fluxes φ_t and φ_r set up by the currents I_t and I_r in each of the two brush axes are themselves alternating at line frequency, but each is stationary in space in its own axis, in exactly the same way as are the main fluxes Φ_t and Φ_r, and like the main fluxes the two leakage fluxes are also equal in magnitude. The alternation of φ_t, for example, will induce in the t axis a reactance voltage I_tX_2, of line frequency proportional to φ_t and lagging 90° behind φ_t, as indicated in Fig. 6-35a; at the same time, rotation through the leakage field φ_r will generate in the t axis an emf proportional to $S\varphi_r$ and in time-phase opposition to φ_r, therefore expressible as SI_rX_2; and since $I_r = I_t$, the net reactance voltage in the t axis is

$$I_tX_2 - I_tSX_2 = I_tX_2(1 - S) = I_tsX_2$$

In exactly similar manner, it may be shown that the net reactance voltage in the r axis is I_rsX_2. These results mean that while all secondary emfs and currents are treated as of line frequency in the machine under consideration, the net reactance voltage varies in proportion to the slip exactly as though the secondary currents were of slip frequency.   In each of the two axes, the relation between current and emf is therefore

$$I_2 = \frac{sE_{2e}}{\sqrt{R_{2e}^2 + s^2 X_{2e}^2}} = \frac{E_{2e}}{\sqrt{(R_{2e}/s)^2 + X_{2e}^2}}$$

or exactly as deduced on the basis of the rotating-field theory; in other words, the secondary current is the same as though the rotor were stationary and the secondary resistance were inversely proportional to the slip.

One point that requires consideration is the question whether the torque developed by the motor is affected by a possible reaction between I_t and φ_r, on the one hand, and between I_r and φ_t, on the other, since in both pairs the constituents are in space quadrature and so advantageously spaced; but reference to Fig. 6-35 shows that in both cases the current and leakage flux are in time quadrature; hence, they contribute nothing to the torque.   The net torque is therefore due wholly to the reaction between I_t and Φ_r and between I_r and Φ_t, each pair contributing half of the total torque.

Since the secondary current is represented by the same equation as that previously deduced by the use of the rotating-field theory, and since conditions in the primary are also the same, the conclusion follows that the equivalent circuit is the same on the basis of both the cross-field theory and the rotating-field theory; and all of the equations and circle diagrams previously deduced are again applicable.

CHAPTER 7

RELATIONS BETWEEN OPERATING PARAMETERS
AND MACHINE DIMENSIONS

7-1. The Output Equation. One of the most striking features in the development of electrical machinery has been the steadily increasing output obtainable from a frame of given dimensions. In the case of induction motors, for example, a frame which in 1903 was rated at 10 hp yielded four times that output about forty years later. This marked increase in weight efficiency was made possible by a combination of several factors, of which the most important include improvements in the magnetic properties of the sheet steel used for core material; the development of insulating materials capable of withstanding relatively high temperature; better provision for ventilation and cooling; and a general tendency toward higher rotative speed.

There is a well-defined relation between the principal dimensions of a rotating machine and its kva or horsepower rating, in terms of quantities which define the specific utilization of the materials of its magnetic and electric circuits. This relation, called the *output equation*,* is derived as follows: The kva rating is given by the expression

$$\text{kva} = m_1 V_1 I_1 \times 10^{-3} \cong m_1 E_1 I_1 \times 10^{-3}$$

where V_1 and I_1 are the rated per-phase values of primary voltage and current, m_1 is the number of primary phases, and E_1 is the primary induced emf which differs from V_1 by the relatively small leakage impedance drop in the primary. Substituting for E_1 the value given by Eq. 4-27,

$$\text{kva} = \sqrt{2}\, \pi m_1 k_{b_1} k_{p_1} f N_1 I_1 \Phi \times 10^{-3} \tag{7-1}$$

where Φ is the flux per pole in webers.

---

* E. Arnold and J. L. LaCour, "Die Wechselstromtechnik," Vol. 4, p. 529, Julius Springer, Berlin, 1913. A. Gray, "Electrical Machine Design," 2d ed., McGraw Hill Book Company, Inc., New York, 1926. A. Still and C. S. Siskind, "Elements of Electrical Machine Design," 3d ed., McGraw Hill Book Company, Inc., New York, 1954. J. H. Kuhlmann, "Design of Electrical Apparatus," 2d ed., John Wiley & Sons, Inc., New York, 1947. P. L. Alger, "The Nature of Polyphase Induction Machines," John Wiley & Sons, Inc., New York, 1951.

Let

d = diameter of the stator bore, m

l = axial length of the core, m

n_s = speed, rps

p = number of poles

B_g = average flux density in the airgap, webers per sq m

The flux per pole is then given by

$$\Phi = B_g \frac{\pi d}{p} l \qquad \text{webers} \qquad (7\text{-}2)$$

In Eq. 7-1, f may be replaced by $pn_s/2$ and N_1 by $2Z_1$, where Z_1 is the number of conductors in series per phase, thus giving

$$\text{kva} = \left(\frac{\sqrt{2}\,\pi^3}{10^3} k_{b_1} k_{p_1} B_g q \right) d^2 l n_s \qquad (7\text{-}3)$$

where $\quad q = \dfrac{m_1 Z_1 I_1}{\pi d}$ = amp-conductors per meter of periphery $\qquad (7\text{-}4)$

Equation 7-3 may then be written

$$\text{kva} = \xi d^2 l n_s \qquad (7\text{-}5)$$

in which form it is referred to as the *output equation*, and the coefficient

$$\xi = \frac{\sqrt{2}\,\pi^3 k_{b_1} k_{p_1}}{10^3} B_g q \qquad (7\text{-}6)*$$

is called the *output coefficient*.

It will thus be seen that when the speed is specified, the output of the machine is determined by the two major dimensions, namely, d and l, and by the values assigned to B_g and q.   The average airgap flux density B_g may be regarded as a measure of the specific utilization of the core material; and it will now be shown that q is a measure of the degree to which the winding is electrically loaded.

Let

a = cross section of a conductor, sq m

h = number of sq m per amp = a/I_1

ρ = resistivity of copper at temperature t

The resistance of a meter length of a single conductor is then ρ/a, and the ohmic loss in this conductor will be $\rho I_1^2/a$ watts.   The number of con-

---

* If the dimensions d and l are expressed in inches, and the speed in rpm is n, Eq. 7-5 becomes

$$\text{kva} = \xi \, d^2 l n \qquad (7\text{-}5a)$$

where $\qquad \xi = \dfrac{\sqrt{2}\,\pi^3 k_{b_1} k_{p_1}}{60 \times 10^{11}} B_g q \qquad (7\text{-}6a)$

where B_g is in cgs lines per square inch, q is in ampere-conductors per inch of periphery, and n is in rpm.

ductors per meter of periphery being q/I_1, it follows that the watts radiated per square meter due to copper loss will be $\dfrac{\rho I_1^2}{a}\dfrac{q}{I_1} = \dfrac{\rho q}{a/I_1} = \dfrac{\rho q}{h}$, and this is a measure* of the resultant rise of temperature which must be kept within allowable limits by appropriate ventilation. It will be seen that unless h is increased in the same proportion that q is increased, the facilities for the dissipation of the greater heating effect must be correspondingly improved, or else the insulating materials must be selected to withstand higher temperature. Furthermore, an increase in the value of h means conductors of larger cross section, which in turn calls for increased slot dimensions; wider slots imply narrower teeth and correspondingly higher flux densities; and deeper slots imply greater leakage reactance.

It will accordingly be evident that the physical dimensions and the quantities characteristic of the magnetic and electric circuits are all intimately interrelated, and that the problem of the designer is to adjust their magnitudes so that they are not only mutually consistent but so that the resultant machine will meet specifications prescribed by American Institute of Electrical Engineers Standards and those of the ASA and the National Electrical Manufacturers Association (NEMA). The problem is further complicated in the case of machines which constitute a line of progressively increased ratings by the consideration that special tooling be held to a minimum, that subassembly parts be used in common as much as possible, and that in general the manufacturing costs be kept down to meet the requirements of a highly competitive field. For all of these reasons, the art of designing calls for great skill, experience, and judgment.

7-2. Calculation of Exciting Admittance and Reactance. Assuming that values of d, l, B_g, and q have been tentatively assigned, the flux per pole, Φ, is fixed by Eq. 7-2. The emf formula, Eq. 4-27, then leads to the main characteristics of the winding as defined by N_1 and by the breadth and pitch factors.

If at this stage the dimensions of all parts of the magnetic circuit were known, the value of Φ would fix the flux density in each of them, and from the magnetization curves of the core material it would be possible to compute the ampere-turns per pole required to maintain the flux; as a first approximation, it may be assumed that the reluctance of the air-gap consumes practically all of the sinusoidally distributed mmf which, by Eq. 4-44, has a crest value

$$A = \frac{2\sqrt{2}}{\pi} k_{b_1} k_{p_1} m_1 \frac{N_1}{p} I_\phi \qquad \text{amp-turns per pole} \qquad (7\text{-}7)$$

---

* If a is expressed in circular mils, h in circular mils per ampere, and q in ampere-conductors per inch of periphery, the value of ρ becomes approximately 1 ohm per cir mil-in. at the working temperature of 75°C and the watts lost per square inch becomes simply q/h.

where I_ϕ is the rms value of the magnetizing component of the no-load current.

Using rationalized mks units, the flux density in an airgap of effective length δ is

$$B = \mu_0 \frac{\text{amp-turns}}{\delta} \tag{7-8}$$

so that if for the ampere-turns there is substituted the value given by Eq. 7-7 the result would be the maximum airgap flux density if the entire reluctance of the magnetic circuit were concentrated in the airgap. To allow for the fact that the iron part of the magnetic circuit consumes a part of the available excitation, we may write

$$(B_g)_{\max} = \frac{\pi}{2} B_g = \mu_0 k \frac{2\sqrt{2}}{\pi} k_{b_1} k_{p_1} m_1 \frac{N_1 I_\phi}{p\delta} \tag{7-9}$$

where k is a factor less than unity.

Substituting in Eq. 7-9 the value of B_g from Eq. 7-2, and solving for I_ϕ, the result is

$$I_\phi = \frac{\pi}{4\sqrt{2}\,\mu_0} \frac{\Phi p^2 \delta}{k k_{b_1} k_{p_1} m_1 N_1 dl} \tag{7-10}*$$

where all quantities are expressed in rationalized mks units, μ_0 being equal to $4\pi \times 10^{-7}$.

Equation 7-10 serves to determine the exciting susceptance B_0 since $B_0 = V_1/I_\phi$.

Calculation of the exciting conductance G_0 requires a knowledge of the flux densities in the several parts of the magnetic circuit in order that the hysteresis and eddy-current losses may be computed; on adding to the core loss the friction and windage (usually estimated from test data on similar machines), the result is the total no-load loss, equal to $m_1 V_1^2 G_0$, from which G_0 may be found. However, since G_0 is usually small in comparison with B_0, the exciting reactance X_0 may be found by the approximate relations

$$X_0 = \frac{B_0}{G_0^2 + B_0^2} \cong \frac{1}{B_0} = \frac{V_1}{I_\phi} \cong \frac{E_1}{I_\phi} = \frac{32\pi}{10^7} \frac{m_1 f k (k_{b_1} k_{p_1} N_1)^2 dl}{p^2 \delta} \tag{7-11}$$

where all dimensions are in meters. If all dimensions are expressed in inches, the formula becomes

$$X_0 = \frac{25.53}{10^8} \frac{m_1 f k (k_{b_1} k_{p_1} N_1)^2 dl}{p^2 \delta} \tag{7-11a}$$

---

* In the mixed system of units still commonly employed in the United States, the flux is expressed in maxwells, and the dimensions d, l, and δ in inches. In terms of these units, Eq. 7-10 takes the form

$$I_\phi = \frac{0.174 p^2 \Phi \delta}{k k_{b1} k_{p1} m_1 N_1 \, dl} \tag{7-10a}$$

Equation 7-11 shows that, other things being equal, the magnetizing reactance varies inversely as the square of the number of poles, which means that low-speed motors, where p is large, will have lower power factor than high-speed motors.   This effect of a large number of poles can be partially counterbalanced by reducing the airgap.

7-3. Winding Resistance.   In the case of ordinary wire windings, it is a simple matter to compute the ohmic (d-c) resistance per phase from a knowledge of the length and cross section of the conductors, including the end connections, in the manner discussed in Art. 1-15.   But since the resistance that must be considered is not the ohmic, but the effective, resistance, the results thus computed must be increased by 10 to 30 per cent to take into account the effect of the irregular distribution of current over the cross section of the conductors.   This increase is less in windings made of small wire, or of stranded wire, than in cases where heavy bar or strap copper is used.

The determination of the equivalent resistance of a squirrel-cage winding presents a special problem which is intimately related to the corresponding problem of computing the leakage reactance of that type of winding; both problems are therefore deferred for later consideration.

7-4. Leakage Reactance.   The importance of the total leakage reactance is evident from the fact that it determines the diameter of the circle diagram, and therefore directly affects all of the operating characteristics illustrated in Fig. 6-26.   It is also a fairly accurate measure of the maximum torque, since the latter approaches the magnitude represented by the radius of the circle diagram.

Just as in the case of the static transformer, the primary leakage reactance of an induction motor is due to that part of the flux produced by the stator mmf (considered to be acting alone) which does not link effectively with the rotor winding; similarly, the secondary leakage reactance is attributed to that part of the flux produced by the rotor mmf (also considered to be acting alone) which does not link effectively with the stator winding.   But except for this basic concept, which applies to both types of apparatus, the motor differs sharply from the static transformer in that part of the primary flux may actually link with the secondary winding without inducing therein an emf of normal rotor frequency, while at the same time this portion of the primary flux does induce in the primary an emf in quadrature with the primary current.   The same thing is true with respect to secondary flux components which do not link effectively with the stator, in the sense that the induced primary emfs are not of line frequency.   These effects are due to the relative motion between primary and secondary as well as to the space distribution of their mmfs.

The stator winding of an induction motor is usually of the two-layer type in which the individual coils have fractional pitch, in the manner indicated in Fig. 7-1a.   The rotor, if the machine is of the wound-rotor type, is similarly wound, except that the number of rotor slots is not the same as in the stator, and the number of rotor phases may differ from the number of stator phases.   But without regard to the details of the windings, the mmfs of both stator and rotor may each be resolved into a sinusoidally distributed mmf spanning a full pole pitch and a series of odd harmonics (excluding the third and odd multiples thereof) in the manner discussed in Arts. 4-16 to 4-18.

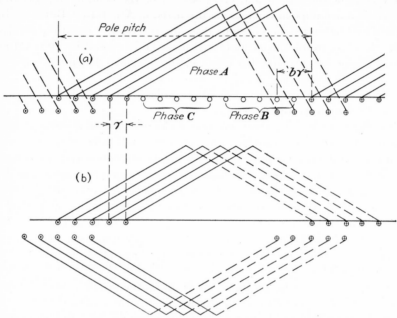

Fɪɢ. 7-1. Equivalent connections, two-layer fractional-pitch distributed winding.

Inspection of the double-layer winding of Fig. 7-1a shows that so far as its magnetizing effect is concerned, it is equivalent to the modified arrangement of Fig. 7-1b.   Each layer, containing half the total turns, is a full-pitch distributed winding having q slots per pole per phase; but the two layers, connected in series, are shifted by an angle $b\gamma$, where b is the number of slots by which the coil throw of the actual winding falls short of full pitch, and γ is the angle, in electrical degrees, from center to center of slots.   The entire winding is therefore equivalent to one in which the breadth factors are

$$k_{b_1} = \frac{\sin\,(q\gamma/2)}{q\,\sin\,(\gamma/2)} \qquad \text{for the fundamental} \qquad (7\text{-}12)$$

$$k_{b_r} = \frac{\sin\,(qr\gamma/2)}{q\,\sin\,(r\gamma/2)} \qquad \text{for the } r\text{th harmonic} \qquad (7\text{-}13)$$

and the corresponding pitch factors are

$$k_{p_1} = \cos\frac{b\gamma}{2} \qquad \text{for the fundamental} \qquad (7\text{-}14)$$

$$k_{p_r} = \cos\frac{br\gamma}{2} \qquad \text{for the } r\text{th harmonic} \qquad (7\text{-}15)$$

It follows from Eqs. 4-44 and 4-46 that the amplitude of the fundamental mmf is

$$A_1 = \frac{2\sqrt{2}}{\pi} k_{b_1} k_{p_1} m \frac{NI}{p} \qquad \text{amp-turns per pole} \qquad (7\text{-}16)$$

while that of the rth harmonic is

$$A_r = \frac{2\sqrt{2}}{\pi}\frac{1}{r} k_{b_r} k_{p_r} \frac{NI}{p} \qquad \text{amp-turns per pole} \qquad (7\text{-}17)$$

Equations 7-12 to 7-17 apply equally to the windings of stator and rotor when the appropriate values of m, q, γ, and N are inserted.

All of these components of the stator and rotor mmfs play a part in producing the actual resultant flux of the machine; but if it is assumed that saturation of the iron may be neglected, the principle of superposition is applicable, and each mmf may then be considered to produce a proportional flux.

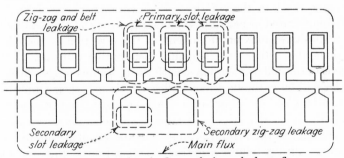

FIG. 7-2. Paths of main flux and airgap leakage flux.

Consider first the fundamental mmfs of the stator and rotor, which are in space opposition but not quite in time-phase opposition, as indicated in the phasor diagram, Fig. 6-15. They combine to give the resultant magnetizing mmf which sets up the mutual flux Φ in the main magnetic circuit, and the mutual flux then serves to transfer energy from the stator to the rotor. But each of these fundamental mmfs also sets up differences of magnetic potential between adjacent teeth (in the peripheral direction), thereby setting up the *slot leakage* flux illustrated in Fig. 7-2. It will be observed that the path of this slot leakage flux lies effectively in the peripheral direction, not in the radial direction of the main flux; if any part of it crossed the gap, it would be a part of the main flux already accounted for. The question might be asked whether some of the slot flux might escape into the airgap and complete its path by following the airgap in the peripheral direction; the answer is that the path would be so long, and would have such small cross section, that the high reluctance would reduce such flux to a negligible amount. In effect, therefore, the essential role of the fundamental mmfs, within the limits of the embedded

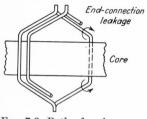

portions of the windings, is completely accounted for in setting up the mutual flux and the slot leakage fluxes.

Beyond the flanks of the core, the end connections of both stator and rotor windings give rise to leakage fluxes in the manner roughly indicated in Fig. 7-3; these fluxes are the *end-connection leakage* fluxes. Their effect in contributing to the total leakage reactance is more difficult to estimate than that of

FIG. 7-3. Path of end-connection leakage flux.

the other leakages, and will therefore be deferred to a subsequent article for discussion.

It remains, then, to consider the effect of the harmonic fluxes, of which only two, the fifth and the seventh, are shown in Fig. 7-4. Coil C represents the single full-pitch coil of one phase of a winding equivalent in its magnetizing effect to that of the actual winding in Fig. 7-1a. At the moment represented in part a of the diagram, the coil C is assumed to be carrying (positive) maximum current in the direction indicated by the conventional dot and cross. The mmf distribution will then be centered on the axis of the coil in accordance with the footnote on page 201, and the harmonics will have the positions indicated, though their amplitudes are not drawn to any particular scale. At the instant represented in Fig. 7-4a, the airgap flux densities due to the harmonic mmfs are all zero at the coil conductors; so the instantaneous emfs due to them will also be zero. The same conclusion follows also from the fact that at the same moment the total flux due to a given harmonic which links with the coil has maximum value, this maximum being proportional to one loop of the curve.

It has been shown in Art. 4-19 that a harmonic of order $r = 6\nu - 1$ (where ν is any integer, such as 1, 2, 3, . . .) travels in a direction opposite to that of the fundamental at a speed equal to $1/(6\nu - 1)$th of synchronous speed; and that a harmonic of order $r = 6\nu + 1$ travels in the same direction as the fundamental at a speed equal to $1/(6\nu + 1)$th of synchronous speed. Consequently, a quarter period later than the instant represented by Fig. 7-4a, when the coil current has decreased to zero, the 5th harmonic will have moved to the left through a distance $\frac{1}{5}(\tau/2)$, where τ is the pole pitch, and the 7th harmonic will have moved to the right through a distance $\frac{1}{7}(\tau/2)$, the resultant distributions of mmf and flux densities taking the form shown in Fig. 7-4b. Accordingly, the coil conductors are at this instant being cut by the maximum flux density of each harmonic, this statement holding true not only for the 5th and 7th harmonics shown in the drawing, but for all the others, 11th and 13th, 17th and 19th, etc. It follows that the emfs induced in the coil also have

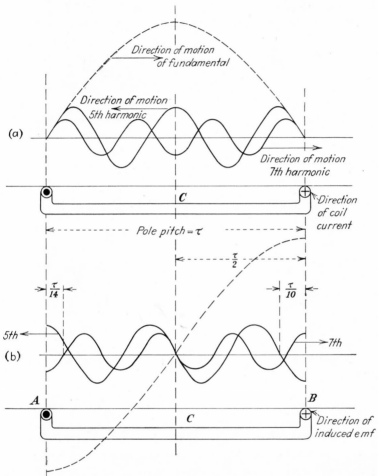

Fig. 7-4. Relative positions of fundamental and harmonics: (a) coil current at positive maximum; (b) coil current zero, quarter cycle later.

maximum positive values (indicated by the dot and cross), from which it may be concluded that these emfs have fundamental frequency and that they lag behind the current by a quarter period. They are therefore reactance voltages, and they are furthermore *leakage* reactance voltages for the reason that the stator harmonic fluxes do not induce rotor voltages of slip frequency, nor do the corresponding rotor harmonics induce stator voltages of line frequency, as will now be shown.

Let coil C in Fig. 7-4 represent a stator coil. Any one of the harmonics of order $6\nu - 1$ travels around the gap at a speed equal to $-1/(6\nu - 1)$th of synchronous speed, the minus sign indicating motion opposite to that of the main rotating field. Harmonics of order $6\nu + 1$ travel in the same direction as the main field at a speed $1/(6\nu + 1)$th of synchronous speed. At the same time, the rotor speed is $1 - s$ times synchronous speed; hence, the frequency of the emf induced in the rotor is in the one case

$$(1 - s) + \frac{1}{6\nu - 1} = \frac{6\nu(1 - s) + s}{6\nu - 1} \times \text{fundamental frequency}$$

and in the other it is

$$(1 - s) - \frac{1}{6\nu + 1} = \frac{6\nu(1 - s) - s}{6\nu + 1} \times \text{fundamental frequency}$$

For example, when $\nu = 1$, the fifth harmonic induces a rotor emf of frequency $\dfrac{6 - 5s}{5} f$, and the seventh harmonic induces a rotor emf of frequency $\dfrac{6 - 7s}{7} f$, both of which are so much greater than the normal slip frequency of the rotor that they must be ruled out of consideration.

In the same way, a rotor harmonic of order $6\nu - 1$ moves, *with respect to the rotor*, at a speed of $s/(6\nu - 1)$ in the direction opposite to that of the rotor, which is itself moving in the direction of the main field at a speed measured by $1 - s$; hence, the speed with respect to the stator is

$$(1 - s) - \frac{s}{6\nu - 1} = \left. \frac{5 - 6s}{5} \right|_{\nu = 1} \neq 1$$

The corresponding rotor harmonic of order $6\nu + 1$ moves relative to the stator at a speed

$$(1 - s) + \frac{s}{6\nu + 1} = \left. \frac{7 - 6s}{7} \right|_{\nu = 1} \neq 1$$

In both cases, the frequency of the emf induced in the stator by the rotor harmonics differs from line frequency and may therefore be disregarded so far as the reactance voltage is concerned.

Finally, it may be observed that the harmonic fluxes illustrated in Fig. 7-4 may be regarded as produced by $6\nu - 1$ and $6\nu + 1$ fictitious poles, the former moving in one direction, the latter in the other. These fluxes cross the airgap radially, but complete their paths in relatively short loops by way of the tooth tips, creating what amount to localized whirls or eddies in the main airgap flux. It is these localized effects which are rather inadequately represented by the leakage fluxes indicated in Fig. 7-2 as zigzag (or tooth-tip) leakage and belt leakage. The preceding analysis shows that both zigzag and belt leakage are fully accounted for by the harmonics.   The fact that stator harmonics produce leakage-reactance voltages only in 'the stator, and that rotor harmonics produce leakage-reactance voltages only in the rotor, accounts for the adoption of the term *differential leakage reactance* as a substitute for the more cumbersome and elusive zigzag and belt leakages.

7-5. Calculation of Slot Leakage Reactance.   *a. Full-pitch Winding.* Consider a two-layer full-pitch winding in partially closed slots of the type shown in Fig. 7-5.   Coil sides A and B occupying the same slot will belong to the same phase and will accordingly carry the same current.   The mmf of the slot currents will set up leakage flux in each of the six paths indicated in the diagram, and these fluxes can be computed if we assume

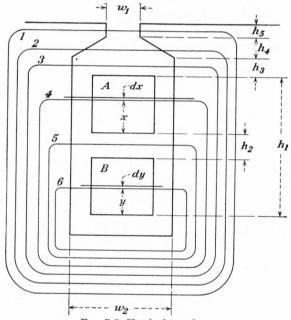

Fig. 7-5. Slot leakage flux.

that the lines of induction pass straight across the slot and that the reluctance of the iron part of the paths is negligible in comparison with that of the air or other nonmagnetic material in the slots.   These fluxes link more or less completely with the slot conductors, and the self-inductance of the embedded length of the slot conductors will therefore be by definition the total number of linkages, in weber-turns per ampere.

Let

$$Z = 2N = \text{number of series conductors per phase}$$
$$q = \text{number of slots per pole per phase}$$
$$m = \text{number of phases}$$
$$z = Z/2pq = N/pq = \text{number of conductors per coil side}$$
$$l = \text{embedded length of conductor}$$

Assuming mks units throughout, the mmf per ampere acting in path 1 is $2z$, the permeance of the path is $\mu_0 l h_5 / w_1$, hence the linkages with the $2z$ conductors are

$$\lambda_1 = \mu_0 (2z)^2 \frac{l h_5}{w_1}$$

The conditions in paths 2 and 3 are similar, except that the permeance of path 2 may be taken to be $\mu_0 l h_4 / \frac{1}{2}(w_1 + w_2)$, while that of path 3 is $\mu_0 l h_3 / w_2$. Hence, the linkages in these paths are

$$\lambda_2 = \mu_0 (2z)^2 \frac{2 l h_4}{w_1 + w_2}$$

$$\lambda_3 = \mu_0 (2z)^2 \frac{l h_3}{w_2}$$

In path 4, the mmf per ampere acting in the elementary path dx is $z + \dfrac{xz}{\frac{1}{2}(h_1 - h_2)}$, the permeance is $\mu_0 l \, dx / w_2$, and the total linkages per ampere are

$$\lambda_4 = \int_0^{\frac{1}{2}(h_1 - h_2)} \mu_0 \left(z + \frac{2xz}{h_1 - h_2} \right)^2 \frac{l \, dx}{w_2} = \mu_0 \frac{z^2 l}{w_2} \frac{7(h_1 - h_2)}{6}$$

Similar procedures with respect to paths 5 and 6 give

$$\lambda_5 = \mu_0 z^2 \frac{l h_2}{w_2}$$

and $$\lambda_6 = \int_0^{\frac{1}{2}(h_1 - h_2)} \mu_0 \left(\frac{2yz}{h_1 - h_2} \right)^2 \frac{l \, dy}{w_2} = \frac{\mu_0 z^2 l}{w_2} \frac{h_1 - h_2}{6}$$

The sum of these six partial linkages gives the slot inductance in henrys, and when the result is multiplied by $2\pi f$ and by the number of slots per phase ($= pq$), the final product is the slot reactance per phase, $(X_1)_{\text{slot}}$; hence,

$$(X_1)_{\text{slot}} = \frac{32\pi^2}{10^7} \frac{N^2 f l}{pq} \left(\frac{h_5}{w_1} + \frac{2h_4}{w_1 + w_2} + \frac{h_3}{w_2} + \frac{h_1}{3w_2} - \frac{h_2}{12w_2} \right) \quad (7\text{-}18)$$

if dimensions are in meters. If lengths are in inches, the numerical coefficient in Eq. 7-18 becomes $32 \times 2.54\pi^2 / 10^9 = 8.02 / 10^7$.

b. *Fractional-pitch Windings.* In this case, some of the slots contain coil sides which belong to different phases, so that the currents in the top and bottom coil sides of these slots are out of phase by an angle θ electrical degrees which is determined by the number of phases; but, for each slot in which the current in B, Fig. 7-3, lags behind that of A, there will be another slot, carrying the return conductors of coil A, in which this phase sequence is reversed (provided the winding is balanced). Consequently, in computing the mutual inductance between the two coil sides under these circumstances, it is only necessary to take into account the in-phase components of the currents, since the out-of-phase components will neutralize each other.

A coil side such as A, occupying the top of a slot as in Fig. 7-5, has a self-inductance proportional to the linkages

$$
\begin{aligned}
\lambda'_A &= \mu_0 z^2 l \left(\frac{h_5}{w_1} + \frac{2h_4}{w_1 + w_2} + \frac{h_3}{w_2} \right) + \int_0^{\frac{1}{2}(h_1 - h_2)} \left(\frac{2xz}{h_1 - h_2} \right)^2 \frac{\mu_0 l \, dx}{w_2} \\
&= \mu_0 z^2 l \left(\frac{h_5}{w_1} + \frac{2h_4}{w_1 + w_2} + \frac{h_3}{w_2} + \frac{h_1 - h_2}{6w_2} \right) \quad (7\text{-}19)
\end{aligned}
$$

while the other side of the same coil, occupying the bottom of another slot in the manner of coil B, Fig. 7-5, has a self-inductance proportional to

$$
\begin{aligned}
\lambda''_A &= \int_0^{\frac{1}{2}(h_1 - h_2)} \left(\frac{2zy}{h_1 - h_2} \right)^2 \frac{\mu_0 l \, dy}{w_2} + \frac{\mu_0 z^2 l}{w_2} \left(h_2 + \frac{h_1 - h_2}{2} + h_3 \right) \\
&\qquad\qquad + \mu_0 z^2 l \frac{2h_4}{w_1 + w_2} + \mu_0 z^2 l \frac{h_5}{w_1} \\
&= \mu_0 z^2 l \left(\frac{h_5}{w_1} + \frac{2h_4}{w_1 + w_2} + \frac{h_3}{w_2} + \frac{4h_1 + 2h_2}{6w_2} \right) \quad (7\text{-}20)
\end{aligned}
$$

The linkages with coil A due to unit current in coil B (which are equal to the linkages with B due to unit current in A) are proportional to

$$
\begin{aligned}
\lambda_{A-B} &= \int_0^{\frac{1}{2}(h_1 - h_2)} z \left(\frac{2xz}{h_1 - h_2} \right) \frac{\mu_0 l \, dx}{w_2} + \mu_0 z^2 l \left(\frac{h_3}{w_2} + \frac{2h_4}{w_1 + w_2} + \frac{h_5}{w_1} \right) \\
&= \mu_0 z^2 l \left(\frac{h_1 - h_2}{4w_2} + \frac{h_3}{w_2} + \frac{2h_4}{w_1 + w_2} + \frac{h_5}{w_1} \right) \quad (7\text{-}21)
\end{aligned}
$$

The total inductance of a single coil which thus occupies a slot together with a coil of another phase is proportional to $\lambda = \lambda'_A + \lambda''_A + 2\lambda_{A-B} \cos \theta$, and from Eqs. 7-19 to 7-21 this is found to be

$$
\begin{aligned}
\lambda = \frac{16\pi}{10^7} z^2 l \Bigg[&\left(\frac{h_5}{w_1} + \frac{2h_4}{w_1 + w_2} + \frac{h_3}{w_2} \right) \frac{1 + \cos \theta}{2} + \frac{h_1}{24w_2} (5 + 3 \cos \theta) \\
&+ \frac{h_2}{24w_2} (1 - 3 \cos \theta) \Bigg] \quad (7\text{-}22)
\end{aligned}
$$

In general, some of the slots of a fractional-pitch winding will be occupied by coil sides belonging to the same phase, the remainder being occupied by coil sides belonging to different phases. The total slot reactance per phase will then be made up of the sum of two parts, one of which is obtained by applying the linkages $\lambda_1 + \lambda_2 + \lambda_3 + \lambda_4 + \lambda_5 + \lambda_6$ to that part of the phase winding in which the two coil sides of a slot belong to the same phase; while the other part is obtained by applying Eq. 7-22 to the remaining coil sides of the same phase.

7-6. Calculation of Differential Leakage Reactance. The amplitude of the fundamental mmf of an m-phase winding having N turns in series per phase is, by Eq. 4-44,

$$A_1 = \frac{2\sqrt{2}}{\pi} k_{b_1} k_{p_1} m \frac{N}{p} I \qquad \text{amp-turns per pole}$$

while that of the rth harmonic is

$$A_r = \frac{2\sqrt{2}}{\pi} \frac{1}{r} k_{b_r} k_{p_r} m \frac{N}{p} I \qquad \text{amp-turns per pole} \qquad (7\text{-}23)$$

The corresponding maximum flux density in an airgap of effective length δ m is therefore

$$(B_r)_{\max} = \frac{\mu_0 k A_r}{\delta} \qquad (7\text{-}24)$$

where k is a factor (less than unity) which takes into account that part of the mmf which is consumed in the iron part of the flux path. The effective gap length δ is equal to the actual gap (namely, the clearance between stator and rotor) multiplied by the Carter coefficient* (greater than unity), which corrects for the effect of the slot openings.

The flux corresponding to one loop of the harmonic (see Fig. 7-4) is therefore

$$\Phi_r = \frac{2}{\pi} (B_r)_{\max} \frac{\tau}{r} l \qquad (7\text{-}25)$$

and the emf induced by this flux is

$$E_r = \sqrt{2}\, \pi k_{b_r} k_{p_r} f N \Phi_r \qquad (7\text{-}26)$$

On substituting for Φ_r from Eq. 7-25, for $(B_r)_{\max}$ from Eq. 7-24, and for A_r from Eq. 7-23, and then dividing through by I, the result is the differential reactance corresponding to the rth harmonic, i.e.,

$$(X_d)_r = \frac{32}{10^7} \frac{mfN^2}{p} \frac{k\tau l}{\delta} \left(\frac{k_{b_r} k_{p_r}}{r} \right)^2 \qquad (7\text{-}27)$$

The total differential reactance per phase of the winding is found by assigning to r all possible values and then adding the results; the final expression is therefore

$$X_d = \frac{32}{10^7} \frac{mfN^2}{p} \frac{k\tau l}{\delta} \sum \left(\frac{k_{b_r} k_{p_r}}{r} \right)^2 \qquad (7\text{-}28)$$

where all linear dimensions (τ, l, and δ) are in meters. If inch units are used, the coefficient 32×10^{-7} must be replaced by $32 \times 2.54/10^9$. Equation 7-28 serves to compute the differential reactance of both the

* Alexander S. Langsdorf, "Principles of Direct-current Machines," 5th ed., p. 404, McGraw-Hill Book Company, Inc., New York, 1940.

primary and the secondary of a wound-rotor machine by substituting the appropriate values for each of the symbols.

7-7. Calculation of End-connection Leakage Reactance. Numerous formulas, more or less empirical, have been proposed for the calculation of end-connection leakage reactance. Parshall and Hobart, who seem to have been the first to attack the problem, recommended as the result of their experimental study that the inductance of the coil ends be computed on the assumption of the linkage of 2 cgs lines per ampere conductor per inch of free length.[*] Other references are scattered widely through the literature.[†]

More recently, P. L. Alger has derived an expression for the total end-connection leakage reactance which is based upon a lengthy mathematical analysis, the details of which are given in his book.[‡] His formula, in terms of the symbols used in this book, is

$$X_{\text{end}} = \frac{18.4mfN^2d_1}{10^8 \times p^2} \left\{ \frac{x\pi - \sin x\pi}{\pi} \left[1 - \left(\frac{0.8d_2}{d_1} \right)^{p/2} \right] \tan \beta \right.$$
$$\left. + 0.93k_p^2 \left(\log \frac{1.4d_1}{d_s} - \frac{d}{d_1} \log \frac{0.54d}{R} \right) \right\} \quad (7\text{-}29)$$

where all dimensions are expressed in inches, and

$R = \sqrt{0.25(d_1 - d_2)^2 + (y_1 - y_2)^2}$

x = coil pitch expressed as a decimal fraction of pole pitch

d_s = depth of slot

and d, d_1, d_2, y_1, y_2, and β have the meanings indicated in Fig. 7-6. Half of X_{end} is included in the stator branch of the equivalent circuit, and half in the rotor branch.

7-8. Resistance and Reactance of a Squirrel-cage Rotor. The discussion of a squirrel-cage winding in Art. 5-11, supplemented by the illustration in Fig. 5-37, shows that as the rotor moves through the sinusoidally distributed main field the slip-frequency emfs and currents in adjacent bars will differ in phase by an angle α which is equal to the rotor slot pitch expressed in electrical degrees. When the slip is small, the emf and current in any one bar will be substantially in phase because under this condition the rotor impedance $R_{2e}/s + jX_{2e}$ is nearly equal to R_{2e}/s. It follows that there will be one bar in each pole pitch in which both the emf and the current will almost simultaneously have maximum values, while on either side of it, within the limits of the full pole pitch, the current and emf decrease sinusoidally to zero. This distribution of rotor current

---

[*] See H. F. Parshall and H. M. Hobart, "Electric Generators," pp. 159, 160, John Wiley & Sons, Inc., New York, 1900.

[†] For a partial list see Langsdorf, *op. cit.*, p. 611; and A. Still, "Elements of Electrical Design," 2d ed., p. 359, McGraw Hill Book Company, Inc., New York, 1932.

[‡] "The Nature of Polyphase Induction Machines," John Wiley & Sons, Inc., New York, 1951.

results in the automatic production of as many rotor poles as there are stator poles, and the squirrel cage must be regarded as a polyphase winding having many more phases than the stator winding.   The number of rotor phases may be computed as follows:

If the total number of rotor bars is Z_r, and the number of stator poles is p, the entire periphery represents a span of $p\pi$ electrical degrees, and

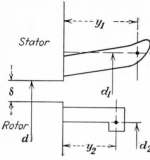

the angle α from bar to bar is

$$\alpha = \frac{p\pi}{Z_r} \qquad (7\text{-}30)$$

In general, since the angle between consecutive phases of an m-phase machine is $2\pi/m$,

$$\alpha = \frac{p\pi}{Z_r} = \frac{2\pi}{m_2}$$

where m_2 is the number of rotor phases, so that

$$m_2 = \frac{Z_r}{p/2} = \text{rotor bars per pair of poles}$$

$$(7\text{-}31)$$

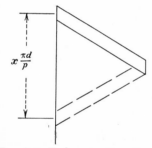

Referring to Eqs. 6-9 and 6-10, it was shown that in general the ratio of voltage transformation is $k_{b_1}k_{p_1}Z_1/k_{b_2}k_{p_2}Z_2$, where Z_1 and Z_2 are the numbers of primary and secondary conductors in series per phase, while the corresponding ratio of current transformation is $m_2 k_{b_2}k_{p_2}Z_2/m_1 k_{b_1}k_{p_1}Z_1$; but since in a squirrel-cage winding $Z_2 = 1$ and

$$k_{b_2} = k_{p_2} = 1$$

FIG. 7-6. End-connection dimensions.

(if there is no skewing), the ratio of voltage transformation is

$$a = k_{b_1}k_{p_1}Z_1 = 2k_{b_1}k_{p_1}N_1 \qquad (7\text{-}32)$$

and the ratio of current transformation is

$$\frac{m_2}{m_1 k_{b_1}k_{p_1}Z_1} = \frac{2Z_r}{pm_1 k_{b_1}k_{p_1}Z_1} = \frac{Z_r}{pm_1 k_{b_1}k_{p_1}N_1} \qquad (7\text{-}33)$$

The factor by which actual rotor resistances and reactances must be multiplied to reduce them to terms of the primary is then $2pm_1(k_{b_1}k_{p_1}N_1)^2/Z_r$ if there is no skewing.

The interconnection between the bars and the end rings of a squirrel cage, as in Fig. 5-37, clearly affects the equivalent resistance and reactance per phase; it is therefore convenient to represent the actual connections in the manner indicated in Fig. 7-7.*   The radial lines represent the rotor

* Arnold and LaCour, *op. cit.*, Vol. V, Part 1.

bars of a two-pole machine as though they had been solidly joined at one end and connected at the other end by a ring each segment of which has twice the resistance and reactance of the segments of one of the actual end rings. The effect is the same as though the radial spokes were the phases of a star-connected generator supplying current to a mesh-connected load.

Let

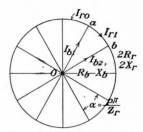

R_b, X_b = resistance and reactance of each bar

$2R_r$, $2X_r$ = resistance and reactance of each segment of ring

I_b = current in bars

I_r = current in ring segments

E_b = emf per bar

Applying Kirchhoff's law, first to the closed circuit Oab (Fig. 7-7), and then to the junction point a,

FIG. 7-7, Diagrammatic representation of two-pole squirrel-cage rotor.

$$\mathbf{E}_{b1} - \mathbf{E}_{b2} = (\mathbf{I}_{b1} - \mathbf{I}_{b2})(R_b + jX_b) + 2\mathbf{I}_{r1}(R_r + jX_r) \qquad (7\text{-}34)$$

and

$$\mathbf{I}_{b1} + \mathbf{I}_{r0} = \mathbf{I}_{r1} \qquad (7\text{-}35)$$

Because of the symmetry of the circuit diagram, the emf and current in any bar will differ in phase from that of the next adjoining bar by the constant angle α; the same thing is true concerning adjacent segments of the ring. It is therefore true that

$$\mathbf{E}_{b2} = \mathbf{E}_{b1}e^{j\alpha} \qquad (7\text{-}36)$$

$$\mathbf{I}_{b2} = \mathbf{I}_{b1}e^{j\alpha} \qquad (7\text{-}37)$$

$$\mathbf{I}_{r1} = \mathbf{I}_{r0}e^{j\alpha} \qquad (7\text{-}38)$$

provided that the sequence of phases is taken clockwise in Fig. 7-7.

From Eqs. 7-35 and 7-38

$$\mathbf{I}_{b1} = \mathbf{I}_{r1} - \mathbf{I}_{r0} = \mathbf{I}_{r1}(1 - e^{-j\alpha})$$

or

$$\mathbf{I}_{r1} = \frac{\mathbf{I}_{b1}}{1 - e^{-j\alpha}} \qquad (7\text{-}39)$$

and from Eqs. 7-36 and 7-37

$$\mathbf{E}_{b1} - \mathbf{E}_{b2} = \mathbf{E}_{b1}(1 - e^{j\alpha}) \qquad (7\text{-}40)$$

$$\mathbf{I}_{b1} - \mathbf{I}_{b2} = \mathbf{I}_{b1}(1 - e^{j\alpha}) \qquad (7\text{-}41)$$

Substituting Eqs. 7-39 to 7-41 in 7-34,

$$\mathbf{E}_{b1}(1 - e^{j\alpha}) = \mathbf{I}_{b1}(1 - e^{j\alpha})(R_b + jX_b) + \frac{2\mathbf{I}_{b1}}{1 - e^{-j\alpha}}(R_r + jX_r)$$

from which

$$\mathbf{E}_{b1} = \mathbf{I}_{b1}\left[R_b + jX_b - \frac{2(R_r + jX_r)}{(e^{j(\alpha/2)} - e^{-j(\alpha/2)})^2} \right] \qquad (7\text{-}42)$$

The relation

$$e^{j(\alpha/2)} - e^{-j(\alpha/2)} = 2j \sin\frac{\alpha}{2} = 2j \sin\frac{\pi}{m_2}$$

then leads to the result

$$\mathbf{E}_{b1} = \mathbf{I}_{b1}\left[R_b + jX_b + \frac{2(R_r + jX_r)}{\left(2 \sin \dfrac{\pi}{m_2}\right)^2} \right] \tag{7-43}$$

which shows that the effect of the end rings is to add to the impedance of each bar an amount $\dfrac{2(R_r + jX_r)}{\left(2 \sin \dfrac{\pi}{m_2}\right)^2}$.

There is of course no difficulty in computing the ohmic resistance and the slot leakage reactance of the individual bars of a squirrel cage. The effective resistance at speeds near synchronism will be only slightly larger than the ohmic resistance unless the bars are very deep; but at low speeds, as at starting, the effective resistance may be so increased because of the crowding of the current to the top of the bars as to increase the starting torque to a considerably higher magnitude than it would otherwise have. Advantage is taken of this fact when larger than normal starting torque is required because of the nature of the load; one form of motor used for this purpose is the *deep-bar* squirrel-cage machine, which is considered more at length in Art. 8-4.

The differential leakage reactance of a squirrel cage requires, however, special consideration because the important rotor harmonics owe their origin to the flux harmonics produced by the stator; for although the normal slip-frequency currents in the rotor bars produce a stepped distribution of mmf in the same general manner as any winding distributed in slots, this particular stepped mmf is itself so nearly sinusoidal (as may be inferred from Fig. 5-37) that its harmonics are negligible.

7-9. Differential Leakage Reactance of a Squirrel-cage Rotor. Figure 7-8 shows two of the large number of stator harmonics which travel around the airgap at different speeds, half of them in one direction, half in the other. The flux due to any one of them, of order r, will induce in the rotor bars emfs and currents which have a frequency equal to $s_r f$, where s_r is the slip of the rotor with respect to the rth stator harmonic and f is the fundamental stator frequency. The current in one particular rotor bar, say, No. 1, may then be assumed to alternate in accordance with the expression $(I_r)_{max} \cos s_r \omega t = (I_r)_{max} \cos s_r \theta$; the mmf produced by this current will have a square-shouldered distribution which may then be resolved into a fundamental and a series of harmonics which in general are of order ρ.

From the discussion in Art. 4-19, and especially from Eq. 4-57, it follows that the mmf of the ρth rotor harmonic at a point P (Fig. 7-8) is

$$a_1 = A_{\rho r} \sin \rho\xi \cos s_r \theta \tag{7-44}*$$

* The arbitrary constants δ and ζ in Eq. 4-57 have for convenience been assigned zero values.

where ξ is the angle, in electrical degrees, measured along the rotor periphery between bar 1 and point P.

As the rotor moves to the right in Fig. 7-8, the time phase of the current in bar 2 will be ahead of that of bar 1 by an angle $r(2\pi/m_2)$ provided that the rotor speed is within the normal working range, i.e., reasonably close to synchronism; but the space-phase position of bar 2 relative to

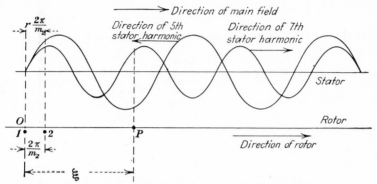

FIG. 7-8. Rotor bars in relation to stator harmonics.

point P is $\rho\xi - \rho(2\pi/m_2)$; so that mmf at point P due to bar 2 is

$$a_2 = A_{pr} \sin\left(\rho\xi - \rho\frac{2\pi}{m_2}\right) \cos\left(s_r\theta + r\frac{2\pi}{m_2}\right) \qquad (7\text{-}45)$$

Similar expressions for successive bars of the squirrel cage give the mmf at point P for each of the m_2 phases included in a double pole pitch. The kth term is

$$a_k = A_{pr} \sin\left[\rho\xi - (k-1)\rho\frac{2\pi}{m_2}\right] \cos\left[s_r\theta + (k-1)r\frac{2\pi}{m_2}\right]$$

$$= \frac{1}{2} A_{pr} \left\{ \sin\left[(\rho\xi + s_r\theta) + (k-1)(r-\rho)\frac{2\pi}{m_2}\right] \right.$$

$$\left. + \sin\left[(\rho\xi - s_r\theta) - (k-1)(r+\rho)\frac{2\pi}{m_2}\right] \right\} \qquad (7\text{-}46)$$

which has the same form as Eq. 4-59. Consequently, when k is assigned all integral values from 1 to m_2 and the results are added by the same procedure which led to Eq. 4-64, the final expression for the mmf at point P is

$$a = \frac{1}{2} A_{pr} \left\{ \frac{\sin(r-\rho)\pi}{\sin\frac{r-\rho}{m_2}\pi} \sin\left[(\rho\xi + s_r\theta) + (r-\rho)\frac{m_2-1}{m_2}\pi\right] \right.$$

$$\left. + \frac{\sin(r+\rho)\pi}{\sin\frac{r+\rho}{m_2}\pi} \sin\left[(\rho\xi - s_r\theta) - (r+\rho)\frac{m_2-1}{m_2}\pi\right] \right\} \qquad (7\text{-}47)$$

which is similar in form to Eq. 4-64, and in general represents two travel-ing waves of mmf, one of which moves along the rotor periphery with an angular velocity equal to $d\xi/dt = -(s_r/\rho)\omega$, the other with an angular velocity $d\xi/dt = +(s_r/\rho)\omega$. It will also be seen from Eq. 7-47 that

$$\frac{\sin (r - \rho)\pi}{\sin \dfrac{r - \rho}{m_2} \pi} = m_2 \tag{7-48}$$

provided that $(r - \rho)/m_2$ is a positive or negative integer, i.e., if

$$\rho = \pm cm_2 + r \tag{7-49}$$

and that

$$\frac{\sin (r + \rho)\pi}{\sin \dfrac{r + \rho}{m_2} \pi} = m_2 \tag{7-50}$$

provided that $(r + \rho)/m_2$ is a positive integer c', in which case

$$\rho = c'm_2 - r \tag{7-51}$$

For all other combinations of r and ρ, the values of the fractions in Eqs. 7-48 and 7-50 are zero.

In order to determine in what manner the differential leakage react-ance of the rotor is dependent upon these rotor harmonics, it must be noted that *only those need be considered which induce quadrature emfs of slip frequency* in the rotor bars. It can easily be seen from the basic phasor diagram, Fig. 6-15, that the flux produced by the stator funda-mental mmf ($r = 1$) would, if acting alone, develop such a quadrature emf of slip frequency if the small phase displacement caused by the mag-netizing current is neglected. Consequently, it is only necessary to con-sider those rotor harmonics of order ρ which satisfy the condition imposed by Eq. 7-49 when $r = 1$, that is,

$$\rho = \pm cm_2 + 1 \tag{7-52}$$

Finally, therefore, it is only necessary to replace primary quantities in Eq. 7-28 by the corresponding quantities for a squirrel cage; specifically, the number of phases becomes $m_2 = 2Z_r/p$, the number of turns in series per phase becomes $\frac{1}{2}$, the breadth and pitch factors become unity, and ρ takes the place of r. Making these substitutions, the differential react-ance per phase, i.e., for a single bar of the unskewed rotor, is

$$(X_d)_{\text{rotor}} = \frac{16}{10^7} \frac{Z_r f}{p^2} \frac{k\tau l}{\varepsilon} \sum \frac{1}{\left(c \dfrac{2Z_r}{p} + 1\right)^2} \tag{7-53}$$

where the summation includes all integral values of c, both positive and negative, but excluding zero.

7-10. The Effect of Skew on Leakage Reactance. In Art. 4-13, it was pointed out that skewing of the rotor slots in the manner illustrated in Fig. 4-29 (and also in Fig. 6-8) serves to prevent undesirable pulsations of flux which are in general caused by the presence of harmonics. These pulsations, if not sufficiently suppressed, may result not only in objectionable noise but also in appreciable negative torques produced by the locking effect between stator and rotor harmonic fluxes which rotate opposite to the direction of the main field. These negative torques, also called parasitic torques, if not minimized, would have the effect of producing more or less pronounced dips in the torque-speed curve (Fig. 6-21) and so interfering with the smooth acceleration of the rotor during the starting period; and without special precautions they may be so serious as to result in subsynchronous crawling. These effects are discussed in greater detail in Art. 8-18.

On the other hand, the beneficial effects of skewing are in part counterbalanced by an increase in the total leakage reactance of the motor, thereby reducing both the starting torque and the pull-out torque, as may be seen from Eqs. 6-26 and 6-30. The reasons for this increased leakage reactance may be very easily understood by considering the case of two parallel plane coils, A and B, which have self-inductances L_1 and L_2 and a mutual inductance M. If the coupling of the coils were perfect, i.e., if there were no magnetic leakage, the equality $L_1L_2 = M^2$ would hold, but in general there is some leakage, and $L_1L_2 > M^2$; if now coil B is turned until its plane becomes perpendicular to that of A, the mutual inductance will decrease from a maximum to zero, which means that more and more of the fluxes linked with A and B become leakage fluxes.

Skewing of the rotor bars is obviously the equivalent of a partial turning of coil B away from parallelism with A, with the result that the coupling between stator and rotor is decreased, and the leakage reactance increased, by an amount which is measured by the change in M^2. To evaluate this change, it is only necessary to observe that while the main flux linked with the stator remains the same whether the rotor is skewed or not, the induced emfs and currents of fundamental frequency in the skewed rotor are reduced by the factor $\dfrac{\sin (\psi/2)}{\psi/2}$ (as explained in Art. 4-13), where ψ is the angle of skew in electrical degrees (see Fig. 4-29a). This means that the mutual inductance between stator and rotor is reduced from its original value, M, to $M\,\dfrac{\sin (\psi/2)}{\psi/2}$, and the increase in the leakage is accordingly measured by the difference between the squares of these quantities; in other words, the increase in the leakage reactance is proportional to $1 - \left[\dfrac{\sin (\psi/2)}{\psi/2}\right]^2$. Since the original value of the exciting (mutual) reactance is X_0, given by Eq. 7-11, the additional leakage reactance caused by skewing is *

$$X_{\text{skew}} = X_0 \left\{ 1 - \left[\frac{\sin (\psi/2)}{\psi/2} \right]^2 \right\} \tag{7-54}$$

and since ψ is a relatively small angle, it follows from Maclaurin's theorem that Eq. 7-54 can be reduced to

$$X_{\text{skew}} = \frac{\psi^2}{12} X_0 \tag{7-55}$$

The fact that in a skewed rotor the breadth factor is $k_{b_2} = \dfrac{\sin (\psi/2)}{\psi/2}$ instead of unity means that the ratios of emf and current transformation given by Eqs. 7-32 and 7-33 must be modified, the former being divided, and the latter multiplied, by the breadth factor k_{b_2}.

* See Alger, *op. cit.*, pp. 207–208.

CHAPTER 8

OPERATIONAL FEATURES OF POLYPHASE
INDUCTION MACHINES

STARTING CONDITIONS

8-1. Starting at Reduced Voltage. The circle diagram discussed in Chap. 6 shows that a squirrel-cage motor designed for low leakage reactance and high magnetizing reactance will have, within the normal operating range, the desirable features of nearly constant speed combined with good efficiency and relatively high power factor at full load. On the other hand, it has the disadvantage that when started from rest with full impressed voltage the starting current is 5 to 8 or more times the rated current, while the starting torque is only 1.5 to about 2 times rated full-load torque. Actually, the first inrush of starting current may considerably exceed the large current predicted by the circle diagram for the same reasons that the starting current of a transformer may be very large during the first few cycles, as explained in Art. 1-22.

The large line current (at low power factor) drawn by such a motor of 5 hp or larger, when started at full voltage, is objectionable because of the possible sharp drop in the voltage of the supply circuit and the con-

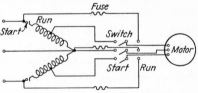

Fig. 8-1. Open-Δ compensator.

sequent dimming of incandescent lamps on the same line as well as undesired effects upon other connected devices. Accordingly, it is customary to start such motors at reduced voltage by means of an auto-transformer which, when used for this purpose, is called a *starting compensator*. Compensators for three-phase motors may be made with two windings in open Δ, as in Fig. 8-1, or with three Y-connected windings, as in Fig. 8-2. Taps in the compensator windings permit the selection of a starting voltage of one-fourth to one-half of rated value, depending upon the starting torque required to bring the motor and its connected load up to speed. If half the line voltage is thus impressed upon the motor terminals, the motor current will be half what it would be with full voltage, but the line current will be cut to one-fourth of the full-voltage value, thus easing the shock upon the supply circuit; however, the starting torque is likewise reduced to one-fourth of what it would otherwise be, with a consequent increase in the time required to attain full speed.   It follows that such motors are suited only to loads such as fans or blowers which require only small starting torque.

The compensators illustrated in Figs. 8-1 and 8-2 have the objectionable feature of opening the circuit during the time required to throw the switch from the starting to the running position.   Though this time may be very short, it is possible that the reclosing of the circuit may result in a transient rush of current sufficiently large to undo the benefit of the origi-

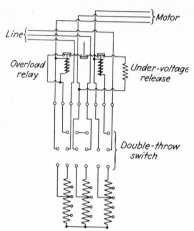

FIG. 8-2. Three-phase autostarter.

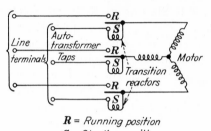

R = Running position
S = Starting position

FIG. 8-3. Starting compensator with transition reactors.

nal reduction of voltage.   This undesirable result can be minimized by inserting a reactor between the starting and the motor terminals of the switch in the manner indicated in Fig. 8-3.

In the starting position, the motor is connected directly to the autotransformer taps without any intermediate fuse protection, and the only line protection is that afforded by the fuse required by the wiring code at the point of connection of the line to the main feeder.   When the starting lever is thrown to the running position, the motor is connected directly to the line through running fuses of proper rating, and the windings of the compensator are entirely disconnected.

8-2. The Y-Δ Connection. A motor which has a Δ-connected stator winding for normal operation can be started with the phases connected in Y, as in Fig. 8-4, provided the reduction in voltage per phase

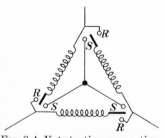

FIG. 8-4. Y-Δ starting connection.

from its normal value V to $V/\sqrt{3}$, and the resultant reduction in starting torque to one-third of its full-voltage value, will permit the motor to accelerate in a reasonable time.   The change from the starting positions, S, of the switches to the running positions, R, is accomplished by means of a triple-pole double-throw switch.   Unless a reactor is used, as in Fig. 8-3, the change-over from the starting to the running position of the switch may cause a large transient current.   The use of this arrangement is limited to small machines connected to loads which require only small starting torque, i.e., less than the available one-third of normal starting torque.

8-3. Starting of Wound-rotor Induction Motors.   It has been shown in Art. 6-7 that the phase resistance of a wound rotor can be varied at will by means of an external rheostat, and that by proper design of this external resistor the torque at starting may be made equal to the maximum (or breakdown) torque that the motor is capable of developing.   This possibility makes wound-rotor motors especially valuable for starting loads which have large initial friction or unusually large inertia, without drawing excessive starting current.   The effects of the high initial resistance not only limit the current but raise the power factor at starting, thereby reducing the initial line disturbance.

The rotor coils of such a motor are formed, placed in the rotor slots, and connected in exactly the same manner as are those of the stator, except that the terminals are connected through slip rings to the external resistor.   While any number of phases (greater than one) may thus be used in the rotor winding, three phases connected in Y are generally employed, as in Fig. 6-6.   The external rheostat is designed so that all three of the Y-connected branches may be simultaneously varied by the same amount so as to preserve the symmetry of the circuit as a whole. The rheostat may be of the faceplate type for machines of moderate current rating, though contactor-type controllers may be used when the current is of considerable magnitude.

Reference to Fig. 6-21 will show that if the external resistance is so selected as to develop maximum torque at the moment of starting the torque will thereafter decrease as the speed rises.   The speed can continue to increase only so long as the motor torque exceeds the resisting torque of the load, in accordance with the fundamental relation

$$T - T_L = \alpha J$$

where T and T_L are the torques due to the motor and to the load, respectively, α is the angular acceleration, and J is the polar moment of inertia of the entire rotating system.*   The speed will become constant when T and T_L are equal.   It is obvious that if the motor is permitted to operate with the initial large starting resistance permanently in circuit the speed regulation will be poor, i.e., the speed will be very sensitive to changes in load; in this respect, it is quite similar to a d-c shunt motor which has a large armature resistance.

Figure 8-5, similar to the speed-torque curves of Fig. 6-21, illustrates

* See Alexander S. Langsdorf, "Principles of Direct-current Machines," 5th ed., pp. 536–545, McGraw-Hill Book Company, Inc., New York, 1940.

the variation of torque with slip for a series of values of rotor resistance. If, starting with the particular resistance R_0 which yields maximum torque at standstill, the resistance is reduced by steps to R_1, R_2, etc., when the speed corresponds to the abscissas of the points of intersection of the successive curves, the torque will vary in the manner indicated by the heavy line; in other words, it may be maintained at a high average value throughout the starting period and thereby limit the time required to reach full speed.

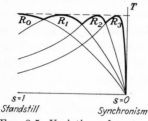

FIG. 8-5. Variation of motor torque from standstill to full speed.

8-4. High-starting-torque Squirrel-cage Rotors. It is easy to see that by a suitable choice of the material and cross section of the bars and end rings of a squirrel-cage rotor it is possible to secure a wide range of performance characteristics. The resistance may be made high by using bars of small section, or by making them of material of high resistivity, or by a combination of both methods; in that case, the torque and power factor at starting can be greatly improved at the same time that the starting current is kept down, but these advantages are secured at the expense of reduced efficiency and poor speed regulation under load conditions. On the other hand, if the rotor resistance is made small by a generous use of copper, high efficiency and practical constancy of speed at normal loads are obtained at the expense of reduced starting torque and large initial current at low power factor.

The size and shape of the slots also play a considerable part in deter mining operating characteristics. Open slots have the effect of reducing the permeance of the slot leakage paths, hence contribute toward reduced leakage reactance; but at the same time they add materially to the gap reluctance and greatly increase the magnetizing component of stator current. Partially or wholly closed slots decrease the magnetizing current but considerably increase the leakage reactance.

FIG. 8-6. (a) Ordinary-purpose rotor punching; (b) high-resistance rotor punching.

For these reasons, the design of an ordinary squirrel-cage motor must be a compromise between conflicting considerations. A "general-purpose" motor provides fairly liberal copper, requiring slots that are deep in comparison with their width, as in Fig. 8-6a, while the slots are overhung by thin bridges which reduce the airgap reluctance and at the same time, because of saturation, interpose considerable reluctance in the path of the slot leakage flux. High-resistance rotors, desirable for applications where high starting torque is important because of frequent starts and stops, will, on the other hand, have small slots, as in Fig. 8-6b, if the rotor bars are made of copper; but a better plan is to use brass or alloy bars, which, because of their greater cross section and mass for the same resistance as the smaller copper bars, will reduce the temperature rise.

The *deep-bar* rotor, in which the depth of the slots indicated in Fig. 8-6a is purposely exaggerated, provides the desirable features of high effective resistance and correspondingly large torque at starting, while under running conditions its resistance is low so that speed regulation and efficiency are not impaired.   This characteristic is the result of the skin-effect phenomenon, which causes the current to be crowded to the top of the bars when the frequency is large, as at starting, while under running conditions, when the frequency is greatly reduced, the current is nearly uniformly distributed over the entire cross section.

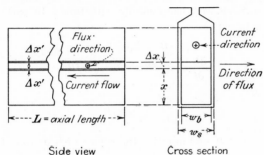

Side view   Cross section
Fig. 8-7. Deep-bar rotor.

In order to determine the manner in which a total current of I amp will be distributed over the cross section of the bar illustrated in Fig. 8-7, let

σ = current density
B = flux density   at distance x above bottom of bar

so that at the distance $x + \Delta x$ above the bottom the current density and the flux density become, respectively,*

$$\sigma_{x+\Delta x} = \sigma + \frac{\partial \sigma}{\partial x} \Delta x \tag{8-1}$$

$$B_{x+\Delta x} = B + \frac{\partial B}{\partial x} \Delta x \tag{8-2}$$

The elementary section of the bar having width w_b and thickness Δx carries the current $\sigma w_b \, \Delta x$, which sets up an equal mmf (in ampere-turns) since the element may be considered to be a single turn.   In accordance with the general formula for a magnetic circuit in air,

$$B = \mu_0 H = \mu_0 \frac{\text{amp-turns}}{\text{length of airgap}}$$

we may write

$$\frac{1}{\mu_0} \left[\left(B + \frac{\partial B}{\partial x} \Delta x \right) - B \right] w_s = \sigma w_b \, \Delta x \tag{8-3}$$

* All quantities are expressed in rationalized mks units.

or
$$\frac{\partial B}{\partial x} = \mu_0 \frac{w_b}{w_s} \sigma \tag{8-4}$$

Directing attention now to the side view of Fig. 8-7, the flux directed at right angles to the elementary strip of length L and width Δx is $BL\,\Delta x$, and the time rate of change of this flux, or $\partial/\partial t\,(BL\,\Delta x)$, is the emf which, by Lenz's law, must be the drop of potential in the strips of thickness $\Delta x'$ and width w_b. Accordingly, if ρ is the resistivity of the material of the bar, in ohm-meters,

$$\frac{\partial}{\partial t}(BL\,\Delta x) = \left[\left(\sigma + \frac{\partial \sigma}{\partial x}\Delta x\right) - \sigma\right] w_b\,\Delta x' \frac{L}{w_b\,\Delta x'} \tag{8-5}$$

from which
$$\frac{\partial B}{\partial t} = \rho \frac{\partial \sigma}{\partial x} \tag{8-6}$$

In the preceding equations, both σ and B are complex quantities, since both represent entities which vary harmonically with time. In particular, the flux density can be expressed as

$$B = B_x e^{j2\pi ft} \tag{8-7}$$

whence
$$\frac{\partial B}{\partial t} = j2\pi f B_x e^{j2\pi ft} = j2\pi f B \tag{8-8}$$

so that by Eq. 8-6

$$\frac{\partial \sigma}{\partial x} = \frac{1}{\rho} j2\pi f B \tag{8-9}$$

Differentiating Eq. 8-9, and inserting the value of $\partial B/\partial x$ from Eq. 8-4,

$$\frac{\partial^2 \sigma}{\partial x^2} = j\frac{2\pi f}{\rho}\frac{\partial B}{\partial x} = j\frac{2\pi\mu_0 f}{\rho}\frac{w_b}{w_s}\sigma \tag{8-10}$$

which may be written

$$\frac{\partial^2 \sigma}{\partial x^2} = 2j\frac{\pi\mu_0 f}{\rho}\frac{w_b}{w_s}\sigma = k^2\sigma \tag{8-11}$$

where
$$k^2 = 2j\frac{\pi\mu_0 f}{\rho}\frac{w_b}{w_s} \tag{8-12}$$

or
$$k = (1+j)\sqrt{\frac{\pi\mu_0 f}{\rho}\frac{w_b}{w_s}}$$

Again, from Eq. 8-1,

$$\frac{\partial^2 B}{\partial x^2} = \mu_0 \frac{w_b}{w_s}\frac{\partial \sigma}{\partial x} \tag{8-13}$$

and, on substituting the value of $\partial \sigma/\partial x$ from Eq. 8-4,

$$\frac{\partial^2 B}{\partial x^2} = 2j\frac{\pi\mu_0 f}{\rho}\frac{w_b}{w_s}B = k^2 B \tag{8-14}$$

The two differential equations, 8-11 and 8-14, have the same form, and their integrals are

$$\sigma = \frac{1}{2k}(Pe^{kx} - Qe^{-kx}) \tag{8-15}$$

and
$$B = \frac{1}{2k}(Me^{kx} - Ne^{-kx}) \tag{8-16}$$

where P, Q, M, and N are constants of integration which must be evaluated in terms of known terminal conditions. Thus, when $x = 0$, it is known that $B = 0$, whence $M = N$; and when $x = h$, $B = \mu_0(I/w_s)$. Consequently

$$B\Big|_{x=h} = \left[\frac{M}{2k}(e^{kx} - e^{-kx})\right]_{x=h} = \frac{M}{2k}(e^{kh} - e^{-kh}) = \mu_0 \frac{I}{w_s}$$

or

$$M = \mu_0 \frac{I}{w_s} \frac{2k}{e^{kh} - e^{-kh}}$$

and the complete solution for B is

$$B = \mu_0 \frac{I}{w_s} \frac{e^{kx} - e^{-kx}}{e^{kh} - e^{-kh}} = \mu_0 \frac{I}{w_s} \frac{\sinh kx}{\sinh kh} \tag{8-17}$$

To evaluate P and Q in Eq. 8-15, note from Eq. 8-9 that when $x = 0$ (and $B = 0$), $\partial\sigma/\partial x = 0$, so that on differentiating Eq. 8-15

$$\frac{\partial\sigma}{\partial x}\Big|_{x=0} = \left[\frac{1}{2}(Pe^{kx} + Qe^{-kx})\right]_{x=0} = \frac{P + Q}{2} = 0$$

whence $P = -Q$, and

$$\sigma = \frac{P}{2k}(e^{kx} + e^{-kx}) \tag{8-18}$$

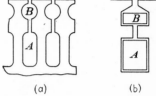

FIG. 8-8. Rotor punchings, double squirrel-cage rotor.

Differentiating Eq. 8-18, and inserting the value of $\partial\sigma/\partial x$ from Eq. 8-9,

$$\frac{\partial\sigma}{\partial x} = \frac{P}{2}(e^{kx} - e^{-kx}) = 2j\frac{\pi f}{\rho}B \tag{8-19}$$

But when $x = h$, $B = \mu_0(I/w_s)$, whence

$$\frac{P}{2} = 2j\frac{\pi\mu_0 f}{\rho}\frac{I}{w_s}\frac{1}{e^{kh} - e^{-kh}} = \frac{k^2 I}{w_b}\frac{1}{e^{kh} - e^{-kh}} \tag{8-20}$$

which, when substituted in Eq. 8-18, gives finally

$$\sigma = k\frac{I}{w_b}\frac{e^{kx} + e^{-kx}}{e^{kh} - e^{-kh}} = (1 + j)\sqrt{\frac{\pi\mu_0 f}{\rho}\frac{w_b}{w_s}}\frac{I}{w_b}\frac{\cosh kx}{\sinh kh} \tag{8-21}$$

The principle of the deep-bar rotor is applied in a different manner in the *double squirrel-cage* rotor, Fig. 8-8, where what would otherwise be a single deep bar is divided into two parts separated by a magnetic bridge. The inner cage, deeply embedded in the rotor iron, has large cross section and low resistance, but at starting its resistance is very large because of the line frequency of the rotor current; the current in the inner cage is therefore limited to a small value which is still further reduced by the screening effect of the current induced in the outer cage. The latter has high resistance and relatively low reactance, so that its influence preponderates, and high starting torque results. As the speed increases, the rotor frequency decreases, permitting the flow of increased current in the inner low-resistance cage, thereby imparting to the motor the characteristics of that type of motor. Actually, both cages carry current when running at full speed, but the greater current will then flow in the inner one. The torque-speed curve of the double-cage motor has the general form shown by the full-line curve of Fig. 8-9; ordinates of this curve may be regarded as the sum of the ordinates of the two dashed curves, one of which has the form characteristic of a high-resistance rotor, the other that of a low-resistance rotor.

The double-cage winding was originally described by Dolivo Dobrowolsky* in 1893, but the publication did not receive the attention that its importance warranted, probably for the reason that the need for the special characteristics of such a motor had not then become acute. Later this type of machine was developed commercially by Boucherot, and it is now frequently referred to as the Boucherot motor.†

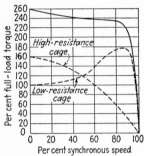

Fig. 8-9. Speed-torque curve of double-cage motor.

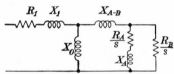

Fig. 8-10. Equivalent circuit of double squirrel-cage motor.

The analytical theory of the double-cage motor has been based by some writers on the theory that the two rotor windings may be considered to be in parallel. Actually, the machine is a modified form of the three-winding transformer discussed in Art. 2-28, so that the mutual induction between the two secondaries must be taken into account. Alger states that a satisfactory form of the equivalent circuit is that of Fig. 8-10, where X_{A-B} is the mutual reactance between the upper and the lower bars (the subscripts A and B refer to Fig. 8-8), and where all the self-reactance of the upper bar, B, is assumed to be mutual with that of the lower bar A.

SPEED CONTROL

8-5. Rheostatic Speed Control. The close resemblance between the induction motor and the d-c shunt motor leads to the conclusion that *rheostatic control* of speed should be possible. This conclusion is in fact supported by the analytical theory leading to the torque-speed curves of Fig. 6-21, but it is evident that the variation of rotor resistance requires the use of a wound rotor connected through slip rings to an external rheo-

* *Elektrotech. Z.*, 1893, p. 185.

† For further details, see F. Punga and O. Raydt, "Modern Polyphase Induction Motors," Sir Isaac Pitman & Sons, Ltd., London, 1933; Miles Walker, "Induction Motors," D. Van Nostrand Company, Inc., New York, 1924; and P. L. Alger, "The Nature of Polyphase Induction Machines," John Wiley & Sons, Inc., New York, 1951.

stat. With any given resistance in circuit with the rotor, operation will be stable only on those portions of the torque-speed curves where the torque decreases as the speed increases. While a wound-rotor machine with auxiliary variable resistor is thus very useful in cases where large starting torque and control of speed are essential, the efficiency is lowered because of the ohmic loss in the rheostat; and the speed regulation is poor for the same reasons that obtain in a d-c shunt motor operated with resistance in series with its armature.

For example, it is well-known that the speed of a d-c shunt motor is determined by the relation*

$$n = \frac{V - I_a R_a'}{\Phi Z'} = \frac{E_a}{\Phi Z'} \tag{8-22}$$

where E_a is the counter emf developed in the armature winding. In the induction motor, the voltage impressed upon the rotor (by induction instead of by conduction) is E_{2e}, and the voltage consumed in the rotor leakage impedance is

$$s\mathbf{E}_{2e} = \mathbf{I}_{2e}(R_{2e} + jsX_{2e})$$

leaving as counter emf

$$\mathbf{E}_{2e}(1 - s) = \mathbf{E}_{2e} - \mathbf{I}_{2e}(R_{2e} + jsX_{2e})$$

which corresponds term by term with $V - I_a R_a'$. Moreover, since

$$\mathbf{E}_{2e} = \mathbf{E}_1 = -jk\mathbf{\Phi} n_1$$

we have
$$\mathbf{E}_{2e}(1 - s) = -jk\mathbf{\Phi} n_1(1 - s) = -jk\mathbf{\Phi} n_2$$

whence
$$n_2 = \frac{\mathbf{E}_{2e} - \mathbf{I}_{2e}(R_{2e} + jsX_{2e})}{-jk\mathbf{\Phi}} \tag{8-23}$$

which corresponds term by term with Eq. 8-22 except that complex quantities replace ordinary magnitudes. It is easy to see, however, in what manner the variation of R_{2e} affects the speed, and why it does so.

8-6. Speed Control by Variation of Rotor Voltage. It is well-known that the speed of a d-c separately excited motor can be controlled far more effectively by varying the voltage impressed upon the armature (V in Eq. 8-22) than by varying the resistance R_a'.† The parallelism between Eqs. 8-22 and 8-23 then indicates that an analogous procedure should be possible in the case of the induction motor by varying E_{2e}, which of course implies the use of a wound rotor. So long as the voltage and frequency impressed upon the stator remain fixed, the flux Φ will be substantially constant, and any change in E_{2e} should then produce a nearly proportional change in the speed n_2.

The rheostatic method of speed control may be regarded as a device for consuming in the control rheostat some of the energy transferred by

* Langsdorf, *op. cit.*, p. 468.
† *Ibid.*, p. 516.

induction from the primary to the secondary, thus decreasing the energy available for the mechanical load and so causing a reduction of speed. On the other hand, all methods of speed control of induction motors which involve variation of rotor voltage are based upon the concept that the energy which would otherwise be wasted in a control rheostat may be usefully returned to the system. Rheostatic control of an induction motor is of course incapable of increasing the speed above synchronism, for that would call for a negative resistance, which is equivalent to a source, as contrasted with a sink, of energy. The equivalent of a negative resistance is, however, represented by a control voltage which is opposite in phase to a control voltage which causes a reduction in speed, and such a reversed control voltage then represents an additional draft of energy from the supply circuit which can then result in speeds above synchronism.

8-7. The Leblanc Exciter. One of the earliest devices for the continuous variation of the speed of induction motors was invented by Maurice Leblanc.* It consists of an auxiliary regulating machine, in

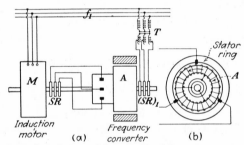

FIG. 8-11. Speed control by means of frequency converter.

reality a frequency converter, which is direct-connected to the shaft of the slip-ring induction motor the speed of which is to be controlled. The Leblanc exciter is open to the objection that the additional cost precludes its use except in the case of very large units, but while it has not been used for its original purpose, it has found an interesting and useful application in one type of frequency converter described in Art. 14-5.

The Leblanc machine has an armature winding (A in Fig. 8-11) exactly like that of an ordinary d-c machine, and is provided with a commutator at one end and slip rings at the other end, in the same manner as a rotary converter. Brushes are disposed around the commutator at intervals of 120 electrical degrees, in the case of a three-phase unit, there being three brushes per pair of poles (the diagram is constructed for the simple case of a two-pole machine) and these brushes are connected to the slip rings of the main motor. The slip rings of the frequency converter are connected through tap-changing transformers, or other voltage-regulating device, to

* B. A. Behrend, "The Induction Motor," 2d ed., pp. 124, 187, McGraw-Hill Book Company, Inc., New York, 1921.

the main supply line having frequency f_1.   The stator frame of the frequency converter is a laminated cylindrical ring without any winding whatever.

In order to understand the operation of this device, refer to Fig. 8-11b, which represents diagrammatically a side view of the frequency converter for the case of a bipolar model.   Current at frequency f_1, supplied from the line through slip rings SR_1, will produce a magnetic field rotating at synchronous speed with respect to the winding A; assume that the magnetic field moves in the clockwise direction relative to A, and that the latter is driven in the counterclockwise direction by the main motor M at the speed $n_2 = n_1(1 - s)$, where n_1 is the synchronous speed of the magnetic field of M.   It follows that if both A and M are wound for the same number of poles, the magnetic field due to winding A will rotate in space at the slip speed $n_1 s$.   The function of the stationary cylindrical smooth-core stator surrounding A is then simply to provide a path of low and uniform reluctance for this magnetic field as it rotates slowly with respect to the brushes on the commutator.   It is then obvious that each of the sections of winding A lying between adjacent brushes always presents the same aspect to the magnetic field which is moving relatively at slip speed, so that the *frequency* of the voltage generated in the turns between brushes is always *slip frequency*.   Because of the fact that the brushes and the slip rings associated with winding A are physically related in the same manner as in a rotary converter, the ratio of the brush voltage to the slip-ring voltage is definitely fixed regardless of the speed; but by rocking the brushes one way or the other, the *phase* of the brush voltage (of slip frequency) can be altered at will through any desired angle.   Finally, by adjusting the ratio of transformation of the regulating transformer T, the magnitude of the brush voltage is likewise brought under control.

The Leblanc a-c exciter therefore makes it possible to inject into the rotor of the induction motor a voltage which may be adjusted over a considerable range, and which always has the proper slip frequency; moreover, its phase is adjustable by rocking the brushes.   Variation of the magnitude of this voltage will then cause the speed of the induction motor to rise or fall as desired, within the limits fixed by the design; the control of the phase of the auxiliary voltage automatically controls the phase of the rotor current of the induction motor, and therefore the phase of the stator current as well, since the mmfs of the rotor and stator currents are tied together by the requirement that their resultant shall yield the (nearly) constant flux; in other words, the power factor of the induction motor can be adjusted as well as its speed.

It is interesting to note that when the induction motor is running at synchronous speed the current supplied by the exciter is continuous (zero-frequency) current.   The exciter really serves a dual function, for it acts simultaneously as a frequency converter and a phase adjuster;

and by changing the number and spacing of the brushes on the commutator it can be made to operate also as a phase converter.

8-8. The Krämer System. * The operation of steel rolling mills calls for large amounts of power coupled with flexible control of speed. One of the first effective methods for meeting the requirements, known as the Krämer system, utilized a commutator machine, direct-connected to the main motor, as in Fig. 8-12. The slip frequency impressed upon the stator winding of the auxiliary machine develops a magnetic field rotating in space at the corresponding slip speed, and because of the presence of the commutator the rotor emf and current will likewise have slip frequency regardless of the actual speed of the shaft. Adjustment of the regulating transformer controls the magnitude of the rotor emf, hence also the speed of the main motor. At speeds below synchronism, the surplus energy in

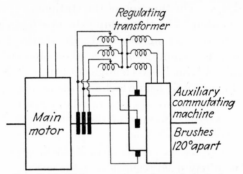

FIG. 8-12. Krämer system of speed control.

the rotor of the main motor is absorbed by the auxiliary machine acting as a motor, thereby causing the auxiliary machine to assume part of the mechanical load and to that extent relieving the main motor. The size of the auxiliary machine is determined by the amount of speed adjustment required; for example, if the speed of the set is to be reduced x per cent below synchronism, its rating must be x per cent of that of the main motor.

Theoretically this arrangement permits power-factor control by shifting the brushes of the commutating machine, but practically this feature is restricted by the circumstance that commutation difficulties limit the possible range of brush shift. It is possible to overcome this difficulty by means of commutating fields or by special phase combinations in the machine itself.

* J. Jonas, Polyphase Commutator Motors, *London Electrician*, **65**:738 (1910). G. A. Maier, Methods of Varying the Speed of A-C Motors, *Trans. AIEE*, **30**(pt. 3): 2455 (1911). F. W. Meyer and W. Sykes, The Economical Speed Control of A-C Motors Driving Rolling Mills, *Trans. AIEE*, **31**(pt. 2):2067 (1912). J. I. Hull, Theory of Speed and Power Factor Control of Large Induction Motors by Neutralized Polyphase A-C Commutator Machines, *Trans. AIEE*, **39**(pt. 2):1135 (1920). See also references to books by B. A. Behrend and Miles Walker.

The chief disadvantage of this system is that the commutated machine must be designed for the same speed as the main motor, which in the case of large rolling mills is low, while in the case of high-speed motors for turbo-compressors, blowers, etc., it becomes practically impossible to design a correspondingly high-speed commutating machine.

Figure 8-13 illustrates a modified form of the system. The slip rings of the main motor are connected to the a-c side of a rotary converter, the d-c side of which feeds a d-c shunt motor direct-connected to the shaft of the main motor. The speed of the set is controlled by varying the field of the d-c motor. Thus, when the field resistance is altered, the d-c voltages of both motor and rotary are correspondingly changed, and therefore also the a-c voltage of the rotary, since the a-c and d-c voltages of a rotary

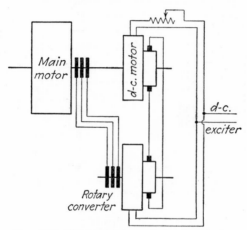

FIG. 8-13. Krämer system of speed control.

have a fixed ratio. This arrangement is suited to a wide range of speed control, as the design of the rotary converter is practically independent of the speed control required.

8-9. The Scherbius System. The Scherbius control, illustrated by the full-line diagram (Fig. 8-14), differs from the Krämer control chiefly in that the commutating machine is not direct-connected to the main motor whose speed is to be controlled; it has the advantage, therefore, that the commutating machine may be designed to run at a speed appropriate to its function.

The commutating machine, excited at slip frequency from the rotor of the main motor, develops a brush voltage of slip frequency which is injected into the rotor circuit of the main motor and so serves to regulate the speed of the latter. The commutating machine is direct-connected to an induction motor supplied from the main line, so that its speed departs from a fixed value only to the extent of the slip of the auxiliary induction machine.

Adjustment of the taps of the regulating transformer (which may take the form of a variable-ratio autotransformer) varies the excitation of the commutating machine, thereby varying the voltage developed in its rotor and so controlling the speed of the main motor. If, for instance, the regulating transformer is so adjusted as to reduce the speed of the main motor, the surplus secondary energy of the latter (which in the case of rheostatic control would be lost in the control resistance) drives the commutating machine as a motor, and the auxiliary induction machine then becomes an induction generator which returns most of this surplus energy

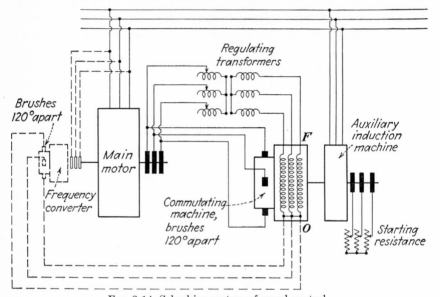

Fig. 8-14. Scherbius system of speed control.

as electrical energy to the supply circuit. This should be contrasted with the action of the Krämer system, which returns the surplus energy in the form of mechanical energy to the load.

For any given setting of the regulating transformer, the speed of the main motor will remain substantially constant regardless of load variation. This can be shown in the following manner:

The voltage induced in the rotor of the main motor is sE_{2e}, where E_{2e} may be taken as substantially constant if the primary leakage-impedance drop is small. If the leakage-impedance drop in the rotor of the main motor is ignored, a voltage proportional to sE_{2e}, and having slip frequency, is thus impressed upon the stator of the commutating machine, which then develops a magnetic field, Φ_c, rotating in space at a speed corresponding to the slip frequency sf_1. In accordance with Eq. 4-27,

$$a(sE_{2e}) = 4.44 k_{b_1} k_{p_1}(sf_1) N_c \Phi_c$$

and since s cancels out, it follows that Φ_c remains substantially constant. If the small variation of speed of the regulating set is neglected, the voltage (of slip frequency) developed in the rotor of the commutating machine also remains nearly constant.   Consequently, the resultant voltage in the secondary circuit of the main motor is also nearly constant, thus corresponding to the condition for substantially constant speed.

For the sake of simplicity, the diagram (Fig. 8-14) indicates only a single polyphase winding of shunt type on the stator of the commutating machine.   In actual practice, because of the large magnitude of the rotor current which must flow through the brushes of this machine, it is necessary to provide neutralizing or compensating windings to overcome the otherwise unduly large reactance drop.

When the circuit diagram has the form shown in full lines in Fig. 8-14, the set is adapted to speed control in the range below synchronism.   The shunt field winding F of the commutated machine is then Y-connected, as at O.   Since the capacity of the regulating machines must be proportional to the speed range desired, it is readily seen that its rating may be reduced by 50 per cent if the speed range is equally above and below synchronism.   To obtain this double-range control, the Y connection at O is opened, and the free terminals of the field windings F are connected to the brushes of a small frequency converter mounted on the extended shaft of the main motor.   Its construction is the same in principle as that of the Leblanc machine (Art. 8-7).   It supplies an excitation of fixed voltage, at slip frequency, to the field F of the commutating machine, and the phase of this voltage can be controlled by shifting the brushes of the frequency converter.

If the load on the main motor is subject to abrupt fluctuations of considerable magnitude, as in rolling-mill operation, it is desirable that a sudden increase of load be accompanied by a correspondingly sharp drop in the speed of the main motor; in this way, the kinetic energy of a heavy flywheel on the main shaft may be drawn upon to relieve the supply circuit of violent fluctuations of current.   This result can be accomplished by compounding (series) windings on the stator of the commutating machine.

8-10. The Schrage Brush-shift Adjustable-speed Motor.   To meet the need for an induction motor of small or moderate size having the desirable feature of flexible speed control without the auxiliary devices described in the preceding articles, K. H. Schrage of Sweden invented the self-contained machine illustrated in Fig. 8-15.   In the United States, this machine is built by the General Electric Company in sizes ranging from 3 to 50 hp, the trade designation being the BTA motor; a few motors of larger rating (100 to 150 hp) have been built, but beyond 150 hp other methods of speed control are preferable.   Ordinarily the General Electric motors of this type are designed for a 3:1 speed range, though a range of

4:1 is available in sizes from 2 to 40 hp.   These motors are designed for three-phase 60-cycle circuits at 220, 440, and 550 volts, though two-phase motors are available.

The diagram of connections of the Schrage motor is shown in Fig. 8-15 for the case of a two-pole model.   It differs from the ordinary polyphase induction motor in that the supply current is conveyed through slip rings to a *primary* winding on the *rotor*, while the phase-wound *secondary* is on the *stator*.   A further difference is the presence in the tops of the rotor slots of an auxiliary *adjusting winding*, entirely similar to an ordinary d-c armature winding, which is tapped to the segments of a commutator in the usual manner.   The commutator is provided with two distinct sets of brushes supported on yoke rings mounted in parallel planes, in such a manner that either set of brushes can be shifted relative to the other in

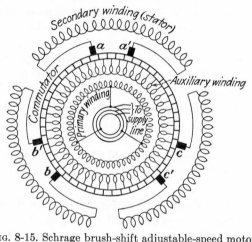

FIG. 8-15. Schrage brush-shift adjustable-speed motor.

either direction.   The individual brushes of each set are successively displaced by 120 electrical degrees, and they are connected, in the manner indicated in Fig. 8-15, to one set of terminals of the secondary (stator) phase windings; the brushes of the other set are similarly connected to the remaining terminals of the secondary phase windings.

Assume for the moment that the brush yokes are adjusted so that the two brushes of a pair which terminate a phase of the secondary winding rest upon one and the same commutator segment; i.e., referring to Fig. 8-15, brushes a and a' lie in the same radial plane, and similarly for the pairs bb' and cc'.   The secondary winding of the motor is then short-circuited.   If reduced voltage from the line is then impressed upon the slip rings, the primary (rotor) current will set up a magnetic field which rotates at synchronous speed relative to the rotor, and if the latter is initially at rest, the magnetic field will rotate at synchronous speed in space. The effect of this synchronously revolving field, at the moment of starting, is to induce emfs and currents of line frequency in the short-circuited secondary, and the reaction between the induced secondary currents and the magnetic field develops a torque in the same manner as in any induction motor; when the speed has reached a sufficient value, full voltage may be applied to the slip rings.

Because of the fact that the secondary winding is in this case embedded in the stator slots, the torque will cause the rotor to accelerate in a direction opposite to that of the revolving magnetic field; the magnetic field itself necessarily continues to rotate at synchronous speed relative to the rotor; consequently, as the latter speeds up more and more in the contrary direction, the speed of the magnetic field in space decreases more and more, and approaches zero as the rotor approaches synchronous speed. In general, the magnetic field rotates in space at slip speed in a direction opposite to that of the rotor core; from this, it follows that the secondary currents and voltages will be of slip frequency, just as in any induction motor, so that when the secondary is short-circuited, with the brush pairs aa', bb', cc' lined up in the positions initially assumed, the motor will run at nearly synchronous speed at all loads within its rated capacity.

It is, of course, evident that the airgap flux, when once established, must thereafter remain substantially constant in magnitude, just as in any induction motor operating with constant primary voltage.

Suppose, now, that the brushes are separated, as indicated in Fig. 8-15. Because of the presence of the commutator, the portion of the auxiliary winding which lies between the two brushes of a pair will always present the same aspect to an observer who is fixed in space, as though the auxiliary winding were itself stationary in the same way as are the secondary windings on the stator; the airgap flux, cutting across it at slip speed, will therefore develop in the auxiliary winding a voltage of the same slip frequency as that induced in the actually stationary secondary winding.

In case the voltages in the secondary and auxiliary windings are additive, the motor speed will be increased, while if they are oppositely directed, the speed will be decreased. If, for example, they are additive under the conditions shown in Fig. 8-15, interchanging the positions of a and a' (and simultaneously those of the other brush pairs) will bring the two voltages into opposition. It is obvious that the magnitude of the regulating voltage thus injected into the secondary windings will be nearly proportional to the chord of the arc subtended by the brush pair, provided the magnetic field is sinusoidally distributed around the airgap.

In a preceding paragraph, reference was made to the starting of the motor at reduced voltage, but this was merely for convenience and simplicity of explanation. In the motor as manufactured by the General Electric Company, starting can be accomplished at full line voltage, without excessive initial rush of current, by first setting the brushes in the low-speed position.   In this way, the starting current will be 125 to 175 per cent of the normal high-speed current, and the starting torque (in the 3:1 range motors) will vary from 200 per cent of normal in the case of the smallest size to 140 per cent of normal in the largest size.   These figures for the starting torque are averages only, for this motor, in common with most induction motors, does not develop the same standstill torque for all positions of the rotor relative to the stator; the static torque will show a variation from a maximum to a minimum value within a small angular range in the rotor position, this effect being due to high-frequency pulsations of the flux caused by the teeth and slots.   The maximum torque of the motor is at least 250 per cent of normal in all sizes when the brushes are in the high-speed position; in the low-speed position, the maximum torque of the smallest size is about 200 per cent of full-load torque, and in the largest size about 140 per cent.

Power-factor Compensation.   In the preceding discussion of the theory of the brush-shift motor, nothing has been said about the phase of the emf contributed by that part of the auxiliary adjusting winding which lies between a pair of brushes.   In fact, Fig. 8-15 has been drawn with the center of winding belt aa' in line with the center of the corresponding phase belt of the secondary, and similarly with respect to the portions bb' and cc'; under such circumstances, the emf, say, of belt aa', will either be in phase with the voltage induced in the corresponding secondary winding, or it will be in phase opposition thereto, depending upon the sense of the two windings.   In either case, the phase of the resultant voltage in the secondary circuit will be the same as that of the secondary winding alone, and the phase of the resultant secondary current will then be determined by the combined resistances and leakage reactances of the two windings in series.   In consequence, the phasor diagram of the motor will have the same form as that of an ordinary induction motor, and its power factor will be governed by the same considerations that have been discussed in Chap. 6.

Suppose, however, that the two brushes of a pair are not symmetrically placed with respect to the center line of the corresponding secondary phase belt.   The phase of the voltage contributed by the adjusting winding will then differ from that of the secondary winding, with the result that the phase of the resultant secondary current will be shifted.   In other words, improvement of power factor can be effected in this type of motor by a suitable adjustment of the brush yokes.

For a given angular spread between the two brushes of a pair, such as aa' (Fig. 8-15), the voltage induced in the intervening part of the auxiliary winding will have the same magnitude without regard to the space position of the brush pair; the only effect of the position of the pair of brushes in question is to alter the phase of the voltage.

8-11. Speed Adjustment by Pole Changing. The fact that the synchronous speed of an induction motor is given by the formula $n = 120f/p$ long ago suggested the possibility of obtaining more than one machine speed by providing the stator with windings so arranged that by suitable switching the number of poles could be changed.

For example, two independent three-phase stator windings, one wound for six poles, the other for eight, can be placed in 72 slots so that synchronous speeds of 1,200 and 900 rpm will result from their connection, one at a time, to a 60-cycle supply line. In order to avoid complications, the rotor of such a two-speed machine would ordinarily be a squirrel cage for the reason that it adjusts itself automatically to any number of poles; but two rotor windings, each with its own slip rings, could be used provided that each winding is designed for the same number of poles as that of the stator winding with which it is to be used. Incidentally, it should be noted that in this example the minimum number of stator slots, S, for integral-slot windings, is determined by the consideration that $S = 3pq$; so if the pole numbers are, as in this case, $p' = 6$ and $p'' = 8$, and the corresponding numbers of slots per pole per phase are q' and q'', it follows that $q'/q'' = p''/p' = \frac{4}{3}$; and since q' and q'' must be integers, the minimum number of slots is $S = 3 \times 6 \times 4 = 3 \times 8 \times 3 = 72$. The two stator windings in this example should be so designed that the individual coils of each of them have the same throw in order to simplify their insertion in the slots; a coil throw of eight slots, for example, would be equivalent to a pitch of $\frac{8}{9}$ for the eight-pole machine, and of $\frac{2}{3}$ for the six-pole machine, both of which are well within practicable limits.

The most common arrangement for multispeed operation utilizes what amounts to a single stator winding in which the coil groups belonging to each phase may be connected to give a 2:1 pole ratio. For example, Fig. 8-16 represents in developed form the coils of one phase of a three-phase winding disposed in 48 slots, with alternate groups in series, thus constituting two distinct circuits, one with terminals x_1y_1, the other with terminals x_2y_2. If these circuits are connected in series, in the order $x_1y_1x_2y_2$, all four groups of coils will magnetize in the same direction (indicated by the poles marked N_t in the diagram), and consequent poles of opposite polarity will accordingly be produced midway between them, thereby giving a total of eight poles; but if the two circuits are connected in series in the order $x_1y_1y_2x_2$, there will be a total of four poles and a corresponding doubling of the speed.

Similarly, if the two circuits of Fig. 8-16 are connected in parallel in the order $(x_1x_2-y_1y_2)$ the number of poles will be eight, while if the order is $(x_1y_2-y_1x_2)$, there will be four poles.

It will be noted that the angle between adjacent slots is 15 electrical degrees in the high-speed (four-pole) connection, and 30 electrical degrees in the low-speed (eight-pole) arrangement, which makes the spread of the phase belts, respectively, 60 and 120 electrical degrees, with corresponding changes in the breadth factors of the windings; further, the four-pole connection has a pitch factor of 50 per cent, while that of the eight-pole machine is 100 per cent.

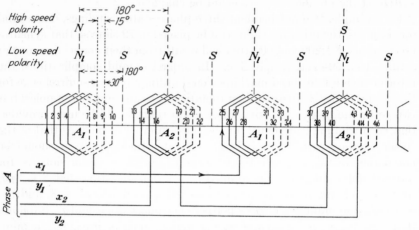

FIG. 8-16. Pole-changing connection diagram, 48-slot 4- and 8-pole machine.

Four possible interconnections of the two circuits of each phase are indicated in Fig. 8-17, and the possible star and Δ combinations of the phases themselves are shown in Figs. 8-18, 8-19, and 8-20. These are, respectively, designated as the *constant-torque*, the *constant-horsepower*,

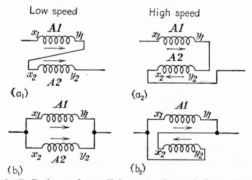

FIG. 8-17. Series and parallel connections of phase circuits.

and the *variable-torque* connections, for the following reasons: Let

$$V = \text{line to line voltage in each diagram}$$
$$I = \text{allowable current per conductor}$$
$$\eta_l, \eta_h = \text{respective efficiencies of low- and high-speed connections}$$
$$\cos \varphi_l, \cos \varphi_h = \text{respective power factors of low- and high-speed connections}$$

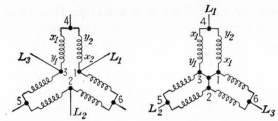

(a) Low speed, series circuit △   (b) High speed, parallel circuit Y

FIG. 8-18. Constant-torque connections.

Referring to Fig. 8-18, it will be seen that

$$\frac{\text{Low-speed output}}{\text{High-speed output}} = \frac{3VI\eta_l \cos \varphi_l}{\sqrt{3}\, V2I\eta_h \cos \varphi_h} = 0.866\, \frac{\eta_l \cos \varphi_l}{\eta_h \cos \varphi_h}$$

Hence, $$\frac{\text{Low-speed torque}}{\text{High-speed torque}} = 1.732\, \frac{\eta_l \cos \varphi_l}{\eta_h \cos \varphi_h}$$

The ratio $\eta_l \cos \varphi_l / \eta_h \cos \varphi_h$ is definitely less than unity, in part because it has been shown that the power factor of a low-speed machine (with its larger number of poles) is inherently lower than that of an otherwise similar high-speed machine, and in part because the efficiency is also affected. In general, this ratio is of the order of 0.7, so that the above torque ratio is of the order $1.73 \times 0.7 = 1.21$, which is close enough to unity to warrant the descriptive term "constant-torque connection" for Fig. 8-18.

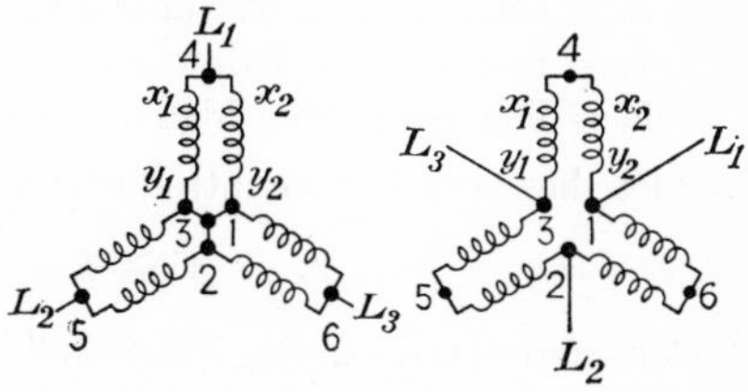

In the same way, reference to Fig. 8-19 shows that

(a) Low speed,   (b) High speed,
parallel circuit Y   series circuit △

FIG. 8-19. Constant-horsepower connections.

$$\frac{\text{Low-speed output}}{\text{High-speed output}} = \frac{\sqrt{3}\, V2I\eta_l \cos \varphi_l}{3VI\eta_h \cos \varphi_h} = 1.15\, \frac{\eta_l \cos \varphi_l}{\eta_h \cos \varphi_h}$$

and $$\frac{\text{Low-speed torque}}{\text{High-speed torque}} = 2.3\, \frac{\eta_l \cos \varphi_l}{\eta_h \cos \varphi_h}$$

so that the above ratio of outputs becomes about $1.15 \times 0.7 = 0.80$, or close enough to unity to warrant the designation "constant-horsepower connection."

Similarly, in Fig. 8-20,

$$\frac{\text{Low-speed output}}{\text{High-speed output}} = \frac{\sqrt{3}\, VI\eta_l \cos \varphi_l}{\sqrt{3}\, V2I\eta_h \cos \varphi_h} = 0.5\, \frac{\eta_l \cos \varphi_l}{\eta_h \cos \varphi_h}$$

and $$\frac{\text{Low-speed torque}}{\text{High-speed torque}} = 1.0\, \frac{\eta_l \cos \varphi_l}{\eta_h \cos \varphi_h} \cong 0.7$$

Relatively, this last ratio of 0.7 is so much less than the corresponding ratio of 1.21 for Fig. 8-18 that the designation "variable-torque connection" is used for Fig. 8-20.

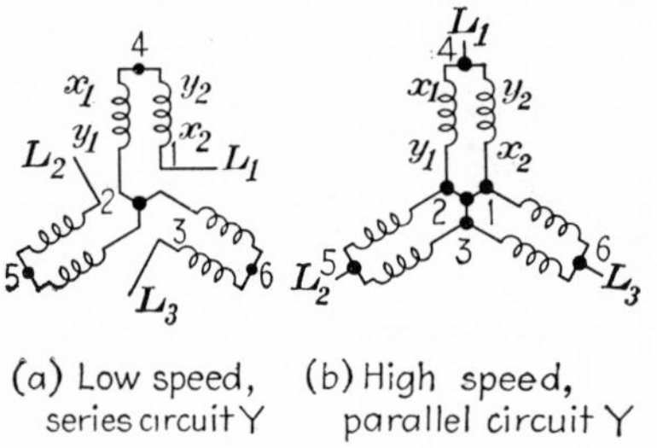

(a) Low speed,   (b) High speed,
series circuit Y   parallel circuit Y

FIG. 8-20. Variable-torque connections.

The constant-torque connection, Fig. 8-18, is applicable to power drives in which the friction load is dominant. The constant-horsepower connection, Fig. 8-19, which yields about twice as much torque at low speed as at high speed, is used to drive machine tools. The variable-torque connection, Fig. 8-20, which gives reduced torque at low speeds, is suited to drive fans, blowers, and similar devices in which the torque decreases rapidly as the speed is reduced.

Example. The fact that the efficiency and power factor are not the same at the high and low speeds is largely a consequence of the change in flux which accompanies the changed connections. In order to investigate this feature, let

N = total number of winding turns per phase

Φ_l = flux per pole at low speed

Φ_h = flux per pole at high speed

and let these symbols be introduced into the general emf formula

$$V \cong E = 4.44 k_b k_p f \Phi N$$

Considering the winding illustrated in Fig. 8-16, it will be seen that in the low-speed connection $q = 4$, $\gamma = 30°$, whence the breadth factor is

$$(k_b)_l = \frac{\sin 4 \times 3\%}{4 \sin 3\%} = 0.837$$

and since the winding has full pitch,

$$(k_p)_l = 1.0$$

In the case of the high-speed connection, where $q = 4$ and $\gamma = 15°$, the breadth factor is

$$(k_b)_h = \frac{\sin 4 \times 15\%}{4 \sin 15\%} = 0.957$$

and since the throw of the coils is one-half of the pole pitch,

$$(k_p)_h = \cos 9\% = 0.707$$

Referring now to Fig. 8-18a,

$$V = 4.44 \times 0.837 f \Phi_l N$$

whereas in Fig. 8-18b

$$\frac{V}{\sqrt{3}} = 4.44 \times 0.957 \times 0.707 f \Phi_h \frac{N}{2}$$

from which $\dfrac{\Phi_l}{\Phi_h} = 0.7$ in the constant-torque connection

Similarly, referring to Fig. 8-19a,

$$\frac{V}{\sqrt{3}} = 4.44 \times 0.837 f \Phi_l \frac{N}{2}$$

while in Fig. 8-19b

$$V = 4.44 \times 0.957 \times 0.707 f \Phi_h N$$

whence $\dfrac{\Phi_l}{\Phi_h} = 0.934$ in the constant-horsepower connection

Finally, from Fig. 8-20a,

$$\frac{V}{\sqrt{3}} = 4.44 \times 0.837 f \Phi_l N$$

and from Fig. 8-20b

$$\frac{V}{\sqrt{3}} = 4.44 \times 0.957 \times 0.707 f \Phi_h \frac{N}{2}$$

whence $\dfrac{\Phi_l}{\Phi_h} = 0.403$ in the variable-torque connection

These changes in the flux per pole on changing from low to high speed are necessarily accompanied by nearly proportional changes in the flux densities in the stator and rotor cores behind the teeth; the depth of the iron behind the teeth must of course be chosen to limit the largest value of flux density to a reasonable amount. But the conditions with respect to the average flux density B_g in the airgap are different because the effective area of a pole is twice as large in the high-speed case as it is in the low-speed case, so that

$$\frac{(B_g)_l}{(B_g)_h} = 1.4 \qquad \text{in the constant-torque connection}$$
$$= 1.87 \qquad \text{in the constant-horsepower connection}$$
$$= 0.81 \qquad \text{in the variable-torque connection}$$

The net result of these considerations is that the design of a multispeed motor must be a compromise which involves the sacrifice of operating characteristics at one or the other, and usually at both, of the two speeds.

8-12. Speed Control by Change of Frequency.

The speed formula, $n = 120f/p$, indicates the possibility of controlling the speed of an induction motor by changing the frequency of the supply circuit; but inasmuch as this method requires a separate variable-speed synchronous alternator for each motor to be independently controlled, it has been applied only in the case of ship propulsion, where each of the driving motors, direct-connected to a propeller shaft, is supplied by its own turbine-driven generator.

If the excitation of the generator is held constant, a change in its speed will alter both its terminal voltage and its frequency in the same proportion, provided that the impedance drop in its armature is neglected;

hence, by Eq. 6-1, the main flux of the driven motor will remain nearly constant. So far as the torque of the motor is concerned, the effect of simultaneous and proportional changes in impressed voltage and frequency may be seen from Eq. 6-26, which, when the slip s is small, may be written in the form

$$T \cong \frac{33,000 m_1 p}{2\pi \times 746 \times 120} \frac{V_1}{f} V_1 \frac{s}{R_{2e}}$$

so that the torque at full speed under the new conditions is proportional to V_1 and therefore also proportional to the impressed frequency and to the speed.

If the motor is started with reduced voltage and frequency, the starting torque becomes

$$T_{s=1} = \frac{33,000 m_1 p}{2\pi \times 746 \times 120} \frac{V_1}{f} V_1 \frac{R_{2e}}{(R_1 + R_{2e})^2 + 4\pi^2 f^2 (L_1 + L_{2e})^2}$$

where L_1 and L_{2e} are the self-inductances of the primary and secondary per phase. Assuming that the resistance $R_1 + R_{2e}$ is small in comparison with the reactance, it will be seen that the starting torque is inversely proportional to the frequency provided that the values of R_1, R_{2e}, L_1, and L_{2e} remain the same as at normal frequency. Actually, they decrease with the frequency because of reduced skin effect.

8-13. Concatenation, or Tandem Control of Speed.* Figure 8-21 is a diagram of two wound-rotor induction motors which are mechanically coupled, either directly or through gears, and which are electrically connected in concatenation (sometimes referred to as "in tandem" or "in cascade"). This arrangement, while formerly used, especially in Europe, has been superseded by other methods for speed control, but it presents features of sufficient interest to justify an analysis of its operation.

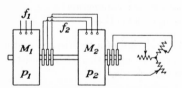

FIG. 8-21. Concatenation of two induction motors, rotor 1 supplying stator 2.

The slip rings of motor M_1 are connected to the stator of motor M_2, and the slip rings of the latter connect to a variable three-phase resistor; with these connections, it is desirable that the ratio of transformation of both motors be unity in order to limit the magnitude of the slip-ring current. The variable resistance is used to start the unit and to obtain speeds intermediate between standstill and the speed corresponding to complete short circuit of the rotor of M_2.

Let p_1 and p_2 be the number of poles and s_1 and s_2 the slips of M_1 and M_2, respectively; then if f_1 and f_2 are the respective frequencies of the

* See Behrend, *op. cit.*, Walker, *op. cit.*, E. Arnold, "Wechselstromtechnik," Vol. V, Julius Springer, Berlin, 1912, for further details.

stator voltages, the following relations are obvious:

$$\text{Synchronous speed of } M_1 = \frac{120f_1}{p_1} = n_1$$

$$\text{Synchronous speed of } M_2 = \frac{120f_2}{p_2} = n_2$$

$$\text{Actual speed of } M_1 = \frac{120f_1}{p_1}(1 - s_1) = n$$

$$\text{Actual speed of } M_2 = \frac{120f_2}{p_2}(1 - s_2) = n$$

Since $f_2 = sf_1$, and the actual speeds of the two machines must be the same, it follows that

$$\frac{1 - s_1}{p_1} = \frac{s_1(1 - s_2)}{p_2}$$

or

$$s_1 = \frac{p_2}{p_1 + p_2 - p_1 s_2} \tag{8-24}$$

When the starting resistance is short-circuited, motor M_2 must operate with very small slip in order that it may have stability, hence s_2 must approach zero, and

$$\text{Limit of } s_1 \rightarrow \frac{p_2}{p_1 + p_2} \tag{8-25}$$

Hence, the actual speed of motor M_1 and of the set as a whole approaches

$$\text{Limit of } n = n_l = \frac{120f_1}{p_1}\left(1 - \frac{p_2}{p_1 + p_2}\right) = \frac{120f_1}{p_1 + p_2} \tag{8-26}$$

The last equation shows that the synchronous speed of the set is the same as that of a single motor which has a number of poles equal to the sum of the numbers of poles of the actual machines. If $p_1 = p_2$, the synchronous speed of the set is half that of either motor when running alone.

The cascade connection of the two identical motors is therefore seen to be quite similar to the first stage of the connection of two series railway motors operated by the familiar series-parallel method of control.

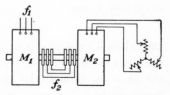

Fig. 8-22. Concatenated motors, rotors electrically connected.

It is readily seen that if p_1 and p_2 are different, the set is capable of operating stably at three different speeds, namely, the nominal synchronous speed of M_1 operating alone, the corresponding speed of M_2 when operating alone, and the speed given by Eq. 8-26 when M_1 and M_2 are connected in cascade.

The diagram of connections shown in Fig. 8-21 may be modified to the form of Fig. 8-22 in case the two motors do not have unit ratios of transformation, but where the two rotors have equal current-carrying capacities.   The two cases are electrically identical when all the motor constants are reduced to a common basis.

The Equivalent Circuit of Concatenated Motors.   Each motor of a concatenated pair such as M_1 and M_2 (Fig. 8-22) will have an individual equivalent circuit of the general type of Fig. 6-17, and it is evident without formal proof that their separate circuits must be coupled in series, the secondary circuit of M_1 being opened to include the circuit of M_2.

It must be remembered, however, that in the circuit of Fig. 6-17b all reactances are computed in terms of the frequency impressed upon the primary, and that the slip s which appears in the term R_{2e}/s is the slip of the rotor with respect to the stator.   It follows, therefore, that if the equivalent circuit of motor M_2 is to be drawn separately, the reactances must be assigned values which correspond to the frequency $f_2 = s_1 f_1$ impressed upon its primary; and if the six principal constants of M_2, reduced to terms of the primary of M_1 (corresponding then to frequency f_1), are

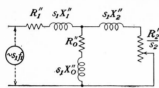

FIG. 8-23. Equivalent circuit of motor M_2 when supplied at frequency $f_2 = s_1 f_1$.

$$R_1'', X_1''; R_0'', X_0''; R_2'', X_2''$$

they become
$$R_1'', s_1 X_1''; R_0'', s_1 X_0''; R_2'', s_1 X_2''$$

when the impressed frequency is $f_2 = s_1 f_1$.   The equivalent circuit of motor M_2, considered separately, then takes the form of Fig. 8-23, and its equivalent impedance at primary frequency f_2 and secondary slip s_2 is

$$Z_e'' = R_1'' + js_1 X_1'' + \cfrac{1}{\cfrac{1}{R_0'' + js_1 X_0''} + \cfrac{1}{\dfrac{R_2''}{s_2} + js_1 X_2''}} \qquad (8\text{-}27)$$

The six principal constants of motor M_1, referred to the primary at frequency f_1, are

$$R_1', X_1'; R_0', X_0'; R_2', X_2'$$

and when it runs at slip s_1, the impedance of its rotor is $R_2' + js_1 X_2'$; but the rotor of M_1 being in series with the whole circuit of M_2, the effect is the same as though the impedance of the secondary of M_1 had been increased to

$$R_2' + js_1 X_2' + Z_e''$$

and it is this entire impedance upon which is impressed the slip voltage, $s_1 E_{2e}'$, developed in the rotor of M_1 by rotation through its revolving magnetic field.   The secondary current of M_1 is therefore

$$\mathbf{I}_2' = \frac{s_1 E_{2e}'}{R_2' + js_1 X_2' + Z_e''} = \frac{E_{2e}'}{\dfrac{R_2'}{s_1} + jX_2' + \dfrac{Z_e''}{s_1}} \qquad (8\text{-}28)$$

and the impedance of the entire secondary of M_1 (including all of M_2), expressed in terms of the primary of M_1, in accordance with Eqs. (8-27) and (8-28), is

$$\left(\frac{R_2'}{s_1} + jX_2'\right) + \left(\frac{R_1''}{s_1} + jX_1'' + \cfrac{1}{\cfrac{1}{\cfrac{R_0''}{s_1} + jX_0''} + \cfrac{1}{\cfrac{R_2''}{s_1 s_2} + jX_2''}}\right) \quad (8\text{-}29)$$

On combining with this impedance the primary leakage impedance and the exciting impedance of M_1, the equivalent circuit of the entire unit

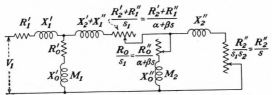

Fig. 8-24. Equivalent circuit of concatenated motors.

consisting of the two concatenated machines takes the form shown in Fig. 8-24, and the expression for the equivalent impedance of the entire set becomes

$$Z_e = R_1' + jX_1' + \cfrac{1}{\cfrac{1}{R_0' + jX_0'} + \cfrac{1}{\cfrac{R_2' + R_1''}{s_1} + j(X_2' + X_1'') + \cfrac{1}{\cfrac{1}{\cfrac{R_0''}{s_1} + jX_0''} + \cfrac{1}{\cfrac{R_2''}{s_1 s_2} + jX_2''}}}} \quad (8\text{-}30)$$

Instead of using the slips s_1 and s_2 of the individual machines M_1 and M_2, it is convenient to work with the slip s of the unit as a whole, which may be defined as

$$s = \frac{n_l - n}{n_l} \quad (8\text{-}31)$$

where n_l is the limiting (synchronous) speed of the set as defined by Eq. 8-26, and n is the actual speed. Since

$$n = \frac{120f_1}{p_1}(1 - s_1) = n_l(1 - s) = \frac{120f_1}{p_1 + p_2}(1 - s)$$

it is readily found that

$$s_1 = \frac{p_2 + p_1 s}{p_1 + p_2} \quad (8\text{-}32)$$

Similarly, since

$$n = \frac{120f_2}{p_2}(1 - s_2) = \frac{120s_1 f_1}{p_2}(1 - s_2) = \frac{120f_1}{p_1 + p_2}(1 - s)$$

the slip s_2 is found to be

$$s_2 = \frac{(p_1 + p_2)s}{p_2 + p_1 s} \tag{8-33}$$

Hence,

$$s_1 s_2 = s \tag{8-34}$$

If

$$\frac{p_2}{p_1 + p_2} = \alpha$$

$$\frac{p_1}{p_1 + p_2} = \beta \tag{8-35}$$

so that $\alpha + \beta = 1$, it is seen from Eq. 8-32 that

$$s_1 = \alpha + \beta s \tag{8-36}$$

and the circuit constants of Fig. 8-24 are accordingly shown in terms of α, β, and s.

It is of course possible to replace the exciting impedance of motor M_1 by the corresponding admittance $Y'_0 = G'_0 - jB'_0$, where

$$G'_0 = \frac{R'_0}{(R'_0)^2 + (X'_0)^2}$$

$$B'_0 = \frac{X'_0}{(R'_0)^2 + (X'_0)^2} \tag{8-37}$$

and in the same way the variable exciting impedance of motor M_2 may be replaced by the corresponding admittance

$$Y''_0 = \frac{R''_0/s_1}{(R''_0/s_1)^2 + (X''_0)^2} - j\frac{X''_0}{(R''_0/s_1)^2 + (X''_0)^2} \tag{8-38}$$

in which both the conductance and the susceptance are variable. This variability of Y''_0 might have been anticipated from the physical fact that the stator of M_2 is excited by a current of variable frequency derived from the rotor of M_1.

The Torque and Division of Load of Concatenated Motors. It has been shown that very little error is introduced by assuming that the exciting admittance may be transferred to the line side of the equivalent circuit. If this approximation is now made with respect to the equivalent circuit Fig. 8-24, the two exciting admittances (or impedances) may be assumed to be in parallel across the primary voltage V_1, and the power absorbed in these parallel branches will differ by only a small amount from the actual friction and core losses of the two machines. The current through the remaining major part of the circuit will then be

$$I_2 = \frac{V_1}{\sqrt{\left(R'_1 + \dfrac{R'_2 + R''_1}{\alpha + \beta s} + \dfrac{R''_2}{s}\right)^2 + (X'_1 + X'_2 + X''_1 + X''_2)^2}} = \frac{V_1}{Z_2}$$

$$\tag{8-39}$$

and the input to this circuit per phase will be

$$P_i = V_1 I_2 \cos \theta_2 \tag{8-40}$$

where $$\cos \theta_2 = \frac{R_1' + \dfrac{R_2' + R_1''}{\alpha + \beta s} + \dfrac{R_2''}{s}}{Z_2} \tag{8-41}$$

It is clear that since friction and core losses have been accounted for by the power absorbed in the exciting impedances, P_i includes the copper losses and the mechanical output (per phase). Substituting Eqs. 8-39 and 8-41 in Eq. 8-40,

$$P_i = \frac{V_1^2 \left(R_1' + \dfrac{R_2' + R_1''}{\alpha + \beta s} + \dfrac{R_2''}{s} \right)}{\left(R_1' + \dfrac{R_2' + R_1''}{\alpha + \beta s} + \dfrac{R_2''}{s} \right)^2 + (X_1' + X_2' + X_1'' + X_2'')^2} \tag{8-42}$$

Now the total copper loss (per phase) in both machines is

$$I_2^2(R_1' + R_2' + R_1'' + R_2'') \tag{8-43}$$

and on subtracting this loss from P_i the total mechanical output per phase is found to be

$$P = I_2^2 \left[(R_2' + R_1'') \frac{\beta(1 - s)}{\alpha + \beta s} + R_2'' \frac{1 - s}{s} \right] \tag{8-44}$$

On comparing Fig. 8-23, which represents the equivalent circuit of motor M_2, with the circuit of Fig. 6-19, it becomes apparent that the output of motor M_2 is given by

$$P_2 = I_2^2 R_2'' \frac{1 - s_2}{s_2} \tag{8-45}$$

and when this is subtracted from the total mechanical power given by Eq. 8-44, the remainder

$$P_1 = I_2^2 \left[(R_2' + R_1'') \frac{\beta(1 - s)}{\alpha + \beta s} + R_2'' \frac{1 - s}{s} - R_2'' \frac{1 - s_2}{s_2} \right] \tag{8-46}$$

is necessarily the mechanical output of motor M_1. These expressions for P_1 and P_2 can be simplified by replacing s_2 by its value in terms of s, in accordance with Eq. 8-33, which can be written in the form

$$s_2 = \frac{s}{\alpha + \beta s}$$

and on making this substitution it is found that

$$P_2 = I_2^2 R_2'' \frac{\alpha(1 - s)}{s} \tag{8-47}$$

$$P_1 = I_2^2 \left(\frac{R_2' + R_1''}{\alpha + \beta s} + \frac{R_2''}{s} \right) (1 - s)\beta \tag{8-48}$$

From the last two equations, it is possible to determine the proportion in which the load on the set as a whole is divided between the two machines; thus,

$$\frac{P_1}{P_2} = \frac{\beta}{\alpha}\left(\frac{R_2' + R_1''}{R_2''} \frac{s}{\alpha + \beta s} + 1\right) \tag{8-49}$$

from which it is seen that in the vicinity of the synchronous speed of the set, i.e., when s approaches zero,

$$\frac{P_1}{P_2} \to \frac{\beta}{\alpha} = \frac{p_1}{p_2}$$

In other words, the two machines divide the load in the ratio of their respective numbers of poles.

The torques developed by the two machines are given by the relations

$$2\pi n_l(1 - s)T_1 = P_1$$
$$2\pi n_l(1 - s)T_2 = P_2$$

where $n_l = 120f_1/(p_1 + p_2)$ is the synchronous speed of the set, and T_1 and T_2 are expressed in terms of "synchronous watts"; if n_l is in rpm, and the torque in pound-feet, an additional factor 746/33,000 would have to be inserted as in Eq. 6-26, from which it follows that

$$\text{Torque in synchronous watts} = \text{torque in lb-ft} \times \frac{746}{33,000}$$

The complete expressions for T_1 and T_2 may be found by substituting for P_1 and P_2 the values determined by Eqs. 8-47 and 8-48, whence

$$T_1 = \frac{V_1^2}{2\pi n_l} \frac{\beta\left(\dfrac{R_2' + R_1''}{\alpha + \beta s} + \dfrac{R_2''}{s}\right)}{\left(R_1' + \dfrac{R_2' + R_1''}{\alpha + \beta s} + \dfrac{R_2''}{s}\right)^2 + (\Sigma X)^2} \tag{8-50}$$

$$T_2 = \frac{V_1^2}{2\pi n_l} \frac{\alpha R_2''/s}{\left(R_1' + \dfrac{R_2' + R_1''}{\alpha + \beta s} + \dfrac{R_2''}{s}\right)^2 + (\Sigma X)^2} \tag{8-51}$$

Curves showing the division of the load between two identical machines are shown in Fig. 8-25, which has been computed for the conditions

$$\alpha = \beta = \tfrac{1}{2}$$
$$R_1' = R_2' = R_1'' = R_2'' = 0.2$$
$$X_1' = X_2' = X_1'' = X_2'' = 1.0$$

and within the range of speed between standstill ($s = 1$) and $s = -1$. Beyond synchronism, there is a region of negative output, corresponding to generator action of the set as a whole, therefore calling for an external prime mover; but beyond this is another region of motor action, and the point of division between generator and motor action may be found from Eq. 8-44 by imposing the condition that the quantity in the brackets shall be zero.   This gives

$$s = -\frac{\alpha}{\beta}\frac{R_2''}{R_2' + R_1'' + R_2'}$$

(8-52)

and in the special case here considered this corresponds to $s = -\frac{1}{3}$.   It is readily seen that when s approaches the value (-1), $s_1 = \alpha + \beta s$ approaches zero for the case $\alpha = \beta$ (equal numbers of poles), which means that motor M_1 is operating under conditions approximating those of an ordinary motor.

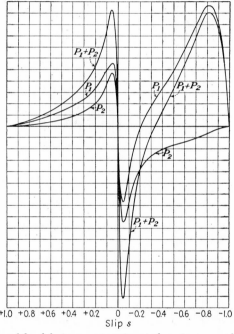

FIG. 8-25. Division of load between concatenated motors, equal numbers of poles.

8-14. Mechanical Control of Speed.   If the stator of an induction motor is mounted on sleeve bearings so that it is capable of rotation around the internally revolving rotor, the actual speed of the latter may be smoothly varied between wide limits, by appropriate control of the speed and direction of rotation of the stator.   For example, when the stator is fixed in position, as in an ordinary machine, the rotor tends to run at nearly synchronous speed in a direction which may be designated as the positive direction; if the stator is mechanically driven in the same direction, the rotor will turn at a speed equal to the stator speed plus its own (nearly synchronous) speed relative to the stator; driving the stator in the reverse (or negative) direction will then cause the rotor to run below its normal speed; when the stator is thus driven at (nearly) synchronous speed in the negative direction, the rotor will be stationary.

As long ago as 1902, B. J. Arnold* proposed such a scheme for smoothly accelerating the speed of railway locomotives driven by single-phase induction motors. In his arrangement, the stators were to be driven forward by compressed-air motors. The Oerlikon Company† of Switzerland has constructed machines in which the rotatable stator is provided with a squirrel-cage winding in its outer surface (in addition to the main

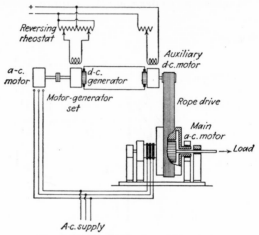

FIG. 8-26. Mechanical speed control.

winding in its inner periphery), the squirrel-cage being caused to rotate by an auxiliary, but fixed, external stator.

A variation of the mechanical method, described by A. M. Rossman,‡ is illustrated in Fig. 8-26. The outer frame of the main a-c motor (which may be of any type, synchronous or induction), which in an ordinary motor would be fixed in position, is belted to an adjustable-speed d-c machine of much smaller rating. This d-c machine is separately excited, and is connected to the d-c end of a motor-generator set whose other unit is in turn connected to the main a-c supply circuit.

In operating this combination, the excitation of the auxiliary d-c machine is held constant, but the voltage impressed upon its armature may be varied from a positive maximum, through zero, to a negative maximum, by means of a suitable rheostat in the field of the generator. When the voltage thus impressed upon the armature of the auxiliary motor is sufficient to drive it as a motor, in such a direction that the frame

* New Electro-pneumatic System of Electric Railway Construction, *Trans. AIEE*, **19**:1003 (1902).

† Walker, *op. cit.*, p. 96.

‡ New System of Speed Control of A-C Motors, *Trans. AIEE*, **50**:162 (1931).

of the main motor turns in the same direction as the rotating magnetic field, the rotor of the main motor will turn at a speed which is the sum of its normal (or base) speed and the speed at which the frame is mechanically driven.   By reducing the d-c voltage impressed upon the auxiliary motor, a condition will be reached at which the frame of the main motor will remain stationary, and further reduction or reversal of the d-c impressed voltage will bring about reversed rotation of the main frame and a correspondingly reduced speed of the driven load.   In that case, the frame of the main motor delivers mechanical energy to the auxiliary d-c machine, driving it as a generator in a direction opposite to that of the main rotor shaft; the d-c machine then delivers energy back to the a-c supply circuit through the medium of the motor-generator set.

ABNORMAL RUNNING CONDITIONS

8-15. Effect of Unbalanced Supply Voltage.   Up to this point, the discussion of the characteristics of the polyphase induction motor has been based upon the assumption that both the phase windings and the impressed phase voltages are symmetrical.   Symmetry of the windings is a necessary consequence of proper design and construction, and always exists in commercial machines, barring accidental short circuits and other forms of mechanical injury.   But unbalanced phase voltages may occur owing to line disturbances or to the presence of unbalanced loads on the system.

The method of symmetrical components described in Chap. 2 is admirably adapted to the analysis of induction-motor performance under the condition of unbalanced terminal voltage.   For it has been shown that in general the actual unequal voltages, whatever their relative phase displacements may be, can be resolved into (1) a set of symmetrical voltages having positive sequence, (2) a symmetrical set having negative sequence, and (3) a set of zero-sequence voltages.   Each of these sets, considered as acting independently of the others, will produce its own set of balanced phase currents, which can thereafter be combined in accordance with the principle of superposition.

Assume the case of a three-phase motor operating on unbalanced supply lines such that the dominant positive-sequence voltage per phase is V_p, and that the corresponding negative- and zero-sequence voltages per phase are V_n and V_0, respectively.   The rotor will then turn in the same direction as the forwardly rotating magnetic field produced by the positive-sequence voltage acting alone; and the negative-sequence voltage, acting alone, will produce a backwardly rotating magnetic field.

So far as the positive-sequence voltage V_p is concerned, the conditions will be the same as in an ordinary motor which has an equivalent circuit of the form shown in Fig. 6-19; the fictitious secondary resistance

$R_{2e}(1 - s)/s$, which in Fig. 6-19 represents the effect of the load, must in the case of voltage V_p be replaced by $R_{2e}(1 - s_p)/s_p$, where s_p is the slip of the rotor with respect to the forwardly rotating magnetic field due to

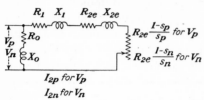

FIG. 8-27. Equivalent circuits for V_p and V_n.

V_p. A similar diagram* will then correctly represent conditions with respect to voltage V_n, provided the load resistance is $R_{2e}(1 - s_n)/s_n$, where s_n is the slip with respect to the backwardly rotating magnetic field due to V_n. Both sets of conditions are indicated in Fig. 8-27.

Since the synchronous speeds due to V_p and V_n have the same absolute value n_1, but have opposite directions, the actual speed, n, is

$$n = n_1(1 - s_p) = -n_1(1 - s_n)$$

whence

$$s_n = 2 - s_p \tag{8-53}$$

and

$$R_{2e}\frac{1 - s_n}{s_n} = R_{2e}\frac{s_p - 1}{2 - s_p} = -R_{2e}\frac{1 - s_p}{2 - s_p} \tag{8-54}$$

The net mechanical output per phase is therefore given by

$$P = I_{2p}^2 R_{2e}\frac{1 - s_p}{s_p} - I_{2n}^2 R_{2e}\frac{1 - s_p}{2 - s_p} \tag{8-55}$$

and the net torque for a three-phase motor is

$$T = \frac{3P}{2\pi n_1(1 - s_p)} = \frac{3R_{2e}}{2\pi n_1}\left(\frac{I_{2p}^2}{s_p} - \frac{I_{2n}^2}{2 - s_p}\right) \tag{8-56}$$

The effect of the negative-sequence voltage is thus seen to be a reduction[†] of the torque and mechanical output, a result which might have been anticipated because of the backwardly rotating magnetic field which it produces. The percentage reduction is generally small with the degree of voltage unbalance usually encountered in practice, V_n being generally less than 10 per cent of V_p. But the copper loss due to the negative-sequence current may at the same time be very appreciable, and so give rise to excessive heating.

Zero-sequence voltages, if present, will not produce any resultant field; hence, they will not affect the torque or mechanical output.

8-16. Effect of Variation of Impressed Voltage and Frequency. The development of analytical relations leading to the circle diagram and the performance characteristics of the polyphase induction motor was based

---

* C. F. Wagner and R. D. Evans, "Symmetrical Components," p. 345, McGraw-Hill Book Company, Inc., New York, 1933.

† S. B. Charters, Jr., and W. A. Hillebrand, Reduction in Capacity of Polyphase Motors Due to Unbalancing in Voltage, *Trans. AIEE*, **28**:559 (1909).

on the tacit assumption that the impressed voltage, V_1, and the line frequency, f_1, are constant, and that the phase voltages are balanced. Inspection of the relations given in Art. 6-5 shows plainly that possible variations in the magnitude of the impressed voltage V_1 will affect merely the scale of the circle diagrams, provided that the constants of the equivalent circuit remain unaltered. Within a moderate range of values of V_1, say, 10 per cent on either side of the normal voltage, this constancy of G_0, B_0, R_1, X_1, R_2, and X_2 may be accepted as sufficiently correct for practical purposes. Strictly, however, any change of V_1 will effect a nearly proportional change in the flux Φ, provided f_1 does not change at the same time; and changes in the flux, because of the effect upon saturation of the teeth, and upon core loss, may be expected to modify G_0 and B_0, and to some extent the leakage reactances as well. If the motor is designed so that the iron of the core is worked below the knee of the magnetization curve, these secondary effects may be neglected. It follows, then, that if a change in V_1 produces merely a proportional change in the scale of the circular current locus, the power and torque scales will change in proportion in V_1^2; in other words, a 10 per cent reduction in line voltage will reduce the torque to 81 per cent of the full voltage value.

Changes in the line frequency, assuming V_1 to remain constant, will produce an inverse change in the flux Φ, but for moderate changes in f_1 there will be no appreciable effect upon core loss and leakage *inductance*. But the leakage *reactances* change in direct proportion to f_1, and the exciting susceptance (B_0) varies (almost) inversely as f_1; so the effect of a change in line frequency is to distort the proportions of the circle diagram, and not merely to alter its scale.

8-17. The Effect of Time Harmonics in the Supply Voltage.* Suppose that the primary voltage V_1 impressed upon the stator of an induction motor consists of a fundamental of effective value V_{11} and some higher harmonic of order s, and effective value V_{1s}, so that

$$V_1 = \sqrt{V_{11}^2 + V_{1s}^2}$$

Each of these voltages may then be assumed to produce primary and secondary currents as though the other were not present, and the resultant current, power, and torque due to the simultaneous action of both fundamental and harmonic voltages may be computed by the principle of superposition.

If the stator and rotor resistances of the motor have a definite set of values corresponding to the fundamental frequency, they will be somewhat higher in the case of the harmonic frequency because of the skin effect; the exciting resistance (R_0 in Fig. 6-17) in the case of the harmonic will be several times greater than in the case of the fundamental. The

---

* L. A. Doggett and E. R. Queer, Induction Motor Operation with Non-Sinusoidal Impressed Voltages, *Trans. AIEE*, **48**:1217 (1929).

reactances, of course, will all be greater for the harmonic voltage than for the fundamental, in the ratio of the frequency of the former to that of the latter.

Notwithstanding the effect of the frequency upon the resistances, it will be assumed that they may be regarded as the same for both the fundamental and harmonic. In the case of the exciting resistance, the effect of the actual variation may be minimized, so far as simplicity of calculation is concerned, by transferring the exciting impedance to the line side of the equivalent circuit. With these approximations, the equivalent circuits for the two impressed frequencies will differ only in that the reactances pertaining to the sth harmonic will be s times as great as those corresponding to the fundamental, and also in that the slip is not the same in the two cases. Corresponding to the fundamental voltage V_{11}, there will be a circle diagram of approximately normal size; and corresponding to the harmonic voltage V_{1s}, there will be another circle diagram, much smaller than the first one for two reasons, namely, that in the expression $V_{1s}/(X_{1s} + X_{2s})$, which fixes the diameter of the circle, the numerator is much smaller than V_{11}, and the denominator is much larger than $X_{11} + X_{21}$. The AIEE Standards specify that V_{1s} must never exceed 10 per cent of V_{11}.

In order to find the slip of the rotor with respect to the harmonic field, use may be made of Tables 4-2 and 4-3, which give the speed and direction of rotation of the field distributions due to any time harmonic. In general, calling this slip s_s,

$$n = n_s(1 - s_s)$$

whence
$$s_s = 1 - \frac{n}{n_s}$$

where n is the actual rotor speed and n_s is the synchronous speed of the magnetic field due to the sth harmonic. It follows that if the rotor of a three-phase motor is running at almost synchronous speed ($n = 100$ per cent), the slip with respect to the fifth time harmonic field is

$$s_5 = 1 - \frac{1}{(-5)} = 1.20$$

while in a two-phase motor it is

$$s_5 = 1 - \frac{1}{(+5)} = 0.80$$

In every case (provided the rotor is running at a speed equal to or less than its normal synchronous speed), the slip with respect to the sth harmonic field is equal to or less than $1 \pm (1/s)$, that is, it approaches unity more and more closely as the order of the time harmonic increases and as its actual speed decreases. This means that while the operating point on the principal circle diagram is in the normal range, the corresponding operating point on the secondary (harmonic) circle diagram is never far removed from the standstill point, and the torque and mechanical power corresponding to the harmonic will therefore always be small. The torque and power due to a time harmonic will be negative (representing braking action) when the slip is greater than unity, and will be positive (representing motor action) when the slip is less than unity.

8-18. The Effect of Space Harmonics in the Field Flux. * The theory of the polyphase induction motor as developed in Chap. 6 is based upon two assumptions: first, that the synchronously rotating mmf produced by the stator is sinusoidally distributed over each of the p principal pole spans; second, that the mmf due to the slip-frequency currents induced in the rotor is similarly distributed over the p induced poles. The principal stator and rotor poles automatically remain in step without regard to the asynchronous speed of the rotor, and it is because of this fact that the resultant torque is called *asynchronous torque*.

That the actual distribution of both stator and rotor mmfs includes a very large number of harmonics indicates that these harmonics may be regarded as the equivalent of additional sets of poles, some of them moving forward in the direction of the main field, others in the backward direction, but all at subsynchronous speeds; the number of poles in any such set is equal to the principal number, p, multiplied by the order of the harmonic to which it is due. Two possible consequences may therefore occur:

a. The interaction between the fictitious stator and rotor poles produced by harmonics of, say, the seventh order will produce a positive torque of the asynchronous type at very low speeds, as at starting, but as the rotor accelerates beyond the synchronous speed of this slowly moving harmonic, the torque will reverse its direction in exactly the manner illustrated in Fig. 6-21 for the case of the principal poles, thereby producing a braking action. The result is the production of a dip in the torque-speed curve at a speed in the neighborhood of one-seventh of normal synchronous speed, in the manner illustrated in Fig. 8-28. The existence of such a dip will cause the motor to "hang" or "crawl" at low speeds for the reason that a net torque which decreases with an increase of speed implies stable equilibrium. The existence of such dips at subsynchronous speeds has long been known, and unless proper precautions are taken to minimize the dangerous harmonics, the acceleration of the motor up to its rated speed will be seriously impaired.

* For further references, see E. E. Dreese, Synchronous Motor Effects in Induction Motors, *Trans. AIEE*, **49**:1033 (1930); G. Kron, Induction Motor Slot Combinations, *Trans. AIEE*, **50**:757 (June, 1931); G. Kron, P. H. Trickey, and R. A. Ball, Irregularities in Speed-torque Curves of Induction Motors, *Elec. Eng.*, December, 1931; M. Liwschitz-Garik and C. C. Whipple, "Electric Machinery," Vol. II, A. C. Machines, D. Van Nostrand Company, Inc., New York, 1946; Alger, *op. cit.*

b. If stator and rotor harmonics of the same order, i.e., having the same number of poles, have different airgap speeds, the torque will be alternately in opposite directions as they move past each other. But if their speeds happen to coincide, they will lock together, if sufficiently powerful,

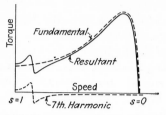

Fig. 8-28. Torque-speed curve as affected by flux harmonics.

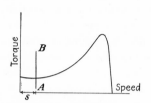

Fig. 8-29. Torque-speed curve showing subsynchronous crawling.

giving rise to the type of *synchronous torque* illustrated in Fig. 8-29, where the torque at a particular slip indicated by *s* may be anywhere between the limits *A* and *B*; in such a case, the motor will crawl at a constant subsynchronous speed.

SPECIAL APPLICATIONS OF POLYPHASE INDUCTION MACHINES

8-19. The Polyphase Induction Voltage Regulator. If the secondaries *S* of a wound-rotor induction machine are connected in series with the same feeder lines which supply the primary windings *P*, in the manner

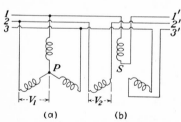

(a)   (b)

Fig. 8-30. Connection diagram, polyphase induction voltage regulator.

indicated in Fig. 8-30, the voltage between lines 1′, 2′, 3′ will be greater or less than that between lines 1, 2, 3, depending upon the relative positions of the stator and rotor. The rotor must of course be blocked to prevent its rotation under the influence of the torque produced by the reaction between the secondary current and the revolving magnetic field.

An induction machine used in this way as a regulator serves to compensate for the line drop in the feeder, and is therefore called upon to supply a secondary voltage amounting only to about 10 per cent of the normal line voltage. The secondary winding must therefore be designed to carry about ten times as much current as the primary; so it is convenient and economical to place the secondaries on the stator and the primaries on the rotor. The secondary terminals (six in a three-phase machine) can then be connected solidly in series with their respective lines, and the primary windings can be supplied with current through slip rings of moderate size. The primary windings are usually Y-connected because of the fewer turns per phase as compared with those of a Δ connection.

The voltage induced in the stationary secondary by the synchronously revolving magnetic field will remain constant in magnitude whatever the relative positions of the stator and rotor may be, but its phase relative to the primary voltage will vary continuously as the rotor is turned. This property is frequently used in laboratory testing when it is required to have available a constant voltage of variable phase. When the connections are made as in Fig. 8-30, it will be seen from Fig. 8-31 that the resultant voltage per phase can be continuously varied from $V_1 - V_2$ to $V_1 + V_2$ as the rotor is turned through an angle of 180 electrical degrees.

Intermediate settings of the rotor will produce a phase shift of the line voltages, indicated by the triangle 1'-2'-3', with respect to the supply voltage 1-2-3.

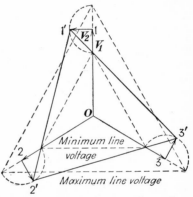

The rotation of the movable member is accomplished by a worm-gear drive, with the gear on the shaft of the rotatable primary. This serves the double purpose of securing fine adjustment and at the same time preventing rotation that would otherwise result from the reaction between primary and secondary. In substation practice, the worm gear is actu-

Fig. 8-31. Phasor diagram, three-phase induction regulator.

ated by a small d-c shunt motor controlled by voltage relays which cause the motor to turn in one direction or the other as occasion demands.

The secondary voltage V_2 changes its phase through the maximum range of 180 electrical degrees when the movable member is turned through the corresponding mechanical angle. Theoretically, therefore, the regulator may be wound for any number of poles, but the usual number is two, though four are occasionally used in the larger sizes. There are several reasons for using a small number of poles. In the first place, the floor space available for such regulators is generally so limited that it is necessary to design the regulator with a vertical shaft and an axial length that is large in comparison with its diameter, which implies a small number of poles. In the second place, the regulator is a transformer with an airgap in its core, which makes its voltage regulation poorer than that of an ordinary transformer, a defect which is aggravated by a large number of poles. In the third place, the actual angular displacement of the movable member is greater with a few poles than would be the case with a larger number, thus contributing to smoothness of adjustment.

8-20. Selsyns. The polyphase induction motor is essentially an asynchronous machine in the sense that its speed is not rigidly fixed by the frequency of the primary supply circuit; but the speed-control systems described in Arts. 8-7 to 8-9 show that the speed of a wound-rotor motor can be held constant at whatever value corresponds to the slip frequency supplied to its rotor. It follows that if two such motors are so connected that both primaries are fed from the same source, and the rotor slip frequencies are forced to be equal, the two machines will run in synchronism with each other at the particular speed determined by the rotor frequency. Induction motors used in this way are called *power selsyns*, the word selsyn being an abbreviation of self-synchronizing.

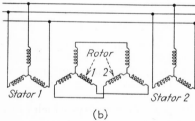

(a)

(b)

FIG. 8-32. Connections of power selsyns.

Consider, for example, the case of the dual drive illustrated in Fig. 8-32a, where each of the two identical main d-c motors is coupled to a wound-rotor induction machine. The stators are connected in parallel to a common source, and the rotors are connected in opposition in the manner shown in Fig. 8-32b. It is very important that the selsyn rotors be so aligned before the set is started that when the speeds of the main d-c machines are equal the opposed emfs of the two rotors will prevent the flow of any current in them and thus also prevent the development of torque; in that case, the two induction machines will "float" on their a-c supply line, which then furnishes only their combined losses.

Suppose, however, that the mechanical load on d-c motor 2 is reduced while that of 1 remains at its normal full-load value, with the result that the speed of set 2 increases, or tends to increase, because of the drooping speed characteristics of the main d-c motors. The immediate effect is to upset the balance of emfs in the local circuit between the two rotors; current will flow through both of them, and the resultant torques will have the proper directions to restore the equality of speeds of the two sets, each rotor forcing its frequency upon the other.

The initial inequality of speeds between the two rotors which is responsible for the synchronizing current implies that the frequencies of the two rotor emfs are not quite the same during the period of readjustment; but if this slight difference is disregarded, the phasor E_{22} in Fig. 8-33 which represents the emf of rotor 2 will have run ahead of its initial position $(E_{22})_0$ when it is in direct opposition to the emf of rotor 1 (represented by E_{21}), *provided that both rotors run in the same direction as their revolving fields.* The resultant voltage E_r in the local circuit of the rotors will set up current I_2 lagging behind E_r, and with components in phase with E_{22} and in phase opposition with E_{21}; accordingly, selsyn 2 becomes a generator and No. 1 a motor. The torque of No. 2 must therefore be supplied by its d-c motor, which is thereby slowed down, while at the same time the motor torque of selsyn 1 helps to drive d-c motor 1, thereby equalizing the electrical input of the two d-c motors.

Power selsyns are used in paper-making machinery, large printing presses, and the like, where different parts of the mechanism, each driven by an individual motor, must main-

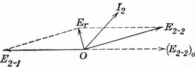

Fig. 8-33. Phasor diagram of Fig. 8-32.

tain the same speeds and the same relative space alignments, as though they were mechanically geared or interlocked.

The restoring torques required for equalization of speeds and loads must be large enough, and must be developed quickly enough, to check any incipient departure from the desired speed of the equipment. For this reason, if the rotors run in the direction of their revolving fields, the selsyns must be so designed that at the normal operating speed of the set the rotor slip is of the order of 50 per cent, to take advantage of the much larger rotor current and torque than corresponds to the small slip of an induction motor operated in the usual manner. It is also possible to design the selsyns so that the rotors run in the direction opposite to their revolving fields at slip frequencies of about 150 per cent; in that case, the roles of the two machines as generator and motor are the reverse of those in the preceding discussion.[*]

Selsyns as Position Indicators. In many installations, it is desirable that the positions of remote movable parts be known at a central control point. To this end, it is possible to use fractional-horsepower units resembling bipolar synchronous motors, except that the shuttle-wound rotors are excited from a single-phase source, as in Fig. 8-34; the stators have three-phase windings, usually Y-connected, with homologous terminals joined together.

Alternation of the magnetic field will induce cophasal emfs in the rotor windings which will be in balance so long as the two rotors are in alignment. But if the rotor of the transmitter is turned through an angle θ by the movement of the device to which it is mechanically linked, the resultant flow of current in the two stators will magnetize along axes which coincide with the changed axis of the transmitter rotor, and the receiver

* See Liwschitz-Garik and Whipple, *op. cit.*, pp. 246–255.

rotor will be subjected to a torque which causes it to rotate to a position paralleling that of the new position of the transmitter.   The rotor of the receiver is provided with a damper winding to prevent oscillations.   One transmitter may actuate any number of receivers provided that it has sufficient capacity to supply the necessary total current.   The movement

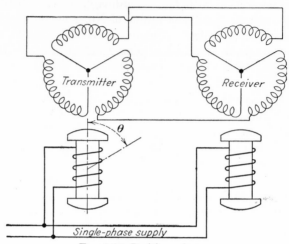

FIG. 8-34. Position selsyns.

of the transmitter, whether forward or backward, steady or intermittent, will be accompanied by a similar movement of the receivers.

The *differential selsyn*, Fig. 8-35, consists of a stator and a rotor each provided with Y-connected windings which have a one-to-one ratio.   It is connected between the stators of two single-phase units like those of

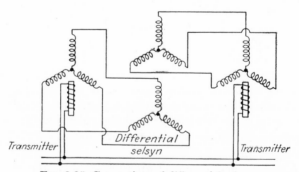

FIG. 8-35. Connections of differential selsyn.

Fig. 8-34, which, when moved independently, will cause the differential unit to indicate either the sum or the difference of their angular positions, depending upon the connections.

8-21. The Asynchronous or Induction Generator.   It has been shown in Arts. 6-6 and 6-7 that when the slip of an induction motor lies between zero and unity, corresponding respectively to synchronism and standstill, both the power and the torque are positive in sign; and that when the slip becomes negative, the power and the torque likewise change from positive to negative, which can have no other meaning than that the machine has become a generator. Negative slip corresponds to a rotor speed greater than synchronous speed, and this in turn means that the rotor is being driven so that it runs ahead of the synchronously rotating magnetic field.

The rotating magnetic field in the polyphase induction motor owes its existence to the magnetizing current supplied to the stator winding from the line, and this supply must continue to be available after the speed passes beyond synchronism and the machine becomes an *induction* or *asynchronous generator*. In other words, a generator of this type is not self-exciting, but must be operated in parallel with other generators which are capable of supplying it with exciting current of *fixed frequency*.

Assume for the moment that a polyphase induction machine is supplied with exciting current of any arbitrarily selected frequency f giving rise to a magnetic field rotating uniformly at a speed n rpm such that $n = 120f/p$. If the slip is zero, there will be no emf or current in the rotor winding, and the stator will draw only the magnetizing current from the supply line. If the speed is increased slightly above synchronism, emf and current of slip frequency will appear in the rotor winding, though they will be reversed in direction with respect to the same quantities at speeds below the synchronous speed. The slip-frequency current in the rotor then produces a rotating mmf moving at slip speed relative to the rotor winding, but in a direction opposite to that which occurs in the case of motor action; the net result is that the rotor mmf moves around the airgap at the same speed as the revolving magnetic field, which means that relative to the stator the rotor current has line frequency. It follows, therefore, that, just as in the case of the motor, there must be a component of primary current which balances the magnetizing effect of the rotor current, the only difference between the two cases being that the direction of energy flow is now from the stator winding to the line. In other words, no matter what the magnitude of the negative slip may be, the primary current will have the frequency that corresponds to the speed of the rotating magnetic field, and this is determined by the frequency of the synchronous generators connected to the line.

A review of the analysis of Chap. 6 will show that while the reasoning was based upon the physical reactions occurring in a motor, the resultant analytical expressions are perfectly general and admit throughout the substitution of negative values of the slip s. Graphical representation of these expressions, which in the case of the circle diagrams, Figs. 6-22 to 6-26, were drawn to illustrate conditions between $s = 0$ and $s = 1$, may then be extended to include all values of s, including those negative values which correspond to generator action. When this is done, the semicircular diagrams become complete circles, and it then becomes a simple matter to investigate the characteristics of the induction generator in complete detail.

The Circle Diagram of the Induction Generator. The complete circular diagram in Fig. 8-36 is an extension of the semicircular diagram in Figs. 6-22 and 6-23, the lettering of the diagrams being the same. Certain differences of interpretation arise because of the transition from motor action in the upper reach between points A and S, to the generator action in the lower reach from A, through B, to C_∞. The latter point is the intersection of line BC_∞ (drawn parallel to the slip line, M_sT) with the circle; it is the point at which the slip would be infinite.

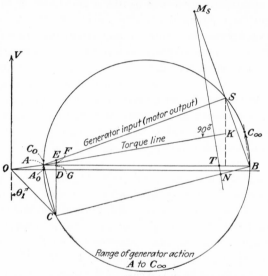

FIG. 8-36. Circle diagram of induction generator.

The stator current of the generator is represented by OC, made up of the components OA and AC, the latter balancing the magnetizing action of the rotor. Line AS, which in the motor diagram defines mechanical output, now serves to fix the mechanical input from the prime mover which drives the induction generator; thus, in Fig. 8-36, when the load conditions are defined by point C, the mechanical input per phase is represented by CE. In the same way, CD represents the electrical power output per phase. The slip is proportional to TN (the scale being fixed by $TM_s = 100$) and is negative since TN is directed downward.

Operating Characteristics of the Induction Generator. Curves showing the variation of speed, power factor, efficiency, primary current, etc., as functions of electrical output can be constructed from the circle diagram in the same manner as has been done for the corresponding case of the motor in Fig. 6-24, but this is left as an exercise for the student. It is more usual, however, to employ the slip as independent variable, and to plot the other quantities in terms of it, for the reason that in practical uses of this type of generator its functioning is completely determined by the speed at which it is driven. Characteristic curves of this type are shown in Fig. 8-37; they are based upon the assumption that the terminal voltage and the frequency are the same as those used in constructing the circle in the first instance. These curves may be obtained experimentally by belting or otherwise mechanically connecting the asynchronous machine to a d-c shunt motor supplied from a constant-voltage circuit; by means of a field rheostat, the excitation of the shunt motor can be varied through a sufficient range to make it function either as a generator or a motor within the approximate speed limits indicated in the diagram.

Assume that an induction machine equipped with a low-resistance squirrel-cage rotor, and otherwise similar in all essential details to the polyphase induction motors described in Chap. 6, is direct-connected to a prime mover such as a turbine which is initially cut off from its source of supply. The unit may be started in the usual way by connecting the induction machine (as a motor) to bus bars energized by independent synchronous generators, whereupon it will attain a speed a little short of synchronism. The operating conditions will then be represented by point C_0 (Fig. 8-36) slightly above the point A, which corresponds to full synchronous speed. The electrical input from the bus bars supplies not

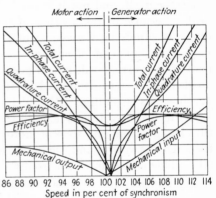

FIG. 8-37. Characteristics of asynchronous generator.

only the quadrature magnetizing current but also the power component required to supply the copper loss, the core loss, and the friction load, including in the latter the friction and windage losses of the idling turbine. If now the throttle of the turbine (steam or hydraulic) is opened just enough to raise the speed to exact synchronism, as at point A, the turbine will supply its own losses, but the energy from the bus bars will supply the core loss and the friction loss of the induction motor, as well as the small copper loss in the stator. A slight additional increase of turbine speed will transfer some of the induction-machine losses from the bus bars to the turbine, and when point A_0 is reached, the bus bars furnish no power at all, but only the quadrature or true magnetizing component of no-load current.

As the speed of the turbine is further increased, the induction machine assumes some of the electrical load previously carried by the synchronous generators alone. The transition from motor to generator action may be made as gradually as desired. The maximum electrical power (per phase) that the machine is capable of delivering is, to the scale of power, less than the radius of the circle by the length DG, but this maximum occurs at a value of primary current much beyond the permissible thermal limit. Practically, the rated load of such a generator corresponds to a negative slip of between 3 and 5 per cent; this means that within the working range of load the quadrature component of stator current does not increase very much beyond the magnetizing current itself.

Power Factor and Quadrature Current. The circle diagram of Fig. 8-36, corresponding to a fixed terminal voltage and frequency, shows that the magnitude and phase of the primary current are not separately variable as they are in the case of a synchronous generator; on the contrary, when the power output has a particular value, the current and the power factor are both completely defined in terms of the constants of the induction generator itself, and not in terms of the resistance and reactance of the load. Because of this feature, it follows that when the induction generator is supplying a given amount of power—and therefore a definite in-phase component of current—the corresponding quadrature component of its current will not in general have any definite relation to the quadrature current demanded by the load, and must be supplied by the synchronous generators with which it is in parallel.

It will be noted from Fig. 8-36 that when the primary current phasor OC changes from the zone of motor action to that of generator action, the angle between it and the impressed voltage OV becomes greater than 90°. This is accounted for from the analytical point of view by the circumstance that the power component of current, which in the case of motor action was taken to be in phase with the voltage, must be considered to be in phase opposition to the same voltage when the machine becomes a generator. That is to say, when the induction *motor* was alone under consideration, the positive direction of energy flow was *into* the machine from the line; when the transition to generator action occurs, the positive direction is *from* the machine to the line. The power factor of the induction generator is then to be considered as the cosine of angle θ_1 (Fig. 8-36). The quadrature component of the induction-generator current continues, as in the induction motor, to be lagging with respect to the terminal voltage of the synchronous generators.

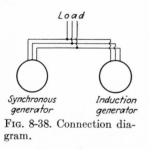

Load

Synchronous   Induction
generator   generator

FIG. 8-38. Connection diagram.

If the load connected to the bus bars of Fig. 8-38 were highly inductive, the synchronous generators would have to supply the quadrature component of the load current in addition to the quadrature component of current required by the induction generator. This would imply such a low power factor for the synchronous generators, with correspondingly poor voltage regulation, that induction generators are not used in such cases but are serviceable only with loads having inherently high power factor. If, on the other hand, the load has capacitative reactance, it will draw from the synchronous generators a leading quadrature current in opposition to the lagging quadrature current taken by the induction generators; if these two currents happen to be exactly equal, the synchronous generators will be relieved of all quadrature current, and the effect is the same as though (1) the induction generator were supplying the leading current to the capacitance of the load; or (2) the load capacitance were supplying the lagging current to the induction generator. If, under these conditions, the voltage being fixed by the synchronous generators, the in-phase component of load current is equal to the in-phase component of the current of the induction machine, the synchronous generators play no part whatever, and may be disconnected from the bus bars. The asynchronous generator will then continue to carry this particular load

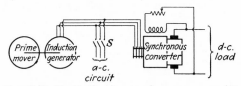

Fig. 8-39. Excitation by synchronous converter.

at the original voltage and frequency, provided the speed of the asynchronous generator remains constant.

*Excitation by Synchronous or Static Condenser.** The reasoning outlined in the preceding paragraph points to the conclusion that if an asynchronous generator and a synchronous converter are connected to an a-c supply circuit, as in Fig. 8-39, overexcitation of the latter may be made to draw just the amount of leading current which is required to balance the lagging quadrature current of the asynchronous generator. If at the same time the speed of the asynchronous machine is increased sufficiently to develop the power required by the converter to carry its own d-c load, the supply circuit may be disconnected at switch *S*. Thereafter, the machines interchange the necessary quadrature current, and conditions will be stable provided at least one of them operates on a part of its magnetization curve* beyond the knee of the curve.

The power developed by the induction generator may be used to supply the d-c load of the converter; or it may drive a mechanical load connected to the shaft of the converter; or it may supply an a-c load tapped off from its terminals as at switch *S*. But it does not follow that such

* See A. S. McAllister, "Alternating Current Motors," McGraw-Hill Book Company, Inc., New York, 1940.

an arrangement as Fig. 8-39 will maintain constant voltage and frequency as in the case of ordinary synchronous machines, as is plain from the circumstance that for fixed frequency the speed of the asynchronous generator must change as the load changes.   If the speed of the generator is kept constant, changing load will result in variable frequency and correspondingly variable speed of the synchronous converter, so that the preservation of constant voltage will then require variable field excitation of the converter.   It must be remembered, too, that a change of frequency will alter all the proportions of the circle diagram of the asynchronous machine, since the magnitudes of G_0, B_0, X_1, and X_2 change as the frequency changes.

The voltage of such a set as Fig. 8-39 is very sensitive to any change in the reactive component of the alternating current supplied to a load. Any lagging current that is required must come from the converter, which means that its field is weakened and its voltage lowered.   Leading current will cause a rise of voltage.

Inasmuch as the overexcited synchronous converter (or synchronous motor) draws a leading current, its effect may be duplicated by means

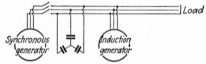

FIG. 8-40. Condenser excitation.

of a static condenser of suitable capacitance.   The connection diagram for such an arrangement may take the form of Fig. 8-40, where the synchronous generator serves to fix the voltage and frequency and initially to excite the asynchronous generator.   After the condenser has been adjusted to supply the requisite quadrature current, the synchronous generator may be disconnected just as in the case of Fig. 8-39.   Variation of the ratio of transformation of the autotransformer that supplies the condenser is equivalent to variation of the capacitance of the condenser.

An asynchronous generator withco ndenser excitation has a drooping voltage characteristic; for any increase of load will produce a drop of voltage owing to the resistance and reactance of the generator itself, and this decreased voltage, acting across the condenser, reduces the exciting current in addition, the joint effect being somewhat the same as in a d-c shunt generator.   The frequency of such a system can remain constant only if the generator speed is appropriately changed as the demands of the load require it.

Inasmuch as the working range of an asynchronous generator is confined within narrow limits of speed variation, the quadrature component of stator current is likewise limited to a moderate range of values, as may be seen either from the circle diagram (Fig. 8-36) or from the characteristic curves of Fig. 8-37. In other words, the quadrature current within the working range does not differ materially from the true magnetizing current at synchronous speed, and as a first approximation it may be treated as constant. In an induction machine, just as in any other type of electromagnetic device, the relation between voltage and exciting current will generally exhibit the phenomenon of magnetic saturation, as illustrated by the saturation curve of Fig. 8-41. If the exciting condenser has a capacitance C farads, the relation between its terminal voltage and current is $I = V\omega C$, where $\omega = 2\pi f$; if frequency is held constant by suitable adjustment of generator speed, the volt-ampere characteristic of the capacitor will be a straight line, as in Fig. 8-41, the slope of the line (tan α in Fig. 8-41) being $1/\omega C$; the resultant voltage of the generator will then be stable at a value determined by the intersection of the saturation curve and the straight line. Obviously, there is a critical value of C below which the straight line will not intersect the curve, in which case the generator voltage will fall to zero.

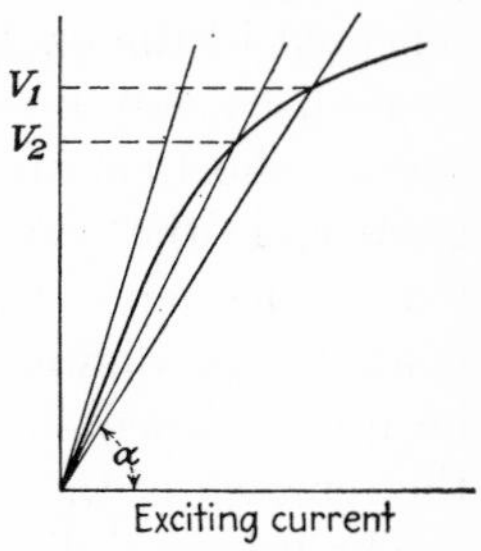

Fig. 8-41. Excitation characteristics.

Condenser excitation is not commercially feasible because of the size and cost of the capacitor, and the possibility is discussed only because of the technical interest it presents; there exists the further disadvantage that a synchronous generator or its equivalent is necessary to produce the initial excitation.

Applications of the Induction Generator. Induction generators have a limited field of usefulness as accessories to systems supplying a load of fairly high power factor, such as substations equipped with synchronous converters or motors, and where synchronous generators are the chief source of energy. In some cases asynchronous generators are driven by hydraulic turbines, and in others the prime mover is an exhaust steam turbine serving the purpose of improving the heat balance of a generating plant; but in any case the prime mover not only requires no governor, but provision must be made for varying its speed in order to make it assume the desired amount of load. This is accomplished by varying the throttle opening, and can be effected either manually or automatically by remote control.

Among the advantages of this type of generator is the fact that it does not have to be synchronized. When connected to the station bus bars with the turbine idling, it will run slightly below synchronism as an induction motor. If the turbine is supplied with just enough steam to keep it at operating temperature, the unit is instantly available for supplying an emergency overload, all that is necessary being to open the throttle. It possesses the added advantage of suitability for high-speed operation because of the simplicity and ruggedness of the squirrel-cage rotor construction; and since its voltage and frequency are controlled by the synchronous generators with which it is in parallel, it requires no attention to these features, hence is well suited to automatic or isolated hydraulic plants controlled from a distant point. Furthermore, the problem of hunting does not arise because of the asynchronous properties of the machine.

Another advantage is due to the characteristics of such a generator in case of a short circuit on the line. The drop of voltage that accompanies a short circuit automatically reduces the excitation and so limits the short-circuit current; the maximum amount of power it can furnish is in any case limited because of the nature of its equivalent circuit as reflected in the circle diagram, and the maximum output can moreover be realized only if the speed is greatly increased. But in case of a very sudden short circuit, the initial rush of current is proportionately just as great as in the case of a synchronous generator, and for much the same reason, namely, that the energy stored in the magnetic field cannot instantly be dissipated; but unlike a synchronous generator, there can be no sustained short-circuit current under such conditions because of the removal of the excitation.

The principal disadvantage of the asynchronous generator is its inherently low power factor.

When polyphase induction motors are used to drive electric locomotives, they become generators if the speed rises above synchronism and so become available for regenerative braking on downgrades.

CHAPTER 9

THE SINGLE-PHASE INDUCTION MOTOR

9-1. Structural Elements and Basic Theory. If, while a polyphase induction motor is running with a moderate or light load, some of the supply lines (one in a three-phase machine) are disconnected so as to leave the equivalent of a single phase connected to the stator winding, it will be found that the motor will continue to run, though at slightly altered speed. In other words, the original polyphase motor has become a single-phase motor. Thus, a three-phase Y-connected winding becomes a single-phase winding having two-thirds of the original coils in circuit if one of the three supply lines is disconnected. A polyphase motor thus converted into a single-phase machine will suffer a reduction in its capacity to carry a load; otherwise stated, a single-phase motor may be expected to have somewhat lower capacity than a polyphase motor of the same weight and dimensions. But whereas the polyphase motor is self-starting, the single-phase motor has no starting torque for reasons explained in Chap. 5; to make it self-starting, the motor must be provided with some auxiliary device which alters its characteristics during the starting period. It follows, therefore, that during the starting period the motor must be converted to a type which is not a single-phase induction motor in the sense in which the term is ordinarily used, and it becomes a true single-phase induction motor only after the speed and torque have been raised to a point beyond which the auxiliary device may be dispensed with. For these reasons, it is necessary to distinguish clearly between the starting period, when the motor is not a single-phase induction motor, and the normal running condition, when it is.

The structural features that must be provided to give adequate starting torque can best be considered later. It is simplest to take up first the physical analysis of the motor as a pure induction machine receiving energy from a single-phase source, starting with the general ideas that have been sketched in Chap. 5. That introductory treatment has already made it plain that the single-phase induction motor in its simplest form is structurally the same as a polyphase induction motor having a squirrel-cage rotor; the only significant difference is that the single-phase motor has a single stator winding which of itself produces mmf stationary in space but alternating in time, whereas a polyphase stator winding carrying balanced currents produces mmf rotating in space around the airgap and unvarying in time with respect to an observer moving with the mmf. Just as in the polyphase motor, the stator winding is disposed in slots around the inner periphery of a laminated ring in the manner indicated in Fig. 9-1, where part a illustrates the case of a bipolar machine and part b shows a four-pole arrangement.

It has been shown in Chap. 5 that the field produced by the single stator winding, when acting alone, is in space quadrature and nearly in time quadrature with the field separately produced by the rotor winding when the latter is in motion. The two fields actually combine to produce a single resultant field which rotates around the airgap, but it has been shown that at rotor speeds differing from synchronism the resultant magnetic field is elliptical in character, therefore not as simple as the circular rotating field encountered in the polyphase induction motor when operating on balanced voltage. While it is possible to analyze the performance of the single-phase induction motor from the point of view of the rotating field, it is on the whole simpler* to approach the problem by considering the component mmfs and fluxes separately contributed by the stator and by the rotor, and this procedure will be followed here. Thereafter, this cross-field theory can be supplemented to advantage by a consideration of the rotating-field theory.

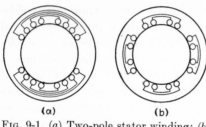

FIG. 9-1. (a) Two-pole stator winding; (b) four-pole stator winding.

9-2. The Cross-field Theory.†   Rotor Stationary. For the sake of simplicity consider the case of the bipolar model shown in Fig. 9-2, where part a indicates a squirrel-cage rotor and part b a wound rotor with commutator and two pairs of brushes, the latter so arranged that one pair is in line with the axis of the stator winding, the other pair displaced from that axis by 90 electrical degrees. In both cases, a and b, a voltage V_1 impressed upon the stator will, in accordance with Lenz's law, induce in the rotor winding a current so directed as to oppose the magnetizing action of the stator current. The conditions are exactly the same as in a short-circuited transformer, for the current in the rotor, which plays the role of the secondary, is limited only by the joint leakage impedance of the primary and secondary. The currents in the squirrel-cage winding of Fig. 9-2a will be distributed symmetrically about an axis in line with the flux

---

* This is a matter of opinion on which there is not complete agreement between writers on this subject. See V. Karapetoff, The Equivalence of the Two Theories of the Single-phase Induction Motor, *Trans. AIEE*, **40**:640 (1921).

† A. S. Langsdorf, The Current Locus of the Single-phase Induction Motor, *Trans. AIEE*, **28**(pt.1):587 (1909).

Φ_t; and in the wound rotor of Fig. 9-2b the current in each part of the winding will have a return path by way of the brushes t, t.

In the case of the squirrel-cage rotor, it is easily seen that the currents in the individual rotor bars have magnitudes ranging from zero in the conductors occupying the Φ_t axis to a maximum midway between the poles; but the joint effect of all the currents is the same as that of a hypo-thetical concentrated coil occupy-ing a plane perpendicular to Φ_t. In Fig. 9-2b, all the armature con-ductors carry current having the same magnitude at a given instant, and their effect is likewise the same as that of a concentrated coil oc-cupying the plane r, r. In either case, therefore, it is possible to consider the actual rotor winding as replaced by an equivalent coil having a 1:1 ratio of turns with respect to the stator, and it is then possible to construct the phasor diagram in Fig. 9-3, showing the relations between stator and (equivalent) rotor currents and emfs. This diagram is the same as that of any trans-former under short-circuit conditions; both the secondary current I_t and the primary current I_1 are large in comparison with normal load current, and they lag heavily behind their corresponding voltages. The only sub-stantial difference between this case and that of an ordinary tranformer is

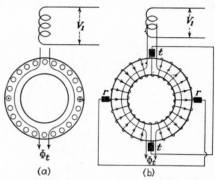

FIG. 9-2. Instantaneous current flow, rotor stationary.

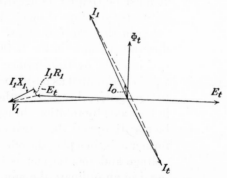

FIG. 9-3. Phasor diagram, rotor stationary.

that here the no-load current I_0 is relatively large because of the airgap between stator and rotor, and the angle α between Φ_t and I_0 is quite small.

Since the space angle between the axes of Φ_t and I_t is zero, the station-ary motor will have no torque.

9-3. Phasor Diagram, Motor Running. Let it be assumed that an external torque is applied to the rotor of Fig. 9-2 so that the rotor is made to turn either in the clockwise direction as in Fig. 9-4a or in the counter-clockwise direction (Fig. 9-4b). Following the usual conventions of car-tesian coordinates, assume that a flux in the transformer axis t, t is positive when directed upward, and that a flux in the speed axis r, r is positive when directed to the right; then in Fig. 9-4a clockwise rotation through the positive flux Φ_t will develop in the speed axis an emf (and current) directed in accordance with the small arrowheads, thereby setting up a

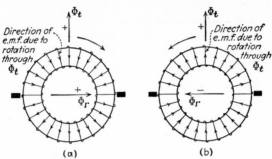

FIG. 9-4. Direction of rotor current and speed field due to rotation through Φ_t.

flux Φ_r directed to the right, hence to be considered positive; and the same clockwise rotation through Φ_r will then develop in the transformer axis an emf directed downward, hence negative. These statements as to direc-tions of emfs and fluxes may be checked quite simply by applying Flem-ing's right-hand rule and Ampère's rule.

Similar considerations applied to the case of counterclockwise rotation (Fig. 9-4b) will show that Φ_r is now directed to the left, which means that

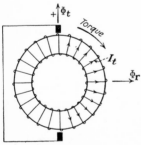

FIG. 9-5. Torque due to I_t and Φ_r, clockwise rotation.

Φ_r must be treated as negative; and counter-clockwise rotation through Φ_r will again de-velop in the transformer axis an emf directed downward just as in Fig. 9-4a. In fact, if the emf induced by transformer action in the t, t axis is designated as positive because it is due to the positive flux Φ_t, the other emf developed in that axis by rotation through Φ_r will always be negative; and these two emfs in the trans-former axis then play the roles of the impressed voltage and counter emf as these are encoun-tered in an ordinary d-c motor.

The original assumption that Φ_t is positively directed has led to the conclusion that the counter emf in the transformer axis is directed down-ward, and this must mean that the impressed voltage (and current) is directed upward, as in Fig. 9-5. Application of Fleming's left-hand rule then shows that the torque due to the reaction between I_t and Φ_r is clock-wise, in other words, it is in the same direction as the initial external torque which started this sequence of phenomena. Had the initial external torque been counterclockwise, as in Fig. 9-4b, the reaction between I_t and Φ_r would also be counterclockwise. Otherwise stated, the motor will automatically develop torque in whichever direction it is given an initial impetus.

The reaction between I_t and Φ_r constitutes the chief source of the motor torque, but it is not the only torque developed. There is also a reaction between I_r and Φ_t since these have axes in space quadrature, but this torque opposes the main torque, as may be verified by applying Fleming's left-hand rule to Figs. 9-4a and 9-5.

Consider now the phase relations between the various fluxes, emfs, and currents, starting, as in Fig. 9-6, with flux Φ_t in any arbitrarily selected position, say, vertically upward. Alternation of this flux will induce an

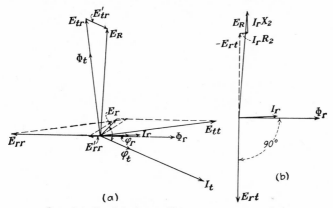

(a)   (b)

Fig. 9-6. Partial phasor diagram, motor running.

emf E_{tt} in the t, t axis, and in accordance with the basic theory of transformers the phase of E_{tt} will be 90° behind that of Φ_t.* At the same time, rotation of the winding through Φ_t will generate in the r, r axis an emf E_{tr}, which may be either in phase with, or in phase opposition to, the flux Φ_t, depending upon the direction of rotation. Figure 9-6 has been constructed by assuming E_{tr} to be in phase with Φ_t.

It may be anticipated that the resultant voltage in the rotor axis t, t will produce a current I_t in that axis and that I_t will lag behind E_{tt} by some angle as yet undetermined; but whatever the phase of I_t may be, it will set up a leakage flux φ_t in time phase with I_t and coaxial in space with Φ_t. Rotation through φ_t will then generate in the r, r axis an emf E'_{tr} in time phase with φ_t (and therefore also with I_t) just as E_{tr} is in time phase with Φ_t. The phasor sum of E_{tr} and E'_{tr} is then the resultant emf E_R developed by rotation in the axis r, r.

* The double subscript, as in E_{tt}, is so arranged that the first subscript indicates the corresponding flux, as Φ_t, to which it is due; and the second subscript indicates whether it is produced by transformer action t or by rotational generation r.

The rotor winding in the r, r axis does not link with any other electric circuit, and it therefore corresponds to the primary winding of an open-circuited transformer. The resultant emf E_R will then produce a magnetizing current I_r, lagging by nearly 90° behind E_R, and I_r will in turn set up the speed field Φ_r nearly, but not quite, in time phase with I_r. The reason for the phase displacement between I_r and Φ_r is that I_r corresponds to the exciting (or no-load) current of a transformer, and it therefore leads the flux by the small angle of hysteretic advance. Alternation of Φ_r will then induce in the r, r axis a transformer emf E_{rt}, lagging behind Φ_r by 90°, and therefore nearly in phase opposition to E_R, as in Fig. 9-6b. The emf E_R must therefore contain as one component an emf equal and opposite to E_{rt}, and in addition a small component $I_r Z_2$ to drive I_r through the local impedance of the rotor circuit. These relations are shown separately in Fig. 9-6b to avoid confusion in the main diagram, Fig. 9-6a.

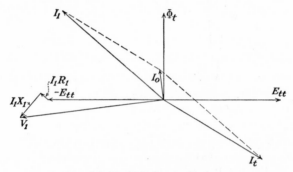

Fig. 9-7. Partial phasor diagram.

The motion of the rotor conductors through the speed field Φ_r generates in the t, t axis an emf E_{rr}, in phase opposition to Φ_r, hence nearly opposed to E_{tt}. But I_r also produces a small leakage flux φ_r in time phase with itself and coaxial in space with Φ_r, so that rotation through φ_r generates in the t, t axis a small additional emf E'_{rr}, opposite in phase to I_r. The resultant of E_{tt}, E_{rr}, E'_{rr} will then be the resultant voltage E_T in the t, t axis, which must drive the current I_t through the local impedance of the rotor. It is therefore clear that E_T must lead I_t by an angle whose tangent is the rotor leakage reactance divided by the rotor resistance. This fact serves to define the phase of I_t, which was originally undetermined, but which must tie in with all the other phase relations that have been thus far qualitatively outlined.

To complete the phasor diagram, it must now be noted that the primary current I_1 must contain a component I_0 (Fig. 9-7) to maintain the transformer flux Φ_t, and another component equal and opposite to I_t (assuming that all secondary quantities are reduced to terms of the primary). Finally, the voltage V_1 impressed upon the stator must balance

E_{tt} and also overcome the leakage-impedance drop $I_1(R_1 + jX_1)$ in the primary.

9-4. Analytical Relations Derived from the Phasor Diagram.

Summarizing the symbols thus far referred to, and adding some others which must now be considered, we have

V_1 = primary impressed voltage

I_1 = primary load current

I_0 = primary exciting current, rotor open-circuited

I_t = rotor current in transformer axis t, t

I_r = rotor current in speed axis r, r

Φ_t = transformer flux in axis t, t

Φ_r = speed flux in axis r, r

E_{tt} = emf induced by transformer effect of Φ_t (in axis t, t)

E_{tr} = emf generated by rotation through Φ_t (in axis r, r)

E_{rt} = emf induced by transformer effect of Φ_r (in axis r, r)

E_{rr} = emf generated by rotation through Φ_r (in axis t, t)

φ_t = leakage flux due to I_t

φ_r = leakage flux due to I_r

E'_{tr} = emf generated by rotation through φ_t (in axis r, r)

E'_{rr} = emf generated by rotation through φ_r (in axis t, t)

$Z_1 = R_1 + jX_1$ = primary leakage impedance

$Z_0 = 1/Y_0$ = primary exciting impedance

$Y_0 = G_0 - jB_0$ = primary exciting admittance

$Z_2 = R_2 + jX_2$ = secondary (rotor) leakage impedance*

$Z_r = 1/Y_r$ = secondary exciting impedance (axis r, r)

$Y_r = G_r - jB_r$ = secondary exciting admittance (axis r, r)

S = speed, in terms of synchronism as unity

Following the same procedure used in analyzing the ordinary transformer, the relations embodied in the phasor diagrams of Figs. 9-6 and 9-7 may now be expressed as complex equations which, when suitably combined, will lead to the formulation of an expression for the equivalent impedance of the motor as a whole; and this will in turn fix the arrangement of the equivalent circuit, from which further deductions can then be drawn.

First, however, it is advantageous to point out a few quantitative relations that follow from the considerations explained in Chap. 4. Thus, by ordinary transformer theory, the magnitude of E_{tt} is directly proportional to Φ_t, and in complex notation

$$\mathbf{E}_{tt} = -jk\boldsymbol{\Phi}_t \tag{9-1}$$

where k is a proportionality constant depending upon the number and distribution of the rotor conductors and upon the frequency of Φ_t. Rota-

---

* Because of the symmetry of the physical construction of the rotor, Z_2 is the same in both the t, t and the r, r axes.

tion of the same conductors at speed S through the flux Φ_t develops the emf E_{tr}, which has been taken to be in phase with Φ_t; consequently,

$$\mathbf{E}_{tr} = kS\mathbf{\Phi}_t \qquad (9\text{-}2)$$

which is numerically the same as E_{tt} at synchronous speed. In exactly the same way,

$$\mathbf{E}_{rt} = -jk\mathbf{\Phi}_r \qquad (9\text{-}3)$$
$$\mathbf{E}_{rr} = -kS\mathbf{\Phi}_r \qquad (9\text{-}4)$$

and from these relations it follows that

$$\mathbf{E}_{tr} = jS\mathbf{E}_{tt} \qquad (9\text{-}5)$$
$$\mathbf{E}_{rr} = -jS\mathbf{E}_{rt} \qquad (9\text{-}6)$$

Furthermore, the reactance voltage $I_t X_2$ may be thought of as due to the synchronous alternation of the leakage flux φ_t through the rotor winding, from which it follows that rotation at speed S through this leakage flux will develop the voltage E'_{tr}, in phase with I_t, such that

$$\mathbf{E}'_{tr} = SX_2\mathbf{I}_t \qquad (9\text{-}7)$$

In the same way, rotation of the winding through the leakage flux φ_r

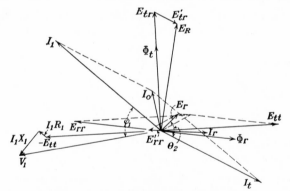

FIG. 9-8. Complete phasor diagram.

(which is in phase with I_r) will develop a voltage E'_{rr}, but in phase opposition to I_r, giving

$$\mathbf{E}'_{rr} = -SX_2\mathbf{I}_r \qquad (9\text{-}8)$$

Inspection of Fig. 9-8 shows that

$$\mathbf{E}_R = \mathbf{E}_{tr} + \mathbf{E}'_{tr} = -\mathbf{E}_{rt} + \mathbf{I}_r Z_2 \qquad (9\text{-}9)$$

and by analogy with transformer theory

$$\mathbf{I}_r = -\mathbf{E}_{rt} Y_r \qquad (9\text{-}10)$$

Substituting Eq. 9-10 in Eq. 9-9 and solving for E_{rt},

$$\mathbf{E}_{rt} = -\frac{\mathbf{E}_{tr} + SX_2\mathbf{I}_t}{1 + Z_2 Y_r} = -\frac{S(j\mathbf{E}_{tt} + \mathbf{I}_t X_2)}{1 + Z_2 Y_r} \qquad (9\text{-}11)$$

The diagram shows that E_T is not only the phasor sum of E_{tt}, E_{rr}, and E'_{rr}, but that it is also the impedance drop in the t, t axis; hence,

$$\mathbf{E}_T = \mathbf{E}_{tt} + \mathbf{E}_{rr} + \mathbf{E}'_{rr} = \mathbf{I}_t Z_2 \qquad (9\text{-}12)$$

On substituting in Eq. 9-12 the values of E_{rr} and E'_{rr} from Eqs. 9-6 and 9-8, and then applying Eqs. 9-10 and 9-11, it is found that

$$
\begin{aligned}
\mathbf{E}_T &= \mathbf{E}_{tt}\left[1 - \frac{S^2(1 + jX_2 Y_r)}{1 + Z_2 Y_r}\right] + \mathbf{I}_t\left[\frac{S^2(jX_2 - X_2^2 Y_r)}{1 + Z_2 Y_r}\right] \\
&= \mathbf{E}_{tt}\left[1 - \frac{S^2(Z_r + jX_2)}{Z_r + Z_2}\right] + \mathbf{I}_t\left[\frac{S^2(jX_2 Z_r - X_2^2)}{Z_r + Z_2}\right] = \mathbf{I}_t Z_2 \quad (9\text{-}13)
\end{aligned}
$$

from which

$$\mathbf{I}_t\left[Z_2 - \frac{S^2(jX_2 Z_r - X_2^2)}{Z_r + Z_2}\right] = \mathbf{E}_{tt}\left[1 - \frac{S^2(Z_r + jX_2)}{Z_r + Z_2}\right] \qquad (9\text{-}14)$$

Again referring to the diagram (Fig. 9-8), it is plain that the primary current is the phasor sum of $\mathbf{I}_0$ and of $-\mathbf{I}_t$ (assuming that all secondary quantities are expressed in terms of the primary); and that the impressed voltage is the phasor sum of $-\mathbf{E}_{tt}$ and $\mathbf{I}_1 Z_1$. Consequently,

$$\mathbf{I}_1 = \mathbf{I}_0 - \mathbf{I}_t = -\mathbf{E}_{tt} Y_0 - \mathbf{I}_t \qquad (9\text{-}15)$$

and

$$\mathbf{V}_1 = -\mathbf{E}_{tt} + \mathbf{I}_1 Z_1 \qquad (9\text{-}16)$$

On combining Eqs. 9-14, 9-15, and 9-16 so as to eliminate E_{tt} and I_t, the result is

$$\mathbf{V}_1 = \mathbf{I}_1\left[Z_1 + \cfrac{1}{Y_0 + \cfrac{1 - \dfrac{S^2(Z_r + jX_2)}{Z_r + Z_2}}{Z_2 - \dfrac{S^2(jX_2 Z_r - X_2^2)}{Z_r + Z_2}}}\right] \qquad (9\text{-}17)$$

9-5. The Equivalent Circuit and the Primary-current Locus. The expression in the brackets in Eq. 9-17 is the equivalent impedance Z_e of the motor as a whole. In this form, it does not lend itself to a determination of the nature of the equivalent circuit, but by a process of repeated division of the final fractional term in the denominator it reduces readily to the form

$$Z_e = Z_1 + \cfrac{1}{Y_0 + \cfrac{1}{Z_2 + \cfrac{1}{\cfrac{1}{S^2(Z_r + jX_2)} + \cfrac{1 - S^2}{S^2 R_2}}}} \qquad (9\text{-}18)$$

Term-by-term examination of Eq. 9-18 shows that the equivalent circuit must have the form of Fig. 9-9 or that of Fig. 9-10 where exciting admittances are indicated instead of the exciting impedances shown in Fig.

9-9. Since the rotor exciting impedance of Fig. 9-9 is given by

$$S^2R_r + jS^2(X_r + X_2) = S^2(Z_r + jX_2)$$

the corresponding admittance is

$$\frac{1}{S^2[R_r + j(X_r + X_2)]} = \frac{R_r - j(X_r + X_2)}{S^2[R_r^2 + (X_r + X_2)^2]}$$

which may be written in the form $(1/S^2)(G_r' - jB_r')$, where

$$\begin{aligned} G_r' &= \frac{R_r}{R_r^2 + (X_r + X_2)^2} \\ B_r' &= \frac{X_r + X_2}{R_r^2 + (X_r + X_2)^2} \end{aligned} \qquad (9\text{-}19)$$

The equivalent circuit of the single-phase induction motor is seen to differ from that of the polyphase induction motor in that it includes an additional branch representative of the exciting circuit in the speed-field

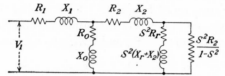

FIG. 9-9. Equivalent circuit, single-phase motor.

axis. It will be noted that this additional branch has an impedance (or admittance) which varies with the load on the motor, since it includes the factor S^2. The principal effect of the load is, however, represented by the variable resistance $S^2R_2/(1 - S^2)$. Under standstill conditions $(S = 0)$, it is seen from Fig. 9-9 that the equivalent circuit takes the

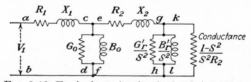

FIG. 9-10. Equivalent circuit, single-phase motor.

same form as that of an ordinary transformer under short-circuit conditions; in other words, the rotor speed axis is then unexcited, as has already been indicated in Art. 9-2 and in Fig. 9-3, and the current taken from the line is mainly determined by the combined stator and rotor leakage impedances. At synchronous speed, $S = 1$ (which could actually be attained only by driving the rotor mechanically), the equivalent load resistance becomes infinite (indicating open circuit), and the rotor exciting impedance in the speed axis becomes $R_r + j(X_r + X_2)$. At synchronism, and at all other speeds differing from zero, the rotor excitation is drawn from the main supply line through the leakage impedances of stator and rotor.

The locus of the primary current may be determined by the same procedure* described in Art. 6-12. Thus, referring to Fig. 9-10, the conductances (or resistances) and the susceptances (or reactances) between the points (a,b), (c,d), etc., have the magnitudes indicated in the following table:†

Points	Conductance or resistance		Susceptance or reactance		Unit
a, b	G		B		mho
c, d	$\dfrac{G}{G^2 + B^2} - R_1 = \alpha$	(9-20)	$\dfrac{B}{G^2 + B^2} - X_1 = \beta$	(9-21)	ohm
e, f	$\dfrac{\alpha}{\alpha^2 + \beta^2} - G_0 = \gamma$	(9-22)	$\dfrac{\beta}{\alpha^2 + \beta^2} - B_0 = \delta$	(9-23)	mho
g, h	$\dfrac{\gamma}{\gamma^2 + \delta^2} - R_2 = \epsilon$	(9-24)	$\dfrac{\delta}{\gamma^2 + \delta^2} - X_2 = \zeta$	(9-25)	ohm
k, l	$\dfrac{\epsilon}{\epsilon^2 + \zeta^2} = \dfrac{G'_r}{S^2} + \dfrac{1 - S^2}{S^2 R_2}$	(9-26)	$\dfrac{\zeta}{\epsilon^2 + \zeta^2} = \dfrac{B_r}{S^2}$	(9-27)	mho

Starting first with Eq. (9-26) and then with Eq. (9-27), and eliminating successively ϵ, ζ, γ, δ, α, and β, there are obtained

$$\frac{K}{L_1}\left(\frac{G'_r}{S^2} + \frac{1 - S^2}{S^2 R_2}\right)\left[\left(G - \frac{M}{K}\right)^2 + \left(B - \frac{P}{K}\right)^2\right]$$
$$+ \left[\left(G - \frac{N_1}{L_1}\right)^2 + \left(B - \frac{Q_1}{L_1}\right)^2 - \frac{1}{4L_1^2}\right] = 0 \quad (9\text{-}28)$$

and $$\frac{K}{L_1}\frac{B'_r}{S^2}\left[\left(G - \frac{M}{K}\right)^2 + \left(B - \frac{P}{K}\right)^2\right]$$
$$+ \left[\left(G - \frac{N}{L}\right)^2 + \left(B - \frac{Q}{L}\right)^2 - \frac{1}{4L^2}\right] = 0 \quad (9\text{-}29)$$

where $M = AR_1 + D$
$\quad\quad N = B_0 R_1 + G_0 X_2 + R_1 X_2 Y_0^2$
$\quad\quad P = AX_1 + C$
$\quad\quad Q = B_0(X_1 + X_2) + X_1 X_2 Y_0^2 + \frac{1}{2}$
$\quad\quad K = AZ_1^2 + 2DR_1 + 2CX_1 + Z_2^2$
$\quad\quad L = X_1 + X_2 + Z_1^2(B_0 + X_2 Y_0^2) + 2X_2(G_0 R_1 + B_0 X_1)$
$\quad\quad L_1 = R_1 + R_2 + Z_1^2(G_0 + R_2 Y_0^2) + 2R_2(G_0 R_1 + B_0 X_1)$
$\quad\quad N_1 = G_0(R_1 + R_2) + R_1 R_2 Y_0^2 + \frac{1}{2}$
$\quad\quad Q_1 = G_0 X_1 + B_0 R_2 + R_2 X_1 Y_0^2$
$\quad\quad A = 1 + 2B_0 X_2 + 2G_0 R_2 + Y_0^2 Z_1^2$
$\quad\quad D = R_2 + G_0 Z_2^2$
$\quad\quad C = X_2 + B_0 Z_2^2$

---

* K. J. Laurell, The Exact Circular Current Locus of the Induction Motor, *Elec. World*, **52**:78 (1908).

† In this table, all quantities are actual (not complex) quantities.

Eliminating S^2 between the pair of simultaneous Eqs. 9-28 and 9-29, the following relation is obtained:

$$\left[G - \frac{M \dfrac{B'_r}{R_2} + N \left(G'_r + \dfrac{1}{R_2} \right) - N_1 B'_r}{K \dfrac{B'_r}{R_2} + L \left(G'_r + \dfrac{1}{R_2} \right) - L_1 B'_r} \right]^2$$

$$+ \left[B - \frac{P \dfrac{B'_r}{R_2} + Q \left(G_r + \dfrac{1}{R_2} \right) - Q_1 B'_r}{K \dfrac{B'_r}{R_2} + L \left(G'_r + \dfrac{1}{R_2} \right) - L_1 B'_r} \right]^2$$

$$= \frac{(B'_r)^2 + \left(G'_r + \dfrac{1}{R_2} \right)^2}{4 \left[K \dfrac{B'_r}{R_2} + L \left(G'_r + \dfrac{1}{R_2} \right) - L_1 B'_r \right]^2} \qquad (9\text{-}30)$$

In this equation, the variable quantities G and B, which are, respectively, the conductance and the susceptance of the motor as measured between line terminals, are seen to be related in accordance with the equation of a circle, shown in Fig. 9-11. Either the coordinates of points on this circle may be read as G (along the vertical axis) and B (along the horizontal axis) or, since

$$\mathbf{I}_1 = \mathbf{V}_1(G - jB) = G\mathbf{V}_1 - jB\mathbf{V}_1$$

the ordinates (magnitude GV_1) may mean the in-phase component of line current, and the abscissas (magnitude BV_1) the corresponding quadrature component of line current, provided that V_1 is drawn along the vertical axis of reference.

Equation 9-30 may be written in the compact form

$$(B - \xi)^2 + (G - \eta)^2 = \rho^2 \qquad (9\text{-}31)$$

where ξ and η are the coordinates of the center of the circle (along the B and the G axes, respectively) and ρ is its radius. The magnitudes of ξ, η, and ρ are seen to be rather complicated functions of the constants of the motor, in accordance with the preceding lists of symbols; in reality, they simplify materially for the reason that in a well-designed motor terms involving Y_0^2 are negligible, and G'_r is small in comparison with $1/R_2$; moreover, because of the symmetry in the transformer and speed axes, $Y_0 = Y_r$ (still assuming that all secondary quantities are expressed in terms of the primary), from which it follows that

$$G'_r = \frac{R_r}{R_r^2 + (X_r + X_2)^2} \cong \frac{R_0}{R_0^2 + X_0^2} = G_0$$

$$B'_r = \frac{X_r + X_2}{R_r^2 + (X_r + X_2)^2} \cong \frac{X_0}{R_0^2 + X_0^2} = B_0 \qquad (9\text{-}32)$$

9-6. Experimental Verification of Circular Current Locus.   To check
the accuracy of the preceding analysis, tests were made on a 60-cycle
Wagner motor rated at 5 hp at 104 volts.   This motor had a wound rotor
provided with commutator and brushes for starting purposes, but
designed to operate with the commutator short-circuited under normal
running conditions, in the manner indicated by Fig. 5-34.   When the
short-circuiting ring is not in use, and the brushes are lifted from the commutator, the motor is equivalent to a transformer with the secondary on
open circuit; hence, the readings of primary voltage, current, and power,
when corrected for primary resistance, will determine R_0 and X_0 (or G_0
and B_0).   With the rotor blocked, and the ring short-circuiting the rotor
winding in the running position, the condition is the same as that of a
short-circuited transformer, thus making it possible to compute the values
of $R_1 + R_2$ and $X_1 + X_2$ from the
observed readings of primary voltage, current, and power.   By measuring the primary resistance R_1 by
the drop-of-potential method, all essential quantities are then determin-
able.   In this way it was found that

$$R_1 = 0.079$$
$$R_2 = 0.167$$
$$X_1 + X_2 = 0.449$$
$$G_0 = 0.029$$
$$B_0 = 0.078$$

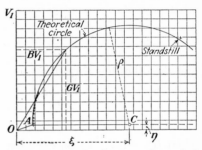

FIG. 9-11. Relation between theoretical
and observed current locus.

Making the approximations indicated in the preceding article, and substituting in the equations listed, the following values are obtained:

$A = 1.045$		$Q = 0.535$	
$C = 0.231$		$K = 0.265$	
$D = 0.169$		$L = 0.462$	
$M = 0.252$		$L_1 = 0.254$	
$N = 0.013$		$N_1 = 0.507$	
$P = 0.466$		$Q_1 = 0.020$	

Hence,
$$\xi = 1.19V_1$$
$$\eta = 0.053V_1$$
$$\rho = 1.04V_1$$

These values of ξ, η, and ρ make it possible to draw the theoretical current
locus, as has been done in Fig. 9-11.   On the same diagram, the points
indicated by small crosses represent observed values of current determined by reading the actual current input and power factor at a series of
loads ranging from no load to somewhat more than full load, while the
impressed voltage was held constant at 105 volts.   While the agreement

between the actual observations and the theoretical locus is not perfect, it is seen to be fairly satisfactory.

9-7. The Circle Diagram by Repeated Inversions. At first sight, it may seem surprising that an equivalent impedance represented by such an apparently complicated expression as Eq. 9-18 actually defines a circular locus of current when a constant voltage is impressed upon it. The analytical proof given in Art. 9-5, while not lacking in rigor, requires somewhat tedious algebraic manipulations which tend to obscure the really simple considerations which lead at once to the conclusion that the locus must be circular provided that the various impedances and admittances remain constant through the entire range of operation.

Thus, referring to Eq. 9-18, the two terms in the final subdenominator represent the admittances of the two parallel branches shown at the right-hand side of Figs. 9-9 and 9-10. One of these branches has the admittance

$$Y'_r = \frac{1}{S^2}(G'_r - jB'_r) \tag{9-33}$$

and the other has the admittance (conductance)

$$Y' = \frac{1 - S^2}{S^2 R_2} = \left(\frac{1}{S^2} - 1\right)G' \tag{9-34}$$

where $G' = 1/R_2$, so that the joint admittance of the two branches is

$$Y'_r + Y' = \frac{1}{S^2}[(G'_r + G') - jB'_r] - G' \tag{9-35}$$

The combined admittance is seen to consist of two parts, one containing the variable factor S, the other being constant. The graphical representation of $(1/S^2)[(G'_r + G') - jB'_r]$ is a line OB (Fig. 9-12) made up of a component $OA = (G'_r + G')/S^2$ drawn along the assumed axis of reference (here taken along the vertical), and a component $AB = B'_r/S^2$ perpendicular thereto, in the clockwise direction. Since the ratio

$$\frac{AB}{OA} = \frac{B'_r}{G'_r + G'} = \tan \alpha$$

is constant, it follows that as S changes the locus of point B is the straight line OB. Combining with OB the fixed length $BC = G'$ drawn parallel (but opposite) to OA in accordance with Eq. 9-35 the resultant OC is the joint admittance of the two parallel branches under consideration; and the locus of OC, as S varies with the load on the motor, is the straight line MC, parallel to OB.

In accordance with the principles discussed in Art. 6-13, the reciprocal of OC may be represented to any desired scale of impedance by a circle the center of which lies on the line OM drawn perpendicular to MC. Strictly speaking, the circle is not the one shown in Fig. 9-12, but the image thereof on the other side of the axis of reference; but this makes no difference so far as the magnitude of the reciprocal is concerned.

It may be noted that at standstill ($S = 0$) points A, B, and C are at an infinite distance above the origin O, and the corresponding standstill point on the impedance circle is at $P_{S=0}$, which is coincident with point O. At synchronous speed ($S = 1$), point C takes the position $C_{S=1}$, and the corresponding point on the circle is $P_{S=1}$. At speeds above synchronism ($S > 1$), the point on the circle moves around in the clockwise direction,

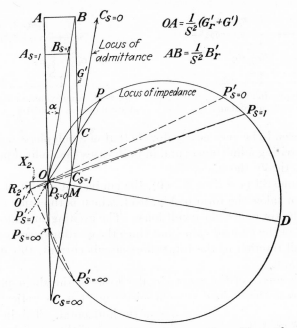

FIG. 9-12. Inversion of admittances varying with speed.

approaching $P_{S=\infty}$ as a limiting position; for the position of point C when the speed is infinite is $C_{S=\infty}$, which in accordance with Eq. 9-35 is fixed by the condition that $OC_{S=\infty} = BC = G'$. Points on the circle in Fig. 9-12 which lie between $P_{S=\infty}$ and $P_{S=0}$ do not represent any actual operating condition, because they correspond to negative values of OA and therefore to negative values of S^2, which is meaningless.

From this stage, the remaining steps are similar to those described in Art. 6-13. Successive inversions involve moving the origin of coordinates to take account of the impedance $R_2 + jX_2$, then the admittance $G_0 - jB_0$, then the impedance $R_1 + jX_1$, and a final inversion to obtain $G - jB$. The essential point is that each such inversion yields a circle because of the circular locus of the impedance in Fig. 9-12.

9-8. The Simplified Circle Diagram. If one compares the circle diagram of Fig. 9-11, which corresponds to the theoretically exact equivalent circuit of Fig. 9-10, with the circle diagram corresponding to the simpler circuit of a polyphase motor, it will be seen that in both cases the circles occupy nearly the same positions with reference to the origin of coordinates. The distinctive, though minor, differences that exist are due to the following considerations:

1. At synchronism ($s = 0$ or $S = 1$), the equivalent circuit of the single-phase motor takes the approximate form shown in Fig. 9-13; and since G'_r and B'_r may be replaced by G_0 and B_0, respectively, the no-load

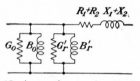

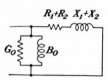

FIG. 9-13. Approximate circuit of single-phase motor at synchronism.

FIG. 9-14. Approximate circuit of single-phase motor at standstill.

current is seen to be very nearly double that of a polyphase motor having the same exciting admittance; and in both cases the no-load power factor will be practically the same.

2. At standstill ($s = 1$ or $S = 0$), the equivalent circuit of the single-phase motor takes the form of Fig. 9-14, which is the same as that of a polyphase motor under like conditions. The exciting current component is only half of the no-load value, but since the exciting current constitutes only a small fraction of the total short-circuit current, this discrepancy is insignificant.

3. The diameter of the exact circular locus of the single-phase motor drawn through the no-load (synchronism) point is theoretically inclined

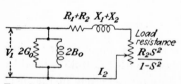

FIG. 9-15. Approximate equivalent circuit of single-phase motor.

below the horizontal. This inclination is in general so slight as to be negligible. For example, referring to the data cited in Art. 9-6, the ordinate of the no-load point A in Fig. 9-11 is, in accordance with Fig. 9-13, $2V_1G_0 = 0.058V_1$, whereas the ordinate of the center of the circle of Fig. 9-11 is $\eta = 0.053V_1$. These test results, do, however, check the theoretical conclusion that the principal diameter of the circle is inclined slightly downward toward the right.

These considerations point to the conclusion that for practical purposes the equivalent circuit of the single-phase induction motor may be drawn in the form of Fig. 9-15, which is of precisely the same type as the equivalent circuit of the polyphase motor. The further conclusion then follows at once that circle diagrams such as Fig. 6-22 are applicable (with exceptions noted hereafter) to the single-phase motor. Thus, Fig. 9-16 has been constructed to show the quantities that may be read directly from the drawing for any condition of loading such as that represented by point C.

The exceptions are concerned with the representation of the torque and the slip. It is plain from Fig. 9-15 that the mechanical output (represented by CE in Fig. 9-16) is

$$P = I_2^2 \frac{R_2 S^2}{1 - S^2} \tag{9-36}$$

whence $\qquad P + I_2^2 R_2 = I_2^2 R_2 \left(\frac{S^2}{1 - S^2} + 1 \right) = \frac{I_2^2 R_2}{1 - S^2} \tag{9-37}$

and $\qquad \dfrac{P}{P + I_2^2 R_2} = \dfrac{CE}{CF} = S^2 \tag{9-38}$

whence the speed is given to scale in Fig. 9-16 by the ratio $\sqrt{CE/CF}$.

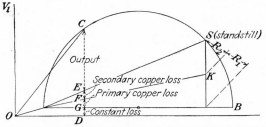

FIG. 9-16. Approximate circle diagram of single-phase induction motor.

Further, the torque developed by the motor must satisfy the relation

$$2\pi n_1 S T = P$$

or $\qquad T = \dfrac{1}{2\pi n_1} \dfrac{I_2^2 R_2 S}{1 - S^2} \tag{9-39}$

where n_1 is the synchronous speed. Now it will be observed that on multiplying Eqs. 9-36 and 9-37 the result is

$$P(P + I_2^2 R_2) = (CE)(CF) = (I_2^2 R_2)^2 \frac{S^2}{(1 - S^2)^2} \tag{9-40}$$

and this is proportional to the square of T as given by Eq. 9-39; hence, the torque is proportional to $\sqrt{CE \cdot CF}$.

9-9. Comparison of Single-phase and Polyphase Motors. The preceding analysis of the operation of single-phase motors indicates that, other things being equal, a single-phase motor will take nearly twice the (per-phase) magnetizing current of a polyphase motor when both are running in the vicinity of synchronous speed. This is borne out by experiment, as may be shown by opening one lead of a three-phase machine which is running without load; the current through the remaining leads increases slightly, but the total volt-amperes remain almost unchanged, and the power factor remains the same as before.   It must be remembered that, under such circumstances (assuming the stator to be Y-connected), the windings of two phases remain in series.

The fact that the magnetizing current is double that of an equivalent polyphase motor then points to the further conclusion (again with the proviso that other things are the same) that the single-phase motor should have a poorer power factor than the polyphase motor.   These considerations are frequently stressed to prove that the single-phase machine is a definitely inferior one.   But when a motor is properly designed, the qualification "other things being equal" does not necessarily apply.   The stator winding of a single-phase motor can be, and is, given a spread to utilize a large part of the available slot space, instead of limiting the winding to the more restricted arc it would occupy if other phase windings had to be accommodated.   This at once reduces the weight of the core.   The real disadvantage of the single-phase motor is the inherent absence of starting torque, which can be overcome only by the use of auxiliary devices to be described later.

The general characteristics of the machine limit its field of usefulness to small ratings.   The upper limit of size is 5 to 10 hp, but millions of fractional-horsepower motors are in use for general purposes, as in refrigerators, sewing and washing machines, desk and ceiling fans, etc.

9-10. Power and Torque Characteristics.   The expressions for power and torque represented by Eqs. 9-36 and 9-39 provide a ready means for fixing the relations between these quantities and the speed.   These equations are based upon the simplified equivalent circuit of Fig. 9-15 and are sufficiently accurate for practical purposes.

Noting from Fig. 9-15 that

$$I_2^2 = \frac{V_1^2}{\left(R_1 + R_2 + \frac{R_2 S^2}{1 - S^2}\right)^2 + (X_1 + X_2)^2}$$

$$= \frac{V_1^2(1 - S^2)^2}{[R_1(1 - S^2) + R_2]^2 + (1 - S^2)^2(X_1 + X_2)^2} \quad (9\text{-}41)$$

it follows that

$$P = \frac{V_1^2 R_2 S^2(1 - S^2)}{[R_1(1 - S^2) + R_2]^2 + (1 - S^2)^2(X_1 + X_2)^2} \quad (9\text{-}42)$$

$$T = \frac{1}{2\pi n_1} \frac{V_1^2 R_2 S(1 - S^2)}{[R_1(1 - S^2) + R_2]^2 + (1 - S^2)^2(X_1 + X_2)^2} \quad (9\text{-}43)$$

Plotting P and T as functions of S, it is seen that both are zero when $S = 0$ and when $S = 1$.   The curves are shown in Fig. 9-17.

9-11. The Rotating-field Theory.   The conclusion drawn from Eq. 9-43 that the torque becomes zero at synchronism ($S = 1$) is very nearly, but not absolutely, correct.   For, on referring to the general phasor diagram in Fig. 9-8, it is to be noted that while the torque of the motor is mainly due to the reaction between the rotor current I_t in the transformer axis and the speed field Φ_r, there is also a torque due to the reaction between I_r (the exciting current in the speed axis) and the transformer flux Φ_t. This latter torque is negative with respect to the main torque, but it was dropped from consideration in making the approximations that led to the simplified equivalent circuit of Fig. 9-15 from which Eq. 9-43 was derived. In other words, the torque curve should theoretically drop to zero value at a speed a trifle short of synchronism, though the discrepancy is of no practical importance.

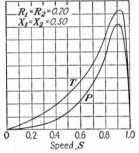

Another, and in some respects a clearer, understanding of the physical phenomena involved may be obtained from the point of view of the revolving field theory. The alternating mmf in the main (transformer) axis, produced by the stator winding (see Fig. 9-2), may be considered to be resolved into two rotating mmfs, each having half the amplitude of the simple alternating mmf, and rotating in opposite directions, but at synchronous speed, around the airgap. If the rotor is stationary, it may then be considered to be subjected simultaneously to the inductive effect of the fields due to these equal and oppositely moving mmfs, and naturally the two sets of induced rotor currents will develop equal and opposite torques.

FIG. 9-17. Torque and power as functions of speed (approximate theory).

If, however, the rotor is given an initial impulse in either direction, its slip with respect to the field turning in the same direction will be less than unity, while at the same time its slip with respect to the oppositely rotating field will be greater than unity. There will then be developed a positive torque in the same direction as the initial impulse, and a negative torque in the opposite direction, but the former will be larger than the latter because of the difference in the slips. It is convenient to consider the actual motor as a composite of two structures, mechanically coupled together, one of which has a rotor subjected to the influence of a stator carrying balanced polyphase currents having positive sequence, while the other rotor is in a field produced by a negative-sequence set of currents.

From this point of view, the speed-torque curve of the actual motor may be obtained by applying the principle of superposition to the hypothetical constituent motors. The difference between these constituent motors is that while one of them is operating at slip s, the other is operating at slip $2 - s$. Their individual speed-torque curves will have the forms indicated in Fig. 9-18, and the algebraic sum of their ordinates will give the resultant torque. It will be observed that this resultant curve crosses the axis of reference just short of synchronism.

It is then possible to determine all other operating characteristics of the hypothetical pair of motors, either analytically with the aid of their equivalent circuits, or graphically from their circle diagrams. This development will not be treated here and may be worked out as an exercise by the reader.

One feature of the revolving-field theory should, however, be noted. It is that, on resolving the original alternating stator mmf into two equal rotating components, the corresponding fluxes in the actual machine will be equal only when the rotor is stationary. Under running conditions (slip approaching zero with respect to the positively rotating field), the operating point on one of the circle diagrams will be close to the no-load point, while on the other circle diagram it will be beyond the standstill point. The circles cannot then be the same in size, because the line representing the primary current must have the same length in both cases, in order to agree with the fact that the primary (stator) mmf was resolved

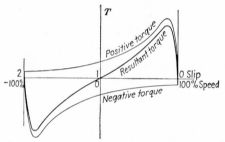

Fig. 9-18. Resultant torque due to oppositely rotating component fields.

into two equal components. It follows, then, that the circle corresponding to the negatively rotating field is much smaller than the other one, and this in turn means that the actual magnitude of the negatively rotating field is small in comparison with that of the forwardly rotating field. This accounts for the fact, capable of experimental verification, that the airgap field of a single-phase motor, when running near synchronism, is actually rotating in the same direction as the rotor itself. It is not constant in magnitude throughout a cycle but varies in the manner of the elliptical field already referred to, thereby checking the conclusions derived from the cross-field theory.

9-12. Starting of Single-phase Induction Motors. Numerous devices have been developed and used to overcome the inherent lack of starting torque of the single-phase induction motor in its pure form. In the course of time, all but a few of them have been discarded because of their cost or clumsiness, with the result that current practice employs those described under the following headings:

The Split-phase Winding. The self-starting properties of a polyphase induction motor can to some degree be imparted to the single-phase motor by providing the latter with two stator windings (the main winding and an auxiliary winding), displaced from each other by 90 electrical degrees; and then exciting the auxiliary winding by means of current which is out of phase with the current in the main winding, both currents being derived from the same supply line. This device, known as the split-phase winding, in the form originally developed by Nikola Tesla, employed windings one of which had relatively high reactance and low resistance, the other lower reactance and higher resistance. One form of this arrangement is illustrated in Fig. 9-19, where M is the main winding and A is the auxiliary winding; during the starting period, the resistor R limits the initial rush of current, and may be cut out of circuit after full speed has been attained, either by means of a man-

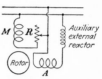

FIG. 9-19. Split-phase winding.

ually or centrifugally operated switch. A motor provided with such a starting resistor is called a *resistance-start motor*.

If one of the windings had pure reactance and the other pure resistance, the two currents would be out of phase by 90°, and the full properties of a two-phase motor would be realized. Obviously, this ideal cannot be attained and the two currents actually differ in phase by 30° or thereabout. The magnetic field is therefore elliptical in nature, equivalent to a pulsating field that is stationary in space upon which is superposed a relatively small rotating field. The torque, due to the latter field, is therefore small, hence, split-phase motors are useful only where the required starting torque is small, as in desk and ceiling fans.

The splitting of the phase can be accomplished equally well or better by means of a capacitor in series with the auxiliary winding, instead of the reactor shown in Fig. 9-19, in which case the arrangement is called a *condenser-start motor;* in this arrangement the auxiliary winding and its capacitor are disconnected after full speed has been reached.

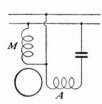

FIG. 9-20. Low-torque capacitor motor.

*The Capacitor Motor.** This type of motor, which has come into wide use, is a modification of the basic split-phase principle. The main winding is designed for direct connection to the line, and the auxiliary winding, in series with a capacitor, remains permanently in circuit as in Fig. 9-20. Motors of this type were designed and built as early as 1901, but did not become commercial until improvements were made in the art of constructing reliable capacitors.

The voltage across the auxiliary winding is the phasor difference between the line voltage and the drop across the capacitor, and is designed

* L. T. Campey, Capacitor Single-phase Motors, *Maintenance Eng.*, September, 1931.

to be nearly in quadrature with the line voltage under full-speed conditions. This, in effect, makes the machine a two-phase motor at full load. The phase relations obviously vary as the load on the motor changes, and at starting the torque is only 40 to 60 per cent of full-load value.

If the capacitance at starting is increased in the manner indicated in Fig. 9-21, the starting torque may be increased to two or three times full-load torque, or even higher. The effect of increased capacitance can also be obtained* by means of an autotransformer, as in Fig. 9-22.

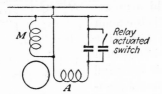
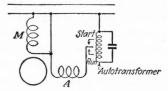

FIG. 9-21. High-torque capacitor motor. FIG. 9-22. High-torque capacitor motor.

The Shaded-pole Motor.† Small motors (fractional horsepower), requiring only small starting torque, may be made to be self-starting by means of shading coils. The stator punchings form a salient-pole structure, as in Fig. 9-23, and low-resistance copper bands, each forming a closed loop, are placed so as to surround approximately half of each pole face.

This arrangement is really a modification of the split-phase principle, the difference being that the auxiliary winding is supplied with its current by induction instead of by conduction; but in order that inductive coupling may exist, the auxiliary winding must be displaced from the main winding by less than 90°, and convenience of construction then dictates the arrangement of Fig. 9-23.

The current induced in the shading coil opposes the change of flux to which it is due; hence, there is a time lag between the phase of the flux included within the shading coil and the flux outside it. This results in a progressive shift of the center of distribution of the flux in the direction from the unshaded to the shaded portion of the pole face, and there is thus established the

FIG. 9-23. Shaded-pole motor (main winding on poles omitted).

equivalent of a weak rotating field superposed upon a stationary flux. The rotor will therefore turn in the direction indicated in the figure.

The Repulsion-start Motor. The general nature of the repulsion motor has been briefly described in Chap. 5 (see Fig. 5-12). It consists of an armature provided with a d-c winding and commutator, the brushes being

* A. S. McAllister, "Alternating Current Motors," p. 89, McGraw-Hill Book Company, Inc., New York, 1940.

† P. H. Trickey, An Analysis of the Shaded Pole Motor, *Elec. Eng.*, September, 1936, p. 1007.

arranged so that during the starting period they are short-circuited along
an axis displaced through a small angle from the axis of the stator winding, as in Fig. 9-24; this has been drawn to represent a bipolar machine,
but if four poles are used, a wave winding, requiring two brushes 90
mechanical degrees apart, is commonly used.   The repulsion motor has
series characteristics, hence develops a large torque per ampere, so that
the motor is capable of starting loads having large inertia or large frictional resistance.

When the motor has attained a speed of about two-thirds of synchronous speed, a centrifugally operated mechanism within the rotor short-
circuits the commutator segments, thereby converting the armature into
the equivalent of a squirrel-cage winding, as explained in Chap. 5.   In
some designs, the brushes are simultaneously lifted from the commutator; in others, they are left in contact with the commutator.   After this
switching operation has been automatically performed, the motor runs
as a single-phase induction motor.   The speed-torque curve of the motor

FIG. 9-24. Connections for repulsion
start.

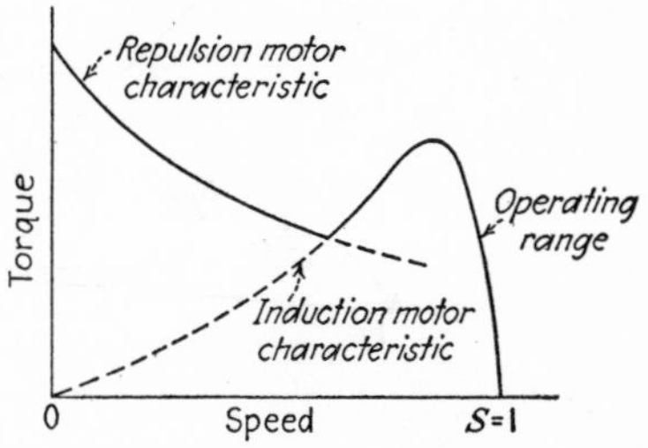

FIG. 9-25. Speed-torque curve, repulsion-
start motor.

is that of the repulsion motor during the starting period, and after the
switching operation it becomes that of the induction motor, as shown in
Fig. 9-25.

Further details concerning repulsion motors will be found in Chap. 15.

9-13. Power-factor Compensation.   The principal reason for the
attention that has been given to the cross-field theory of induction-
motor action is that it provides the most direct approach to an understanding of methods for the control of the power factor and speed of a-c
motors in general.   Power-factor control will be considered in this section, and speed control in the next, though the latter topic has been discussed to some extent in Art. 8-6.   The importance of maintaining a
high power factor has given rise to a large amount of study for the purpose of improving the power factor of all types of a-c motors.

The general phasor diagram in Fig. 9-8, which is reproduced with a
few changes as Fig. 9-26, shows clearly that the primary power factor
($\cos \varphi_1$) of the single-phase induction motor depends largely upon the
phase position of the rotor current (I_t) in the transformer axis, except,

of course, at light loads, when the magnetizing current is dominant.   The phase of I_t is in turn fixed by that of E_T, the phase angle between them being constant and equal to $\varphi_2 = \tan^{-1}(X_2/R_2)$.   But the phase of E_T is itself determined in part by E_{tt} and E_{rr}, both of which are nearly constant in magnitude and phase within the normal range of speed, but principally by E'_{rr}, a small voltage whose phase is opposite to that of the exciting current I_r in the speed axis.   In fact, the phase of E'_{rr} exerts such a critical effect upon the phase of E_T that a very slight change in the phase of the former will have a disproportionately large effect upon the phase of the latter and therefore upon the primary power factor. The conclusion is obvious that effective control of power factor depends upon control of the phase of I_r, therefore upon that of the resultant voltage in the speed axis, or E_R.

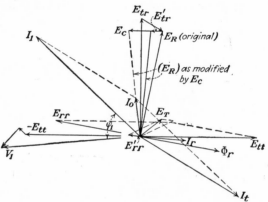

Fig. 9-26. Phase of excitation voltage E_R modified by control voltage E_c.

The simplest way to alter the phase position of E_R is to inject into the rotor speed axis the additional voltage indicated by E_c, whose phase is opposite to that of E_{tt}.   Such a control voltage may be obtained in the manner shown in Fig. 9-27, but it is evident that in order to introduce it into the rotor circuit the latter must be constructed with a commutator and two sets of brushes.

The power factor may be adjusted by means of the voltage E_c to any desired value at any particular load, but unless E_c is varied as the load changes, the power factor will not remain constant.   The setting of the power-factor compensator, if adjusted for unity power factor at average load, will result in leading power factor on one side of the average and lagging power factor on the other.

Instead of using an auxiliary regulating transformer in the manner indicated in Fig. 9-27, the control voltage may be obtained by means of taps in the main stator winding M.

9-14. Speed Control.   The single-phase induction motor of the usual type is characterized by a nearly constant magnetic field in much the same way as is an ordinary d-c shunt motor. Its substantial constancy of speed may therefore be accounted for by the consideration that the counter emf, itself necessarily nearly equal to the constant impressed voltage, is proportional to the product of flux and speed. Hence, if speed regulation is to be attained notwithstanding the maintenance of constant primary voltage and flux, the voltage impressed upon the armature circuit must be varied independently of the constant stator voltage. The

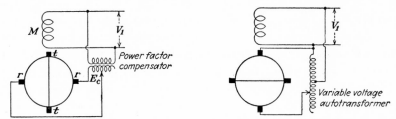

FIG. 9-27. Connections for power-factor compensation.   FIG. 9-28. Connections for speed control.

d-c analogue is the separately-excited motor whose field excitation is held constant.

The conclusion to be drawn from these considerations is that the voltage impressed upon the transformer axis t, t in Fig. 9-27 must be variable at will, instead of being maintained at the value E_{tt} in Fig. 9-26, fixed by the nearly constant transformer flux Φ_t. This result can be accomplished in the manner indicated in Fig. 9-28, the control voltage being derived from an autotransformer (or an equivalent variable-ratio two-winding transformer) supplied from the same source to which the stator winding M is connected.

CHAPTER 10

THE SYNCHRONOUS GENERATOR

10-1. Types and Construction of Alternators. A d-c generator of the usual type, having a closed-coil armature winding, may be made to serve as an a-c generator if it is provided with slip rings suitably connected to the winding. For example, if the armature is lap-wound, the machine will serve as a single-phase generator if it has two slip rings, one of them connected to all points of the winding which are 360 electrical degrees apart (i.e., which are separated by a double pole pitch), the other similarly connected to points midway between the first set; upon adding two additional slip rings, similarly connected to points intermediate between those to which the first pair of rings are connected, a quarter-phase (or two-phase) relation is established. Similarly, the machine will deliver three-phase alternating current if it is provided with three slip rings tapped into points of the winding separated from each other by 120 electrical degrees.

An example of this type of a-c machine, but used as a motor, is found in the synchronous converter (Chap. 13); in general, however, a-c generators as well as synchronous motors are separately excited and are of the rotating-field type, since it is easier and simpler to insulate the armature winding when it is a part of the stationary structure; and the only sliding contacts then required are the slip rings for the low-voltage exciting current of the field winding. Such machines are called synchronous alternators because the speed and the frequency have a fixed relation, determined by the equation $f = pn/120$. A further distinction between the synchronous machine and the d-c type is that in the former the armature winding is almost always of the open types illustrated in Chap. 4; in three-phase alternators, for example, the Y connection is practically universal.

The revolving-field type of alternator may be divided into two classes, the vertical and the horizontal. The vertical type is used mostly in connection with water wheels, Fig. 10-1 representing the Hoover Dam generators. Some of the original turbo-generator units of the Curtis type were built with vertical shafts, and with the generator above the turbine, but this construction has been superseded by the horizontal type. Figure 10-2, for example, shows a slow-speed engine-driven alternator, and

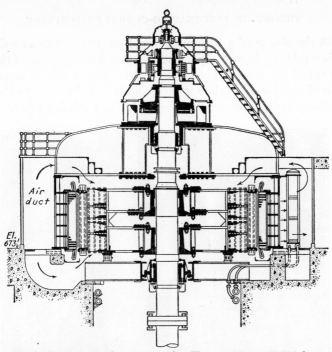

FIG. 10-1. Vertical water-wheel generator for Hoover Dam: 82,500 kva, 150 rpm, 13,800 volts, 50 cycles; or 180 rpm, 16,500 volts, 60 cycles; 40 poles. (*Courtesy of General Electric Company.*)

FIG. 10-2. Low-speed engine-driven alternator. (*Courtesy of General Electric Company.*)

Fig. 10-3 the stator of a turbine-driven generator. The superiority of
the horizontal type depends upon the fact that developments of the steam
turbine called for speeds much higher than were common prior to the
adoption of this form of prime mover; and it is plain that the horizontal
design affords better opportunity than does the vertical for providing the

FIG. 10-3. Stator for 25,000 kw 3,600 rpm hydrogen-cooled turbine generator. (*Courtesy of Allis-Chalmers Manufacturing Company.*)

necessary strength of frame, freedom from vibration, and simplicity of
bearing construction.

The inductor type of alternator is illustrated in Fig. 10-4. Its distinguishing characteristic is that both the armature and field windings are
stationary, therefore requiring no sliding contacts of any kind. The variation of the flux linked with the armature winding is due to the rotation of two sets of laminated lugs. It will be seen from the figure that
the polarity of the lugs does not change, those on one side being permanently of north polarity, those on the other side of south polarity.

Because of this fact, each inductor of the armature winding is subjected to a flux which pulsates from a maximum to a minimum value, but which does not reverse.   If there were no fringing of the flux between adjacent lugs, the minimum value of the field intensity between them would be zero, in which case the inductor alternator would require just twice as many inductors in its armature winding as an ordinary machine, assuming the same airgap field intensity in both cases.   Owing to the fact that the flux of the inductor alternator pulsates, but does not reverse, it is possible to use higher flux densities, for the same core loss, than in the ordinary type, and this consideration, together with the higher speed made possible by the rugged construction of the rotor, tends to reduce the disparity in the required number of armature inductors.   The serious objection to the inductor type arises from the fact that the flux between adjacent inductor lugs of the same polarity has a minimum value which

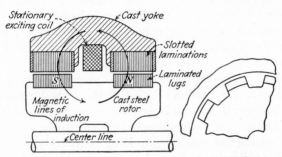

FIG. 10-4. Section of inductor-type alternator.

is not only far from the ideal zero value, but which increases with increasing excitation; it follows that armature inductors situated between the lugs, and which for best results should have no emf induced in them, are actually cut by a flux which generates an emf directly opposed to the flow of current.   This effect results in such poor voltage regulation that this type of machine is no longer used in systems for the generation and distribution of power, but it finds a useful application in connection with induction heating, which requires the use of frequencies much higher than the 25, 50, and 60 cycles used in transmission and distribution networks.

10-2. Armature Construction.   Provisions for Cooling.   Figures 10-1 to 10-3 show in a general way the essential features of the alternator as a whole.   The armature core, whatever the type of machine, is built up of sheet-steel punchings about 0.014 in. thick which are rigidly keyed to the frame.   In some designs, the dovetail projections on the core punchings fit into slots milled in the housing; in others, projections on the housing engage slots in the punchings.   In building up the core to the required thickness, successive layers are arranged so that the butt joints between adjacent segments of one layer come midway between those of the next, the dovetail projections and the slots for their reception being so positioned as to make this arrangement possible. The laminations are clamped tightly together by means of through bolts and end plates, the latter being provided with projecting fingers which serve to support the armature teeth.

The external frame, or housing, which supports the armature core is currently built up of steel plates which are electrically welded together, instead of the more expensive cast-steel frames formerly used. In the case of large turbo-generators where forced ventilation becomes a necessity, the interior design of the frame must provide adequate passages for the free movement of the large volume of cooling air or hydrogen gas, and the frame must accordingly be totally enclosed.

In the case of water-wheel or engine-driven alternators of low or medium speed, characterized by large diameter and small axial length, there is no special difficulty in providing sufficient ventilation to hold the operating temperature to safe values. In addition to the large areas available for direct radiation, there is the fanning action of the rotating field, which may be increased (at the expense of added friction loss) by the provision of fan blades around the periphery. If the axial length of the core is small, the heat developed in the embedded portion of the armature winding will be conducted to the end connections and there dissipated if the fanning action is sufficient; ordinarily, however, it is necessary to subdivide the core by providing ventilating ducts at intervals of about 3 in. to permit the flow of cooling air radially through the core. The provision of adequate cooling facilities becomes a problem of prime importance in the design of high-speed turbo-generators of large capacity. The output equation*

$$kva = \xi d^2 ln$$

shows that the effect of the high speed, n, is to reduce the amount of active material (determined by the diameter d and axial length l) much below that required in a slow-speed machine of the same capacity, thereby greatly reducing the area available for direct radiation. The diameter must be kept small enough to keep the peripheral speed of the rotor within safe limits, so that for large capacity the axial length must be considerable. This adds to the difficulty of cooling the central portion of the core, which is too far from the end connections to permit the heat to be conducted along the armature inductors to the end connections with moderate difference of temperature between the middle point and the ends. All of these considerations point to the necessity of completely enclosing the machine in order to permit the use of forced ventilation to carry away the heat; and here the designer is confronted with the

* See Art. 7-1.

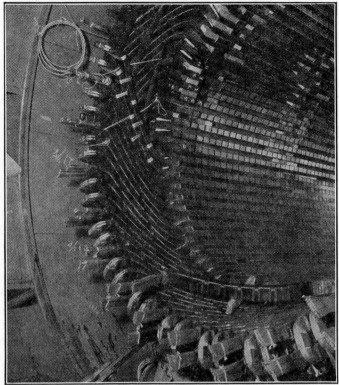

Fig. 10-5. Partly-wound stator of hydrogen-cooled turbo-generator, 112,500 kva, 13,800 volts, four poles, 1,800 rpm, showing bracing of end turns. (*Courtesy of General Electric Company.*)

difficulty of providing air ducts of sufficient section to carry the required volume of air. The amount of cooling air required may be computed from the following considerations:

Weight of 1 cu ft of dry air at 60°F and 28.5 in. Hg = 0.07272 lb
Specific heat of air = 0.2418
1 Btu ≡ 778 ft-lb

Energy required to raise 100 cu ft of air through 1°C
$$= 0.07272 \times 100 \times 0.2418 \times 778 \times \tfrac{9}{5} = 2,462 \text{ ft-lb}$$
$$\equiv 2,462 \times \frac{0.746}{33,000} \text{ kw-min} \equiv 0.0559 \text{ kw-min}$$

Consequently, a loss of 1 kw will raise the temperature of 100 cu ft of air through 1/0.0559 = 18°C in 1 min. If the temperature of the air is higher, the weight per cubic foot will be less than the figure used above, in which case the rise of temperature corresponding to a given loss will be higher in inverse ratio to the decreased specific weight.

As an example of the volume of cooling air required, consider the case*
of a 1,500-rpm 25-cycle 15,000-kva machine having an efficiency of 96.5
per cent. The total loss in the machine is

$$\frac{15,000}{0.965} - 15,000 = 545 \text{ kw}$$

calling for 54,500 cu ft of air per min, with a difference of 18°C between
the temperatures of outgoing and incoming air, or about 50,000 cu ft per
min for a temperature rise of 20°C.   Assuming an average air velocity
of 6,000 ft per min (values of 5,000 to 6,000 ft per min are common), the
area of cross section of the air passages must be 8⅓ sq ft, or much more
than can be provided with the ordinary method of *radial* ventilation

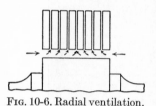

FIG. 10-6. Radial ventilation.

(Fig. 10-6), where the cooling air enters the
ducts through the stator core by way of the
airgap.   Thus, if the peripheral velocity of the
rotor of the above machine is assumed to be
20,000 ft per min, the diameter will be 51 in.,
and with an airgap of 1 in. (iron to iron), and
assuming the air to be supplied from each end,
the available cross section is 2.22 sq ft, or
only a little more than one-quarter of the required area.   So far as the
rotor itself is concerned, there would be no difficulty in providing sufficient cooling air, for the rotor losses constitute only about 10 per cent of
the total loss, therefore requiring only about 5,000 cu ft of air per min,
corresponding to a duct area of about 0.83 sq ft, or well within the

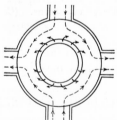

FIG. 10-7. Circumferential ventilation.

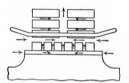

FIG. 10-8. Axial ventilation.

amount available; the difficulty arises from the much larger amount of
cooling air required by the stator.

The limitations of the radial method led to the development of the *circumferential* and *axial* methods of cooling, as illustrated in Figs. 10-7 and
10-8.   In the former, air is supplied to one or more points on the outer
periphery of the stator core, and is forced circumferentially through the
ducts between the laminations to suitable outlets.   If this method is
combined with the radial system, the stator ducts will have to carry the

* B. G. Lamme, High-speed Turbo-alternators—Designs and Limitations, *Trans.
AIEE*, **32**:11 (1913).

two streams of air indicated in Fig. 10-7, and the resultant interference will detract from the effectiveness of both of them. To avoid this interference, some machines have been built in the manner indicated in Fig. 10-9, alternate radial ducts being closed at the outer surface, and all of them being closed at the airgap. The large central duct provides an outlet for the cooling air for the rotor. This method is subject to the disadvantage that the stator ducts are not all in parallel, which means a reduction in the available area and an increase in length of path.

In the *axial* method, the stator cooling air is forced in the axial direction through the passages formed by the holes in the stator punchings shown in Fig. 10-8. This design has the great advantage that the stator heat, which flows much more freely along the laminations than across them, finds its way directly to the axial openings with considerably smaller temperature drop than is necessary to make it flow across the laminations.

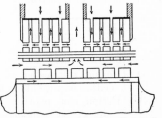

FIG. 10-9. Combined radial and circumferential ventilation.

In cases where the cooling air used for the forced ventilation of generators contains an appreciable amount of solid matter in suspension, as in smoky or dusty surroundings, the cooling air must be filtered or washed to prevent the eventual clogging of the ducts in the core. Filters made of cheesecloth have been used, but they are troublesome because of the frequency with which they must be renewed if the air is dirty. Washing the air by making it pass through a spray chamber is an effective remedy, for at the same time that the dust is removed, the initial temperature of the air is appreciably reduced, thereby increasing the output of the generator without exceeding the allowable limit of temperature at the hottest spot.

In the case of generators and motors of large capacity, the circulation of the cooling air requires considerable power and correspondingly expensive auxiliary equipment. With air as the cooling medium, there is an ultimate limit of rating beyond which it would not be possible to keep within safe temperature limits. Further increase in rating calls for a cooling medium having a greater specific heat and a lower density than air. Hydrogen, which has a specific heat of 3.409 (about $14\frac{1}{2}$ times that of air) and a density of 0.005611 lb per cu ft at 0°C and 760 mm Hg, fulfills these requirements, and is used for cooling large synchronous condensers and generators. Its use calls for completely enclosed explosion-proof designs, with the provision of cooling coils (carrying circulating water or oil) inside the casing to extract the heat from the circulating atmosphere of hydrogen.*

* M. D. Ross, Application of Hydrogen Cooling to Turbine Generators, *Trans. AIEE*, **50**:381 (1931).

10-3. Armature Insulation. The requirements to be met in the selection and disposition of the insulating materials are so closely related to the thermal conditions in the machine that it is not possible to consider these two features independently. For each class of organic material used for insulating purposes, there exists a limiting temperature beyond which deterioration sets in and progresses rapidly, so that in general the conditions which determine the maximum rise of temperature determine the material to be used. The insulation must, of course, have sufficient dielectric strength to withstand the electrical stresses, and be strong enough mechanically to withstand the physical stress and vibration to which it is subjected.

The AIEE Standards classify insulating materials into five groups, to four of which there have been assigned definite temperature limits for purposes of standardization, in accordance with the following table:

Class	Material	Limiting temperature
O	Cotton, silk, paper, and similar organic materials when neither impregnated nor immersed in oil	90°C
A	Cotton, silk, paper, and similar organic materials when impregnated or immersed in a liquid dielectric; also enamel applied to conductors	105°C
B	Inorganic materials such as mica, fiber glass, and asbestos in built-up form combined with binding substances	130°C
C	Inorganic materials such as pure mica, porcelain, quartz, etc.	Not designated
H	Inorganic materials such as mica, asbestos, and fiber glass combined with binding substances composed of silicone compounds which may be in rubbery or resinous forms	180°C

Alternating-current machines of low and moderate voltages, comparable with those encountered in d-c machines, present no special difficulties so far as insulation is concerned, and the same materials are used in both, such, for example, as vulcanized fiber, horn and fish paper, and varnished cambric and paper. But in high-voltage machines the conditions are complicated by the fact that an increase in the thickness of the insulation is not accompanied by a proportional increase in disruptive strength, so that a point is soon reached where the space limitations demand the use of insulating materials having substantially greater dielectric strength per mil of thickness. Mica is the best material not only with respect to this consideration but also because of its ability to withstand high temperature. For these reasons, mica is relied upon to the practical exclusion of other materials for the insulation of high-voltage alternators, especially turbo-alternators where high temperatures are unavoidable. The brittleness of mica makes it necessary to build up the required thickness by using thin flakes cemented together by varnish or bakelite, generally with a backing of thin paper or cloth, and then baking it under pressure. Before the binding material has hardened, the material is plastic and can be formed when hot into tubes or troughs for slot linings, which become rigid on baking.   The organic material constituting the binder serves a structural purpose only, and since it occupies only a small part of the space taken by the insulation as a whole, is not relied upon for dielectric strength.   In the case of one of the first Niagara generators, which was put into service in August, 1895, an inspection made during the summer of 1914 showed that the cambric binder had everywhere lost its mechanical strength, was entirely gone in some places, and in others had been reduced to a fine powder;* notwithstanding this condition, and that the cambric had originally constituted 25 per cent of the total insulating material, the insulated bars of the armature winding were tight in the slots.   In this particular machine, the insulation had been hand-wrapped, whereas present practice makes use of the Hoefler process of machine wrapping, in which the insulation is rolled hot on the straight part of the coils occupying the slots; this gives a much more compact structure than hand wrapping, and removes entirely any need for relying upon the cloth or paper backing as a spacer.

When high-voltage alternators were first developed, it was found that the slot insulation was subject to serious injury from the effects of corona discharge, which in turn caused the formation of ozone, with consequent oxidation and pitting of the insulation.   The damage was most pronounced where the conductors were opposite sharp edges of the core, as at the ends of the core and at the edges of air ducts through the core; this is natural, since corona discharge sets in when the concentration of dielectric flux exceeds a definite limit, and the presence of sharp edges of metal promotes the concentration of dielectric flux.   Lamme† maintained that the use of mica insulation, suitably applied, was sufficient to overcome this difficulty, and pointed to machines thus insulated which were free from this trouble at voltages as high as 13,000 volts above ground. The certain prevention of corona formation requires that the dielectric flux density be kept below the critical value, and this can be accomplished, as has been done in some designs, by wrapping with tin foil those parts of the coil which occupy the slots, thus forming a continuous metallic sheath without sharp edges; the tin foil, if used, is just inside the outer layer of protecting tape, and is grounded to the core of the machine.

When an alternator is suddenly short-circuited, the armature current increases sharply to a transient value which may be many times larger than the steady or permanent value of short-circuit current, and the

* F. D. Newbury, Experimental Data Concerning the Safe Operating Temperature for Mica Armature-coil Insulation, *Trans. AIEE,* **34**(pt. II):2747 (1915).

† *Op. cit.,* p. 29.

forces developed by the leakage flux associated with the armature current, being proportional to the square of the current, may reach destructive magnitude. For reasons to be developed later, but which are obviously associated in part with the amount of power normally developed by the machine, these forces are particularly severe in large turbo-alternators, and require very rigid bracing of the end connections as shown in Figs. 10-3 and 10-5.

10-4. Construction and Insulation of the Field System. The rotating field structure of slow- and moderate-speed machines of standard design consists of laminated poles projecting radially from an annular steel core forming part of the spider, the general arrangement being shown in Fig. 10-2. The punchings constituting the pole cores are made of thicker material than those of the armature core and are provided with overhanging tips which serve not only to distribute the airgap flux but also to support the field windings. The pole cores are attached to the spider either by bolts or by means of keys in connection with dovetail projections forming an integral part of the punchings. In small machines of this type, the field winding consists of double-cotton-covered wire, with paper insulation between layers, but wherever conditions warrant, the winding is made of bare ribbon conductor wound on edge, successive turns being insulated from each other by thin strips of insulating material such as asbestos paper.

From the relation $f = pn/120$, it follows that in 25-cycle alternators $pn = 3,000$, while in 60-cycle alternators $pn = 7,200$. Bearing in mind that steam turbines are inherently high-speed machines, it follows that turbo-alternators must in general have two to six poles. While some 60-cycle machines of this type have been built with six salient poles for speeds of 1,200 rpm, present practice makes use of cylindrical rotors with the exciting winding embedded in slots, a construction which provides greater mechanical strength and permits more accurate balancing; incidentally, the smooth surface of a cylindrical rotor conduces to quiet running, though the suppression of noise is to a large extent accomplished by completely enclosing the machine.

The rotor design of the early high-speed turbo-generators included some of the features common to the standard designs of low-speed machines, particularly the through-shaft construction. This had the effect of seriously limiting the output for which these machines could be built, since the small rotor diameter fixed by the high speed greatly restricted the space available for the teeth and slots and the depth of the core below them. This limitation was overcome by abandoning the through-shaft construction, using in lieu thereof, in the smaller sizes, a rotor comprising a core and shaft made from a solid forging and, in the larger sizes, a core made up of plates or disks bolted together and with bolted-on shaft extensions.* In this way, it became possible to use shaft

* For a full account of these developments, see Lamme, *op. cit.*, p. 1.

diameters considerably larger than were feasible with the through-shaft design, thus resulting in greater stiffness with correspondingly reduced trouble from vibration.

Figure 10-10 is in part a cross section of a bipolar rotor, but with the addition of a perspective sketch showing the end turns of two of the coils of the exciting winding, which, because of its spread, yields a stepped mmf distribution approximating the desired sinusoidal form (see Art. 4-18). The importance of this consideration depends upon the fact that the wave form of emf of an a-c generator should conform as closely as possible to a sine curve, since the absence of harmonics reduces the possibility of undesirable complications in the behavior of connected apparatus and because of the greater ease and simplicity with which necessary calculations can be made. There is the further fact that the AIEE Standards specify that the deviation factor* of the open-circuit terminal-voltage wave of synchronous machines shall not exceed 10 per cent unless otherwise specified.

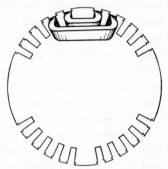

FIG. 10-10. Bipolar radial-slot rotor.

The free ends of the exciting coils must be rigidly supported by steel or bronze rings of high-grade material, not only because of the large centrifugal forces due to high speed of rotation, but also because of the still larger forces to which the coils are subjected in case of a sudden short circuit on the circuit supplied by the alternator. For it will be shown later that the effect of such a sudden short circuit, in addition to causing a transient armature current of large magnitude, is to induce in the field winding a transient unidirectional current and voltage which may be many times larger than the normal values. The transient voltage due to this cause will in general be within the puncturing limits of the insulation, since considerations of mechanical strength call for quality and thickness of material more than sufficient to withstand the dielectric stress; but the mechanical stresses on the insulation, as well as on the coils themselves, are very severe, and these conditions, in combination with the high operating temperature, preclude the use of insulating material other than mica.

It may be noted further that the metallic structure which forms the core end of the bolted-on shaft extension bridges the magnetic poles of the rotor, hence must be made of nonmagnetic material, such as bronze,

---

* "The deviation factor of a wave is the ratio of the maximum difference between corresponding ordinates of the wave and of the equivalent sine wave to the maximum ordinate of the equivalent sine wave when the waves are superposed in such a way as to make this maximum difference as small as possible" (AIEE Standards, No. 503, Par. 1.190, June, 1945).

to avoid undue shunting of the magnetic flux away from the main magnetic circuit.

10-5. Voltage Regulation of Alternators. When a-c generators first came into general use, the variation of terminal voltage caused by changes in the magnitude and power factor of the consumer demand was a source of annoyance, largely because of the resultant unsteadiness of the light of incandescent lamps, which then constituted a major part of the load.   One of the early attempts to overcome this difficulty employed a series transformer the primary of which was inserted in the outgoing line and, with its secondary connected through a commutating device on the generator shaft, supplying unidirectional current to a compounding winding on the field poles.   The trouble with this arrangement, and with other more elaborate schemes developed later, was that the compounding, while responsive to changes in current, was incapable of counteracting the demagnetizing (or magnetizing) effect of changing power factor of the load.

Because of these circumstances the problem of predetermining the voltage regulation of alternators was of great importance both to designers and to operators, with the result that the early literature of the subject is very extensive.   *Voltage regulation* is defined as the rise of voltage, expressed in per cent of rated voltage, when the load is reduced to zero, the field excitation and frequency remaining at their initial values.   It is to be noted, however, that the phrase "rise of voltage" in this definition presupposes an inductive or noninductive load, because if the load is sufficiently capacitative, the magnetizing effect of a leading current may cause the voltage under load conditions to be higher than at no load; in that case, the effect of reducing the load to zero is to produce a fall of voltage, and the regulation must then be treated as negative instead of positive.

The advent of automatic regulators of the Tirrill type transferred attention from voltage regulation per se to the closely related matter of the change in field excitation required either to maintain constant terminal voltage or to produce a specified degree of compounding.   The importance of the subject is further emphasized by the fact that the voltage regulation, and its counterpart in changed excitation, are closely related to the amount of current produced by an alternator under short-circuit conditions.

The regulation of a completed machine can theoretically be determined by actually loading it and observing the change in terminal voltage when the load is disconnected, the speed and excitation remaining fixed; but this method is out of the question under full-load conditions, except in the case of small machines, because of the cost of providing motive power and auxiliary apparatus for absorbing the output.   Large machines may be tested at low power factor by methods to be described later, but in general their regulation at high-power-factor loads must be computed.

The factors which enter into the determination of alternator regulation are the armature reaction, the armature leakage impedance, and the change in field leakage which accompanies changes in excitation. These are fundamentally the same as those involved in the corresponding case of d-c generators, the differences being due to the effect of power factor upon armature reaction, and the substitution of armature impedance in place of the armature resistance of d-c machines. It is to be noted also that the problem resembles the corresponding determination of the regulation of transformers.

10-6. Phasor Diagram of Alternator with Nonsalient Poles. It has been shown in Arts. 8-7 to 8-9 that a wound-rotor induction motor may be made to run at any desired speed by supplying its rotor with voltage and current of the corresponding slip frequency. If that slip frequency happens to be zero, i.e., if the rotor is supplied with continuous (or direct) current, the motor will run at synchronous speed. In that event, the induction motor becomes structurally identical with an alternator which has a cylindrical rotor of the type which is illustrated in Fig. 10-10 for the special case of a two-pole machine. The conclusion follows immediately that the phase relations between the stator and the rotor mmfs of the synchronous machine will then be the same as in the phasor diagrams of the induction motor, Figs. 6-15 and 6-16; and these mmfs may be combined as phasors for the same reason as in those diagrams, namely, that because of the concentric cylindrical shapes of the stator and rotor their mmfs act upon magnetic circuits which have equal reluctance in all axes, as explained in Art. 6-4 and illustrated in Fig. 6-14. It is to be noted, however, that whereas the stator of an induction motor is the primary and the rotor is the secondary, these roles are reversed when the machine becomes a synchronous generator. The rotor of the revolving-field alternator is the primary, not only because it supplies the excitation for the magnetic field, but also because the mechanical energy imparted to it by the prime mover is the source of the electrical energy developed in the stator.

The distribution of the mmf produced by the rotor exciting winding and by the stator (armature) current will both be of the stepped types, some of which were discussed in Chap. 4; both mmfs may therefore be resolved into fundamentals of full pitch and a series of higher space harmonics; but for the time being let it be assumed that the harmonics may be neglected and that attention may be restricted to the sinusoidally distributed fundamentals. The fundamental mmf of the rotor, moving with the latter, is alternating with respect to the stationary armature winding, and may therefore be represented by a phasor F, as in Fig. 10-11; and the armature mmf, also rotating at synchronous speed with respect to the stator winding, and therefore stationary with respect to the poles, may in like manner be represented by the phasor A, which is (1) in time phase with the stator current I and (2) displaced from F by an angle $90 + \psi$.

The two statements in the preceding sentence are explained (1) by the footnote on page 201 (Art. 4-16), where it was pointed out that whenever the current of a particular phase passes through its positive maximum the axis of the resultant mmf of all phases coincides with the center line of that winding; and (2) by Fig. 4-33 (page 197), which shows that the armature mmf (there represented by the symbol A_2) is displaced by the angle $90 + \psi$ from the axis of the field excitation F.   The angle ψ is the

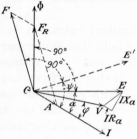

FIG. 10-11. General (Potier) phasor diagram of alternator with nonsalient poles.

phase displacement between the armature current and the emf E' that would be generated if the field excitation were acting alone.

Again referring to Fig. 10-11, the resultant of mmfs F and A is F_R, which is then responsible for the flux (per pole) Φ; the latter, alternating with respect to the armature winding, induces the emf per phase, E, which lags 90° behind Φ, and leads current I by an angle α (assuming that the load on the alternator is sufficiently inductive to account for the larger angle ψ).   Deducting from E the ohmic drop IR_a and the reactance drop IX_a, where R_a and X_a are, respectively, the effective resistance and leakage reactance of the armature winding per phase, the result is V, the terminal per-phase voltage of the machine. Voltage V leads the current I by an angle φ, such that $\cos \varphi$ is the power factor of the load.

If, under the conditions represented by Fig. 10-11, the load is disconnected, the speed and the field excitation F remaining the same, the terminal voltage per phase will increase from V to E', the latter lagging 90° behind F; and if V and I are the rated voltage and current of the machine, the per cent regulation for the power factor $\cos \varphi$ will be

$$\frac{E' - V}{V} \times 100$$

The resemblance between Fig. 10-11 and the phasor diagrams of the transformer and of the induction motor is so clear as to require no comment.   One slight distinction is that in Fig. 10-11 the flux Φ is drawn in phase with the resultant magnetizing mmf F_R instead of lagging behind it by an angle of hysteretic advance.   This is due to the fact that the airgap of an alternator is so much larger than in the induction motor that (except for the effect of saturation of the iron) the flux may be considered to be proportional to the resultant mmf.   Another feature of Fig. 10-11 which differs from the corresponding diagram of the induction motor is that the resultant mmf F_R is relatively much larger than $N_1' I_0$ in Fig. 6-15, likewise because of the large airgap of the typical alternator.

10-7. The Open-circuit and Short-circuit Characteristics. The simi-
larities between the phasor diagram of the alternator, on the one hand,
and the corresponding diagrams for the stationary transformer and the
induction motor, on the other, lead quite naturally to the conclusion that
the open-circuit and short-circuit tests which were useful in the two latter cases are likewise applicable to the alternator.

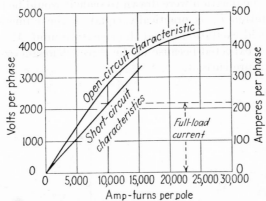

FIG. 10-12. Open- and short-circuit characteristics.

The *open-circuit characteristic* of an alternator (also called the no-load,
or the saturation, characteristic), Fig. 10-12, shows the relation between
the field excitation and the emf developed when the machine is driven at
rated speed with its terminals on open circuit. In Fig. 10-12, the excitation is shown in terms of ampere-turns per pole, though in some cases the
excitation is given in terms of the field current in amperes; and the emf
is expressed in volts per phase, though it is common to use volts between
lines if the winding is Y connected.

The open-circuit characteristic will usually be
more or less curved because of saturation of the iron
part of the magnetic circuit; but the initial straight
part of the curve, if extended, yields the *airgap characteristic* since it represents the relation between the
voltage (and therefore the airgap flux) for the condition of zero reluctance of the iron.

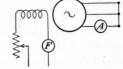

FIG. 10-13. Connec-
tions for short-circuit
test.

The *short-circuit characteristic* shown in Fig. 10-12 is obtained experimentally by running the machine at its rated speed with its terminals
short-circuited as in Fig. 10-13, and observing the current by means of
ammeter A when the excitation F is varied from zero to an amount sufficient to circulate about 125 to 150 per cent of full-load current. The
short-circuit characteristic is normally a straight line through the origin
because the excitation is so small that there is no saturation to affect the
resistance and reactance of the short-circuited armature.

Under the short-circuit conditions of Fig. 10-13, the terminal voltage V is zero, and the phasor diagram, Fig. 10-11, accordingly reduces to the form shown in Fig. 10-14. The emf generated by the resultant excitation F_R is just sufficient to overcome the internal impedance drop $I(R_a + jX_a)$. In practice, X_a is so much greater than R_a (ten times or more) that the current I lags behind E by an angle not much less than 90°, so that if the diagram were drawn to scale it would be found that the effective excitation F_R is practically equal to the numerical difference between the field excitation F and the armature mmf A. This result is what would be expected because of the direct demagnetizing effect of a lagging quadrature current.

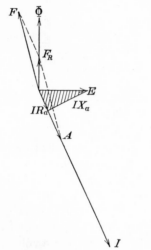

FIG. 10-14. Phase relations, short-circuit conditions.

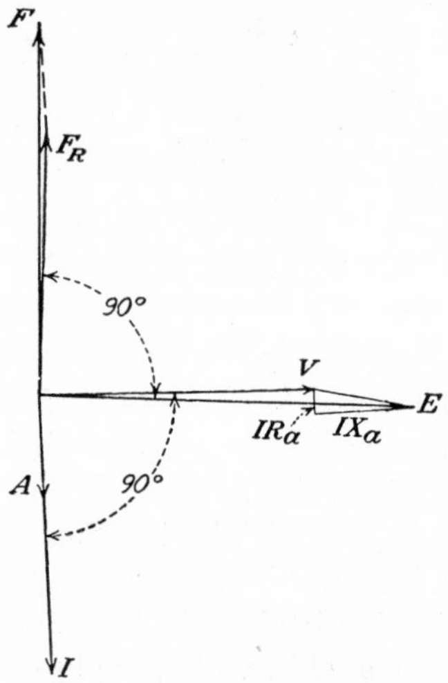

FIG. 10-15. General phasor diagram, zero power factor.

10-8. Load Characteristics and the Potier Triangle.

Let the alternator (of the cylindrical-rotor type) be connected to a load consisting of a purely inductive reactor, so that the armature current I lags 90° behind the terminal voltage V. The general phasor diagram, Fig. 10-11, then takes the form of Fig. 10-15, which shows that for practical purposes the net excitation F_R is the numerical difference between the mmfs of field and armature, and that the terminal voltage V may be taken to be the numerical difference between the induced emf E and the armature reactance drop IX_a.

If now the external reactive load is varied, while at the same time the field excitation F is so adjusted that the current I remains constant at its rated value, the graph of the relation between the terminal voltage V and the field excitation F will take the form shown in Fig. 10-16 as the curve $F_0P''P$, which is called the *zero-power-factor characteristic*.

Figure 10-16 shows that when the field excitation is equal to OF (to which there corresponds the open-circuit voltage FR), the net excitation is OM, which is less than OF by the armature mmf A. The net excitation induces voltage $E = MN$, but from this amount must be deducted $IX_a = NQ$, leaving as the terminal voltage $MQ = FP = V$, and P is therefore a point on the zero-power-factor characteristic.

It is easy to see that if the current I is kept constant, other points on the zero-power-factor characteristic such as P' and P'' may be located by sliding the triangle NQP, called the *Potier triangle*, parallel to itself so that point N remains on the open-circuit characteristic. Point P' is of particular interest, for it corresponds to the excitation OF_0, which is just sufficient to circulate full-load current when the machine is short-cir-

cuited, and the magnitude of OF_0 may accordingly be found from the short-circuit characteristic, as indicated in Fig. 10-12.

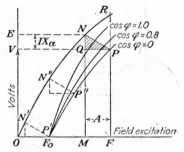

FIG. 10-16. Load characteristics of alternator.

Figure 10-16 includes two additional load characteristics, one of them for the case of noninductive load (cos φ = 1), the other for a load power factor cos φ = 0.8 (lagging), but in both cases with the current held constant at its full-load value. Points on these curves must in general be computed in the manner outlined in the examples given in the following article, because of the practical impossibility of obtaining actual test readings under controlled conditions, at least in the case of large machines.

The zero-power-factor characteristic may, however, be obtained experimentally by direct observation provided there are available one or more synchronous motors of sufficient current-carrying capacity to absorb the generator current output. For it may be inferred from Art. 4-14, particularly in connection with Fig. 4-31, that if these motors are operated without load and with reduced excitation (or with no excitation at all), the motors will draw a heavily lagging current which will supply their excitation.* The power factor of this motor load will not be zero, since the motor losses due to friction and windage, copper and iron losses must be supplied by the generator under test, but the resultant power factor can be held to 20 per cent or less, to which there corresponds an angle φ in Fig. 10-11 of about 80°, in which case the conditions are not materially different from those shown in Fig. 10-15. It will be observed further that in Fig. 10-16 the load characteristic for cos φ = 0.8 lies more than halfway between the curves for cos φ = 1 and cos φ = 0, which means that the terminal voltage, while very sensitive to changes of

* This effect is treated in full detail in the subsequent chapter The Synchronous Motor.

power factor at or near unity, is very insensitive when the power factor approaches zero.

The construction of the zero-power-factor characteristic shown in Fig. 10-16 may be applied in reverse manner for the experimental determination of both X_a, the armature leakage reactance, and the armature mmf A, which corresponds to the rated current I. Thus, in Fig. 10-17, curve C_0 is the experimentally determined open-circuit characteristic, and curve C_0' is the zero-power-factor characteristic. It is not necessary to determine the whole of curve C_0'; two points are sufficient, one of them being point F_0 obtained from the short-circuit characteristic; the other, such as point P, is obtained by means of a load of underexcited synchro-

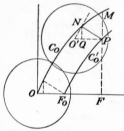

FIG. 10-17. Potier method of determining armature reaction and leakage reactance.

nous motors, such that the field excitation OF of the alternator is approximately equal to its normal full-load value. Then, make a tracing of the part of the drawing in the vicinity of origin O (as indicated by the circle surrounding the origin), and slide this tracing parallel to its original position until point F_0 coincides with point P, with point O of the tracing at O'. The dashed line $O'N$, which represents the lower part of the open-circuit characteristic transferred to the tracing, will intersect curve C_0 at the point N, and the Potier triangle is therefore NQP, and it may there-

after be transferred back to the origin. In this way, $NQ = IX_a$, and $QP = A$, the armature mmf corresponding to current I. The value of A thus determined experimentally should check the value given by Eq. 4-44, namely,

$$A = \frac{2\sqrt{2}}{\pi} m k_{b_1} k_{p_1} N_p I \qquad \text{amp-turns per pole}$$

The reactance determined in this way is called the *Potier reactance*.

10-9. Calculation of Load Characteristics and Voltage Regulation. The relations implicit in the general phasor diagram, Fig. 10-11, lead readily to the calculation of points on the load characteristics and incidentally the voltage regulation for any specified power factor of the load. Consider, for example, a two-pole three-phase Y-connected turbo-generator rated at 2,500 kva, 6,600 volts between terminals, at 3,000 rpm. The frequency is $f = pn/120 = 50$ cycles. The armature winding is distributed in 60 slots, with four conductors per slot, and its effective resistance and reactance per phase are 0.073 and 0.87 ohm, respectively. The open-circuit characteristic, shown in Fig. 10-12, is plotted in terms of ampere-turns per pole, with the ordinates representing volts per phase, i.e., from line to neutral. The rotor, illustrated in Fig. 10-10, has a winding distributed in 10 slots per pole, and its fundamental mmf, F, is computed by substituting $r = 1$ in Eq. 4-51, together with the appropriate values of q, ϵ, and γ (see Fig. 4-46).

It is required to compute the field excitation necessary to develop rated terminal voltage and rated current when the power factor of the load is (a) 80 per cent, lagging; (b) 100 per cent; (c) zero; and in each case to determine the voltage regulation.

a. *Load Power Factor* = $\cos \varphi = 0.8$. From the given data, the rated terminal voltage per phase is

$$V = \frac{6,600}{\sqrt{3}} = 3,810$$

and the rated current per phase is

$$I = \frac{2,500,000}{3 \times 3,810} = 219 \text{ amp}$$

The ohmic and reactive drops per phase are

$$IR_a = 219 \times 0.073 = 16 \text{ volts}$$
$$IX_a = 219 \times 0.87 = 190 \text{ volts}$$

For a power factor of 80 per cent ($\cos \varphi = 0.8$, $\sin \varphi = 0.6$), the complex expression for V, referred to the current I as axis of reference, is

$$\mathbf{V} = 3,810 (\cos \varphi + j \sin \varphi) = 3,048 + j2,286$$

and the impedance drop is

$$\mathbf{I}(R_a + jX_a) = (I + j0)(R_a + jX_a) = 16 + j190$$

The induced emf is therefore

$$\mathbf{E} = \mathbf{V} + \mathbf{I}(R_a + jX_a) = (3,048 + 16) + j(2,286 + 190)$$
$$= 3,064 + j2,476$$

and
$$E = \sqrt{3,064^2 + 2,476^2} = 3,940 \text{ volts}$$

Referring to the open-circuit characteristic, Fig. 10-12, it is seen that this voltage corresponds to an excitation of 17,500 amp-turns per pole, which when added geometrically to $-A$ gives the field excitation F. To compute A, it is to be noted that the entire winding comprises $60 \times 4 = 240$ conductors, or 120 turns, so that N_p = turns per pole per phase = $120/(3 \times 2) = 20$. Since q = number of slots per pole per phase = $60/(2 \times 3) = 10$ and γ = angle between slots = $360/60 = 6°$,

$$k_{b_1} = \frac{\sin (q\gamma/2)}{q \sin (\gamma/2)} = \frac{\sin 30°}{10 \sin 3°} = 0.955$$

and therefore, by Eq. 4-44,

$$A = \frac{2\sqrt{2}}{\pi} \times 3 \times 0.955 \times 20 \times 219 = 11,300 \text{ amp-turns per pole}$$

From Fig. 10-11, A is in phase with I, so that

$$\mathbf{A} = 11,300 + j0$$

The resultant excitation F_R is 90° ahead of E, and E is ahead of I by an angle α such that

$$\cos \alpha = \frac{3,064}{3,940} = 0.778$$

$$\sin \alpha = \frac{2,476}{3,940} = 0.628$$

Therefore
$$\mathbf{F}_R = F_R e^{j(\alpha+90)} = F_R(-\sin \alpha + j \cos \alpha)$$
$$= 17,500(-0.628 + j0.778)$$
$$= -10,990 + j13,615$$

Hence,
$$\mathbf{F} = \mathbf{F}_R - \mathbf{A} = -22,290 + j13,615$$
$$F = \sqrt{22,290^2 + 13,615^2} = 26,120$$

The open-circuit voltage corresponding to this excitation, determined from Fig. 10-12, is 4,450 volts; hence, the regulation is

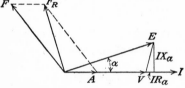

FIG. 10-18. General phasor diagram, unity power factor.

$$\frac{4,450 - 3,810}{3,810} \times 100 = 16.8\%$$

b. *Load Power Factor* $= \cos \varphi = 1.0$. The general phasor diagram, Fig. 10-11, takes the form of Fig. 10-18 when $\varphi = 0$. Taking the current I as the axis of reference,

$$\mathbf{I} = 219 + j0$$
$$\mathbf{V} = 3,810 + j0$$

and
$$\mathbf{E} = \mathbf{V} + \mathbf{I}(R_a + jX_a) = 3,810 + 16 + j190$$
$$= 3,826 + j190$$

whence
$$E = \sqrt{3,826^2 + 190^2} = 3,830$$

This emf leads the current by an angle α such that

$$\cos \alpha = \frac{3,826}{3,830} = 0.9989$$

$$\sin \alpha = \frac{190}{3,830} = 0.0496$$

and corresponding to E is the resultant excitation $F_R = 16,500$ amp-turns per pole, from Fig. 10-12. Since F_R leads E by 90°, it leads the current by $90 + \alpha$; hence,

$$\mathbf{F}_R = F_R[\cos(90 + \alpha) + j \sin(90 + \alpha)] = F_R(-\sin \alpha + j \cos \alpha)$$
$$= 16,500(-0.0496 + j0.9989)$$
$$= -818 + j16,482$$

The field excitation is therefore

$$\mathbf{F} = \mathbf{F}_R - \mathbf{A} = -12{,}118 + j16{,}482$$
$$F = \sqrt{12{,}118^2 + 16{,}482^2} = 20{,}457$$

and corresponding thereto is the open-circuit voltage 4,150. The regulation is therefore

$$\frac{4{,}150 - 3{,}810}{3{,}810} \times 100 = 8.9\%$$

c. *Load Power Factor* $= \cos \varphi = 0$. The phasor diagram for this case, Fig. 10-15, as previously discussed, shows that it is sufficiently accurate to write

$$E = V + IX_a = 3{,}810 + 190 = 4{,}000$$

whence the value of F_R from Fig. 10-12 is 18,000 amp-turns per pole, from which

$$F = 18{,}000 + 11{,}300 = 29{,}300 \text{ amp-turns per pole}$$

to which there corresponds the open-circuit voltage of 4,500 volts. The regulation is then

$$\frac{4{,}500 - 3{,}810}{3{,}810} \times 100 = 18.1\%$$

10-10. The EMF Phasor Diagram. Synchronous Impedance. Assuming as before that the alternator has nonsalient poles, and adding the further assumption that the magnetic circuit is unsaturated, it is possible to analyze the performance characteristics in a simpler way than the one described in the preceding sections, but at the expense of accuracy if the assumptions are not in accord with actual facts. As a matter of fact, the procedure about to be described was at one time used to compute the performance of salient-pole machines having more or less saturated magnetic circuits, but it had to be abandoned because of the erratic results, which, in retrospect, might have been expected. The method is included here because it involves the concept of synchronous impedance, useful in other applications.

The assumption of a cylindrical rotor makes it possible to combine the mmfs of stator and rotor by the method of phasor addition; and the assumption of an unsaturated magnetic circuit makes it possible to consider that the individual mmfs set up proportional fluxes, each of which then develops a proportional emf which may be appropriately combined with other emfs to obtain their resultant. In other words, the mmfs may be replaced by the emfs they produce, and it is for this reason that the procedure has been called the emf method.

From Fig. 10-11, it is seen that

$$\mathbf{F}_R = \mathbf{F} + \mathbf{A} \tag{10-1}$$

and

$$\mathbf{E} = \mathbf{V} + \mathbf{I}(R_a + jX_a) \tag{10-2}$$

both of which relations are still valid under the conditions here assumed. It is also true that

$$\mathbf{A} = k\mathbf{I} \tag{10-3}$$

since the armature mmf is in phase with I; and the proportionality constant k is given by

$$k = \frac{2\sqrt{2}}{\pi} m k_{b_1} k_{p_1} N_p$$

Since the magnetic circuit has been assumed to be unsaturated, the open-circuit characteristic is a straight line, which means that the emfs are proportional to the mmfs which produce them; and since any harmonically varying emf lags 90° behind the flux (and the mmf) which produces it, we may write

$$\mathbf{E} = -jc\mathbf{F}_R \tag{10-4}$$

where c is a proportionality constant equal to the slope of the open-circuit characteristic.

Substituting Eqs. 10-3 and 10-4 in 10-1,

$$\frac{\mathbf{E}}{-jc} = \mathbf{F} + k\mathbf{I}$$

and replacing $\mathbf{E}$ by its value from Eq. 10-2, and transposing,

$$-jc\mathbf{F} = \mathbf{V} + \mathbf{I}[R_a + j(X_a + ck)] \tag{10-5}$$

But in accordance with the reasoning upon which Eq. 10-4 depends, the term $-jc\mathbf{F}$ in Eq. 10-5 is the emf due to F acting alone, which means that it is the open-circuit voltage, represented by E' in Fig. 10-19; hence,

$$\mathbf{E}' = \mathbf{V} + \mathbf{I}[R_a + j(X_a + ck)] \tag{10-6}$$

The significant feature of Eq. 10-6 is that the equivalent impedance of the machine is $R_a + j(X_a + ck)$; in other words, the leakage reactance X_a has been increased by the amount ck. This term, ck, arises from the armature reaction A, which, in accordance with this particular theory, must be thought of as itself producing a flux and an emf; this emf, by analogy with Eq. 10-4, is

$$-jc\mathbf{A} = -jck\mathbf{I}$$

Hence, the total emf must include an equal and opposite component, $+jck\mathbf{I}$, to balance it, thereby accounting for the term ck in Eq. 10-6. The latter may be written

$$\mathbf{E}' = \mathbf{V} + \mathbf{I}[R_a + j(X_a + X_A)] \tag{10-7}$$

where
$$X_A = ck \tag{10-8}$$

is a fictitious reactance equivalent in its effect to the armature reaction.

The total equivalent reactance $X_a + X_A$ may be expressed as

$$X_s = X_a + X_A \qquad (10\text{-}9)$$

where X_s is called the *synchronous reactance* and the equivalent imped-ance, $R_a + jX_s = Z_s$, is called the *synchronous impedance*.

It will be observed that the phase relations between the voltages and currents in Fig. 10-19 are of the same nature as those of the correspond-ing quantities in Fig. 1-15 which determine the regulation of a trans-former. In Fig. 10-19, E' is the emf developed by the field excitation under open-circuit conditions; it corresponds to the voltage impressed upon the primary of a transformer, and is supposed to remain constant under any load, provided F is not changed. As a matter of fact, E' has no real existence under load conditions, for the effect of armature reac-tion is to change the actual excitation from F to F_R, and the latter alone sets up a flux and an equivalent emf.

The impedance triangle of Fig. 10-19 corresponds to the combined impedance triangles of primary and secondary in Fig. 1-15, which sug-gests that X_s may be obtained from a short-circuit test just as is done in

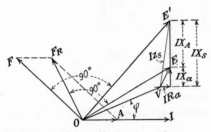

FIG. 10-19. Phasor diagram, synchronous-impedance method.

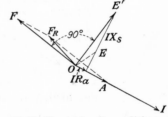

FIG. 10-20. Short-circuit conditions, syn-chronous-impedance method.

the case of the transformer. The phasor diagram corresponding to short-circuit conditions is shown in Fig. 10-20, which is derived from Fig. 10-19 by imposing the condition $V = 0$. The original assumptions then lead to the conclusion that the entire emf induced in the winding is consumed by the internal synchronous impedance. Since R_a is small in comparison with X_a and still smaller in comparison with X_s, it is sufficiently accurate to say that the entire emf induced by the field excitation F is consumed by the synchronous reactance.

The test procedure for measuring Z_s and X_s, as indicated by this the-ory, calls for the determination of the short-circuit and the open-circuit characteristics, as in Fig. 10-21 (which is the same as Fig. 10-12 except for a change of scale). The open-circuit characteristic, contrary to the assumption of no saturation, shows the curvature ordinarily encountered. If now the voltage ordinate corresponding to any value of field excitation is divided by the short-circuit current for the same excitation, the quotient should be the synchronous impedance (or reactance); repeating this process for several values of F, the curve of synchronous impedance shown in Fig. 10-21 will be obtained.

If both the open-circuit and short-circuit characteristics were straight lines, the quotient

$$Z_s = \sqrt{R_a^2 + X_s^2} = \frac{E(\text{open circuit})}{I(\text{short circuit})}$$

would be constant. Actually, it is variable, decreasing with increasing excitation. This is due to the fact that the working range of the open-circuit characteristic includes a partially saturated condition, while the whole range of the short-circuit characteristic, even up to currents two or more times the full-load value, corresponds to an unsaturated condition; for under short-circuit conditions the armature mmf A is nearly equal and opposite to F, leaving only the small residual excitation F_R.

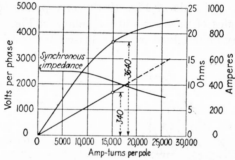

Fig. 10-21. Variation of synchronous impedance.

It appears, therefore, that unless the machine is designed for low flux densities at the largest excitation within the working range, the characteristic curves of Fig. 10-21 cannot be obtained under identical conditions, so that the synchronous impedance calculated from them will be too large. The result is that the computed regulation is poorer than it is in reality, thus giving rise to the designation *pessimistic method* as a synonym for the emf or synchronous-impedance method.

Since the synchronous impedance changes with varying excitation when saturation is present, and only one value can be used in making the calculations, it is logical to select a value corresponding as nearly as possible to the average excitation under load conditions. This means the selection of that value of synchronous impedance which is determined by the largest short-circuit current that can be observed without serious overheating of the armature winding; hence, from the curve of Fig. 10-21,

$$Z_s = \frac{3,640}{340} = 10.7 = \sqrt{0.073^2 + X_s^2}$$

from which $X_s = 10.7$

To find the regulation at full-load current and 80 per cent power factor (lagging), using the current I of Fig. 10-19 as the axis of reference, we have

$$\mathbf{V} = V(\cos \varphi + j \sin \varphi) = 3,810(0.8 + j0.6)$$

and
$$\mathbf{E}' = \mathbf{V} + \mathbf{I}(0.073 + j10.7)$$
$$= 3,810(0.8 + j0.6) + 219(0.073 + j10.7)$$
$$= 3,064 + j4,629$$
$$E' = \sqrt{3,064^2 + 4,629^2} = 5,640$$
$$\text{Regulation} = \frac{5,640 - 3,810}{3,810} \times 100 = 48\%$$

which is very different from the result found in Art. 10-9 for the same load.

10-11. Load Characteristics, EMF Method. In the case of a purely inductive load (cos $\varphi = 0$), the diagram of Fig. 10-19 takes the form shown in Fig. 10-22; and since IR_a is negligible in comparison with IX_s,

$$V \cong E' - IX_s$$

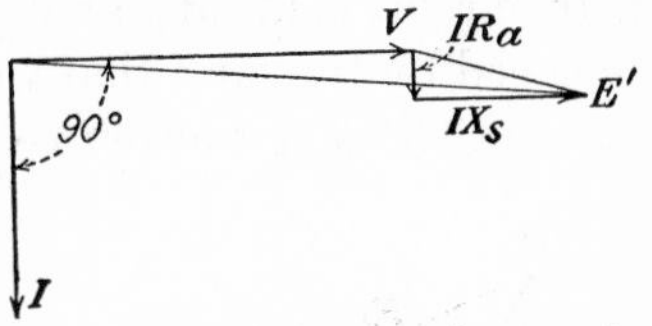

The emf method therefore leads to the conclusion that the zero-power-factor characteristic may be obtained from the open-circuit characteristic by the construction

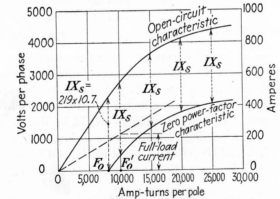

Fig. 10-22. Diagram for purely inductive load, emf method.

shown in Fig. 10-23, i.e., by shifting the no-load characteristic vertically downward by an amount equal to IX_s on the voltage scale. The difference between this construction and the diagonal shift in Fig. 10-16 shows

Fig. 10-23. Construction of zero-power-factor characteristic, emf method.

clearly why the emf method leads to pessimistic conclusions as to the regulation when the no-load characteristic is curved because of saturation.

An obvious inconsistency, caused by the variable nature of the synchronous impedance, is brought to light on considering the location of the point F_0. For X_s was found from Fig. 10-21 by using the largest available value of F, thereby making IX_s smaller than if a lower excitation had been chosen, and this brings F_0 closer to the origin O than would otherwise be the case. In accordance with this theory, the ordinate at F_0 should be the open-circuit voltage induced by the same excitation which on short circuit produces full-load current; but it is plain from the short-circuit characteristic of Fig. 10-21, reproduced as a dashed line in Fig. 10-23, that full-load current on short circuit corresponds to excitation F_0'. Thus, the selection of a small value of X_s for the purpose of obtaining greater accuracy at normal field excitation introduces additional error when the excitation is moderate.

10-12. The MMF Method.   The emf method is based upon the idea that each mmf acting upon the unsaturated magnetic circuit can be replaced by the emf it would produce if it acted separately. The converse of this proposition, likewise subject to the condition that the magnetic circuit is unsaturated, leads to the conclusion that each emf can be replaced by the mmf that would produce it, and this idea is therefore the basis of the *magnetomotive-force*, or *mmf, method* for determining regulation and the load characteristics.

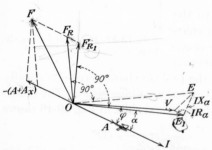

The phasor diagram of Fig. 10-24 shows the same fundamental relations embodied in Fig. 10-11, namely, that

$$\mathbf{F}_R = \mathbf{F} + \mathbf{A} \qquad (10\text{-}10)$$
$$\mathbf{E} = \mathbf{V} + \mathbf{I}(R_a + jX_a) \qquad (10\text{-}11)$$

and also that $\mathbf{E}$ is 90° behind $\mathbf{F}_R$, this fact being expressed by

$$\mathbf{E} = -jc\mathbf{F}_R \qquad (10\text{-}12)$$

FIG. 10-24. Phasor diagram, mmf method.

If a search coil of fine wire were placed in the same slots occupied by the conductors of one of the phase windings, a voltmeter connected to its terminals would read the actual voltage induced in the winding (corrected, if necessary, by applying a factor equal to the ratio of turns of the two windings). This actual voltage would be due to all the flux linked with the main winding, including the leakage flux as well as the main flux, and it would therefore be equal to the emf indicated by E_1 in Fig. 10-24. But E_1 is seen to be the resultant of V and IR_a, so that

$$\mathbf{E}_1 = \mathbf{V} + \mathbf{I}R_a \qquad (10\text{-}13)$$
and
$$\mathbf{E} = \mathbf{E}_1 + j\mathbf{I}X_a \qquad (10\text{-}14)$$

The evidence presented by the reading of the voltmeter connected to the search coil is proof of the fact that the emf E_1 has a real existence, and that E and IX_a must be regarded as fictitious components, useful for purposes of analysis, but without independent existence as separate entities. The actually induced emf E_1, in terms of the mmf theory, must then be considered to be produced by a resultant mmf F_{R_1}, leading E_1 by 90°, so that by analogy with Eq. 10-12 we may write

$$\mathbf{E}_1 = -jc\mathbf{F}_{R_1} \qquad (10\text{-}15)$$

The reactance voltage IX_a, itself fictitious, may in the same way be considered to be produced by a fictitious mmf A_x, such that

$$-j\mathbf{I}X_a = -jc\mathbf{A}_x \qquad (10\text{-}16)$$

Substituting Eqs. 10-12, 10-15, and 10-16 in Eq. 10-14, we have

$$-jc\mathbf{F}_R = -jc\mathbf{F}_{R_1} + jc\mathbf{A}_x$$

whence
$$\mathbf{F}_R = \mathbf{F}_{R_1} - \mathbf{A}_x \qquad (10\text{-}17)$$

and from Eq. 10-10

$$\mathbf{F} = \mathbf{F}_{R_1} - (\mathbf{A} + \mathbf{A}_x) \qquad (10\text{-}18)$$

The form of Eq. 10-18 indicates that the effective armature reaction A has been increased by the amount A_x, this increase taking into account the effect of the leakage reactance of the armature winding. In other

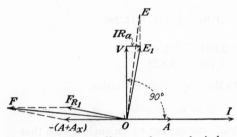

FIG. 10-25. Phasor diagram for purely inductive load, mmf method.

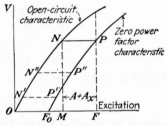

FIG. 10-26. Determination of armature-demagnetizing ampere-turns, mmf method.

words, whereas the emf method replaced armature reaction by an equivalent reactance, the mmf method replaces the armature reactance by an equivalent reaction.

For the case of a purely reactive load ($\cos \varphi = 0$), the diagram, Fig. 10-24, takes the form of Fig. 10-25. The terminal voltage V is practically equal to E_1, and the latter is due to the net excitation F_{R_1}, which is in turn nearly equal to the numerical difference between F and $A + A_x$. These facts indicate that the zero-power-factor characteristic can be found by the construction shown in Fig. 10-26, where OF represents any value of field excitation and $MF = A + A_x$ is the constant demagnetizing mmf of the armature. The difference between OF and MF, that is, OM, is the net excitation F_{R_1}, and this induces the emf $MN = E_1 = V$; therefore, by projecting point N upon the ordinate at F, there is located a point P on the zero-power-factor characteristic. A like construction for other values of F shows that the process is equivalent to shifting the no-load characteristic horizontally to the right by the constant amount $MF = OF_0 = A + A_x$.

The construction indicated in Fig. 10-26 assumes that $A + A_x$ is known. If it is not known, one way of finding it for a given machine is to obtain by test the open-circuit and zero-power-factor characteristics, plotting them as in Fig. 10-26, and measuring the horizontal displacement between two points such as N and P, where MN is the normal voltage of the machine. Another method for finding $A + A_x$ makes use of the open-circuit and short-circuit characteristics of Fig. 10-23; for it will be seen from Fig. 10-25 that if V is made equal to zero, as at short circuit, F_{R_1} and E_1 likewise become substantially zero, and $A + A_x$ then equals F; practically, this means that $A + A_x$ is the excitation required to circulate full-load current when the machine is short-circuited. Figure 10-23 shows that on this basis $A + A_x = 10,000$ amp-turns per pole.

Example. Let it be required to find the regulation of the machine described in Art. 10-9 at full kva load and at 80 per cent power factor, lagging.

Referring all quantities to an axis of reference coinciding with current I, we have from Fig. 10-24 that

$$\mathbf{V} = 3,810(0.8 + j0.6) = 3,048 + j2,286$$
$$IR_a = 16 + j0$$
$$\mathbf{E}_1 = \mathbf{V} + IR_a = 3,064 + j2,286$$
$$E_1 = \sqrt{3,064^2 + 2,286^2} = 3,822$$

From Fig. 10-13, there corresponds to this voltage an excitation

$$F_{R_1} = 16,500 \text{ amp-turns per pole}$$

which is 90° ahead of E_1; the latter leads the current by an angle α such that

$$\cos \alpha = \frac{3,064}{3,822} = 0.802$$

$$\sin \alpha = \frac{2,286}{3,822} = 0.598$$

whence $\mathbf{F}_{R_1} = F_{R_1}[\cos(90 + \alpha) + j\sin(90 + \alpha)] = F_{R_1}(-\sin \alpha + j\cos \alpha)$
$$= 16,500(-0.598 + j0.802)$$
$$= -9,867 + j13,233$$

The equivalent armature reaction $A + A_x = 10,000$ is in phase with the current I; hence,

$$\mathbf{F} = \mathbf{F}_{R_1} - (\mathbf{A} + \mathbf{A}_x) = -19,867 + j13,233$$
$$F = \sqrt{19,867^2 + 13,233^2} = 23,870$$

to which there corresponds an open-circuit voltage of 4,330 volts. The regulation is therefore

$$\frac{4,330 - 3,810}{3,810} \times 100 = 13.7$$

which, when compared with the computed regulation of 16.8 per cent by the general method (Art. 10-9), and 48 per cent by the emf method (Art. 10-10), explains why the mmf method, as here developed, came to be called the *optimistic method*.

10-13. Comparison of the General, the EMF, and the MMF Methods. The three methods for constructing the zero-power-factor characteristic, based upon the theories that have been discussed in the preceding articles, are all indicated in Fig. 10-27, which shows clearly why the emf method leads to pessimistic, and the mmf method to optimistic, results. Both methods were initially based upon the assumption of an unsaturated magnetic circuit; therefore, neither can be expected to give reliable results when saturation is present even to a moderate degree. If the open-circuit characteristic were a straight line, as in Fig. 10-28, all three methods would obviously give the same results.

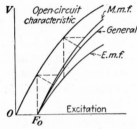

FIG. 10-27. Comparison of constructions for zero-power-factor characteristics.

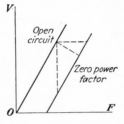

FIG. 10-28. Construction of zero-power-factor characteristics, unsaturated magnetic circuit.

10-14. The ASA Modification of the MMF Method. The preceding discussion of the original emf and mmf methods for computing voltage regulation and load characteristics serves to make it abundantly clear that neither of the two methods, in the forms in which they were originally developed, is capable of giving reliable results. Their shortcomings stem largely from the unrealistic assumption of an unsaturated magnetic circuit; and when they were applied, as was regularly done, to salient-pole machines before the cylindrical-rotor type was developed, the erratic nature of their predictions was still further emphasized. One feature that may be mentioned at this point is that in a salient-pole machine it is not correct to combine the actual field ampere-turns of the exciting winding which are concentrated on a pole core with the ampere-turns of the distributed armature winding; it will be shown later (Art. 10-15) that the armature mmf of a salient-pole machine must be taken to be

$$A = 0.75 m k_{b_1} k_{p_1} N_p I$$

the coefficient 0.75 taking the place of $2\sqrt{2}/\pi = 0.9$ in Eq. 4-44. Furthermore, even when this correction is applied, the field and armature mmfs act upon magnetic circuits which in general do not have the equal reluctances encountered in the cylindrical-rotor machine, without which equality the phasor combination of field and armature mmfs is not fully justified.

Notwithstanding their inherent shortcomings, the simplicity of the constructions to which they lead have a strong appeal, and this is largely the reason for the adoption by the ASA of a modified form of the mmf method for the calculation of voltage regulation.

Referring to the mmf diagram (Fig. 10-24), it will be seen that the field excitation F is the phasor sum of F_{R_1} and $-(A + A_x)$; these relations are reproduced in Fig. 10-29, where it is also shown that the angle between $-(A + A_x)$ and a perpendicular to F_{R_1} (which in Fig. 10-24 is equal to α) may be taken to be equal to φ, where $\cos \varphi$ is the power factor of the load; this approximation is justified because the ohmic drop IR_a is very small.   But the field excitation OF thus determined by Fig.

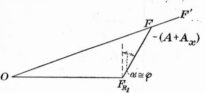

10-29 is based upon the assumption of an unsaturated magnetic circuit, and it must therefore be increased by an amount FF' if the additional excitation required by the partially saturated magnetic circuit is to be taken into account.

FIG. 10-29. Determination of field excitation, ASA method.

Before proceeding to the determination of this additional excitation FF', consider Fig. 10-30a, which shows the no-load (saturation) characteristic and the zero-power-factor characteristic.   The former may be computed from the design data of the machine, or it may be determined experimentally.   Only two points on the zero-power-factor characteristic need be known: one of them, F_0, is found by measuring the field excitation required to circulate full-load current when the armature is short-circuited, thus fixing the value of $A + A_x$; the other, point P, is found by loading the alternator with an underexcited synchronous motor of sufficient capacity to draw full-load current at a low power factor, and at normal voltage.   It is then possible to construct the Potier triangle as described in Art. 10-8, thereby fixing the magnitude of the armature reactance drop IX_a.   At the same time, the value of F_{R_1} corresponding to normal voltage is equal to the abscissa of point Q, Fig. 10-30a, where a horizontal line drawn at normal voltage intercepts the airgap characteristic.

In Fig. 10-30b, the open-circuit characteristic is reproduced, and on the same diagram the rated terminal voltage OV is drawn at angle φ above the horizontal (which represents the armature current as reference axis); added geometrically to V are IR_a and IX_a, the latter obtained from the Potier triangle, thus giving the magnitude of the induced emf E, which is then transferred to the vertical axis by striking the arc EE_i;

through the point E_i draw the horizontal line intersecting both the air-gap characteristic and the open-circuit characteristic. The distance between the two points of intersection, in terms of the scale of field excitation, is then the additional excitation FF' (see Fig. 10-29) required to compensate for the partial saturation of the machine, and therefore gives the total excitation, OF', needed to yield rated terminal voltage. When OF' (from Fig. 10-29) is laid off in Fig. 10-30b as an abscissa of the open-circuit characteristic, it fixes the open-circuit voltage of the machine when the load is reduced to zero; and this in turn determines the regulation for rated kva load at the power factor, cos φ, used in the construction of the diagrams.

This method, now official in the United States, gives results which are reliable for both salient- and nonsalient-pole machines.

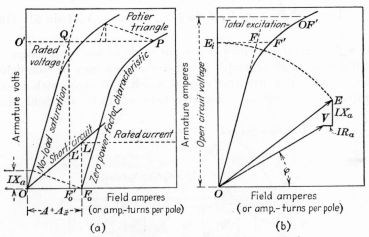

FIG. 10-30. ASA diagram for determining regulation.

10-15. The Blondel Two-reaction Method for Salient-pole Machines.
In all of the preceding discussion of the effects of armature reaction, emphasis has been placed upon the obvious fact that the mmfs of armature and exciting windings can be combined phasorially only when they act upon the same magnetic circuit. This condition is substantially met in the case of alternators having nonsalient poles, but it is by no means fulfilled in machines of the salient-pole type. It is therefore not surprising that the application of the original emf and mmf methods to salient-pole generators gave discordant and erratic results.

The first satisfactory analysis of the disturbing effects caused by salient-pole construction was the work of André Blondel;[*] the method he devised is called the *two-reaction* method because it takes into account

* *Trans. Intern. Elec. Congr.*, St. Louis, **1**:635 (1904). See also *L'Industrie élec.*, **8**:481, 529 (1899).

the fact that the armature mmf contains in general a quadrature (cross-magnetizing) and a direct (demagnetizing or magnetizing) component which produce effects of different kinds. Thus, referring to Fig. 4-39 (page 204) and to Eq. 4-44, it will be noted that of the total armature mmf

$$A = \frac{2\sqrt{2}}{\pi} mk_{b_1}k_{p_1}N_pI$$

the component

$$A_q = \frac{2\sqrt{2}}{\pi} mk_{b_1}k_{p_1}N_p(I \cos \psi) = 0.9mk_{b_1}k_{p_1}N_p(I \cos \psi) \quad (10\text{-}19)$$

exerts a true cross-magnetizing effect; and the component

$$A_d = \frac{2\sqrt{2}}{\pi} mk_{b_1}k_{p_1}N_p(I \sin \psi) = 0.9mk_{b_1}k_{p_1}N_p(I \sin \psi) \quad (10\text{-}20)$$

exerts a demagnetizing effect if ψ is an angle of lag, or a magnetizing effect if ψ is an angle of lead. The factor $I \cos \psi$ may be considered to be the component of armature current which is in phase with a voltage generated by the original undistorted field set up by the field winding

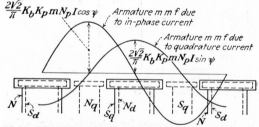

FIG. 10-31. Fictitious field poles equivalent to armature mmf.

alone; and $I \sin \psi$ is similarly the component of armature current in quadrature with the same emf. In other words, ψ is the angle between the center line of a phase coil when it is carrying maximum current and a line midway between the poles. Both of these components of armature reaction rotate at synchronous speed with respect to the armature winding, and each of them may be looked upon as due to a fictitious set of poles; the set producing the direct (demagnetizing or magnetizing) effect is marked N_d, S_d in Fig. 10-31, and is necessarily in alignment with the main poles; the other set, producing the cross-magnetizing effect, is marked N_q, S_q and lies midway between the main poles.

It is at once apparent that the two sinusoidally distributed mmfs of which the maximum values are given by Eqs. 10-19 and 10-20 act on magnetic circuits which have radically different reluctances. The magnetic circuit associated with A_d is the same as the main magnetic circuit of the machine, while that associated with A_q is made up in large part of the air space between the main poles. Their magnetizing effects being entirely different, it is quite clear why their resultant does not have a relation to the mmf of the field winding that is sufficiently real to justify on theoretical grounds the geometrical combination of F and A.

The direct component of armature reaction being equivalent to that of the fictitious poles N_d, S_d which are in alignment with the main poles and move with them, the net mmf acting on the main magnetic circuit is the same as though the excitation of the main poles were changed by an amount equal to the excitation of these fictitious poles, i.e., weakened if the phase angle ψ is one of lag, strengthened if it is an angle of lead. Looked at in another way, the excitation of the main poles, when acting alone, may be supposed to produce an emf E_f (Fig. 10-32); this excita-

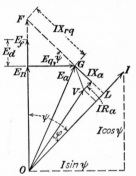

tion is then so reduced (if the current lags) that the net excitation produces the emf E_n, the difference, $E_d = E_f - E_n$, being attributable to the direct component of armature mmf.

The transverse component of armature mmf may be replaced by the equivalent effect of the fictitious poles N_q, S_q, which will generate in the armature winding an emf E_q (Fig. 10-32), which is in quadrature with, and lagging behind, the emf E_f due to the main field; the quadrature relation between E_q and E_f is easily seen from Fig. 10-31, since the poles N_q, S_q are halfway be-

Fig. 10-32. Phasor diagram, salient-pole alternator, Blondel two-reaction method.

tween the main poles. The resultant emf generated in the armature winding is then E_a, the phasor sum of E_n and E_q, and the terminal voltage V is found in the usual manner by subtracting geometrically from E_a the drops due to the ohmic resistance and the leakage reactance of the armature winding. Figure 10-32 is therefore the phasor diagram of the alternator based on the original two-reaction theory.

The question now arises how to determine the actual magnitudes of the emfs E_f, E_d, and E_q, taking into account the fact that E_f is an emf of fundamental frequency produced by a concentrated winding of, say, M amp-turns per pole applied to the salient poles, while A_d and A_q, given by Eqs. 10-19 and 10-20, represent sinusoidally distributed mmfs set up by the currents spread over the armature periphery. It is clearly inadmissible to subtract A_d directly from M for the purpose of computing the net excitation acting on the main magnetic circuit under load conditions, because of the wholly different space distributions of the two mmfs; similarly, A_q acts upon a magnetic circuit that is physically quite unlike the main magnetic circuit. A method for reconciling these differences has been given by J. A. Schouten,* which, while not as rigorous

* Über den Spannungsabfall mehrphasiger synchroner Maschinen, *Elektrotech. Z.,* **31**:877 (1910).

as some later studies, is a fairly close approximation and is outlined in the following paragraphs.

Curve B in Fig. 10-33 represents the no-load distribution of field intensity in the airgap produced by the concentrated excitation of the field poles. It is assumed that when the excitation is increased to meet the requirements of increasing load, the curve retains its original form, in other words, changes in saturation are ignored. Consequently if the excitation is M amp-turns per pole, the airgap field intensity due to it may be expressed as $cMf(\alpha)$, where $f(\alpha)$ is a Fourier series made up of sine terms because of the symmetry of curve B about its middle point; as a matter of fact, ordinates of curve B may be looked upon as proportional to the permeances of the corresponding tubes of induction due to an excitation whose axis coincides with the pole axis, and the curve may be constructed by mapping the lines of force. At the point where $\alpha = \pi/2$, $f(\alpha) = 1$. From this point of view, the ordinates of the sinusoidal curve A_d in Fig. 10-33 may then be multiplied by $cf(\alpha)$ to obtain the flux distribution (curve A) that would be produced by the direct component of armature mmf if it were acting alone. The net airgap induction then becomes

$$B_g = c[Mf(\alpha) - A \sin \psi f(\alpha) \sin \alpha] \quad (10\text{-}21)$$

where $A = 0.9mk_{b_1}k_{p_1}N_pI$.

The distribution represented by Eq. 10-21 may now be resolved into a fundamental and higher odd harmonics, the amplitude of the fundamental being

$$B_{g_1} = \frac{2}{\pi} \int_0^\pi B_g \sin \alpha \, d\alpha$$

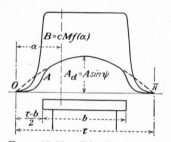

FIG. 10-33. Distribution of effective part of direct armature mmf.

and the average value of the fundamental over a pole pitch is $(2/\pi)B_{g_1}$. If the length of the armature core parallel to the shaft (corrected for fringing) is l, the fundamental flux per pole is

$$\Phi_{d_1} = \frac{2}{\pi} B_{g_1}l\tau = \frac{4cl\tau}{\pi^2} \int_0^\pi [Mf(\alpha) \sin \alpha - A \sin \psi f(\alpha) \sin^2 \alpha] \, d\alpha$$

$$= \frac{4cl\tau}{\pi^2} \left[M - A \sin \psi \frac{\int_0^\pi f(\alpha) \sin^2 \alpha \, d\alpha}{\int_0^\pi f(\alpha) \sin \alpha \, d\alpha} \right] \int_0^\pi f(\alpha) \sin \alpha \, d\alpha \quad (10\text{-}22)$$

Writing

$$\alpha_M = \int_0^\pi f(\alpha) \sin \alpha \, d\alpha$$

$$\alpha_A = \int_0^\pi f(\alpha) \sin^2 \alpha \, d\alpha$$

it will be seen from Eq. 10-22 that so far as the fundamental is concerned, the field mmf M has been decreased by an amount

$$A'_d = \frac{\alpha_A}{\alpha_M} A \sin \psi \text{ amp-turns per pole} \qquad (10\text{-}23)$$

which means that the armature demagnetizing mmf, $A \sin \psi$, actually distributed over a full pole pitch, must be multiplied by the factor α_A/α_M to convert it into an equivalent mmf concentrated upon the field poles. For the special case in which curve B is a sine curve, the factor becomes

$$\frac{\alpha_A}{\alpha_M} = \frac{\displaystyle\int_0^\pi \sin^3 \alpha \, d\alpha}{\displaystyle\int_0^\pi \sin^2 \alpha \, d\alpha} = 0.85$$

which means that 85 per cent of the armature mmf, $A \sin \psi$, must be deducted* from the field excitation M in order to find from the no-load characteristic (Fig. 10-21) the resultant value of emf E_n (Fig. 10-32). This refers to the fundamental only, for it is ordinarily not necessary to consider the effect of higher harmonics, which are generally too small to affect the result appreciably. In case it is desired to include some of the higher harmonics, it follows from Eq. 10-21 that the amplitude of the rth harmonic of airgap intensity is

$$B_{g_r} = \frac{2}{\pi} \int_0^\pi B_g \sin r\alpha \, d\alpha$$

and its average value over a span equal to τ/r is $(2/\pi)B_{g_r}$. The flux Φ_{d_r} which then develops the harmonic emf E_r is

$$\Phi_{d_r} = \frac{2}{\pi} B_{g_r} \frac{l\tau}{r} = \frac{4cl\tau}{\pi^2 r} \int_0^\pi [Mf(\alpha) \sin r\alpha - A \sin \psi f(\alpha) \sin \alpha \sin r\alpha] \, d\alpha$$

$$= \frac{4cl\tau}{\pi^2} \frac{1}{r} \left[M - A \sin \psi \frac{\displaystyle\int_0^\pi f(\alpha) \sin \alpha \sin r\alpha \, d\alpha}{\displaystyle\int_0^\pi f(\alpha) \sin r\alpha \, d\alpha} \right] \int_0^\pi f(\alpha) \sin r\alpha \, d\alpha$$

$$(10\text{-}24)$$

This shows that the armature mmf must now be multiplied by the factor α_{Ar}/α_{Mr} before deducting it from M. Furthermore, the voltage corresponding to this modified value of M, as picked from the no-load characteristic, must be multiplied by the ratio

$$\frac{\displaystyle\int_0^\pi f(\alpha) \sin r\alpha \, d\alpha}{\displaystyle\int_0^\pi f(\alpha) \sin \alpha \, d\alpha}$$

* This reduction of $A \sin \psi$ to 85 per cent of its normal value changes the coefficient $2\sqrt{2}/\pi$ from 0.9 to $0.9 \times 0.85 = 0.765$, and the latter figure is rounded off to 0.75, as was pointed out in Art. 10-14.

and also by the ratio $\dfrac{k_{b_r}k_{p_r}}{k_{b_1}k_{p_1}}\,r$.   The final value of E_n thus computed will be

$$E_n = \sqrt{E_{n_1}^2 + E_{n_3}^2 + E_{n_5}^2 + \cdots}$$

which is the effective value of the equivalent sine wave of fundamental frequency.   In three-phase machines, the third harmonic will cancel out in the line voltage, but it may be present in the phase voltage (line to neutral).   If there is a 5th harmonic amounting to 13 per cent of the fundamental, and a 7th harmonic of 5 per cent, the error due to neglecting them will be only 0.97 per cent; hence, the fundamental is usually sufficient for practical purposes.

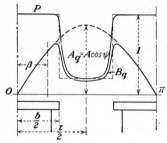

FIG. 10-34. Distribution of effective part of transverse armature mmf.

By mapping the lines of force* that would be produced by an excitation whose axis lies midway between the poles, a permeance distribution curve such as P, Fig. 10-34, may be constructed.   It may be represented as a function of β, say, $P(\beta)$, where β is measured from the center line of a pole, and where $P(\beta) = 1$ when β is zero and π.

Now the cross-magnetizing effect of the armature is represented by the sine curve of amplitude $A_q = A \cos \psi$, and at any point β the ordinate is $A \cos \psi \sin \beta$.   The corresponding field intensity is then

$$b_q = cA \cos \psi \, P(\beta) \sin \beta \tag{10-25}$$

represented by the curve B_q in Fig. 10-34.   This saddle-shaped curve can now be resolved into a fundamental and harmonics, the amplitude of the fundamental being

$$B_{q_1} = \frac{2}{\pi} \int_0^\pi B_q \sin \beta \, d\beta$$

The average value of the field intensity of the fundamental over a pole pitch is $(2/\pi)B_q$, and the fundamental flux, per pole pitch, due to the cross ampere-turns, then is

$$\Phi_{q_1} = \frac{4cl\tau}{\pi^2} A \cos \psi \int_0^\pi P(\beta) \sin^2 \beta \, d\beta \tag{10-26}$$

Since the fundamental emf due to an excitation M on the main poles is proportional to $(4cl\tau/\pi^2)M\alpha_M$, it follows that in order to read off E_{q_1} from the no-load characteristic the cross-magnetizing ampere-turns $A \cos \psi$

---

* R. W. Wieseman, Graphical Determination of Magnetic Fields; Practical Applications to Salient-pole Synchronous Machine Design, *Trans. AIEE*, **46**:141 (1927).

must be multiplied by the factor

$$\frac{\int_0^\pi P(\beta) \sin^2 \beta \, d\beta}{\alpha_M} = \frac{\int_0^\pi P(\beta) \sin^2 \beta \, d\beta}{\int_0^\pi f(\alpha) \sin \alpha \, d\alpha} \qquad (10\text{-}27)$$

where α and β are obviously complementary angles. Suppose, for example, that the actual curve $P(\beta)$ is replaced by the square-cornered curve shown in dashed lines in Fig. 10-34, such that

$$P(\beta) = 1 \qquad \text{from} \qquad \beta = 0 \qquad \text{to} \qquad \beta = \frac{b}{\tau}\frac{\pi}{2}$$

$$P(\beta) = \frac{1}{5} \qquad \text{from} \qquad \beta = \frac{b}{\tau}\frac{\pi}{2} \qquad \text{to} \qquad \beta = \pi - \frac{b}{\tau}\frac{\pi}{2}$$

$$P(\beta) = 1 \qquad \text{from} \qquad \beta = \pi - \frac{b}{\tau}\frac{\pi}{2} \qquad \text{to} \qquad \beta = \pi$$

and suppose that $f(\alpha) = \sin \alpha$. The factor given by the expression 10-27 then becomes

$$\frac{1}{5}\left(1 + 4\frac{b}{\tau}\right) - \frac{4}{5\pi} \sin \frac{b}{\tau} \pi$$

Consequently, the equivalent excitation for determining the fundamental E_{q_1} becomes

for $b/\tau = 0.6$, $0.439A \cos \psi$
and for $b/\tau = 0.67$, $0.515A \cos \psi$

Reference to Fig. 10-32 will make it quite clear that the value of E_q is an important factor in fixing the value of the angle ψ, upon which in turn the demagnetizing (or magnetizing) and the cross-magnetizing effect of the armature mmf depend. For this reason, it is necessary to fix E_q as accurately as possible, and if calculations or measurements are concerned with the currents and voltages per phase, it may not be sufficient to assume that E_q can be computed from the fundamental (E_{q_1}) alone. Curve B_q of Fig. 10-34 shows clearly that there is present in the cross field a prominent space harmonic of considerable amplitude which will develop a third harmonic emf E_{q_3}. The effective value of the equivalent sine wave which represents E_q will therefore be more nearly equal to $\sqrt{E_{q_1}^2 + E_{q_3}^2}$ than to E_{q_1} alone; so it may become necessary to find E_{q_3} if the latter is appreciable. The amplitude of the third space harmonic of curve B_q is

$$B_{q_3} = \frac{2}{\pi}\int_0^\pi B_q \sin 3\beta \, d\beta = \frac{2}{\pi}\int_0^\pi cA \cos \psi \, P(\beta) \sin \beta \sin 3\beta \, d\beta \qquad (10\text{-}28)$$

and E_{q_3} will be proportional to the product of B_{q_3} and the winding factor $k_{b_3}k_{p_3}$. Remembering that the fundamental voltage due to the excitation M on the main field winding is an emf proportional to the fundamental of curve B in Fig. 10-33, i.e., to

$$\frac{2}{\pi} \int_0^\pi cMf(\alpha) \sin \alpha \, d\alpha = \frac{2}{\pi} cM\alpha_M$$

and also proportional to $k_{b_1}k_{p_1}$, it follows that E_{q_3} can be read from the no-load characteristic by using as excitation

$$\frac{k_{b_3}k_{p_3}}{k_{b_1}k_{p_1}} \frac{\int_0^\pi P(\beta) \sin \beta \sin 3\beta \, d\beta}{\alpha_M} \tag{10-29}$$

If the function $P(\beta)$ is the same as that used in the preceding example, $\alpha_M = \pi/2$ corresponding to $f(\alpha) = \sin \alpha$, and

$$\frac{k_{b_3}k_{p_3}}{k_{b_1}k_{p_1}} = \frac{0.67}{0.96}$$

so that expression 10-29 becomes

for $b/\tau = 0.6$, $\qquad\qquad$ $0.222A \cos \psi$
and for $b/\tau = 0.67$, $\qquad$ $0.230A \cos \psi$

These values are approximately half of the corresponding figures for the fundamental, so that E_{q_3} is about half of E_{q_1} and

$$E_q = \sqrt{E_{q_1}^2 + E_{q_3}^2}$$

is therefore about 12 per cent greater than E_{q_1} subject to the assumed conditions.

10-16. Special Cases of Phasor Diagram, Two-reaction Theory. In order to apply the two-reaction theory to the calculation of the regulation of an alternator at a specified load and power factor, it is necessary to fix a relation between φ, the phase angle of the load circuit, and the angle ψ which enters into the expressions for A_d and A_q. This relation is inherent in the geometry of Fig. 10-32 and in the fact that E_q, and the transverse armature mmf A_q which is responsible for it, together define a point on the lower straight part of the open-circuit characteristic. The emf due to this transverse mmf is proportional to $A \cos \psi$, and may be expressed as a constant times $A \cos \psi$, as in Eq. 10-27; consequently, E_q is itself proportional to $A \cos \psi$, or

$$E_q = X_{rq}(I \cos \psi) = I_q X_{rq} \tag{10-30}$$

where the proportionality constant X_{rq} is obviously of the nature of a reactance, expressible in ohms, and $I_q = I \cos \psi$ is the in-phase (cross-magnetizing) component of current.

It will therefore be seen from Fig. 10-32 that the line LG (extended) makes an angle ψ with E_q; hence, by Eq. 10-30, the intercept GF must be equal to IX_{rq}, which, for a given current, will be constant for all values of the terminal voltage V. The point F thus determined, which lies on the phasor E_f (extended), has been called the Joubertian point. Hence, from Fig. 10-32,

$$\tan \psi = \frac{FL}{OL} = \frac{V \sin \varphi + I(X_a + X_{rq})}{V \cos \varphi + IR_a} \qquad (10\text{-}31)$$

The quantity $X_a + X_{rq}$ in Eq. 10-31 is similar to the term $X_a + ck$ in Eq. 10-5; but whereas the term ck there represented the *entire* arma-

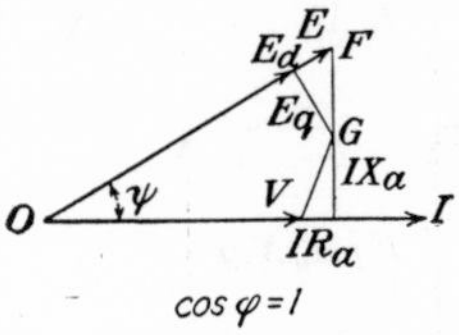

FIG. 10-35

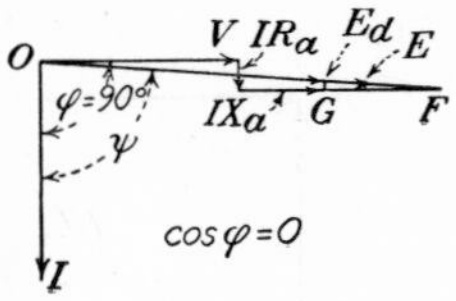

FIG. 10-36

FIGS. 10-35 and 10-36. Two-reaction diagrams for $\cos \varphi = 1$ and $\cos \varphi = 0$.

ture reaction $A = kI$, the corresponding term X_{rq} in Eq. 10-31 derives only from the cross-magnetizing component of armature reaction.

Special cases of the general diagram, Fig. 10-32, are shown in Figs. 10-35 to 10-39. Figures 10-35 and 10-36 show the form of the diagram when the loads are respectively noninductive ($\cos \varphi = 1$) and completely inductive ($\cos \varphi = 0$). Figure 10-37 represents the short-circuit condition, $V = 0$. Figures 10-38 and 10-39 present the case of leading current, the former for a general value of $\cos \varphi$, the latter the special case where $\varphi = 90°$, that is, a completely capacitive load. It will be noted that, for some value of φ between those shown in the last two diagrams, the angle ψ becomes zero; when ψ becomes leading, beyond this zero value, the direct component of armature

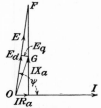

FIG. 10-37. Short-circuit conditions.

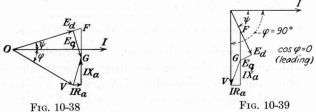

FIG. 10-38

FIG. 10-39

FIGS. 10-38 and 10-39. Two-reaction diagrams for leading current.

mmf changes sign, i.e., becomes magnetizing instead of demagnetizing, and E_f is accordingly less than E_d, instead of greater. The particular value of leading power factor which marks this transition may be found from Eq. 10-31 by imposing the condition $\tan \psi = 0$; this can occur only when the numerator is zero, i.e., when

$$V \sin \varphi = -I(X_a + X_{rq})$$

or when the reactance drop in the load circuit is equal and opposite to the drop in the equivalent internal reactance $X_a + X_{rq}$.

10-17. Modified Phasor Diagram, Two-reaction Theory. Figure 10-40 is a modification of the phase relations shown in Fig. 10-32, but

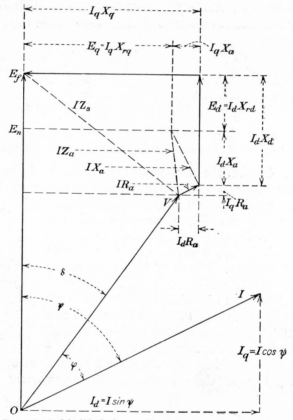

FIG. 10-40. Modified phasor diagram, two-reaction theory.

the two diagrams are basically the same. The principal difference is that Fig. 10-40 shows that the drop of voltage, E_d, caused by the direct component of current, is represented by $I_d X_{rd}$, where X_{rd} is a reactance equivalent to the demagnetizing effect of I_d, just as X_{rq} was a reactance equivalent to the cross-magnetizing effect of I_q.

Inspection of Fig. 10-40 shows that if

$$X_d = X_a + X_{rd}$$

and
$$X_q = X_a + X_{rq} \tag{10-32}$$

the terminal voltage V may be considered to be what is left of the total induced emf E_f after deducting (1) the ohmic drop IR_a, (2) the reactive drop I_dX_d in quadrature with I_d, and (3) the reactive drop I_qX_q in quadrature with I_q. It is also to be seen that the resultant of these three components of the internal drop of voltage is IZ_s, where Z_s is the same synchronous impedance which is the basis of the emf method of computing regulation (see Fig. 10-19). These facts bring out clearly the essential difference between the emf method and the two-reaction method; for whereas the former lumps the entire mmf of the armature as a single equivalent reactance, the latter introduces two reactances, one associated with the direct component of armature mmf, the other with the transverse or quadrature component.

10-18. Relations between Z_s, X_d, and X_q.   Let

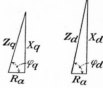

$$Z_d = \sqrt{R_a^2 + X_d^2}$$
$$Z_q = \sqrt{R_a^2 + X_q^2}$$
so that $\qquad R_a = Z_d \cos \varphi_d = Z_q \cos \varphi_q \qquad (10\text{-}33)$
$$X_d = Z_d \sin \varphi_d$$
$$X_q = Z_q \sin \varphi_q$$

FIG. 10-41. Direct and quadrature impedances.

as illustrated in Fig. 10-41.

From the geometry of Fig. 10-40, it is readily seen that

$$V \sin \delta = I_q X_q - I_d R_a \qquad (10\text{-}34)$$
and $\qquad E_f - V \cos \delta = I_d X_d + I_q R_a \qquad (10\text{-}35)$

and since $I_q = I \cos \psi$ and $I_d = I \sin \psi$, the last two equations may be written

$$V \sin \delta = IZ_q \sin (\varphi_q - \psi) \qquad (10\text{-}36)$$
$$E_f - V \cos \delta = IZ_d \cos (\varphi_d - \psi) \qquad (10\text{-}37)$$

But, from Fig. 10-40,

$$(V \sin \delta)^2 + (E_f - V \cos \delta)^2 = (IZ_s)^2 \qquad (10\text{-}38)$$

so that, from Eqs. 10-36 and 10-37,

$$Z_s^2 = Z_d^2 \cos^2 (\varphi_d - \psi) + Z_q^2 \sin^2 (\varphi_q - \psi) \qquad (10\text{-}39)$$

which shows that Z_s is the hypotenuse of a right triangle the sides of which are $Z_d \cos (\varphi_d - \psi)$ and $Z_q \sin (\varphi_q - \psi)$. Moreover, Eq. 10-39 will be recognized as the polar equation of an ellipse referred to its center as origin, the variables being Z_s and ψ.

The construction of point P of this ellipse, based upon the relations in the preceding equations, is shown in Fig. 10-42.

Equation (10-39) can be simplified by using the trigonometric identities

$$\cos^2 x = \frac{1 + \cos 2x}{2}$$

$$\sin^2 x = \frac{1 - \cos 2x}{2}$$

which, when substituted in Eq. 10-39, together with the relations in Eq. 10-33, give

$$Z_s^2 = \frac{Z_d^2 + Z_q^2}{2} + (X_d - X_q)\sqrt{R_a^2 + \left(\frac{X_d + X_q}{2}\right)^2}\,\sin{(2\psi - \alpha)} \quad (10\text{-}40)$$

where α, shown in Fig. 10-42, is defined by the relation

$$\tan \alpha = \frac{\frac{1}{2}(X_d + X_q)}{R_a} \quad (10\text{-}41)$$

It will be seen that the *square* of Z_s is equal to a constant average value $\frac{1}{2}(Z_d^2 + Z_q^2)$ upon which is superposed a variable amount that

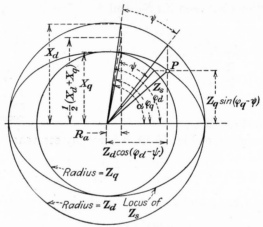

Fig. 10-42. Elliptical variation of synchronous impedance.

changes cyclically as the angle ψ changes with the load.   The maximum and minimum values of Z_s^2 occur when the sine term, $\sin{(2\psi - \alpha)}$, is equal to $+1$ and -1, respectively, so that

$$(Z_s^2)_{\max} = \frac{Z_d^2 + Z_q^2}{2} + (X_d - X_q)\sqrt{R_a^2 + \left(\frac{X_d + X_q}{2}\right)^2} \quad (10\text{-}42)$$

$$(Z_s^2)_{\min} = \frac{Z_d^2 + Z_q^2}{2} - (X_d - X_q)\sqrt{R_a^2 + \left(\frac{X_d + X_q}{2}\right)^2} \quad (10\text{-}43)$$

and if R_a is sufficiently small,

$$(Z_s)_{\max} \cong X_d \quad (10\text{-}44)$$
$$(Z_s)_{\min} \cong X_q \quad (10\text{-}45)$$

It will also be seen that if $X_d = X_q$, which is the condition that obtains in a cylindrical-rotor machine, the value of Z_s as defined by Eq. 10-40 is a constant, or

$$(Z_s^2)_{X_d = X_q} = \frac{Z_d^2 + Z_q^2}{2} \cong \frac{X_d^2 + X_q^2}{2} = X_d^2 = X_q^2 \quad (10\text{-}46)$$

The nature of the variation of Z_s as a function of ψ can be analyzed in another way. For it will be seen from Fig. 10-42 that Z_s, when expressed as a complex quantity, is given by

$$Z_s = Z_d \cos (\varphi_d - \psi) + jZ_q \sin (\varphi_q - \psi) \qquad (10\text{-}47)$$

which, when expanded, and with substitutions from Eq. 10-33, becomes

$$Z_s = \left(R_a + j\frac{X_d + X_q}{2} \right) e^{-j\psi} - j\frac{X_d - X_q}{2} e^{j\psi} \qquad (10\text{-}48)$$

The geometrical interpretation of this equation is shown in Fig. 10-43a. The term $R_a + j\dfrac{X_d + X_q}{2}$ is represented by the line OL when $\psi = 0$, for it has a horizontal component R_a and a vertical component $\frac{1}{2}(X_d + X_q)$; and the term $-j\dfrac{X_d - X_q}{2}$ is a vertical line LP_0, directed downward when $\psi = 0$. Consequently when $\psi = 0$, Z_s is represented by the line $OP_0 = (Z_s)_0$.

When angle ψ is assigned a value such as ψ_1, OL turns clockwise to the position OL_1, and simultaneously LP_0 turns counterclockwise to position L_1P_1, with the result that Z_s becomes $OP_1 = (Z_s)_1$. Similarly, when ψ becomes ψ_2 and ψ_3, Z_s takes the values indicated by OP_2 and OP_3, and the locus of all points such as P_0, P_1, P_2, etc., is the ellipse shown in Fig. 10-42.

So far as the magnitude of Z_s is concerned, it will be seen that the construction of Fig. 10-43a is the same as though the line

$$OL = \sqrt{R_a^2 + \left(\frac{X_d + X_q}{2} \right)^2}$$

were stationary, as in Fig. 10-43b, with the line $LP = \frac{1}{2}(X_d - X_q)$ rotating around point L with an angular movement proportional to 2ψ. The diagram shows clearly that the maximum and minimum values of Z_s have the magnitudes

$$(Z_s)_{\max} = \sqrt{R_a^2 + \left(\frac{X_d + X_q}{2} \right)^2} + \frac{X_d - X_q}{2} \cong X_d \qquad (10\text{-}49)$$

$$(Z_s)_{\min} = \sqrt{R_a^2 + \left(\frac{X_d + X_q}{2} \right)^2} - \frac{X_d - X_q}{2} \cong X_q \qquad (10\text{-}50)$$

and that the average value of Z_s is

$$(Z_s)_{\mathrm{av}} = \sqrt{R_a^2 + \left(\frac{X_d + X_q}{2} \right)^2} \cong \frac{X_d + X_q}{2} \qquad (10\text{-}51)$$

Finally, when the values of Z_s as a function of ψ are plotted in cartesian coordinates, as in Fig. 10-44, there is obtained a curve which, while it

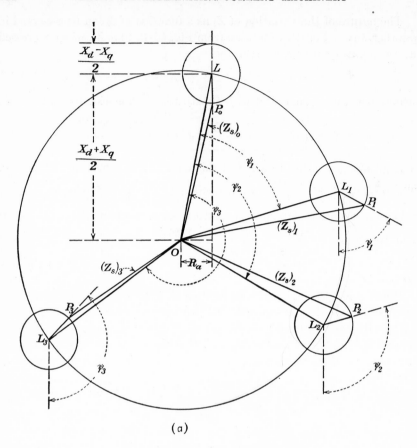

(a)

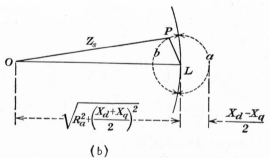

(b)

Fig. 10-43. Variation of synchronous impedance with angular position of rotor.

looks like an ordinary sinusoid, is really a function of the double angle 2ψ. Otherwise expressed, the angular spread of the loops above the mean value (shown as a in Fig. 10-44) is greater than the spread b of the loops below the mean value. The reason for this lack of symmetry is indicated in Fig. 10-43b, where the angles a and b are obviously unequal.

10-19. The Slip Test. The variation of the synchronous impedance Z_s as the angle ψ is changed can be observed experimentally in salient-pole machines by an ingenious method known as the *slip test*.* Assuming the case of a three-phase machine, subnormal voltage (of rated frequency) is impressed upon the armature terminals with the field exciting winding open, while the rotor is driven by an auxiliary d-c motor in the same direction as the synchronously revolving field produced by the armature current, but at a speed slightly different from synchronism. The speed of the rotor may be slightly greater or slightly less than synchronous speed, but in either case the slip should be very small.

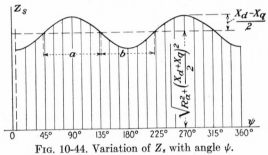

Fig. 10-44. Variation of Z_s with angle ψ.

As the rotor poles slip slowly through the consequent poles produced by the armature current, the two sets of poles will be alternately in line and in space quadrature. When they are in line, the armature mmf acts through the main magnetic circuit, and at that instant the impressed armature voltage, divided by the corresponding armature current, will be equal to X_d, the direct-axis synchronous reactance.† When the two sets of poles are in space quadrature, the ratio of armature volts to armature current will be X_q, the quadrature-axis synchronous reactance.

If the slip is sufficiently small, the pointers of an indicating voltmeter and an ammeter, connected as in Fig. 10-45, will swing slowly from a maximum to a minimum, the voltage being least when the current is greatest, and vice versa; for best results, the slip should be so small that the inertia of the moving parts of the instruments will not introduce errors into the readings. Instead of using indicating instruments, oscil-

* The first description of the slip test occurs in an article by K. H. Haga in *L'Éclairage élec.*, **11**(9) (1909). See also R. H. Park and B. L. Robertson, Synchronous Machines, *Trans. AIEE*, **47**(2):516 (1927).

† Actually, the quotient is Z_d, but R_a is usually small enough to justify the approximation.

lograph records of the armature voltage and current may be taken, as in Fig. 10-45.* This diagram indicates a slip much larger than would be used in practice and is intended to serve as illustrative only; actual oscillograms of this kind are shown in Fig. 11-30.

The voltage induced in the open field winding is the result of the varying flux linked with it as the field poles slip through the revolving armature field.

[This] voltage may reach dangerous values when the slip is increased, or from the switching surge when the a-c lines are opened, and to guard against damage from high voltage a short-circuiting switch (such as a hook-operated disconnect switch) should be connected across the field, and should be closed except when it is known that the slip is low and readings are being taken. All instruments should be disconnected from the field circuit except when it is known that induced voltages are less than the voltage ratings of the instruments.†

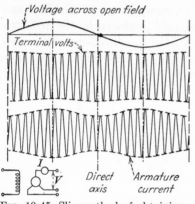

FIG. 10-45. Slip method of obtaining X_d and X_q.

The quadrature-axis synchronous reactance, X_q, equals the minimum ratio of armature voltage and current in Fig. 10-45; the correct ratio occurs when the induced field voltage is a maximum, positive or negative, but it must correspond to the condition that the current is the rated armature current of the machine. Similarly, the direct-axis synchronous reactance, X_d, equals the maximum ratio of armature voltage and current; the correct ratio occurs when the induced field voltage is zero.

Because of uncertainties in the calibration of the oscillograms, the AIEE Standards recommend that they be used to obtain the ratio X_q/X_d rather than to determine the reactances separately. This ratio, when multiplied by the value of X_d from the synchronous impedance test, will then give X_q.

The unsaturated value of the direct-axis impedance, Z_d, is by definition equal to the ratio

$$Z_d \cong X_d = \frac{\text{open-circuit voltage from airgap characteristic}}{\text{corresponding short-circuit current}}$$

or, referring to Fig. 10-30a,

$$X_d = \frac{F'_0 Q}{F'_0 L'} = \frac{V}{F'_0 L'}$$

* This drawing is a reproduction of an illustration in the AIEE Test Code for Synchronous Machines, No. 503, July, 1945.

† From AIEE Test Code for Synchronous Machines, Par. 1.825 (1945).

where V is the rated voltage of the machine.   But it will be seen from Fig. 10-30a that

$$\frac{F_0'L'}{OF_0'} = \frac{F_0L}{OF_0} = \frac{I}{OF_0}$$

where I is the rated current; therefore,

$$X_d = \frac{V}{I}\frac{OF_0}{OF_0'} \qquad (10\text{-}52)$$

In per-unit notation, V and I are the unit values of voltage and current, respectively, so that V/I is the unit impedance (or reactance).   Hence,

$$(X_d)_{\text{per-unit}} = \frac{OF_0}{OF_0'} \qquad (10\text{-}53)$$

The reciprocal of the ratio appearing in Eq. 10-53, i.e., OF_0'/OF_0, is called the *unsaturated short-circuit ratio;* in other words,

Unsaturated short-circuit ratio

$$= \frac{\text{field current for rated open-circuit voltage on airgap characteristic}}{\text{field current for rated armature current on}}$$
$$\text{sustained symmetrical short circuit}$$

The *short-circuit ratio* in general is the ratio of the field current for rated open-circuit voltage (from the no-load characteristic) to the field current for rated armature current on sustained symmetrical short circuit.   In both cases, the measurements must correspond to rated frequency.

10-20. The Armature Leakage Reactance, X_a.   The armature leakage reactance, X_a, which appears in all of the diagrams showing the phase relations between current and voltage, is attributable to the leakage flux associated (*a*) with the embedded part of the armature winding and (*b*) with the end connections.   The *slot leakage reactance* can be computed by the same formulas (Eqs. 7-18 to 7-22 in Art. 7-5) previously derived in connection with induction-motor theory.   The *end-connection* reactance may be estimated* by a formula derived by P. L. Alger,

$$X_{\text{end}} = 0.3(3y - 1)\left(\frac{8\pi^2 m}{10^9}\right)\frac{fDZ^2}{p^2} \qquad (10\text{-}54)$$

where y = winding pitch expressed as a decimal
  D = diameter of the airgap, cm

10-21. The Reaction Reactances, X_{rd} and X_{rq}.   The two-reaction theory brings into consideration, in addition to X_a, the *reaction reactances* X_{rd} and X_{rq}, which together with X_a determine the direct-axis and the quadrature-axis reactances X_d and X_q.   The relations between X_{rd} and

---

* P. L. Alger, The Calculation of the Armature Reactance of Synchronous Machines, *Trans. AIEE*, **47**:493 (1928).

X_{rq} are implicit in Fig. 10-40 but are more clearly shown in Fig. 10-46, where $I_d X_{rd}$ and $I_q X_{rq}$ are represented by the equivalent expressions ΣE_d and ΣE_q, respectively. The summation symbol indicates that each of these reactive components of emf, the former associated with I_d, the latter with I_q, are made up of a series of quadrature voltages induced by the fundamental and higher harmonic components of armature mmf in much the same way as has been described in Art. 7-6 in connection with the differential leakage reactance of induction motors. The derivation of the magnitudes of ΣE_d and ΣE_q by Doherty and Nickel* is here given in condensed form.

Stated as briefly as possible, the theory takes into account that both the in-phase and quadrature components of armature current, I_q and I_d, set up sinusoidal space distributions of mmf which rotate at various speeds with respect to the armature surface, and at still different speeds with respect to the poles; the fundamentals, of course, are stationary with respect to the poles. In accordance with the principles explained at the close of Art. 4-20, any sinusoidal wave rotating with respect to the poles can be resolved into two components which are stationary relative to the poles, and in space and time quadrature with each other. In this way, all the different harmonic distributions of mmf due to the entire armature current can be resolved into a series of stationary but alternating mmfs, and to each of them there will correspond some permeance

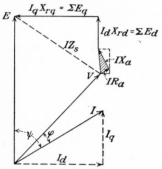

FIG. 10-46. Modified phasor diagram, two-reaction theory.

distribution curve such as is exemplified by P in Fig. 10-34. The product of the ordinates of each stationary mmf by the corresponding ordinates of its appropriate permeance curve will then give the distribution of radial field intensity in the airgap, and these fluxes will in turn generate in the armature winding emfs covering a considerable range of frequencies. Those emfs which are of fundamental frequency are then incorporated in the phasor diagram of the type shown in Fig. 10-46. While some features of this general theory are inherent in the analysis worked out by Schouten, discussed in Art. 10-15, the Doherty-Nickle treatment goes much more thoroughly into the intimate details of machine performance and has shown itself capable of predicting actual operating characteristics with an accuracy that is quite remarkable.

Equation 4-64 of Art. 4-19 is a general expression for the distribution of any space harmonic of armature mmf produced by any time harmonic in the current wave. Since in the Doherty-Nickle theory only the time

* R. E. Doherty and C. A. Nickel, Synchronous Machines, *Trans. AIEE*, **45**:912 (1926).

fundamental of current is considered, it is then sufficient to substitute $s = 1$, thus obtaining

$$a_r = \frac{A_{r1}}{2} \left\{ \frac{\sin (r-1)\pi}{\sin \dfrac{(r-1)\pi}{m}} \sin \left[P - \frac{(m-1)(r-1)\pi}{m} \right] \right.$$

$$\left. + \frac{\sin (r+1)\pi}{\sin \dfrac{(r+1)\pi}{m}} \sin \left[Q - \frac{(m-1)(r+1)\pi}{m} \right] \right\} \qquad (10\text{-}55)$$

where $P = r(\alpha - \delta) + (\theta - \zeta)$
  $Q = r(\alpha - \delta) - (\theta - \zeta)$
  $A_{r1} = \dfrac{4}{\pi}\dfrac{1}{r} k_{b_r} k_{p_r} N_p I_m = \dfrac{4\sqrt{2}}{\pi r} k_r N_p I$
  r = order of harmonic ($= 1, 5, 7, 11, 13, 17, 19, \dots$)
  k_r = winding factor, including breadth and pitch factors
  N_p = turns per phase per pole
  I = effective value of current fundamental

Equation 10-55 is sufficient to determine the distribution of any space harmonic of mmf due to the actual current I in the armature winding; but since we are here concerned with the separate effects of $I_d = I \sin \psi$ and $I_q = I \cos \psi$, it is necessary to resolve the distribution represented by Eq. 10-55 into two components, one of which, a_{rq}, is attributable to the cross-magnetizing current I_q; the other, a_{rd}, to the directly demagnetizing current I_d (assuming that ψ is an angle of lag). To accomplish this resolution, the current I appearing as a factor in A_{r1} is in the one case replaced by I_q, in the other by I_d; but in making this substitution it is necessary to distinguish between the values of δ and ζ in the two cases, for I_q and I_d are in time quadrature.

On referring back to the derivation of Eq. 4-64, and especially to Fig. 4-51, it will be observed that the origin of coordinates was an arbitrarily selected point *on the armature surface* defined by the angle δ, to which can be assigned any value that happens to be convenient; in like manner, angle ζ was arbitrary, since it merely defines the phase of the time fundamental of current in phase 1 at the moment from which time is counted. If, for example, it is decided to make $\delta = 0$ and $\zeta = 0$ in Eq. 4-57, the physical meaning is that the displacement α, measured in electrical degrees along the armature surface toward the right, is reckoned from the point on the armature where the sinusoidally distributed mmf of phase 1 is zero (and increasing) at the instant when the fundamental current in that phase is passing through its positive maximum. In the case of the current component I_q, such a reference point corresponding to $\delta = 0$ and $\zeta = 0$ is at O (Fig. 10-47a); hence, in applying Eq. 10-55 for I_q,

$$P = P_q = r\alpha + \theta$$
$$Q = Q_q = r\alpha - \theta$$

So far as component I_d is concerned, the distribution of the space harmonics is the same function of α as in the case of I_q, but since I_d is 90° behind I_q in time phase, the time-phase angle to be used is $\theta - (\pi/2)$ instead of θ. Consequently for the case of I_d,

$$P = P_d = r\alpha + \left(\theta - \frac{\pi}{2}\right)$$

$$Q = Q_d = r\alpha - \left(\theta - \frac{\pi}{2}\right)$$

Now it will be remembered that in three-phase machines $(m = 3)$, substitution of various values of r in Eqs. 4-64 and 10-55 always gives rise to a factor $m/2 = 3/2$, which becomes a part of the coefficient A_{r1}. For convenience, therefore, in what follows

$$A_{rq} = \frac{3}{2}\frac{4}{\pi}\frac{\sqrt{2}}{r} k_r N_p I_q = \frac{2.7}{r} k_r N_p I_q \tag{10-56}$$

$$A_{rd} = \frac{2.7}{r} k_r N_p I_d \tag{10-57}$$

Substituting successively* $r = 1, 5, 7, 11, 13, 17, 19$, the equations of the space harmonics of mmf, referred to point O *on the armature surface*, become for a three-phase machine:

TABLE 10-1. MMF WAVES REFERRED TO ARMATURE

Order of harmonic	Space harmonic due to I_q	Space harmonic due to I_d
1	$a_{1q} = A_{1q} \sin(\alpha + \theta)$	$a_{1d} = -A_{1d} \cos(\alpha + \theta)$
5	$a_{5q} = A_{5q} \sin(5\alpha - \theta)$	$a_{5d} = +A_{5d} \cos(5\alpha - \theta)$
7	$a_{7q} = A_{7q} \sin(7\alpha + \theta)$	$a_{7d} = -A_{7d} \cos(7\alpha + \theta)$
11	$a_{11q} = A_{11q} \sin(11\alpha - \theta)$	$a_{11d} = +A_{11d} \cos(11\alpha - \theta)$
13	$a_{13q} = A_{13q} \sin(13\alpha + \theta)$	$a_{13d} = -A_{13d} \cos(13\alpha + \theta)$
17	$a_{17q} = A_{17q} \sin(17\alpha - \theta)$	$a_{17d} = +A_{17d} \cos(17\alpha - \theta)$
19	$a_{19q} = A_{19q} \sin(19\alpha + \theta)$	$a_{19d} = -A_{19d} \cos(19\alpha + \theta)$

In accordance with the general outline of the theory as given in an earlier paragraph in this article, the next step is to refer these space harmonics, including the fundamental, to a reference point or origin *on the field system* instead of to the origin O on the armature itself. Let the new reference point be O' (Fig. 10-47), i.e., on the axis of a pole. At the instant $t = 0$, or $\theta = \omega t = 0$, O' is in line with O, but thereafter, at any

---

* The third space harmonic and all odd multiples thereof have been shown to be absent in a three-phase machine.

general time t, the displacement between O and O' is $\theta = \omega t$ since the poles are moving to the left with angular velocity ω; consequently, at a general time t, the displacement of a point K from origin O' will be

$$\alpha' = \alpha + \omega t = \alpha + \theta$$

or
$$\alpha = \alpha' - \theta \qquad (10\text{-}58)$$

When this value of α is substituted in the equations in Table 10-1, they take the forms shown in Table 10-2.

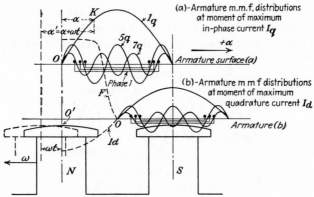

FIG. 10-47. (a) Relative positions of armature and field for maximum I_q. (b) Relative positions of armature and field for maximum I_d.

All of the equations in Table 10-2, except those of the fundamental, represent waves traveling with respect to the reference point and therefore rotating with respect to the poles. The negative sign of the θ terms

TABLE 10-2. MMF WAVES REFERRED TO POLES

Order of harmonic	Space harmonic due to I_q	Space harmonic due to I_d
1	$a_{1q} = A_{1q} \sin \alpha'$	$a_{1d} = -A_{1d} \cos \alpha'$
5	$a_{5q} = A_{5q} \sin (5\alpha' - 6\theta)$	$a_{5d} = +A_{5d} \cos (5\alpha' - 6\theta)$
7	$a_{7q} = A_{7q} \sin (7\alpha' - 6\theta)$	$a_{7d} = -A_{7d} \cos (7\alpha' - 6\theta)$
11	$a_{11q} = A_{11q} \sin (11\alpha' - 12\theta)$	$a_{11d} = +A_{11d} \cos (11\alpha' - 12\theta)$
13	$a_{13q} = A_{13q} \sin (13\alpha' - 12\theta)$	$a_{13d} = -A_{13d} \cos (13\alpha' - 12\theta)$
17	$a_{17q} = A_{17q} \sin (17\alpha' - 18\theta)$	$a_{17d} = +A_{17d} \cos (17\alpha' - 18\theta)$
19	$a_{19q} = A_{19q} \sin (19\alpha' - 18\theta)$	$a_{19d} = -A_{19d} \cos (19\alpha' - 18\theta)$

shows that all of them are moving in a direction opposite to that of the poles themselves. But by expanding the sine and cosine terms, for example those associated with a_{5q} and a_{5d}, they take the forms

$$a_{5q} = A_{5q} \sin 5\alpha' \cos 6\theta - A_{5q} \cos 5\alpha' \sin 6\theta \qquad (10\text{-}59)$$
$$a_{5d} = A_{5d} \cos 5\alpha' \cos 6\theta + A_{5d} \sin 5\alpha' \sin 6\theta \qquad (10\text{-}60)$$

which may also be written in the equivalent forms

$$a_{5q} = A_{5q} \sin 5\alpha' \cos 6\theta + A_{5q} \cos 5\alpha' \cos \left(6\theta + \frac{\pi}{2} \right) \quad (10\text{-}61)$$

$$a_{5d} = A_{5d} \cos 5\alpha' \cos 6\theta + A_{5d} \sin 5\alpha' \cos \left(6\theta - \frac{\pi}{2} \right) \quad (10\text{-}62)$$

This last pair of equations shows clearly that a_{5q} consists of two components, one of which has a variable amplitude $A_{5q} \cos 6\theta$, the other a variable amplitude $A_{5q} \cos (6\theta + \pi/2)$, so that the two are in time quadrature; and the space distributions of the two are also in quadrature, since the first varies as $\sin 5\alpha'$, the other as $\cos 5\alpha'$. Similar considerations hold with respect to a_{5d}, except that the time relations between the

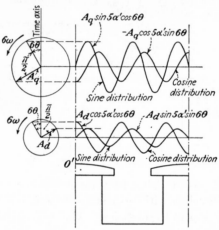

Fig. 10-48. Relative time and space relations of stationary components of fifth harmonic.

two members of the pair have a sequence opposite to that of a_{5q}. These relations are shown in Fig. 10-48, which includes at the left a polar diagram showing how the amplitudes of the stationary sinusoids vary with time. It will be understood that a corresponding set of relations holds for the four constituent stationary waves set up by each of the other orders of harmonics.

If at a given instant the ordinates of each of these stationary (with respect to the poles) mmf distributions, such as illustrated in Fig. 10-48, are multiplied by the corresponding ordinates of the permeance distribution curve (which must of course be referred to the same origin O'), the product will in each instance be the radial component of airgap field intensity, point by point along the pole span. The question arises whether the permeance distribution is the same for the "sine" as for the "cosine" distributions indicated in Fig. 10-48, and also whether these permeance distributions are the same or different for the various orders of harmonics. These questions are answered in the Doherty-Nickle paper (part 1) and particularly in Appendix B contributed by P. L. Alger and R. H. Park, which should be studied as collateral reading. Here it must suffice to say that the permeance distribution is so nearly the same for the sine and cosine distributions of a given harmonic, beginning with the fifth, that they may be taken to be identical; but the permeance curves are not the same for the different orders of harmonics. These permeance distributions are illustrated in Fig. 10-49. The absolute values of permeance in a given machine will obviously depend upon the physical dimensions, particularly upon the length of the airgap, the ratio of pole arc to airgap, and the ratio of pole arc to pole pitch. But in any case the permeance curve is a periodic function of the independent variable α', and it is seen from Fig. 10-49 that it describes one complete cycle of changes in the space of a single-pole pitch; hence it has a

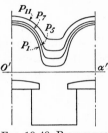

FIG. 10-49. Permeance distribution curves.

"space frequency" double that of the space fundamental of mmf. Accordingly, the permeance curve for the rth space harmonic can be represented as a Fourier series of the form

$$p_r = P_{0r} + P_{2r} \cos 2\alpha' + P_{4r} \cos 4\alpha' + \cdots \qquad (10\text{-}63)$$

where the coefficients P_{0r}, P_{2r}, P_{4r}, . . . take different values for each value of r.

It is possible to form the products $b_{5q} = a_{5q}p_5$ and $b_{5d} = a_{5d}p_5$ by actually multiplying first Eqs. 10-59 and 10-63, and then 10-60 and 10-63, and thereafter making the necessary algebraic and trigonometric reductions. But if this is done, a similar procedure must be followed for each of the other orders of harmonics in Table 10-2; so a shorter and more direct process is preferable.

It will be observed that the equations in Table 10-2 exhibit a special kind of progression so far as the numerical coefficients of α' and θ are concerned, and also that the harmonics, beginning with the fifth, group naturally in pairs as indicated by the braces at the left of the first column. The coefficients of θ in the successive pairs are 6, 12, 18, . . . , suggesting therefore that the coefficient of θ is in general $6n$, where n may take the successive values 1, 2, 3, ... The coefficients of the angle α' are always either $6n - 1$ or $6n + 1$, that is,

$$r = 6n - 1$$

for the lower-ordered mmf of a pair; and

$$r = 6n + 1$$

for the higher-ordered mmf of the same pair. It follows, therefore, that the equation for the rth space harmonic of mmf due to I_q (taken from Table 10-2) may be written*

$$a_{rq}^- = A_{rq} \sin [(6n - 1)\alpha' - 6n\theta] \qquad (10\text{-}64)$$

or
$$a_{rq}^+ = A_{rq} \sin [(6n + 1)\alpha' - 6n\theta] \qquad (10\text{-}65)$$

while the corresponding equations for I_d are

$$a_{rd}^- = +A_{rd} \cos [(6n - 1)\alpha' - 6n\theta] \qquad (10\text{-}66)$$
$$a_{rd}^+ = -A_{rd} \cos [(6n + 1)\alpha' - 6n\theta] \qquad (10\text{-}67)$$

Concentrate attention first upon Eq. 10-64, which must be multiplied by Eq. 10-63 to obtain the field intensity distribution $b_{rq}^- = a_{rq}^- p_r$. The first step is to expand Eq. 10-64, obtaining

$$a_{rq}^- = A_{rq} \sin (6n - 1)\alpha' \cos 6n\theta - A_{rq} \cos (6n - 1)\alpha' \sin 6n\theta$$

and on multiplying this by p_r the result is

$$b_{rq}^- = A_{rq} \cos 6n\theta [P_{0r} \sin (6n - 1)\alpha' + P_{2r} \sin (6n - 1)\alpha' \cos 2\alpha'$$
$$+ P_{4r} \sin (6n - 1)\alpha' \cos 4\alpha' + \cdots]$$
$$- A_{rq} \sin 6n\theta [P_{0r} \cos (6n - 1)\alpha' + P_{2r} \cos (6n - 1)\alpha' \cos 2\alpha'$$
$$+ P_{4r} \cos (6n - 1)\alpha' \cos 4\alpha' + \cdots]$$

While the last equation has a rather formidable aspect, it simplifies enormously when it is noted that the terms in the first bracket are all of the form

$$P_{hr} \sin (6n - 1)\alpha' \cos h\alpha'$$

and those in the second are

$$P_{hr} \cos (6n - 1)\alpha' \cos h\alpha'$$

where h takes in succession the even values 0, 2, 4, 6, ... So the equation for b_{rq}^- becomes

$$b_{rq}^- = A_{rq} \cos 6n\theta \sum_h P_{hr} \sin (6n - 1)\alpha' \cos h\alpha'$$

$$- A_{rq} \sin 6n\theta \sum_h P_{hr} \cos (6n - 1)\alpha' \cos h\alpha'$$

$$= \tfrac{1}{2} A_{rq} \cos 6n\theta \sum_h P_{hr}[\sin (6n - 1 + h)\alpha' + \sin (6n - 1 - h)\alpha']$$

$$- \tfrac{1}{2} A_{rq} \sin 6n\theta \sum_h P_{hr}[\cos (6n - 1 + h)\alpha' + \cos (6n - 1 - h)\alpha'] \qquad (10\text{-}68)$$

This equation tells a very interesting story; for since $6n - 1$ is always an odd number, while h is even, terms like $6n - 1 \pm h$ are always odd; moreover, if n, for example, is 1, so that

$$r = 6n - 1 = 5$$

* The minus and plus signs in a_{rq}^- and a_{rq}^+ indicate that in the former case $r = 6n - 1$, while in the latter $r = 6n + 1$.

meaning that we are dealing with the fifth space harmonic of mmf, it is seen that when $h = 4$ there appear terms involving the sines and cosines of α' and $9\alpha'$. Similarly, if $n = 2$,

$$r = 6 \times 2 - 1 = 11$$

and if $h = 10$, we find terms involving the sines and cosines of α' and $21\alpha'$. In other words, the flux produced by any rth space harmonic of mmf contains *all* the odd harmonics, including one of full-pitch span, but they are all alternating with frequency $6n\omega$; all of these component fluxes represented by the summation of terms in Eq. 10-68 are stationary with respect to the poles since they are referred to origin O' in Fig. 10-48.

If in Eq. 10-68 the terms $\cos 6n\theta$ and $\sin 6n\theta$ are now transferred behind the summation sign, there will appear products of the type

$$P_{hr} \sin (6n - 1 \pm h)\alpha' \cos 6n\theta = \frac{P_{hr}}{2} \{\sin [(6n - 1 \pm h)\alpha' + 6n\theta] + \sin [(6n - 1 \pm h)\alpha' - 6n\theta]\}$$

and

$$P_{hr} \cos (6n - 1 \pm h)\alpha' \sin 6n\theta = \frac{P_{hr}}{2} \{\sin [(6n - 1 \pm h)\alpha' + 6n\theta] - \sin [(6n - 1 \pm h)\alpha' - 6n\theta]\}$$

which, considered separately, represent eight flux waves rotating at various speeds; however, some of them mutually cancel, for on substituting the above expansions in Eq. 10-68 the latter reduces to

$$b_{rq}^- = \frac{A_{rq}}{2} \sum_h P_{hr}\{\sin [(6n - 1 + h)\alpha' - 6n\theta] + \sin [(6n - 1 - h)\alpha' - 6n\theta]\} \quad (10\text{-}69)$$

Remembering that b_{rq}^+ differs from b_{rq}^- only in that $6n + 1$ takes the place of $6n - 1$, it follows at once that

$$b_{rq}^+ = \frac{A_{rq}}{2} \sum_h P_{hr}\{\sin [(6n + 1 + h)\alpha' - 6n\theta] + \sin [(6n + 1 - h)\alpha' - 6n\theta]\} \quad (10\text{-}70)$$

In exactly the same way, starting with Eqs. 10-66 and 10-67, it is found that

$$b_{rd}^- = \frac{A_{rd}}{2} \sum_h P_{hr}\{\cos [(6n - 1 + h)\alpha' - 6n\theta] + \cos [(6n - 1 - h)\alpha' - 6n\theta]\} \quad (10\text{-}71)$$

$$b_{rd}^+ = -\frac{A_{rd}}{2} \sum_h P_{hr}\{\cos [(6n + 1 + h)\alpha' - 6n\theta] + \cos [(6n + 1 - h)\alpha' - 6n\theta]\} \quad (10\text{-}72)$$

The four equations, 10-69 to 10-72, give the complete account of all the flux waves referred to origin O' on the field system. If we now transfer the origin back again to O, i.e., on the armature, the equations will be made to show the speed with which these fluxes cut the armature winding, and this will in turn determine the magnitude and frequency of the emfs they generate.

Substituting

$$\alpha' = \alpha + \theta$$

which follows from Eq. 10-58, the last four equations become

$$b_{rq}^- = \frac{A_{rq}}{2} \sum_h P_{hr}\{\sin\left[(6n - 1 + h)\alpha + (h - 1)\theta\right]$$

$$+ \sin\left[(6n - 1 - h)\alpha - (h + 1)\theta\right]\} \quad (10\text{-}73)$$

$$b_{rq}^+ = \frac{A_{rq}}{2} \sum_h P_{hr}\{\sin\left[(6n + 1 + h)\alpha + (h + 1)\theta\right]$$

$$+ \sin\left[(6n + 1 - h)\alpha - (h - 1)\theta\right]\} \quad (10\text{-}74)$$

$$b_{rd}^- = \frac{A_{rd}}{2} \sum_h P_{hr}\{\cos\left[(6n - 1 + h)\alpha + (h - 1)\theta\right]$$

$$+ \cos\left[(6n - 1 - h)\alpha - (h + 1)\theta\right]\} \quad (10\text{-}75)$$

$$b_{rd}^+ = -\frac{A_{rd}}{2} \sum_h P_{hr}\{\cos\left[(6n + 1 + h)\alpha + (h + 1)\theta\right]$$

$$+ \cos\left[(6n + 1 - h)\alpha - (h - 1)\theta\right]\} \quad (10\text{-}76)$$

As h takes all possible values $(0, 2, 4, 6, \ldots)$ in these final general equations, all the possible flux waves, referred to the armature, will be determined. But in accordance with the theory as originally outlined, interest is confined to those particular flux waves which generate emfs of fundamental frequency. To find these waves, it must be remembered that if the flux from the poles contains, say, a kth space harmonic, rotation through it at synchronous speed will develop an emf of k times normal frequency; if such a flux harmonic is to produce an emf of fundamental frequency, its speed relative to the armature must be $1/k$ times synchronous speed. The equation of a flux wave having this speed relative to the armature is, however, of the form

$$b = B \sin (k\alpha \pm \theta)$$
or
$$b = B \cos (k\alpha \pm \theta) \quad (10\text{-}77)$$

from which it follows that the only values of h that need be considered are those which in Eqs. 10-73 to 10-76 reduce the coefficient of θ to plus or minus unity.

Take Eq. 10-73 as an example. Let $n = 1$, which means that we are dealing with the fifth space harmonic of mmf ($r = 6n - 1 = 5$). There are only two values of h which yield the type form 10-77, namely, $h = 0$ and $h = 2$, and the result of substituting them is

$$b_{5q} = A_{5q}P_{05} \sin (5\alpha - \theta) + \tfrac{1}{2}A_{5q}P_{25} \sin (7\alpha + \theta) \qquad (10\text{-}78)$$

In exactly the same manner, Eqs. 10-74 to 10-76 give for $n = 1$

$$b_{7q} = A_{7q}P_{07} \sin (7\alpha + \theta) + \tfrac{1}{2}A_{7q}P_{27} \sin (5\alpha - \theta) \qquad (10\text{-}79)$$
$$b_{5d} = A_{5d}P_{05} \cos (5\alpha - \theta) + \tfrac{1}{2}A_{5d}P_{25} \cos (7\alpha + \theta) \qquad (10\text{-}80)$$
$$b_{7d} = -A_{7d}P_{07} \cos (7\alpha + \theta) - \tfrac{1}{2}A_{7d}P_{27} \cos (5\alpha - \theta) \qquad (10\text{-}81)$$

These four equations bring out in simple fashion the curious and interesting result that the only terms of the infinite permeance series (Eq. 10-63) which affect the desired result are the first and the second; the equations show also that the fifth space harmonic of mmf produces two flux waves (see Eqs. 10-78 and 10-80), one a fifth harmonic, the other a seventh, rotating in opposite directions, each of which develops an emf of fundamental frequency. Similarly, Eqs. 10-79 and 10-81 show that the seventh harmonic of mmf produces harmonic flux waves of the fifth and seventh orders, rotating oppositely, and generating fundamental emfs.

Going back to the general formulas 10-73 to 10-76 and substituting $n = 2$, corresponding to the 11th and 13th space harmonics of mmf, it is again found that $h = 0$ and $h = 2$ are the only significant values; in fact, it is clear from their form that these are the only values of h that can be concerned no matter what n may be. Consequently, the results may be summarized for all the significant flux harmonics in the *single pair* of general equations:

$$b_{(6n\mp1)q} = A_{(6n\mp1)q}\{P_{0(6n\mp1)} \sin [(6n \mp 1)\alpha \mp \theta]$$
$$+ \tfrac{1}{2}P_{2(6n\mp1)} \sin [(6n \pm 1)\alpha \pm \theta]\} \qquad (10\text{-}82)$$
$$b_{(6n\mp1)d} = \pm A_{(6n\mp1)d}\{P_{0(6n\mp1)} \cos [(6n \mp 1)\alpha \mp \theta]$$
$$+ \tfrac{1}{2}P_{2(6n\mp1)} \cos [(6n \pm 1)\alpha \pm \theta]\} \qquad (10\text{-}83)$$

where the upper signs are first to be used throughout, then the lower signs throughout.

Substituting successively the values $n = 1, 2, 3$, the resultant equations for the higher harmonic flux waves which generate emfs of fundamental frequency are as shown in Table 10-3.

This analysis has thus far been concerned with the effects of the higher space harmonics of the armature mmf, beginning with the fifth, since in a three-phase machine there are no third space harmonics or odd multiples thereof. Nothing has yet been said concerning the space fundamental of mmf, though naturally its effects constitute by far the greater part of the whole. The procedure to be followed in determining the flux wave due to it is essentially the same as for the higher harmonics, though the actual derivation is much simpler. Thus, referring to the first line of Table 10-2, the fundamental space waves of mmf referred to an origin

TABLE 10-3. FLUX WAVES WHICH DEVELOP EMF OF FUNDAMENTAL FREQUENCY

Produced by mmf harmonic of order	Higher harmonic flux waves due to I_q
5	$b_{5q} = A_{5q}[P_{05} \sin (5\alpha - \theta) + \frac{1}{2}P_{25} \sin (7\alpha + \theta)]$
7	$b_{7q} = A_{7q}[P_{07} \sin (7\alpha + \theta) + \frac{1}{2}P_{27} \sin (5\alpha - \theta)]$
11	$b_{11q} = A_{11q}[P_{011} \sin (11\alpha - \theta) + \frac{1}{2}P_{211} \sin (13\alpha + \theta)]$
13	$b_{13q} = A_{13q}[P_{013} \sin (13\alpha + \theta) + \frac{1}{2}P_{213} \sin (11\alpha - \theta)]$
17	$b_{17q} = A_{17q}[P_{017} \sin (17\alpha - \theta) + \frac{1}{2}P_{217} \sin (19\alpha + \theta)]$
19	$b_{19q} = A_{19q}[P_{019} \sin (19\alpha + \theta) + \frac{1}{2}P_{219} \sin (17\alpha - \theta)]$

Produced by mmf harmonic of order	Higher harmonic flux waves due to I_d
5	$b_{5d} = A_{5d}[P_{05} \cos (5\alpha - \theta) + \frac{1}{2}P_{25} \cos (7\alpha + \theta)]$
7	$b_{7d} = -A_{7d}[P_{07} \cos (7\alpha + \theta) + \frac{1}{2}P_{27} \cos (5\alpha - \theta)]$
11	$b_{11d} = A_{11d}[P_{011} \cos (11\alpha - \theta) + \frac{1}{2}P_{211} \cos (13\alpha + \theta)]$
13	$b_{13d} = -A_{13d}[P_{013} \cos (13\alpha + \theta) + \frac{1}{2}P_{213} \cos (11\alpha - \theta)]$
17	$b_{17d} = A_{17d}[P_{017} \cos (17\alpha - \theta) + \frac{1}{2}P_{217} \cos (19\alpha + \theta)]$
19	$b_{19d} = -A_{19d}[P_{019} \cos (19\alpha + \theta) + \frac{1}{2}P_{219} \cos (17\alpha - \theta)]$

on the poles are

$$a_{1q} = A_{1q} \sin \alpha'$$
$$a_{1d} = -A_{1d} \cos \alpha' \tag{10-84}$$

The permeance distribution curve for full-pitch distribution is

$$p_1 = P_{01} + P_{21} \cos 2\alpha' + P_{41} \cos 4\alpha' + \cdots \tag{10-85}$$

Consequently,

$$b_{1q} = A_{1q}(P_{01} \sin \alpha' + P_{21} \sin \alpha' \cos 2\alpha'$$
$$+ P_{41} \sin \alpha' \cos 4\alpha' + \cdots)$$
$$b_{1d} = -A_{1d}(P_{01} \cos \alpha' + P_{21} \cos \alpha' \cos 2\alpha'$$
$$+ P_{41} \cos \alpha' \cos 4\alpha' + \cdots) \tag{10-86}$$

and these reduce to

$$b_{1q} = A_{1q}\left[\left(P_{01} - \frac{P_{21}}{2}\right) \sin \alpha' + \frac{1}{2} (P_{21} - P_{41}) \sin 3\alpha' \right.$$
$$\left. + \cdots \right] \tag{10-87}$$
$$b_{1d} = -A_{1d}\left[\left(P_{01} + \frac{P_{21}}{2}\right) \cos \alpha' + \frac{1}{2} (P_{21} + P_{41}) \cos 3\alpha' \right.$$
$$\left. + \cdots \right]$$

Here the only terms that need be considered are the first ones in each expression, since the others, being higher harmonics in the flux wave of the poles, generate emfs of corresponding frequency. Hence, the significant fundamental flux waves due to armature reaction are

$$b_{1q} = A_{1q}\left(P_{01} - \frac{P_{21}}{2}\right)\sin\alpha' \tag{10-88}$$

$$b_{1d} = -A_{1d}\left(P_{01} + \frac{P_{21}}{2}\right)\cos\alpha' \tag{10-89}$$

It is left to the student to prove that if the two Fourier series in Eq. 10-87 are analyzed for the magnitudes of the fundamentals, using the basic formula (Eq. 4-10), the results will be the same as Eqs. 10-88 and 10-89. This is in reality the procedure that was followed by Schouten in the paper referred to (Art. 10-15).

10-22. Magnitude and Phase of the EMFs in the Doherty-Nickle Theory. All of the flux waves of fundamental (full span) and higher harmonic space distribution which generate in the armature winding appreciable emfs of fundamental frequency are accounted for by Eqs. 10-88 and 10-89 and those listed in Table 10-3. It is now necessary to determine from these flux equations the magnitudes and phases of the emfs they generate.

Take the flux fundamental first. It consists of the two parts represented by Eqs. 10-88 and 10-89, the former due to I_q, the latter to I_d. These two distributions, which are stationary with respect to the poles and move with them, are shown in their proper space relation by the curves $1q$ and $1d$ of Fig. 10-47, which, though originally drawn for the purpose of showing armature mmf due to phase 1, may still serve to show flux relations provided the scale is so altered that the amplitude of curve $1q$ is $A_{1q}(P_{01} - \frac{1}{2}P_{21})$ and that of $1d$ is $A_{1d}(P_{01} + \frac{1}{2}P_{21})$. At the instant represented in Fig. 10-47a, the coils of phase 1 have maximum linkage with the flux b_{1q}, and the emf due to it is therefore zero; but at the same instant the conductors of phase 1 are cutting the main field flux (curve F) at the greatest rate, and the emf E_f (Fig. 10-42) is a maximum. It is obvious from the relative positions of curves F and $1q$ (the latter trailing after the former by a space angle of 90°) that the emf E_{1q} due to flux b_{1q} lags 90° behind E_f, and therefore by the same angle behind I_q. The same reasoning serves to show that the emf E_{1d} generated by b_{1d} lags 90° behind I_d; for in Fig. 10-47 curve $1d$ trails behind curve $1q$ by 90°, therefore generates an emf lagging 90° behind E_{1q}, hence lagging behind I_d by the same angle. These phase relations are shown in Table 10-4 by operator $-j$ prefixed to expressions for E_{1q} and E_{1d}, since such an operator serves to rotate through 90°, in a clockwise direction, the phasor quantity to which it is attached.

As to the magnitudes of E_{1q} and E_{1d}, it is clear that they are respectively proportional to the flux amplitudes,

$$A_{1q}(P_{01} - \tfrac{1}{2}P_{21}) \quad \text{and} \quad A_{1d}(P_{01} + \tfrac{1}{2}P_{21})$$

in exactly the same way that the emf E_f is proportional to the amplitude B_1 of the space fundamental of curve F in Fig. 10-47. Therefore,

$$E_{1q} = \frac{A_{1q}(P_{01} - \tfrac{1}{2}P_{21})}{B_1} E_f \tag{10-90}$$

$$E_{1d} = \frac{A_{1d}(P_{01} + \tfrac{1}{2}P_{21})}{B_1} E_f \tag{10-91}$$

Consider next the flux b_{5q} (Table 10-3), produced by the fifth space harmonic of mmf, and composed of the fifth and the seventh flux harmonics represented in the expression

$$b_{5q} = A_{5q}P_{05} \sin (5\alpha - \theta) + \tfrac{1}{2}A_{5q}P_{25} \sin (7\alpha + \theta) \tag{10-92}$$

both rotating with respect to the armature winding. At the instant $t = 0$ represented in Fig. 10-47a, the two curves marked $5q$ and $7q$ correctly represent the space distributions of these two flux waves, though not to scale so far as their ordinates are concerned, since they were drawn originally to represent mmfs and not fluxes. The fifth flux harmonic, $A_{5q}P_{05} \sin (5\alpha - \theta)$, is moving to the right* relative to the armature at one-fifth synchronous speed, and the seventh flux harmonic,

$$\tfrac{1}{2}A_{5q}P_{25} \sin (7\alpha + \theta)$$

is moving to the left at one-seventh synchronous speed. Consequently, the emfs which they generate, E_{5q5} and E_{5q7}, respectively,† both of fundamental frequency, are in the case of the former one-fifth as large as would be generated by an equal fifth flux harmonic in the main flux wave F; and in the case of the latter it is one-seventh as large as would be produced by a like seventh harmonic in curve F. Applying Eq. 4-28 for the magnitude of the emf due to harmonics in the main flux wave, it follows that

$$E_{5q5} = \frac{A_{5q}P_{05}}{5B_1} \frac{k_5}{k_1} E_f \tag{10-93}$$

and

$$E_{5q7} = \frac{1}{2} \frac{A_{5q}P_{25}}{7B_1} \frac{k_7}{k_1} E_f \tag{10-94}$$

Referring back to Eqs. 10-56 and 10-57 (page 438) it will be noted that coefficients of the type A_{rq} can all be referred to the single coefficient A_{1q} by the relation

$$A_{rq} = \frac{A_{1q}}{r} \frac{k_r}{k_1} \tag{10-95}$$

* Because if $5\alpha - \theta = $ constant, $d\alpha/dt = +\tfrac{1}{5}\omega$.

† The first subscript indicates the order of the space harmonic of mmf responsible for the flux, and the last indicates the order of the space harmonic of flux which develops the emf.

and in the same manner

$$A_{rd} = \frac{A_{1d}}{r} \frac{k_r}{k_1} \qquad (10\text{-}96)$$

whence, on substituting these relations in 10-93 and 10-94,

$$E_{5q5} = \frac{A_{1q}P_{05}}{25} \frac{k_5^2}{k_1^2} \frac{E_f}{B_1} \qquad (10\text{-}97)$$

$$E_{5q7} = \frac{A_{1q}P_{25}}{70} \frac{k_5 k_7}{k_1^2} \frac{E_f}{B_1} \qquad (10\text{-}98)$$

It is now a simple matter to determine the phases of these two emfs with respect to the current I_q originally responsible for them. For it will be seen from Eq. 10-88 that the flux fundamental is represented by

$$b_{1q} = A_{1q}(P_{01} - \tfrac{1}{2}P_{21}) \sin \alpha' = A_{1q}(P_{01} - \tfrac{1}{2}P_{21}) \sin (\alpha + \theta) \quad (10\text{-}99)$$

which is known to be a flux wave of full span like curve $1q$ of Fig. 10-47a, rotating to the left with the poles. Assuming that the left side of phase belt 1 in that diagram is at the reference point O, the field intensity at that point contributed by flux wave b_{1q} will be found from Eq. 10-99 by substituting $\alpha = 0$ in that equation, the result indicating that the field intensity at that point is proportional to $\sin \theta$; but Eq. 10-92 shows that at the point $\alpha = 0$ the field intensity contributed by b_{5q} is

$$(b_{5q})_{\alpha=0} = A_{5q}P_{05} \sin (-\theta) + \tfrac{1}{2}A_{5q}P_{25} \sin \theta \qquad (10\text{-}100)$$

which because of the negative sign of θ in the first term on the right-hand side shows that the coil side at O is being cut by the fifth flux harmonic in a phase opposite to that of the fundamental, while at the same time the phase of the seventh flux harmonic is the same as that of the fundamental. Since the motion of the fifth flux harmonic is opposite to that of the fundamental, while that of the seventh is the same, it follows that both these fluxes generate emfs having the same phase as that of E_{1q}, therefore lagging behind I_q by 90°. These facts are shown by the operator $-j$ prefixed to the magnitudes of E_{5q5} and E_{5q7} in Table 10-4. Similar reasoning leads to the determination of the magnitudes and phases of the remaining emfs (all of fundamental frequency) generated by the other flux harmonics produced by current I_q. The results are listed in the second column of Table 10-4.

The third column of Table 10-4 gives the magnitudes and phases of the emfs of fundamental frequency due to current I_d. There is no difficulty in obtaining the magnitudes of these emfs from the corresponding fluxes listed in Table 10-3, since they are deduced in the manner already explained; but the sequence of signs is not quite the same. Consider the equations

$$b_{1d} = -A_{1d}(P_{01} + \tfrac{1}{2}P_{21}) \cos (\alpha + \theta)$$
$$\overleftarrow{}$$

$$b_{5d} = A_{5d}P_{05} \cos (5\alpha - \theta) + \tfrac{1}{2}A_{5d}P_{25} \cos (7\alpha + \theta)$$
$$\overrightarrow{} \qquad\qquad\qquad\qquad \overleftarrow{}$$

the first obtained from Eq. 10-89 by substituting $\alpha' = \alpha + \theta$, the second from Table 10-3.   The arrows under the trigonometric terms indicate the direction of motion of the corresponding flux waves in accordance with the conventions indicated in Fig. 10-47.   If, as has already been shown, the flux b_{1d}, with its negative sign and left-hand motion, generates an emf E_{1d} lagging 90° behind I_d, then the flux $+ A_{5d}P_{05} \cos (5\alpha - \theta)$, with a positive sign and a right-hand motion, will also generate an emf lagging 90° behind I_d; the reversal of direction of motion is neutralized by the change of sign.   But the flux $\frac{1}{2}A_{5d}P_{25} \cos (7\alpha + \theta)$, with positive sign and left-hand motion, generates an emf of reversed phase, thus accounting for the negative sign between the terms constituting the second item in the I_d column of Table 10-4.   Similar considerations govern the remaining items in the table.

TABLE 10-4. MAGNITUDES AND PHASES OF FUNDAMENTAL EMFs DUE TO
ARMATURE REACTION

(Factor E_f/B_1 is omitted throughout)

Order of mmf harmonic	Magnitude and phase of fundamental emf due to flux harmonic produced by I_q	Magnitude and phase of fundamental emf due to flux harmonic produced by I_d
1	$-jA_{1q}(P_{01} - \frac{1}{2}P_{21})$	$-jA_{1d}(P_{01} + \frac{1}{2}P_{21})$
5	$-jA_{1q}\left(\dfrac{P_{05}}{25}k_5^2 + \dfrac{P_{25}}{70}k_5k_7\right)\dfrac{1}{k_1^2}$	$-jA_{1d}\left(\dfrac{P_{05}}{25}k_5^2 - \dfrac{P_{25}}{70}k_5k_7\right)\dfrac{1}{k_1^2}$
7	$-jA_{1q}\left(\dfrac{P_{07}}{49}k_7^2 + \dfrac{P_{27}}{70}k_5k_7\right)\dfrac{1}{k_1^2}$	$-jA_{1d}\left(\dfrac{P_{07}}{49}k_7^2 - \dfrac{P_{27}}{70}k_5k_7\right)\dfrac{1}{k_1^2}$
11	$-jA_{1q}\left(\dfrac{P_{011}}{121}k_{11}^2 + \dfrac{P_{211}}{286}k_{11}k_{13}\right)\dfrac{1}{k_1^2}$	$-jA_{1d}\left(\dfrac{P_{011}}{121}k_{11}^2 - \dfrac{P_{211}}{286}k_{11}k_{13}\right)\dfrac{1}{k_1^2}$
13	$-jA_{1q}\left(\dfrac{P_{013}}{169}k_{13}^2 + \dfrac{P_{213}}{286}k_{11}k_{13}\right)\dfrac{1}{k_1^2}$	$-jA_{1d}\left(\dfrac{P_{013}}{169}k_{13}^2 - \dfrac{P_{213}}{286}k_{11}k_{13}\right)\dfrac{1}{k_1^2}$
17	$-jA_{1q}\left(\dfrac{P_{017}}{289}k_{17}^2 + \dfrac{P_{217}}{646}k_{17}k_{19}\right)\dfrac{1}{k_1^2}$	$-jA_{1d}\left(\dfrac{P_{017}}{289}k_{17}^2 - \dfrac{P_{217}}{646}k_{17}k_{19}\right)\dfrac{1}{k_1^2}$
19	$-jA_{1q}\left(\dfrac{P_{019}}{361}k_{19}^2 + \dfrac{P_{219}}{646}k_{17}k_{19}\right)\dfrac{1}{k_1^2}$	$-jA_{1d}\left(\dfrac{P_{019}}{361}k_{19}^2 - \dfrac{P_{219}}{646}k_{17}k_{19}\right)\dfrac{1}{k_1^2}$

Finally, therefore, if the summations of the two columns of emfs listed in Table 10-4 are symbolized as ΣE_q and ΣE_d, the former due to I_q the latter to I_d, the complete phasor diagram in accordance with the two-reaction theory takes the form already shown in Fig. 10-46.

10-23. Sudden Short Circuit of a Synchronous Generator.   The material thus far presented in this chapter has outlined the various theories, substantially in the order of their historical development, which sought to explain and to predict the performance of synchronous generators under *steady-state* conditions of operation. It will have been observed that the factors chiefly concerned in the several analyses pertained to the stator, namely, the armature current and voltage, the armature resistance and leakage reactance, and the armature reactions as represented by the synchronous reactance and by the direct-axis and quadrature-axis reactances. The rotor has until now not entered the picture except in so far as the field current produced the working flux in the main magnetic circuit.

Inspection of Fig. 10-31 will show, however, that any sudden change of load or power factor, or both, which affects the magnitude and phase of the armature current will produce equally sudden changes in the mmfs of the fictitious poles N_d, S_d, and N_q, S_q. Any change in the mmf of the first pair obviously tends to change the flux linked with the main field winding, but in accordance with Lenz's law this change is resisted by an induced current which is immediately called into being in the rotor winding. This means that the field winding becomes the secondary of a transformer, and continues that role during the time required for the armature current to settle down to its permanent steady value; when that condition is finally reached, the armature mmf again becomes constant in magnitude and fixed in position with respect to the poles, and transformer reactions thereupon cease.

The same sudden change of armature mmf which induces transient current in the field winding also induces similar transient current in the permanently short-circuited damper (amortisseur) winding if one is present, and also eddy currents in the pole faces and adjacent metal parts, and these play the part of an additional secondary linked with the armature winding as primary.

If the sudden change of load which brings about these reactions in the direct axis occurs when the angle ψ (see Fig. 10-31) differs from 90° so that cos ψ is appreciable, somewhat similar results ensue because of the change in mmf of the fictitious poles N_q, S_q (in Fig. 10-31), but with the important difference that the induced secondary currents can appear only in the damper winding and in adjacent metal parts.

With these considerations in mind, let it be assumed that a three-phase alternator, driven at constant (rated) speed, is excited so that its open-circuit voltage is the rated voltage E of the machine; and that subject to these conditions its terminals are suddenly short-circuited. At the first instant, the armature current is limited only by the internal leakage impedance of the armature winding, Z_a, but since R_a is very small in comparison with X_a, it is sufficiently accurate to use X_a instead of Z_a, and it may therefore be concluded that the short-circuit current will lag by an angle $\psi = 90°$ behind the induced voltage; accordingly, $I_d = I$, and $I_q = 0$. It would be an oversimplification, however, to say that the initial rush of current per phase would be $I = E/Z_a \cong E/X_a$; for it must be remembered that when an alternating voltage is suddenly applied to an inductive circuit the initial current depends upon the magnitude of the voltage at that instant; i.e., it depends upon the point of the voltage wave at which the circuit is closed. If, for example, the closure occurs at the instant when the current corresponding to voltage E and reactance X_a would normally be at its maximum, but is actually zero at that moment, the resultant transient current will be double the current normally due to E and X_a. It may therefore be said that the initial rush of current (per phase) will be somewhere between E/X_a and $2E/X_a$.

Subject to the assumptions of the preceding paragraph, a symmetrical short circuit applied simultaneously to all three phases does not disturb the balanced nature of the armature circuit as a whole, with the result that the algebraic sum of the instantaneous currents in all three phases remains at all times equal to zero; the peak values of all three of the phase currents will be substantially the same and during the first few cycles after the short circuit occurs may be anywhere from ten to twenty times normal full-load current, depending upon the design of the machine.

The initial enormous rush of current, lagging by almost 90° behind the voltage, creates a proportionally large demagnetizing mmf in the direct axis, and tends to reduce the flux per pole, Φ, below its original value. But this flux represents a very considerable amount of stored energy which cannot instantly be dissipated; so while Φ promptly begins to decrease, it does so very slowly, at a rate which depends upon the *time constants* of the associated electrical circuits, i.e., upon the ratio inductance/resistance of these circuits. The tendency of the flux Φ to be thus sustained means that the exciting current must automatically jump from its original value to a much larger value, and at a correspondingly higher voltage, but with the same direction of flow as before, in order to balance the suddenly increased demagnetizing mmf of the armature current. At the same time, the eddy currents in the damper and the adjacent metal parts likewise increase in obedience to Lenz's law, thus assisting the rotor field winding to sustain the flux Φ.

Since the rotor field winding thus becomes the secondary of a transformer in which the armature winding is the primary, it is important to investigate the factors upon which its leakage impedance depends. The rotor field current is supplied by an exciter which has very low resistance and inductance as compared with the corresponding values of the rotor winding itself; consequently, the effect at the time the short circuit occurs is the same as though the field winding were short-circuited. There is no difficulty in determining the resistance of the rotor field winding, which must, of course, be reduced to terms of the armature as primary by applying the appropriate conversion factor. The leakage reactance of the field winding is due to that part of the total flux per pole, Φ_t, which is represented by φ in the equation

$$\Phi_t = \Phi + \varphi = \Phi\left(1 + \frac{\varphi}{\Phi}\right)$$

where $1 + (\varphi/\Phi) = \sigma =$ leakage factor of the field system. Both φ and σ can be computed from the physical dimensions of the machine. Knowing the value of the leakage flux φ, the equivalent inductance is determined by the relation that inductance (L) is equal to the leakage-flux* linkages per ampere of the corresponding field current, and the leakage reactance is then $2\pi fL$, which must also be reduced to terms of the armature as primary.

10-24. Transient and Subtransient Reactances. The first rush of current, many times larger than full-load current, is followed by a period during which the armature current decays gradually to the sustained short-circuit value which corresponds to the initial excitation; for as the armature current falls from its initial large value, the transient field current which balances its demagnetizing effect also decreases to its original magnitude. The gradual decay of both currents is a consequence of the fact that the energy stored in the original field Φ is dissipated, in a logarithmic manner, in the resistances of the armature and field windings, the damper, and the eddy-current paths.

When, at the end of the transient period, the armature current settles down to its final steady-state value, the phasor diagram, Fig. 10-46, collapses to a form in which $V = 0$, $I_q \cong 0$, $I_d \cong I$, and $I_q R_{rq} \cong 0$, and if IR_a is neglected, the result is that the induced emf

$$E = I(X_a + X_{rd}) = IX_d$$

The transformer action between the armature and field windings has then disappeared because the steady armature current produces an unvarying armature mmf which is stationary with respect to the poles; the effect is the same as though the secondary of the transformer had been opened. The series relation shown by the term $X_a + X_{rd}$ in the above expression points to the conclusion that the equivalent circuit of this open-circuited transformer is shown by Fig. 10-50, where X_{rd}, the reactance equivalent to the armature mmf in the direct axis, plays the part of the *exciting reactance* of the transformer of which the field winding is the secondary. The steady-state short-circuit reactance is therefore $X_d = X_a + X_{rd}$.

When the alternator is suddenly short-circuited, the approximate equivalent circuit for a brief time thereafter is shown by Fig. 10-51, where it will be noted that for simplicity the resistances associated with each of the branches have been omitted. The conditions in the machine

---

* Flux expressed in webers.

are those of a three-winding transformer, the armature being the primary, and the two secondaries consisting of (*a*) the field winding having reactance X_f and (*b*) the damper winding having reactance X_D. The mutual inductance between the two secondaries may be safely omitted. The equivalent reactance of the circuit is

$$X_d'' = \frac{1}{(1/X_{rd}) + (1/X_f) + (1/X_D)} \tag{10-101}$$

and this is called the *subtransient direct-axis reactance*. It is obviously considerably smaller than $X_d = X_a + X_{rd}$ represented by Fig. 10-50.

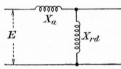

FIG. 10-50. Approximate equivalent circuit of alternator, steady-state short circuit.

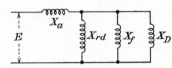

FIG. 10-51. Approximate equivalent circuit, initial stage of sudden short circuit, direct-axis subtransient reactance.

The effect of the damper winding and the eddy currents in the pole faces disappears after the first few cycles because the resistances associated with these secondary circuits are relatively much larger than the resistance of the field winding (reduced to terms of the primary). Accordingly, after the first few cycles the equivalent circuit takes the form of Fig. 10-52, and the equivalent reactance

$$X_d' = \frac{1}{(1/X_{rd}) + (1/X_f)} \tag{10-102}$$

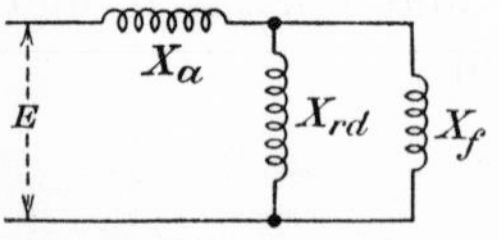

FIG. 10-52. Approximate equivalent circuit, direct-axis transient reactance.

is called the *transient direct-axis reactance*. It is likewise smaller than X_d, the steady-state short-circuit reactance.

In general, the rapid decay of the effect of the damper is equivalent to a rapid increase of X_D from its initial value to infinity; the slower decay of the effect of the field winding is equivalent to a slow increase of X_f from its initial value to infinity.

10-25. Current Variation during Sudden Symmetrical Short Circuit. Figure 10-53 is a sketch showing the general nature of the current variation in one of the three phases when the terminals are suddenly short-circuited, subject to the condition that the field excitation is sufficient to develop the rated open-circuit voltage. During the first few cycles, the wave form of armature current will depend upon the point in the emf cycle at which the short-circuiting switch is closed. In the other two phases, the wave forms of armature current will differ from the one shown in Fig. 10-53 because of the fact that at any given moment along the time axis the algebraic sum of the three corresponding phase currents must be zero. Since the curve in the illustration starts off in the positive direction, at least one of the others will start in the negative direction.

Each of the oscillograms shows that the peak values of current define the envelopes represented by curves *ab* and *ef*. The curve *cd*, midway between the envelopes, therefore represents a slowly decaying *unidirectional* (i.e., direct) current, upon which is superposed a slowly decaying alternating current shown by the wave form of Fig. 10-54. The latter

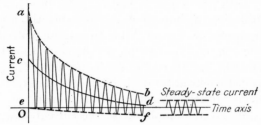

FIG. 10-53. Typical oscillogram of armature current.

curve is constructed by laying off the amplitudes of the a-c component of Fig. 10-53 above and below the axis *c'd'* (which takes the place of curve *cd* in Fig. 10-53). The envelopes of the new curve, one of them marked *a'b'*, will be symmetrical about the time axis.

The ordinates of the unidirectional curve *cd* of Fig. 10-53 represent a d-c component of the phase current there shown. There will be similar d-c components in each of the other phases, but the magnitudes and signs

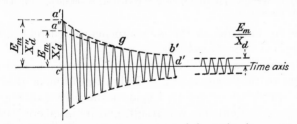

FIG. 10-54. Alternating component of short-circuit current.

of all three of them must conform with the requirement that their algebraic sum is always zero. These three d-c components produce a resultant decaying mmf in the direct axis; for they may be regarded as the "frozen" instantaneous values of hypothetical alternating currents which, if they existed, would magnetize in the direct axis. This resultant decaying mmf of the d-c components must be balanced by a corresponding d-c component of current in the field winding. The a-c components of the phase currents, typified by the wave form of Fig. 10-54, combine to produce an additional decaying mmf in the direct axis, which must be balanced by an additional d-c component of the field current. An oscillogram of the field current, taken at the same time as those of the three phase currents, would accordingly have a logarithmic form of the type of curve cd, but its ordinate at any time t would have a magnitude and sign equivalent to a field mmf equal and opposite to the corresponding resultant mmf of the phase currents at the same instant.

The decay of the a-c component of the short-circuit current (Fig. 10-54) is logarithmic, but in general the rate of decay is not the same during the first few cycles, as in part $a'g$, as it is during the remaining interval indicated by gb'. The difference is due to the fact that part $a'g$ is influenced by both reactances X_f and X_D (Fig. 10-51), while the effect of X_D drops out during the interval gb'. Consequently, if the logarithms of the peak amplitudes of curve $a'b'$, Fig. 10-54, are plotted against time as in Fig. 10-55a, the resultant graph will be curved in the portion $a'g$ but will be a straight line thereafter in the portion gb'. If the straight part $b'g$ is extended backward until it intersects the axis of ordinates at a'', it will therefore give the logarithm of the ordinate $c'a''$ in Fig. 10-54, and this is accordingly the amplitude of the current that would flow if X_D were infinite, i.e., if the *transient reactance* X'_d were alone operative.

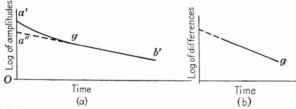

FIG. 10-55. (a) Determination of direct-axis transient reactance. (b) Determination of subtransient reactance.

In that case, the envelope of the a-c component of current in Fig. 10-54 would be the curve shown as $a''gb'$.

The difference between the amplitudes of curves $a'b'$ and $a''b'$ (Fig. 10-54) is due to the effect of X_D. If the logarithm of this difference between the amplitudes is plotted against the corresponding times, as in Fig. 10-55b, a straight line will result, and its intercept with the vertical axis determines the point a' in Fig. 10-54.

In case the symmetrical short circuit occurs at a distance from the generator, the resistance of the intervening line may be sufficient to reduce the phase angle ψ appreciably below 90°. In that case, there will be a quadrature-axis component of current, I_q, in addition to the direct-axis component I_d, and the effect of the I_q will be to induce corresponding neutralizing currents of a rapidly decaying nature in the damper winding and adjacent metal parts. The transient component of quadrature-axis current must then be combined with the direct-axis component to determine the resultant armature current.

10-26. Measurement of Direct-axis Subtransient Reactance, X''_d.
The AIEE Test Code for Synchronous Machines describes several procedures for measuring X''_d, one of them based upon the test connections

shown in Fig. 10-56. The field winding is short-circuited, and a single-phase voltage is impressed across two armature phase windings in series (connected for 120° phase displacement). The rotor is blocked in the angular position for maximum induced field current. The subtransient reactance X_d'' is then equal to half the applied voltage divided by the resulting armature current.

10-27. Unsymmetrical Short Circuit of Three-phase Generator. If a three-phase Y-connected generator is driven at rated speed and with an excitation sufficient to develop its rated voltage on open circuit, a sudden short circuit across any two of its terminals, or between one line and the neutral, will cause it to function as a sin-

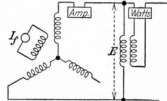

FIG. 10-56. Measurement of X_d''.

gle-phase machine, thereby upsetting the balanced circuit conditions discussed in the preceding articles, and bringing into play a different set of reactions.

The single-phase armature current set up under the conditions specified in the preceding paragraph produces an mmf which alternates at normal frequency but which is stationary with respect to the armature winding. In accordance with the principles discussed in Chap. 4, especially in Art. 4-16 and as illustrated in Fig. 4-36, this alternating but stationary mmf may be resolved into two components, each having half the amplitude of the alternating original mmf, one of them revolving at synchronous speed in the same direction as the rotor, the other at equal speed in the opposite direction.

The former component, moving in step with the rotor, will therefore react with the rotor field winding in the same way as in the case of a balanced three-phase circuit, so that the wave form of the armature short-circuit current may be expected to include as one component a curve of the type illustrated in Fig. 10-53. The field current may also be expected to include a unidirectional transient current similar in form to curve cd of that figure.

The backwardly rotating armature mmf produces a flux which varies from a maximum value when it is lined up with the poles to a minimum when it is in the mid-pole position (assuming that the generator is of the salient-pole type). It will therefore induce in the rotor field winding an emf and current of double frequency, but with amplitudes decreasing exponentially to the magnitudes characteristic of steady-state conditions in a single-phase generator. The double-frequency component of the resultant field current will in turn produce a triple-frequency harmonic in the voltage wave of the armature.

The analytical solution of problems involving single-phase short circuits, or unbalanced conditions in general, is most effectively handled by resolving the unbalanced current, by the method of symmetrical components, into a set of positive-, negative-, and zero-sequence currents (see Arts. 2-29 to 2-31). The positive-sequence components constitute a balanced set of three-phase currents which produce an mmf moving in step with the rotor field, and they will accordingly result in reactions already considered in Arts. 10-23 to 10-25. The negative-sequence components produce an armature mmf revolving at synchronous speed in the direction opposite to that of the rotor, and therefore set up double-frequency emfs and currents in the field winding, in the damper winding, and in the eddy-current paths. But the impedances which correspond to the negative-sequence currents are not the same as those which pertain to the positive-sequence currents, at least in the case of salient-pole machines, though in cylindrical-rotor machines there is not much difference. The zero-sequence components of armature current all have the same time phase, with the result that the mmfs due to these zero-sequence phase currents are mutually 120° apart in space phase, and accordingly annul one another. The impedances corresponding to these zero-sequence currents are different from those corresponding to either of the other sets.

10-28. Measurement of Negative-sequence Impedance. The negative-sequence impedance may be determined experimentally by applying balanced negative-sequence voltage to the armature terminals while the machine is driven at rated speed with its field winding short-circuited. The negative-sequence impedance is then the quotient obtained by dividing the observed impressed voltage per phase by the current per phase.

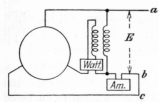

FIG. 10-57. Measurement of negative-sequence impedance.

A simultaneous wattmeter reading will give the I^2R loss, and from this reading it is possible to compute the resistance per phase and thereby fix the value of the reactance per phase.

The AIEE Test Code for Synchronous Machines (Paragraph 1.884) gives other methods for measuring negative-sequence impedance, one of them as follows:

Referring to Fig. 10-57, the Y-connected machine is driven at rated speed with two of its terminals, b and c, short-circuited. Voltage E is applied between terminal a and the junction of terminals b and c. An ammeter and the current coil of a wattmeter are connected in the short-circuited phases, and the potential coil of the wattmeter is connected across voltage E. The negative-sequence impedance is then given by

$$z_2 = \frac{E}{\sqrt{3}\,I} \tag{10-103}$$

and if P is the reading of the wattmeter, the negative-sequence reactance is

$$x_2 = z_2 \frac{P}{EI} \qquad (10\text{-}104)$$

In making the test, the rotor must be watched for serious overheating, and in the case of turbine generators it may be necessary to use low values of current and so obtain only the unsaturated values of impedance. It is also to be noted that the results may be influenced by the presence of harmonics.

10-29. Measurement of Zero-sequence Reactance.* The machine is driven at rated speed with its field winding short-circuited. With all phases connected in series, single-phase current is circulated by impressing a voltage upon the open terminals. The zero-sequence reactance is then

$$x_0 = \frac{E}{3I} \qquad (10\text{-}105)$$

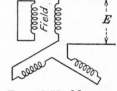

Practically the same results will be obtained with the rotor stationary or with the rotor entirely removed.

Fig. 10-58. Measurement of zero-sequence reactance.

In some cases, it may be convenient to connect the phases in parallel instead of in series. In that case, the voltage required will be one-third of that required for series connection, and the current will be three times larger. In both cases, the connections must be checked to be certain that the currents simultaneously flow in the same direction from the line terminals.

10-30. Losses and Efficiency. While the efficiency of any machine is the ratio of its output to its input, it is much more convenient to express it in the form

$$\eta = \frac{\text{output}}{\text{output} + \text{losses}} \qquad (10\text{-}106)$$

In the case of a large generator, it is wholly impracticable to determine its efficiency by direct measurement of input and output because of the cost of such a test even if all facilities were available; and even if they were, the mechanical input cannot readily be measured. On the other hand, most of the losses can be computed or measured, though some of them which can be neither calculated nor easily measured are assigned conventional values based upon experience. Efficiency computed on the basis of conventional losses is therefore designated as *conventional efficiency*.

The losses directly chargeable to a synchronous generator include:

1. I^2R losses, (*a*) in the armature winding; (*b*) in the field winding; (*c*) at the contact between brushes and slip rings.

* AIEE Test Code for Synchronous Machines, No. 503. Par. 1.892 (1945).

2. Core loss.

3. Friction and windage loss, including the loss due to the circulation of cooling air through a closed ventilating system, and also the brush friction loss at the slip rings.

4. The stray-load loss caused by eddy currents in the armature conductors and by additional core loss due to the distortion of the magnetic field under load conditions.

In the case of large machines, there are certain additional losses associated with their operation, such as (1) the loss in the field-regulating rheostat and (2) the loss in ventilating ducts external to the machine itself, as when two or more machines are supplied with cooling air from a common blower system. These losses are charged against the plant as a whole, not against the individual machines.

The copper (I^2R) losses in the armature and field windings are computed by using the d-c values of resistance corrected to the working temperature of 75°C.

The core loss, including hysteresis and eddy-current losses, is that which corresponds to the main flux at rated frequency when the machine develops an open-circuit (no-load) voltage per phase equal to the phasor sum of its rated voltage per phase and the ohmic drop per phase.

The stray-load loss per phase, added to the armature copper loss (at 75°C) per phase, and the sum divided by the square of the current, yields the effective value of armature resistance.

Brush contact losses of synchronous machines are usually small enough to be safely neglected, but in case they must be considered, the AIEE Standards specify that they may be computed by assuming a drop of (a) 1 volt per collector ring if carbon or graphite brushes with attached pigtails are used, or (b) $1\frac{1}{2}$ volts if pigtails are not attached, or (c) $\frac{1}{4}$ volt if metal-graphite brushes are used.

Bearing friction can theoretically be calculated, but practically it is variable with the load and is dependent upon uncertain conditions of lubrication. Windage loss, ordinarily small except in turbo-alternators unless hydrogen cooling is used, cannot be computed. The combined value of friction and windage is either measured, as described below, or estimated on the basis of experience with similar machines, and in either case this loss is treated as a constant in computing conventional efficiency.

10-31. Measurement of Losses. *a. By Rated Motor.* Friction, windage, and core loss are easily measured by driving the generator on open circuit by a d-c shunt motor which has already been calibrated* to determine its own internal losses. With any given excitation applied to the synchronous machine, the electrical input to the armature of the shunt motor, minus its armature copper loss, brush contact loss, core

* See A. S. Langsdorf, "Principles of Direct-current Machines," 5th ed., p. 621, McGraw-Hill Book Company, Inc., New York, 1940.

loss, and stray-power loss, is equal to the sum of the friction, windage, and core losses of the synchronous machine. Friction and windage loss can thus be determined by driving the synchronous machine at its rated speed with its field circuit open; hence, the core loss with the field excited is the difference between the output of the driving motor and the constant friction and windage loss. The core loss thus determined is plotted as a function of the terminal voltage, and from the curve so determined it is possible to read off the loss corresponding to rated voltage, corrected to take into account the ohmic drop.

To measure the stray-load loss, the terminals of the synchronous machine are short-circuited, and the excitation is varied over a sufficient range to circulate current from zero to somewhat more than full-load value. When thus driven at rated speed, the output of the d-c motor will include the friction and windage loss plus the load losses of the synchronous machine; hence, the load losses are determined by subtracting the previously measured friction and windage loss. The load losses thus measured include the ohmic loss of the armature winding (computed by using its d-c resistance) and the stray-load loss; hence, the latter can be found by subtraction. It is to be noted that a correction for core loss is not needed, because the flux in the main magnetic circuit is so small under the conditions of sustained short circuit that core loss is negligible. The load loss thus measured under short-circuit conditions is due to the local distortions of flux caused by armature reaction; if it may be assumed that these distortions are the same as under normal full-load running conditions (the armature current being the same in both cases), it would follow that the observed load loss per phase, divided by the square of the current (per phase), will be the effective resistance of the armature per phase.

b. *By Retardation Method.* It is well-known from the study of applied mechanics that in order to impart an angular acceleration α to a body of polar moment of inertia J, which at the moment is rotating with angular velocity ω, power must be applied to the extent required by the expression

$$P = J\omega\alpha \qquad (10\text{-}107)$$

Conversely, if the rotation is being slowed down, α becomes angular retardation (negative acceleration) and P becomes the power developed at the expense of the decreased kinetic energy of rotation, $\frac{1}{2}\omega^2 J$.

Assuming for the moment that the moment of inertia J is known, Eq. 10-107 provides means for measuring the power loss, P, of a synchronous machine if simultaneous values of ω and α are known. Suppose, for example, that the open-circuited machine is excited to a sufficient extent to make its core loss correspond to its rated terminal voltage (corrected to take account of ohmic drop) when it is running at its synchronous speed, i.e., when $\omega = 2\pi f$. Let the machine be driven in any convenient manner at a speed slightly above synchronism, and then be allowed to coast by removing the driving power. The speed will immediately begin to decrease in the manner indicated by the curve *edf* in Fig. 10-59. In order to plot this speed-time curve, it is necessary to observe the time corresponding to accurately known speeds, preferably measured by some form of stroboscope. Small machines will lose speed more quickly than large turbo-generators, which will ordinarily take a long time to come to

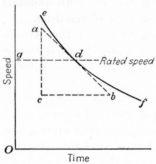

FIG. 10-59. Retardation method.

rest, so the curve *ef* will be flat. But at the point *d*, where the curve crosses the line of rated speed *(Og)*, the angular velocity ω equals $2\pi f$, and α is the slope of the tangent line *adb*, i.e.,

$$\alpha = \frac{ca}{cb}$$

Hence, if J is known, the power calculated by Eq. 10-107 is the friction, windage, and core loss.

The determination of the value of J can be made by applying a known power load to the shaft of the machine and observing its speed-time curve as it coasts from slightly above synchronism; but a simpler method is to run the machine as an unloaded synchronous motor with its field excitation adjusted for minimum armature current (see Art. 11-8 and Fig. 11-12). Under this condition, the power input to the armature includes the friction and windage, the core loss that corresponds to the excitation, and a negligible copper loss, all corresponding to synchronous speed. The machine is then speeded up somewhat above synchronism, and then allowed to coast while its field excitation remains the same as before. Consequently, on plotting the speed-time curve as in Fig. 10-59, the point *d* will correspond to known values of P, ω, and α, hence, by Eq. 10-107 the value of J can be found.

CHAPTER 11

THE SYNCHRONOUS MOTOR

11-1. General Physical Considerations. Assume for the sake of simplicity that a multipolar synchronous generator is provided with a concentrated single-phase winding of full pitch, as in Fig. 11-1. At the particular instant shown in the diagram, the emf developed in the winding by the field acting alone will have maximum value, and for counterclockwise rotation of the field poles will be directed in the manner indicated by the conventional dots and crosses. If it is further assumed that the radial component of airgap flux is sinusoidally distributed, the emf will vary harmonically. Let it be now assumed that the armature winding is connected to an external circuit of such character that the current is in phase with this emf; then as the winding moves relative to the poles, the

FIG. 11-1. Generator emf and current.

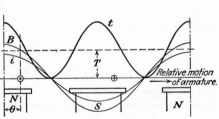

FIG. 11-2. Generator torque, $\psi = 0$.

simultaneous values of the current (i) in the coil and the field intensity (B) in which it is situated are shown by the ordinates of the sinusoidal curves i and B in Fig. 11-2. Each conductor will therefore be acted upon by a tangential force $F = Bli$ newtons, all quantities being expressed in mks units. Applying Fleming's left-hand rule to the conditions shown in Fig. 11-2, the force on the conductors is toward the left, or in opposition to their motion relative to the poles. The effect is therefore the same as though the field system of Fig. 11-1 experiences a torque in the clockwise direction, which must be balanced by the oppositely directed driving torque of the prime mover.

If the total number of armature conductors is Z, and the radius of the armature bore is r m, the total instantaneous torque is

$$t = ZBlri \qquad \text{newton-m} \qquad (11\text{-}1)$$

Since from the specified conditions

$$B = B_m \cos \theta$$
$$i = I_m \cos \theta$$

it follows that the instantaneous torque is

$$t = ZB_mI_mlr \cos^2 \theta$$
$$= \frac{1}{2}ZB_mI_mlr(1 + \cos 2\theta) \tag{11-2}$$

and since $\theta = \omega t$, where ω is the angular velocity in electrical radians per second, it is clear that the torque has a frequency double that of the emf and current and that its average value is

$$T = \frac{1}{2}ZB_mI_mlr \tag{11-3}$$

or half of the maximum value as shown in Fig. 11-2.

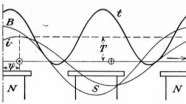

FIG. 11-3. Generator torque, $\psi > 0$.

If the external circuit which determines the current is now adjusted so that the current reaches its maximum $\psi°$ later than the emf, as in Fig. 11-3, the instantaneous torque is

$$t = ZB_mI_mlr \cos \theta \cos (\theta - \psi)$$
$$= \frac{1}{2}ZB_mI_mlr[\cos \psi + \cos (2\theta - \psi)] \tag{11-4}$$

and the average torque becomes

$$T = \frac{1}{2}ZB_mI_mlr \cos \psi \tag{11-5}$$

The torque curve in Fig. 11-3 is the same as in Fig. 11-2, but it is shifted downward and to the right, so that the torque is negative for a part of the time. This is analogous to the variation of power in a single-phase circuit, and cos ψ is a "torque factor" just as cos φ is a power factor. For the special case represented by $\psi = \pi/2$, the average torque is zero, and the instantaneous torque varies as a double-frequency harmonic function, being equally positive and negative every half cycle. When the torque is positive, the generator is driven by its prime mover, but when the torque is negative, the circuit is the source of power.

Suppose that while the generator is running under the conditions represented in Fig. 11-3 the power supply to the prime mover is suddenly cut off and that at the same time the armature current is reversed in direction but otherwise remains the same as before, as in Fig. 11-4. The torque reverses its sign and becomes motor torque, but the speed and the direction of rotation remain the same as before. The fact that the speed remains at its original synchronous value may be explained in several ways: one way that has already been mentioned is that the machine becomes the same as an induction motor in which the wound rotor is supplied with zero-frequency (continuous) current, and which is thereby forced to run in synchronism with the revolving field supplied by its stator. But it is also evident that the armature current must reverse its direction each time that a conductor passes from the influence of one pole to that of the next pole in order that the torque may remain predominantly of one sign, as in Fig. 11-4; or, looked at in another way, the magnetic field set up by the single-phase armature current is stationary in space but alternating in time, hence may be resolved into two rotating fields, each traveling at synchronous speed but in opposite directions.

The field poles must lock into step with one of these component fields which moves in the same direction as the initial rotation of the machine; and the other component of the armature field moves backward at double synchronous speed with respect to the field poles, giving rise to a double-frequency torque which is directed first one way, then the other, thus

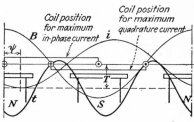

Fig. 11-4. Motor torque, $\psi > 0$.

again accounting for the torque curve of double frequency shown in Fig. 11-4.

In Fig. 11-3, illustrating generator action, the current, displaced in phase from the emf by angle ψ, has an in-phase component which magnetizes in the quadrature axis, and skews the main field in the direction of rotation, increasing the field intensity at the trailing tips and decreasing it at the leading pole tips; and the quadrature component, magnetizing in the direct axis of the field poles, demagnetizes the main field when ψ is an angle of lag, and magnetizes when ψ is an angle of lead. But in the case of Fig. 11-4, illustrating motor action, the conditions are different. In the first place, while the emf generated by the field flux (assumed to be acting alone) is still a maximum when the coil sides are opposite the middle of the poles, this emf is now the counter emf of the motor, and the impressed voltage must be opposite in phase, ignoring for the moment the effect of impedance drop. This means that the conditions shown in Fig. 11-4, so far as direction of current is concerned, illustrate the case of armature current lagging by angle ψ behind the impressed terminal voltage. It will be noted that the conditions are the exact opposite of those for generator action in Fig. 11-3; in other words, the in-phase component of current, while still magnetizing in the quadrature axis, skews the main field in a direction *opposite* to the direction of rotation, increasing the field intensity at the leading tips of the poles, and decreasing it at the trailing tips, exactly as in a d-c motor. And the quadrature component of current *magnetizes* the main field when ψ is an angle of lag, and demagnetizes when ψ is an angle of lead.

11-2. Physical Conditions in the Polyphase Synchronous Motor. If the motor of Fig. 11-4 is now provided with additional phase windings so that there are in all m phases displaced from each other by $2\pi/m$ electrical radians, each of them will develop a torque similar to that indicated in Eq. 11-4, but the variable phase angle will be successively θ, $\theta \pm \dfrac{2\pi}{m}$, . . . , $\theta \pm \dfrac{m-1}{m} 2\pi$. The sum of all the m expressions for torque may then be obtained by procedures already explained in Chap. 4 for similar types of trigonometric series, giving for the total torque

$$T = \frac{m}{2} Z B_m I_m lr \cos \psi \qquad \text{newton-m} \qquad (11\text{-}6)$$

which is independent of the variable angle $\theta = \omega t$, hence is unvarying with respect to time.   The double-frequency pulsations due to any one of the phase windings are exactly annulled by the combined effect of all the others.

Looked at in another way, a balanced polyphase current flowing in a symmetrically disposed winding sets up a magnetic field rotating at synchronous speed with respect to the winding.   This armature field consists of a set of consequent poles equal in number to that corresponding to the winding arrangement, and there is a tendency for the field poles (assumed to be excited) to lock into position with the armature poles, a north pole due to the armature holding on, as it were, to a south pole of the field system.   It is easy to see, however, that while this locking action is powerful if the field system is already up to synchronous speed when the armature current is flowing, there can be no torque when the field poles (assumed to constitute the rotor) are originally stationary; for under this condition the armature poles, as they sweep across the field poles, will urge the latter first in one direction, then in the other.   The synchronous motor is therefore not inherently self-starting, but must be equipped with some form of auxiliary starting device, to be described later.

While it is true that because of the interlocking action between the armature and the field poles the motor must either run at synchronous speed, or not run at all, it is not to be assumed that the engagement between the armature field and the rotor field is an absolutely rigid one. The angular velocity of the rotating magnetic field set up by the armature current is strictly equal (or proportional) to the corresponding angular velocity of the generator which supplies the current, and there may be slight pulsations of the line frequency because of the nature of the prime mover.   But even if the frequency, and therefore the angular velocity of the motor's armature field, is absolutely uniform, the coupling between the armature and rotor is represented by the drag between two sets of poles of opposite polarities, and it is well-known that the pull between such poles acts as though the lines of magnetic force were stretched elastic bands. It follows that the rotor position may at any instant be either slightly ahead of, or slightly behind, the corresponding position of the armature field, which means that the speed of the synchronous motor may oscillate, or hunt, being first slightly greater, then slightly less, than that of the assumed uniform speed of the rotating armature field. The effect is the same as though the shafts of the prime mover and of the synchronous motor were elastically, instead of rigidly, coupled.

11-3. Torque and Power Relations. The torque equation 11-6 was derived from fundamental considerations for the particular case of a concentrated full-pitch winding. It is possible to modify it to a more convenient form by observing that the average field intensity over a pole pitch is $B_{av} = (2/\pi)B_m$ and that the flux per pole is therefore

$$\Phi = B_{av}l\tau = \frac{2}{\pi} B_m l \frac{2\pi r}{p} = \frac{4B_m lr}{p}$$

from which

$$T = \frac{mp\Phi Z I_m}{2 \times 4} \cos \psi \tag{11-7}$$

or, for a given machine,

$$T = k\Phi I \cos \psi \tag{11-8}$$

where k may take values which will convert the torque to pound-feet or any other suitable unit.

It follows from the principles of mechanics that the mechanical power developed is

$$P = 2\pi \frac{n}{60} T \qquad \text{watts}$$

Substituting the value of T from Eq. 11-7, and at the same time inserting the relations $f = pn/120$, $I_m = \sqrt{2}\, I$, $Z = 2N$, the above expression for the power reduces to

$$
\begin{aligned}
P &= \sqrt{2}\, \pi m f \Phi N I \cos \psi \\
&= mEI \cos \psi
\end{aligned}
\tag{11-9}
$$

in accordance with the fundamental formula for the generated emf.

Because of the constant speed of a synchronous motor, the total torque developed is always directly proportional to the electrical power determined by the product of counter emf and the component of current in phase therewith. The total torque is greater than the torque actually available at the shaft because the total torque includes the amount consumed in overcoming the drag due to core losses, windage, and bearing friction; and the electrical power (per phase) represented by the product $EI \cos \psi$ is less than the power supplied from the line by the I^2R_a

loss in the armature winding. If the torque and power, per phase, are indicated by T and P, respectively, it follows that

$$P = \frac{2\pi n}{60} T \quad \text{watts}$$

where T is expressed in units which may be called *synchronous watts;* further,

$$VI \cos \varphi = P + I^2 R_a \tag{11-10}$$

where V is the impressed voltage per phase at the armature terminals and φ is the angle of phase displacement between V and I.

11-4. Transition from Generator to Motor Action. The preceding discussion emphasizes the fact that a synchronous machine will operate reversibly either as a generator or a motor, just as in the case of a shunt-wound d-c machine. That is to say, if the load on a generator is gradually reduced to zero so that the current likewise becomes zero, a reversal of the load from electrical to mechanical character will cause a reversal

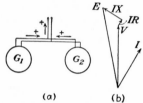

(a)   (b)

FIG. 11-5. Generators in parallel.

FIG. 11-6. Series connection of generator and motor.

of the current supplied to it, provided the machine is connected to bus bars which continue to be supplied with constant voltage from another generator of sufficient capacity; but the machine whose load has been thus reversed continues to run at the original speed and in the original direction, the change from generator to motor action occurring insensibly if it is sufficiently gradual.

Suppose, for example, that two identical generators, G_1 and G_2 (Fig. 11-5a), are connected in parallel to an external load circuit and that the bus-bar voltage is maintained at V volts per phase. The phase relations between the generated emf E, the terminal voltage V, and the current I of each machine will then be as represented in Fig. 11-5b, which should be compared with the general diagram of an alternator (Fig. 10-11). The arrows in Fig. 11-5a indicate the positive directions with respect to the external load circuit.

If the power supply to generator G_2 is now cut off, and generator G_1 is so regulated that the terminal voltage remains unaltered, generator G_2 becomes a synchronous motor M (Fig. 11-6) and the voltage E which it develops becomes a counter emf which must be considered to have a negative sign with respect to the local circuit between the two machines. The terminal voltage V and the current I taken by the motor, considered with respect to this local circuit, have the same signs as before the change from generator to motor action. It is then obvious that

$$\mathbf{E}_{G_1} - \mathbf{I}Z_{G_1} = \mathbf{V} = -\mathbf{E}_M + \mathbf{I}Z_M \qquad (11\text{-}11)$$

where the subscripts G_1 and M refer to the generator and motor, respectively. Equation 11-11 is a statement of the fact that the terminal voltage V contains a component equal and opposite to the counter emf of the motor and a component to overcome the internal impedance of the armature winding. This equation may be written

$$\mathbf{E}_{G_1} + \mathbf{E}_M = \mathbf{I}(Z_{G_1} + Z_M) \qquad (11\text{-}12)$$

which is merely a statement of the fact that the phasor sum of the emfs generated in the two machines (taken with respect to the local circuit in which they act) is equal to the impedance drop in the entire local circuit. It is important to understand that Z_{G_1} includes not only the impedance of the generator itself but also that of the line and bus bars up to the point at which the terminal voltage is measured; similarly, that Z_M includes the impedance of the motor armature and that of the line connecting it to the terminal points at which V is measured.

When the change from generator to motor action occurs, the counter emf of the motor will remain equal in magnitude to the original generated emf, assuming that there has been no change of excitation. It

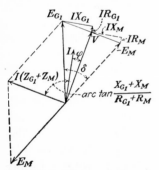

FIG. 11-7. Phase relations in general.

follows, therefore, since the resultant of E_{G_1} and E_M must be sufficient to drive the current through the total impedance $Z_{G_1} + Z_M$ of the local circuit of Fig. 11-6, that E_M must change its phase position in the manner indicated in Fig. 11-7. In other words, the generated emfs E_{G_1} and $E_{G_2} = E_M$, which were originally numerically equal and in exact phase opposition (with respect to the local circuit), must now fall short of exact phase opposition. Ordinary considerations of mechanical realities are sufficient to indicate that when the driving power is cut off from generator G_2 its rotor must drop back relative to the rotor of G_1, which may be assumed to continue to be driven with unvarying speed; if G_2, which now becomes motor M, then assumes a mechanical load, its rotor system must drop back still further, the end result being that E_M (reversed) lags behind E_{G_1} by an angle δ (Fig. 11-7). The actual existence of this physical displacement can be observed by means of a stroboscope; or if the two identical machines, both assumed to be of the open type of construction, are placed with their shafts in line, then on viewing the motor through the pole system of the generator, the motor poles will appear to be stationary, but displaced backward.

The construction of Fig. 11-7 is in strict accord with Eqs. 11-11 and 11-12. The current I lags behind the resultant of E_{G_1} and E_M by an angle whose tangent is $(X_{G_1} + X_M)/(R_{G_1} + R_M)$, and it will be noted that with the dimensions that have been selected the line current I leads the terminal voltage by angle φ. Had the angle δ been differently chosen, E_{G_1} and E_M retaining the same magnitudes, both I and V would change in magnitude and phase, and under certain conditions the angle φ could become an angle of lag. But whatever the phase positions of V and I may be, the power (per phase) supplied to the motor terminals is $VI \cos \varphi$. It is clear, therefore, that the primary cause of the varying values of δ and φ is the varying load on the motor, other conditions (such as field excitation) remaining the same.

CYLINDRICAL-ROTOR THEORY

11-5. Phasor Diagram. The diagram of Fig. 11-7 has been drawn subject to the assumption that E_{G_1} and E_M remain constant so far as magnitudes are concerned. Ordinarily, however, the motor is operated with constant voltage V applied to its terminals, the internally generated emf E_{G_1} being left to take care of itself. If, therefore, V is treated as constant, there are two independent variables that enter into the analysis of the motor behavior, one of them being the load on the motor and the other the rotor (field) excitation; the dependent variables are then (1) the current taken by the motor and (2) the angle of phase displacement between terminal voltage and current.

Let it now be assumed that the characteristics of the motor can be analyzed with sufficient accuracy by means of the synchronous-impedance method described in Art. 10-10, and that the synchronous imped- ance and synchronous reactance of the motor are to be found in precisely the same manner as has been described for the case of a generator. The phasor diagrams for the motor, analogous to the general diagram in Fig. 10-19, then take the forms indicated in Figs. 11-8 and 11-9, the former illustrating the case of lagging current, the latter that of leading current. It is desirable now to modify the original symbols, and to represent by E the counter emf previously designated as E_M. Since this counter emf (reversed) is one component of the terminal voltage, the other compo- nent being the synchronous impedance, it follows that E must be con- ceived as due to the flux produced by the field excitation F and that $-E$ must therefore lead F by 90°. The phasor sum of F and the armature excitation A must then be the resultant excitation F_R, and F_R must accordingly lag by 90° behind $-E_a$, which is equal and opposite to the emf actually generated in the armature winding; in other words, X_a indicated in the diagrams is the true leakage reactance.

The two diagrams (Figs. 11-8 and 11-9) bring out clearly several interesting facts. One is that in the case of lagging current (Fig. 11-8) the resultant excitation F_R is greater than the field excitation F, whereas in the case of leading current (Fig. 11-9) F_R is less than F. These results are in agreement with the conclusion, previously deduced, that in the case of a synchronous motor a lagging current magnetizes the field poles, whereas a leading current demagnetizes them. It will also be noted that while the terminal voltage and current are numerically the same in both cases, the field excitation F must be greater when the current leads than when it lags. The power absorbed by the motor is the same in both cases, since V, I, and φ have the same magnitudes. Consequently it is

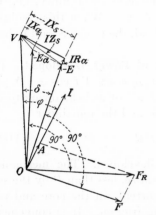

FIG. 11-8. Synchronous-impedance diagram, current lagging.

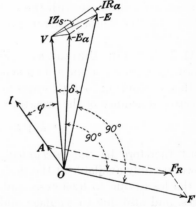

FIG. 11-9. Synchronous-impedance diagram, current leading.

seen that other things remaining the same, *an increase in the field excitation is capable of changing the phase displacement between terminal voltage and current from an angle of lag to an angle of lead.* This is an extremely important characteristic of the synchronous motor, for by the simple expedient of overexciting its field winding the machine may be made to draw a leading current from the source of supply and thus neutralize in whole or in part, or even overcompensate, the effect of other inductive loads on the system. A synchronous motor used in this way is called a *synchronous condenser.*

There is nothing mysterious about this property of a synchronous motor, and it is possible to explain it in an even simpler manner than that involving the use of phasor diagrams. For in general the counter emf of any motor must be very nearly equal and opposite to the impressed terminal voltage, so that if the latter is constant, the counter emf will be substantially constant. (The phasor difference is in any case the relatively small leakage-impedance drop.) Now the counter emf is proportional to the speed and to the field flux, and since the speed is constant in the case of the synchronous motor, the field flux must likewise be substantially constant within the normal limits of operation. It follows, then, that if the field excitation is increased, thereby tending to increase the field flux that can vary only slightly, there must be an automatic change of the armature mmf in order to offset the effect of the increased field excitation; the armature current must therefore contain a leading component, since it has already been shown by simple physical considerations that a leading current in a synchronous motor exerts a demagnetizing effect. By the same reasoning, it follows that a weakening of the field excitation tends to draw a lagging current from the source of supply. For any set of operating conditions, there will be some value of field excitation which will cause the power factor to be unity, i.e., the current to be in phase with the terminal voltage. When this condition exists while the motor is carrying its rated load, the motor is said to have normal excitation.

11-6. Armature Current as a Function of Power Developed. The power (per phase) supplied to a synchronous motor is $VI \cos \varphi$. A part of this, amounting to $I^2 R_a$ watts per phase, is lost as heat owing to the effective resistance of the armature winding, and the remainder

$$P = VI \cos \varphi - I^2 R_a \qquad (11\text{-}13)$$

must therefore be the *mechanical power* developed. The mechanical power usefully available at the shaft is, of course, less than P by the sum of the losses due to hysteresis and eddy currents in the core and pole faces, and also due to windage and bearing friction. It is convenient, however, to deal not with the power at the shaft but with the total power developed, in accordance with the above equation.

Equation 11-13 can be written in the form

$$I^2 - \frac{V}{R_a} I \cos \varphi = -\frac{P}{R_a} \qquad (11\text{-}13a)$$

and by adding to both sides the term $(V/2R_a)^2$ it becomes

$$I^2 + \left(\frac{V}{2R_a}\right)^2 - 2\left(\frac{V}{2R_a}\right) I \cos \varphi = \left(\frac{V}{2R_a}\right)^2 - \frac{P}{R_a} \qquad (11\text{-}14)$$

The constant quantity $V/2R_a$ is of the nature of current, expressible in amperes, and it is clearly a current in phase with V since the denominator is a pure resistance. The left-hand member of Eq. 11-14 is then the sum of the squares of two currents, minus twice their product times the cosine of the phase angle between them; so if $V/2R_a$ and I are regarded as two sides of a triangle, as in Fig. 11-10, the third side must be $\sqrt{(V/2R_a)^2 - P/R_a}$. If the condition is imposed that P is to remain constant, both $V/2R_a$ and $\sqrt{(V/2R_a)^2 - P/R_a}$ are constant, and the locus of the current phasor I, as φ changes, must therefore be a circle having a radius $\sqrt{(V/2R_a)^2 - P/R_a}$ and with its center at point C. It is clear that when $P = 0$, corresponding to an ideal no-load condition, the circle has a radius $V/2R_a$, therefore passing through point O. The limiting (maximum) value of power is that which reduces the radical $\sqrt{(V/2R_a)^2 - P/R_a}$ to zero, for any greater value of P would lead to imaginary quantities; accordingly, the maximum value of power is

$$P_{max} = \frac{V^2}{4R_a} \qquad (11\text{-}15)$$

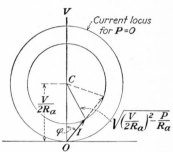

and corresponding to this value the circular locus of I degenerates to one of zero radius, i.e., it becomes the point C itself. This means that the current corresponding to maximum power is $V/2R_a$, and the power input would then be $V(V/2R_a)$, or twice the mechanical power developed;

FIG. 11-10. Current locus, constant power.

the excess input is accounted for by the ohmic loss in the winding, amounting to

$$I^2R_a = \left(\frac{V}{2R_a}\right)^2 R_a = \frac{V^2}{4R_a}$$

or the same as the mechanical power itself, and the efficiency is therefore 50 per cent. The maximum power is of theoretical interest only, for it is much beyond the practical rating determined by temperature limitations in an actual machine.

When Eq. 11-14 is solved for I, the result is

$$I = \frac{V}{2R_a} \cos \varphi \pm \sqrt{\left(\frac{V}{2R_a} \cos \varphi\right)^2 - \frac{P}{R_a}} \qquad (11\text{-}16)$$

showing that for given values of P and φ there are always two values of current, as indicated in Fig. 11-10.

11-7. Armature Current as a Function of Excitation. It is clear from Figs. 11-7 to 11-9 that V, the terminal voltage, is the phasor sum of the reversed counter emf and the synchronous impedance drop; this is in accordance with Eq. 11-10, which in terms of the modified symbols becomes

$$\mathbf{V} = -\mathbf{E} + \mathbf{I}Z_s$$

where $Z_s = R_a + jX_s$ is the synchronous impedance of the armature. The counter emf E is proportional to, and in quadrature with, the field excitation F, so that, so far as mere magnitudes are concerned, it is possible to write

$$E = cF$$

where c is a proportionality constant implying that the magnetic circuit of the machine is unsaturated. The complex expression is

$$-\mathbf{E} = jc\mathbf{F} \tag{11-17}$$

The phase relations between V, E, and I are shown in modified form in Fig. 11-11, from which it may be seen that IZ_s is always one side of a triangle (OQV) whose other two sides are V and $cF = E$, and which include between them the variable angle δ; therefore,

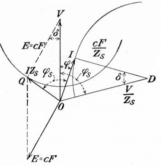

$$
\begin{aligned}
(IZ_s)^2 &= V^2 + (cF)^2 - 2V(cF) \cos \delta \\
&= V^2 + E^2 - 2VE \cos \delta
\end{aligned}
\tag{11-18}
$$

If the excitation F (and therefore also E) is held constant as the load changes, the locus of point Q (the end of the IZ_s phasor) is a circle having its center at V

Fig. 11-11. Current locus, constant excitation.

and a radius equal to the constant length $cF = E$.

To determine the locus of the current phasor I, it may be observed that since the locus of IZ_s is a circle, that of I must be another circle; this circle may be fixed by observing that Eq. 11-18 can be written

$$I^2 = \left(\frac{V}{Z_s}\right)^2 + \left(\frac{cF}{Z_s}\right)^2 - 2\left(\frac{V}{Z_s}\right)\left(\frac{cF}{Z_s}\right) \cos \delta \tag{11-19}$$

which states that I is one side of a triangle whose other two sides, including between them the variable angle δ, are the constant lengths V/Z_s and $cF/Z_s = E/Z_s$, both of which are of the nature of current. Consequently, the locus of the current I is a circle of radius cF/Z_s having its center at D, where the current phasor $OD = V/Z_s$ lags behind V by an angle $\varphi_s = \tan^{-1} X_s/R_a$.

Another way to determine the locus of I follows from the fact that if each side of triangle OQV is divided by the complex expression for the impedance Z_s, namely, $Z_s \epsilon^{j\varphi_s}$, the effect is the same as multiplying them by $(1/Z_s)\epsilon^{-j\varphi_s}$; that is, each side of the triangle OQV is changed in scale by the multiplier $1/Z_s$ and at the same time rotated clockwise through angle φ_s.

The variable angle δ is evidently a function of the load, for when F (and E) are constant in magnitude, the phase position of E relative to V must be determined by the angle through which the field system drops back in order that the resultant of V and E may yield sufficient current to develop the necessary torque.

It follows, then, that as F takes all possible values from zero to the maximum amount consistent with permissible temperature rise, the locus of I is a family of concentric circles having point D in Fig. 11-11 as center.

11-8. The V and O Curves of the Synchronous Motor. Figures 11-10 and 11-11 show separately the relation of the dependent variable I to the two independent variables P and F. On superposing these diagrams, the two families of circles, one for various values of power, the other for various values of field excitation, take the positions shown in Fig. 11-12,

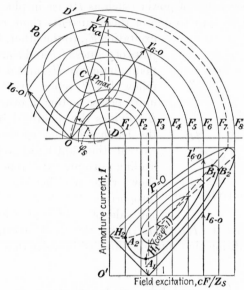

Fig. 11-12. Construction of V and O curves.

where D, the center of the excitation circles, falls on the circle for zero power. The proof of this fact follows from the relation

$$OD = \frac{V}{Z_s} = \frac{V}{R_a}\frac{R_a}{Z_s} = \frac{V}{R_a}\cos\varphi_s$$

It will be observed that for any excitation such as is represented by the radius of circle F_6, there are in general two values of armature current for any given power such as $P = 0$. Two such paired values of current are indicated by the phasors I_{60} and I'_{60}, one of them leading the terminal voltage V, the other lagging behind it. These two values of current are also shown in the cartesian diagram in Fig. 11-12, the construction of which is evident without further explanation. Each of the curves in the cartesian diagram shows the relation between field excitation and armature current for a fixed value of the mechanical power developed; because of the shape of the lower portions of the loops they are usually called the V curves of the synchronous motor; when considered as a whole, the oval shape has given rise to the term O curves. The V curves possess a number of interesting and important geometrical properties, which will now be investigated.

11-9. Condition for Unity Power Factor. It will be noted that there are two points on each loop in Fig. 11-12, such that at one of them the current is a minimum, as at A_1, while at the other the current is a maximum, as at B_1. The locus of all such points is indicated as a dashed line H_1. Now it is clear from Fig. 11-13, which is a small-scale reproduction of part of Fig. 11-12, that minimum and maximum values of current corresponding to any value of power (such as P) are in phase with the terminal voltage; and that to one of these currents there corresponds the

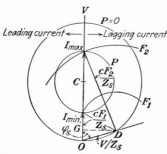

FIG. 11-13. Condition for $\cos \varphi = 1$.

excitation F_1, to the other, F_2. It is these pairs of values of I and F which determine points on curve H_1, and it must therefore follow that H_1 represents the condition for unity power factor; in other words, curve H_1 divides the quadrant into two zones, the left-hand zone representing lagging current, the right-hand zone representing leading current. Reference to Fig. 11-13 shows that in either case the excitation (proportional to cF/Z_s) is represented by one side of a triangle whose other two

sides are the current ($I_{\min}$ or $I_{\max}$) and the fixed length V/Z_s; consequently, the condition that must be satisfied in order that the power factor shall be unity is

$$\left(\frac{cF}{Z_s}\right)^2 = \left(\frac{V}{Z_s}\right)^2 + I^2 - 2\frac{V}{Z_s} I \cos \varphi_s \qquad (11\text{-}20)$$

This equation, regarded as a relation between the two variables cF/Z_s and I, represents curve H_1, which is accordingly a hyperbola. Equation 11-20 can be rewritten in the form

$$\left(\frac{cF}{Z_s}\right)^2 - \left(I - \frac{V}{Z_s} \cos \varphi_s\right)^2 = \left(\frac{V}{Z_s} \sin \varphi_s\right)^2 \qquad (11\text{-}21)$$

which shows that the vertex of the curve (Fig. 11-12) has the coordinates

$$\frac{cF}{Z_s} = \left(\frac{V}{Z_s}\right) \sin \varphi_s = \frac{V X_s}{Z_s^2}$$

and

$$I = \left(\frac{V}{Z_s}\right) \cos \varphi_s = \frac{V R_a}{Z_s^2}$$

These values follow also from Fig. 11-13, from which it may be seen that the minimum excitation consistent with the condition $\cos \varphi = 1$ is DG, drawn perpendicular to OV, thus giving $(cF/Z_s)_{\min} = (V/Z_s) \sin \varphi_s$.

11-10. Minimum and Maximum Excitation for Given Power. Condition for Stability. Again referring to Fig. 11-12, each of the V or O curves is characterized by two points, such as A_2 and B_2, which correspond to minimum and maximum excitation for the power corresponding to the loop considered. The construction of Fig. 11-14 shows that for this condition the excitation circles F_1 and F_2 are tangent to the particular power circle under consideration, and that the current (I_1 or I_2) is represented by one side of a triangle whose other two sides are cF/Z_s and V/Z_s, which

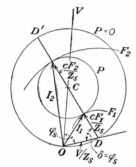
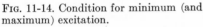

FIG. 11-14. Condition for minimum (and maximum) excitation.

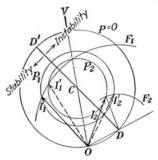

FIG. 11-15. Stability diagram.

include between them the constant angle φ_s. The general relation determining the locus of all such points, indicated by curve H_2 (Fig. 11-12), is then

$$I^2 = \left(\frac{V}{Z_s}\right)^2 + \left(\frac{cF}{Z_s}\right)^2 - 2\frac{V}{Z_s}\frac{cF}{Z_s}\cos\varphi_s \tag{11-22}$$

which may be written

$$I^2 - \left(\frac{cF}{Z_s} - \frac{V}{Z}\cos\varphi_s\right)^2 = \left(\frac{V}{Z}\sin\varphi_s\right)^2 \tag{11-23}$$

which is the equation of a hyperbola whose vertex has the coordinates $cF/Z_s = (V/Z_s)\cos\varphi_s$, and $I = (V/Z_s)\sin\varphi_s$.

It will be noted that Eqs. 11-23 and 11-21 are alike in form but that the variables cF/Z_s and I are simply interchanged. This means that the two curves H_1 and H_2 are one and the same curve in two different positions, and that they are symmetrical with respect to a 45° line through origin O'.

The curve H_2 of Fig. 11-12 has its counterpart in the diameter DD' of Fig. 11-14. The significance of these lines may be seen in Fig. 11-15. For suppose that a motor developing power P_1 (Fig. 11-15) draws I_1 amp when the excitation is F_1; any increase of load will cause a momentary slowing down of the rotor, and because of the increase in angle δ the current will change to some such value as I_1' provided the excitation F_1 remains unaltered; the end of the current phasor then lies upon a power circle P_2, which because of its smaller radius represents greater power than P_1; hence, the increase of load is accompanied by an increase in the power and torque developed, which means stable operation. If on the other hand the motor were operating with power P_2, excitation F_2, and current I_2, an increase of load would cause the current phasor to swing backward to a position such as I'_2, and the power developed would then decrease. It follows, therefore, that the portions of the O curves lying above curve H_2 (Fig. 11-12) are of theoretical interest only and cannot be obtained experimentally by ordinary test methods* because the motor would fall out of synchronism and stall before the upper parts of the curves could be reached; moreover, the upper portions of the curve correspond to values of armature current much beyond the limits prescribed by considerations of temperature rise.

11-11. Additional Geometrical Properties of V Curves. The condition represented by $P = 0$ in the preceding discussion is, of course, purely theoretical, because the motor must develop enough mechanical power to overcome its own core loss and friction loss if it is to continue to run. The condition represented by $P = 0$ might be realized if the motor were driven by another motor which supplies these losses. In any case, the condition $P = 0$ is not a hard and fast limit which cannot be overstepped, for when $P < 0$ (that is, negative) the motor becomes a generator, and $P = 0$ then characterizes the boundary between motor and generator action of a reversible machine.

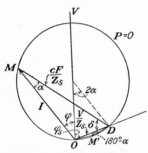

FIG. 11-16. Phasor diagram for zero power.

Now it will be seen from Fig. 11-16 that when $P = 0$ the phasor representing current I terminates on the circle for zero power, and the phasor representing the field excitation, cF/Z_s, drawn from point D, must terminate at the same point. In the triangle formed by I, cF/Z_s, and the fixed length $OD = V/Z_s$, the angle at point M is constant and equal, say, to α, for all values of the phase angle φ provided point M remains above the line OD; when the terminal point of the current phasor I lies below OD, as at M', the angle at M' is also constant, but it is equal to $180 - \alpha$. The geometry of the figure shows that

$$\alpha = 90 - \varphi_s \tag{11-24}$$

In the first case, when M is above OD, the cosine law applied to triangle ODM gives

$$I^2 + \left(\frac{cF}{Z_s}\right)^2 - 2I\frac{cF}{Z_s}\cos\alpha = \left(\frac{V}{Z_s}\right)^2$$

* See J. F. H. Douglas, E. D. Engeset, and R. H. Jones, Complete Synchronous Motor Excitation Characteristics, *Trans. AIEE*, **44**:164 (1925).

and in the second case, when M' is below OD,

$$I^2 + \left(\frac{cF}{Z_s}\right)^2 - 2I\,\frac{cF}{Z_s}\cos\,(180 - \alpha) = \left(\frac{V}{Z_s}\right)^2$$

Substituting the relation given by Eq. 11-24, the last two equations become

$$I^2 + \left(\frac{cF}{Z_s}\right)^2 - 2I\,\frac{cF}{Z_s}\sin\,\varphi_s = \left(\frac{V}{Z_s}\right)^2 \qquad (11\text{-}25)$$

and

$$I^2 + \left(\frac{cF}{Z_s}\right)^2 + 2I\,\frac{cF}{Z_s}\sin\,\varphi_s = \left(\frac{V}{Z_s}\right)^2 \qquad (11\text{-}26)$$

which represent a pair of ellipses, as in Fig. 11-17. Only those portions shown in full lines have any physical significance so far as the synchronous motor is concerned, and these portions define the complete V curve for zero power. They are the same curves shown in Fig. 11-12, though to a different scale. By applying the usual methods of analytic geometry, it is readily shown that the major axes of both ellipses are inclined to the reference axes at angles of 45°, and that the squares of the lengths of the major and minor axes are, respectively, $\dfrac{(V/Z_s)^2}{1 - \sin\,\varphi_s}$ and $\dfrac{(V/Z_s)^2}{1 + \sin\,\varphi_s}$, which reduce to $V^2/Z_s(Z_s - X_s)$ and $V^2/Z_s(Z_s + X_s)$.

Since the current I is a function of two independent variables, P and F, it is possible to represent the relations between them as a three-dimensional surface referred to P, F, and I as coordinate axes. The V or O curves of Fig. 11-12 are in fact the projections of contour lines of this surface, each one corresponding to a particular value of power plotted at right angles to the plane of I and F (or cF/Z_s). The power circles of Fig. 11-12, reproduced as part of Fig. 11-18, have been drawn for convenience with uniform spacing between them, but it does not

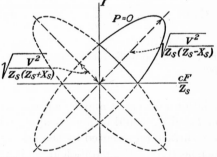

FIG. 11-17. Elliptical V curves, zero power.

follow that the power scale corresponding to them is uniform, and in fact it is not. For these circles derive from Eq. 11-13a, namely,

$$I^2 - \frac{V}{R_a}\,I\cos\,\varphi = -\frac{P}{R_a}$$

which, when regarded as a relation between two variables, I and P (V, R_a, and φ being constant), is the equation of a parabola. In particular, when $\cos\,\varphi = 1$, the parabola takes the form shown in Fig. 11-18, which may be considered to be the vertical cross section of a paraboloid of revolution, horizontal sections of which constitute the power circles of Fig.

11-12.   The power scale, plotted to the left in Fig. 11-18, then increases uniformly from zero at the base of the paraboloid to $P_{max} = V^2/4R_a$ at the vertex; for example, in Fig. 11-18 three uniformly spaced power circles have been drawn between the zero-power circle and the center, and they correspond, in order of increasing power, to $\frac{7}{16}P_{max}$, $\frac{3}{4}P_{max}$, and $\frac{15}{16}P_{max}$.

Since the power circles of Fig. 11-12 may be regarded as sections (or contour lines) of a paraboloid like that of Fig. 11-18, it follows naturally that the family of concentric excitation circles (Fig. 11-12) are to be considered as the projections of a family of concentric cylinders whose common axis is perpendicular to the plane of the drawing through the point D.   Any one of these cylinders, representing a fixed value of excitation, will then intersect the paraboloid in a space curve defining the relation between I and P subject to the condition of constant excitation; this

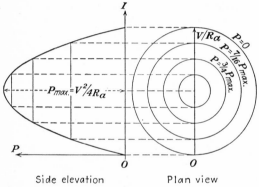

Side elevation   Plan view

FIG. 11-18. Parabolic relation between current and power.

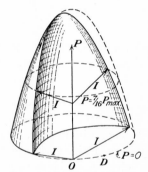

FIG. 11-19. Freehand perspective of paraboloid cut away by cylinder.

relation between I and P, when transferred to a plane through the axes of I and P, would be a vertical section, perpendicular to the axis of F, of the surface represented by the nest of V curves, Fig. 11-12.   A freehand perspective of the paraboloid, as it appears when cut away by an intersecting cylinder, is shown in Fig. 11-19, which includes an attempt to show how, as the power increases, the current changes in magnitude and in phase, there being two values of current for each value of power.

11-12. Effect of R_a and X_s.   Graphical Construction for Torque.   All of the preceding analysis of motor performance has been based upon simple geometrical properties of the diagrams derived from the fundamental phasor diagrams Figs. 11-8 and 11-9.   It is apparent that the motor constants R_a and X_s play an important part in the development of the theory; so it is desirable to investigate their effects in greater detail than has yet been done.   To this end, Fig. 11-11 has been redrawn in the modified form of Fig. 11-20.

From Fig. 11-20, as well as from Eq. 11-10, it is seen that

$$\mathbf{V} = -\mathbf{E} + \mathbf{I}(R_a + jX_s) \tag{11-27}$$

and
$$-\mathbf{E} = E \sin \delta + jE \cos \delta \tag{11-28}$$

provided that V is drawn vertically upward, so that

$$\mathbf{V} = 0 + jV \tag{11-29}$$

From these relations, it follows that

$$\mathbf{I} = \frac{\mathbf{V} + \mathbf{E}}{R_a + jX_s} = \frac{-E \sin \delta + j(V - E \cos \delta)}{R_a + jX_s} \tag{11-30}$$

which, when rationalized, gives

$$\mathbf{I} = \frac{(V - E \cos \delta)X_s - ER_a \sin \delta}{R_a^2 + X_s^2}$$
$$+ j \frac{(V - E \cos \delta)R_a + EX_s \sin \delta}{R_a^2 + X_s^2} \tag{11-31}$$

The mechanical power developed by the motor may be obtained by taking the real part of the product formed by multiplying the complex expression for $-\mathbf{E}$ by the conjugate of $\mathbf{I}$. The result is

$$P = \frac{VE(R_a \cos \delta + X_s \sin \delta) - E^2 R_a}{R_a^2 + X_s^2} \tag{11-32}$$

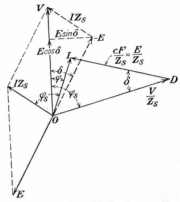

FIG. 11-20. Modified phasor diagram of synchronous motor.

and on substituting $R_a = Z_s \cos \varphi_s$ and $X_s = Z_s \sin \varphi_s$ it becomes

$$P = \frac{VE \cos (\varphi_s - \delta)}{Z_s} - \frac{E^2 \cos \varphi_s}{Z_s} \tag{11-33}$$

This equation gives the same mechanical power as that involved in Eq. 11-13, namely,

$$P = VI \cos \varphi - I^2 R_a$$

but it has the advantage of introducing a different set of variables, particularly the torque angle δ.

For example, assume that a motor is operating with fixed values of V, E, R_a, and X_s; then the only variable dependent upon the load is angle δ. The condition for maximum power consistent with the set of constant parameters is

$$\frac{dP}{d\delta} = \frac{VE}{Z_s} \sin (\varphi_s - \delta) = 0$$

from which it is seen that $\delta = \varphi_s$. This result has already been anticipated, for it follows from Fig. 11-14 that for a given excitation the power will have its greatest value when the power circle and the excitation circle are tangent to each other, in which case $\delta = \varphi_s$. Assuming that $\delta = \varphi_s$, Eq. 11-33 reduces to

$$P_m = \frac{VE - E^2 \cos \varphi_s}{Z_s} = \frac{VE}{Z_s} - \frac{E^2 R_a}{Z_s^2} \tag{11-34}$$

where P_m is the largest value of power consistent with the excitation corresponding to the counter emf E. The larger the value assigned to E, the smaller will be the value of P_m; consequently, the largest possible value of E is that which reduces P_m to zero, or

$$\frac{VE_{\max}}{Z_s} - \frac{E_{\max}^2 R_a}{Z_s^2} = 0$$

whence
$$E_{\max} = V \frac{Z_s}{R_a} \tag{11-35}$$

which is several times as great as the impressed voltage V. The same result is deducible from Fig. 11-14, where the largest possible excitation circle has a radius (to the scale of amperes)

$$DD' = \frac{cF_{\max}}{Z_s} = \frac{E_{\max}}{Z_s}$$

and this must equal, to the same scale, the diameter of the zero-power circle V/R_a, from which $E_{\max} = VZ_s/R_a$. It must be remembered, however, that this maximum value of counter emf has no practical significance, for it corresponds to values of armature current far in excess of permissible limits. Moreover, when $\delta = \varphi_s$, the machine is operating on the dividing line between stability and instability, which is in itself impracticable.

Equation 11-34 can be written

$$P_m = \frac{VE}{\sqrt{R_a^2 + X_s^2}} - \frac{E^2 R_a}{R_a^2 + X_s^2} \tag{11-36}$$

and if it is assumed that V, E, and R_a are constant, there will be some value of X_s for which P_m will have its greatest value. Thus, setting $dP_m/dX_s = 0$, the result is

$$X_s = R_a \sqrt{\frac{4E^2}{V^2} - 1} \tag{11-37}$$

which leads to the conclusion *that if $E = V$ it would follow that $X_s = \sqrt{3} \, R_a$, or $\varphi_s = \tan^{-1}(X_s/R_a) = 60°$*. The physical meaning of this result is shown in Fig. 11-21a; it implies that the terminal point of phasor $DC = CF/Z_s = E/Z_s$ is at the center of the system of power circles, and that the power is the maximum which the motor is theoretically capable of developing. There would then be no overload capacity, the motor would be operating on the verge of instability, and the current would be $V/2R_a$, much beyond the allowable limit. The conditions in an actual motor are somewhat like those shown in Fig. 11-21b, where P_r is approximately the position of the circle of *rated* power; and where, for

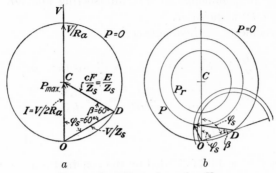

FIG. 11-21. Effect of varying X_s.

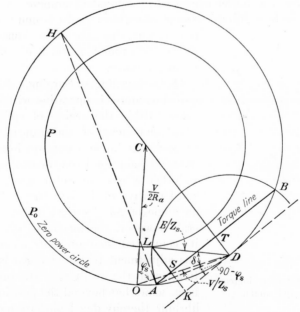

FIG. 11-22. Construction of torque line.

some intermediate power indicated by circle P, there is the possibility of drawing leading current from the line with only moderate excitation, thus utilizing to advantage one of the most valuable characteristics of the synchronous motor.

The Torque Diagram. Figure 11-22, which is basically the same as Fig. 11-11, illustrates the conditions when the motor has a field excitation $DL = E/Z_s$, and is carrying a load to which there corresponds the power circle P. The armature current, OL, is fixed by the point of intersection of the excitation circle (radius DL) and the power circle P. The excitation circle intersects the zero-power circle in the points A and B, thus fixing the line AB (perpendicular to CD). From point L, the line LSK is drawn perpendicular to AB, intersecting line DK (drawn perpendicular to CD) at point K.

From the geometry of the diagram,

$$LK = \frac{E}{Z_s} \sin\left[\delta + (90 - \varphi_s)\right] = \frac{E}{Z_s} \cos\left(\delta - \varphi_s\right)$$

and

$$TD = SK = \frac{(DA)^2}{DH} = \frac{(DL)^2}{DH} = \frac{(E/Z_s)^2}{V/R_a} = \frac{E^2}{VZ_s} \cos \varphi_s$$

Consequently,

$$LS = LK - SK = \frac{E}{Z_s} \cos\left(\delta - \varphi_s\right) - \frac{E^2}{VZ_s} \cos \varphi_s$$

which is equal to Eq. 11-33 divided by the constant impressed voltage V. Therefore, the line LS is proportional to the power represented by the circle P; it is the power expressed in equivalent amperes, and may be read in watts by a suitable change of scale; it is also proportional to the torque, which because of the constant speed of the synchronous motor is directly proportional to power.

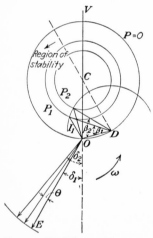

FIG. 11-23. Effect of increase of load on torque angle.

11-13. Hunting, or Surging. When a synchronous motor is operating with fixed excitation within the region of stability, Fig. 11-23, an increase of load from P_1 to P_2 calls for a change in the rotor position from that defined by angle δ_1 to one defined by $\delta_1 + \Delta\delta$. In other words, the rotor must slip backward relative to the armature field through an angle of $\Delta\delta$ electrical degrees. In general, however, the inertia of the rotor and its connected load prevents an instantaneous adjustment to the changed load conditions, with the result that the rotor swings back somewhat beyond the position of equilibrium, thereby developing torque in excess of the load requirement and so not only checking the initial reduction of speed but increasing it slightly above synchronous speed. In this manner, there is set up a periodic swinging of the rotor first to one side, then to the other, of the new position of equilibrium, this oscillation being superposed upon the uniform synchronous speed of rotation. Looked at in another way, the armature field produced by the line current rotates at constant angular velocity, and the rotor field, moving in space with the armature field, has a relative to-and-fro motion with respect to the latter.   Eddy currents are therefore produced in the pole faces, which, in accordance with Lenz's law, are always so directed as to oppose their cause and therefore tend to damp out these oscillations.   Changes in the angle δ are accompanied by changes in the armature current, as is clear from Fig. 11-23, and this entire phenomenon, called *hunting*, can be observed by the slow periodic swinging of the ammeter pointer.   Hunting is, of course, objectionable, and in order to suppress it more effectively than by eddy currents in the pole faces, synchronous motors are always provided with *damping grids*, or *amortisseur windings*, of the type illustrated in Fig. 4-37.   They consist of low-resistance copper bars embedded in slots in the pole faces, the projecting ends of the bars being connected to end rings in the manner of the squirrel-cage windings commonly used in induction motors.   The damping effect of such windings is much more powerful than that of mere eddy currents in the pole faces, and they contribute moreover a self-starting characteristic that would otherwise not exist.   It is obvious that there is no current in the amortisseur winding when the rotor is moving uniformly at synchronous speed; and that when hunting occurs the current in the damper winding has the low frequency of the oscillation.

The power (per phase) developed by the motor, as given by Eq. 11-33, is

$$P = \frac{VE \cos (\varphi_s - \delta) - E^2 \cos \varphi_s}{Z_s}$$

which shows the manner in which the power developed (and the torque) is related to the torque angle δ.   Differentiating this expression with respect to δ,

$$\frac{dP}{d\delta} = \frac{VE}{Z_s} \sin (\varphi_s - \delta)$$

or since φ_s is ordinarily nearly $90°$,

$$\frac{dP}{d\delta} = \frac{VE}{Z_s} \cos \delta \qquad\qquad (11\text{-}38)$$

The derivative $dP/d\delta$ means the change in the power developed per unit change of the torque angle, and the greater it is, the stiffer will be the elastic coupling between the motor and the generating system which drives it.   In other words, a stiffly coupled motor tends to follow every variation of speed of the generators which drive it, or if the generators supply constant frequency, it tends to maintain its own speed at a constant value no matter how its mechanical load may fluctuate.   Too much stiffness may therefore cause undue mechanical stress in the moving parts, and in the windings as well.   Inspection of Eq. 11-38 shows that the stiffness (or rigidity) factor is directly proportional to $E(= cF)$, so that an overexcited motor is more stiffly coupled than one having smaller field excitation; conversely, the stiffness factor varies inversely as Z_s, and since Z_s is practically equal to X_s, it is plain that a large synchronous reactance exerts a cushioning effect. The length of the airgap between stator and rotor has a decided effect upon the stiffness of coupling; for, other things being equal, a large airgap requires a larger field excitation (F) than a smaller one, and E, being equal to cF, it also greater. The combination of a large airgap and a small synchronous reactance accordingly implies stiff coupling, and vice versa.

The stiffness or coupling factor represented by Eq. 11-38 is seen to be a function of δ, and it becomes zero when $\delta = \varphi_s$. This checks with results already arrived at by other methods, for when $\delta = \varphi_s$, the stability limit has been reached. This means that the torque angle can never exceed φ_s without causing the motor to drop out of step. Some references in the literature of this subject state that the torque angle can never exceed 90 electrical degrees, but this is a rather loose way of saying that φ_s, which is the limiting value of δ, is usually not much under 90°.

11-14. Periodicity of Hunting.* The mathematical analysis of hunting has as objective the determination of the manner in which angle θ in Fig. 11-23 varies with time, counting from the moment when the load is changed from P_1 to P_2. The method is based upon the principle of the conservation of energy, which when applied to the case of rotating bodies leads to the well-known equation of mechanics

Polar moment of inertia $\times$ angular acceleration = accelerating torque†

Assume that the motor is developing power corresponding to circle P_1, Fig. 11-23, and that an additional load equivalent to a torque T_L is suddenly applied. At any general time t thereafter, the rotor will be displaced from its initial position (relative to the synchronously rotating armature field) by an angle θ electrical degrees, which is equivalent to an actual space angle of $(2/p)\theta$, when p is the number of poles. The angular acceleration is accordingly $\dfrac{2}{p}\dfrac{d^2\theta}{dt^2}$, and the accelerating torque is $\dfrac{2J}{p}\dfrac{d^2\theta}{dt^2}$, where J is the polar moment of inertia‡ of the rotor, *including its connected load.*

In accordance with D'Alembert's principle, all of the couples acting upon the rotating system constitute a set of moments which are in equilibrium. The externally applied torque T_L must then be equal to the

---

*See C. P. Steinmetz, "Theory and Calculation of Electrical Apparatus," pp. 288–299; also A. F. Puchstein and T. C. Lloyd, "Alternating Current Machines," 2d ed., p. 482, John Wiley & Sons, Inc., New York, 1942.

† The acceleration may, of course, be negative, i.e., a retardation.

‡ The symbol J is used instead of the customary I because the latter has been assigned to represent current.

sum of the internally developed torques. In addition to the inertial torque $\dfrac{2J}{p}\dfrac{d^2\theta}{dt^2}$, these include the restoring couple due to the elastic pull of the magnetic field upon the field poles, and the frictional or braking torque due to currents induced in the damping winding. These will be considered in the order mentioned.

When the rotor torque angle increases from δ to $\delta + \theta$, the power developed increases from

$$P_\delta = \frac{VE}{Z_s} \cos (\varphi_s - \delta) - \frac{E^2 \cos \varphi_s}{Z_s}$$

to

$$P_{\delta+\theta} = \frac{VE}{Z_s} \cos (\varphi_s - \delta - \theta) - \frac{E^2 \cos \varphi_s}{Z_s}$$

and the increment is

$$P_{\delta+\theta} - P_\delta = \frac{VE}{Z_s} [\cos (\varphi_s - \delta - \theta) - \cos (\varphi_s - \delta)]$$

$$= \frac{2VE}{Z_s} \sin \frac{\theta}{2} \sin \left(\varphi_s - \delta - \frac{\theta}{2} \right) \qquad (11\text{-}39)$$

The torque developed by the motor increases by a proportional amount, which is seen to be proportional to $\sin (\theta/2)$; but for the small values of θ encountered in ordinary cases, $\sin (\theta/2) = \theta/2$ and

$$\sin \left(\varphi_s - \delta - \frac{\theta}{2} \right) = \sin (\varphi_s - \delta)$$

whence

$$\frac{P_{\delta+\theta} - P_\delta}{\theta} = \frac{VE}{Z_s} \sin (\varphi_s - \delta) \qquad (11\text{-}40)$$

This is the same result as Eq. 11-38,

$$\frac{dP}{d\delta} = \frac{VE}{Z_s} \sin (\varphi_s - \delta)$$

which represents the change in power per radian of torque angle, and is a measure of the stiffness of the elastic coupling. In order to convert Eq. 11-40 to equivalent torque per radian of displacement, it is to be noted that in general

$$T = \frac{muP}{2\pi(n/60)} = \frac{mpu}{4\pi f} P \qquad (11\text{-}41)$$

where m is the number of phases and u is a factor for converting T to the desired unit; $u = 10^7$ if T is to be expressed in dyne-centimeters;

$$u = \frac{10^7}{980 \times 10^3 \times 10^2} = 0.102 \text{ to convert it to kilogram-meters; and}$$

$$u = \frac{10^7}{980 \times 453.6 \times 30.48} = 0.74 \text{ to convert it to pound-feet.}$$

The braking torque is produced by the reaction of the current induced in the damping winding upon the main field. This current is proportional to the voltage induced in the winding, and the voltage is proportional to the relative velocity of the rotor with respect to the armature field, i.e., to $d\theta/dt$. Consequently, the braking torque may be taken equal to $k\ d\theta/dt$.

The complete equation of motion may then be written as

$$\frac{2J}{p}\frac{d^2\theta}{dt^2} + k\frac{d\theta}{dt} + \frac{mpu}{4\pi f}\theta\frac{VE}{Z_s}\sin(\varphi_s - \delta) = T_L \qquad (11\text{-}42)$$

which may be transformed to

$$(D^2 + 2aD + b)\theta = T_L\frac{p}{2J} \qquad (11\text{-}43)$$

where

$$a = \frac{kp}{4J}$$
$$b = \frac{mp^2u}{8\pi fJ}\frac{VE}{Z_s}\sin(\varphi_s - \delta) = \frac{p}{2J}\frac{mpu}{4\pi f}\frac{VE}{Z_s}\sin(\varphi_s - \delta) = \frac{p}{2J}K \qquad (11\text{-}44)$$

Equation 11-43 will be recognized as a linear differential equation of the second order. But it is approximate only, and holds only for small values of θ; the more accurate form, calling for the use of Eq. 11-39 instead of 11-40, would lead to elliptic integrals. The complete solution of Eq. 11-43, assuming that T_L is constant, is

$$\theta = A\epsilon^{(-a+\sqrt{a^2-b})t} + B\epsilon^{(-a-\sqrt{a^2-b})t} + \frac{T_L}{K} \qquad (11\text{-}45)$$

where A and B are constants of integration which can be evaluated if two conditions of the problem are specified. The form of the solution shows that the angular displacement θ consists of two parts: a transient displacement, represented by the exponential terms which disappear after a theoretically infinite time, but practically within a very short time; and a permanent displacement such that $T_L = K\theta_L$, so that the torque angle, which was originally δ_1, becomes ultimately $\delta_1 + \theta_L$.

Three possibilities occur, defined by the conditions

(1) $a^2 > b$
(2) $a^2 = b$
(3) $a^2 < b$

Case 1. If $a^2 > b$, which means physically that the damping or braking is large in comparison with the elastic coupling, both exponential terms in Eq. 11-45 have negative exponents, though one is numerically greater than the other. The graph of θ as a function of time may be determined as follows: Assume that when $t = 0$ (the instant at which the disturbance begins) the machine is running with torque angle δ_1, so that $\theta = 0$; and that at this particular instant the speed of the rotor is exactly synchronous, so that $d\theta/dt = 0$. These two conditions, namely, $\theta = 0$ when $t = 0$ and $d\theta/dt = 0$ when $t = 0$, when substituted in Eq. 11-45 give

$$A = -\frac{T_L}{2K}\left(\frac{a}{\sqrt{a^2 - b}} + 1\right)$$

$$B = \frac{T_L}{2K}\left(\frac{a}{\sqrt{a^2 - b}} - 1\right)$$

(11-46)

and it then becomes possible to plot the curve of θ and t as in Fig. 11-24. The change in θ occurs as a logarithmic, nonoscillatory adjustment to the new load conditions, the rotor settling down to its new torque angle by a drifting process.

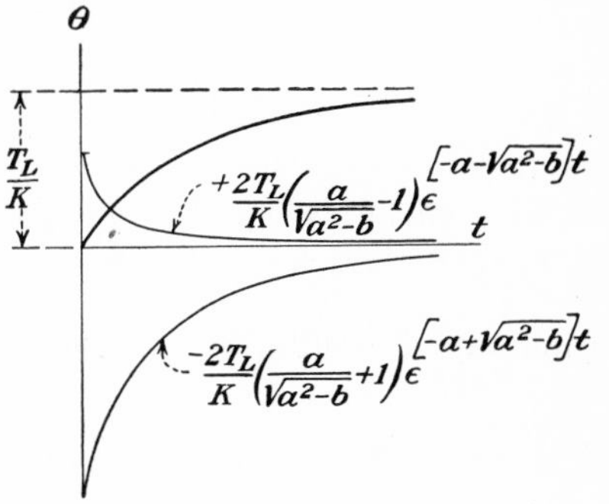

Case 2, corresponding to the condition $a^2 = b$, is a boundary condition between case 1 and case 3, and will not be considered here. The analysis is left as an exercise for the student.

Case 3, defined by the condition

FIG. 11-24. Logarithmic or nonoscillatory transient.

$a^2 < b$, leads to imaginary exponents in Eq. 11-45, which may then be written

$$\theta = \epsilon^{-at}(A\epsilon^{j\sqrt{b-a^2}\,t} + B\epsilon^{-j\sqrt{b-a^2}\,t}) + \frac{T_L}{K}$$

$$= \epsilon^{-at}[(A + B)\cos\sqrt{b - a^2}\,t + j(A - B)\sin\sqrt{b - a^2}\,t] + \frac{T_L}{K} \quad (11\text{-}47)$$

If, as in case 1, the initial conditions are defined by $\theta = 0$ when $t = 0$ and $d\theta/dt = 0$ when $t = 0$, it is found that

$$A + B = -\frac{T_L}{K}$$

$$j(A - B) = -\frac{a}{\sqrt{b - a^2}}\frac{T_L}{K}$$

Hence, $\quad \theta = \dfrac{T_L}{K} - \dfrac{T_L}{K}\sqrt{\dfrac{b}{b - a^2}}\,\epsilon^{-at}\cos(\sqrt{b - a^2}\,t - \gamma) \quad (11\text{-}48)$

where $\tan\gamma = a/\sqrt{b - a^2}$.

Equation 11-48 indicates that θ approaches its ultimate or steady-state value of T_L/K by a transient series of oscillations of decreasing amplitude, and that the frequency of the oscillations is

$$f_t = \frac{\sqrt{b - a^2}}{2\pi} \qquad (11\text{-}49)$$

The time period of a complete oscillation is the reciprocal of f_t, i.e.,

$$T_{f_t} = \frac{2\pi}{\sqrt{b - a^2}} \qquad (11\text{-}50)$$

and if the braking factor, represented by a, is sufficiently small the period becomes (see Eq. 11-44)

$$T_{f_t} = \frac{2\pi}{\sqrt{b}} = 2\pi \sqrt{\frac{8\pi f J Z_s}{mp^2 u V E \sin (\varphi_s - \delta)}} \qquad (11\text{-}51)$$

The period as given by Eq. 11-51 is only approximate because of the assumptions that have been made, (1) that θ is small* and (2) that the braking effect is negligible in comparison with the elastic restoring torque. In case a^2, though small, is not negligible in comparison with b, the initial (undamped) oscillation will have an amplitude $\dfrac{T_L}{K} \sqrt{\dfrac{b}{b - a^2}}$ in accordance with Eq. 11-48, and this is approximately equal to $\dfrac{T_L}{K} \left(1 + \dfrac{1}{2}\dfrac{a^2}{b}\right)$, or greater than the permanent angular displacement T_L/K. If the initial displacement of the rotor (that is, δ_1) is initially large, this may cause angle $\delta_1 + \theta$ to exceed φ_s, in which case the motor would break out of synchronism since it then comes within the region of instability.

An additional approximation in Eq. 11-51 is due to the fact that Z_s is not strictly constant as has been tacitly assumed. The eddy currents in the pole faces and in the amortisseur winding act like the short-circuited secondary of a transformer and so tend to reduce the apparent primary impedance, represented in this case by Z_s.

11-15. Variable-torque Loading. When a synchronous motor is used to drive a compressor, the resisting torque due to the load will vary from instant to instant because of valve action. In general, such a variable torque is equivalent to an average torque, T_{av}, upon which is superposed a more or less extensive series of harmonically varying torques, say, n in all, including one of fundamental frequency† and others of higher frequency. The general expression for such a variable torque is

$$T = T_{av} + \sum_{r=1}^{r=n} T_r \sin (r\omega_1 t + \varphi_r) \qquad (11\text{-}52)$$

---

* The results here derived should be compared with those involved in the calculation of the period of a pendulum, where similar approximations are usually made.

† This frequency is, of course, wholly independent of the frequency of the current that drives the motor.

where r fixes the order of the harmonic, φ_r determines the phase of this harmonic at the initial moment $t = 0$, and T_r is its amplitude in the torque units to be used. The angular velocity of the fundamental torque is ω_1.

The general equation of motion of the rotor, by analogy with Eq. 11-43, becomes

$$(D^2 + 2aD + b)\theta = \left[T_{av} + \sum_{r=1}^{r=n} T_r \sin (r\omega_1 t + \varphi_r) \right] \frac{p}{2J}$$

and the solution, assuming that the oscillatory case $(a^2 < b)$ only need be considered, is

$$\theta = \epsilon^{-at}(M \cos \sqrt{b - a^2}\, t + N \sin \sqrt{b - a^2}\, t) + \frac{T_{av}}{K}$$

$$+ \sum_{r=1}^{r=n} \frac{pT_r \sin (r\omega_1 t + \varphi_r - \gamma_r)}{2J \sqrt{(r^2\omega_1^2 - b)^2 + 4a^2 r^2 \omega_1^2}} \quad (11\text{-}53)$$

where
$$\tan \gamma_r = \frac{2ar\omega_1}{b - r^2\omega_1^2} \quad (11\text{-}54)$$

The physical meaning of Eq. 11-53 is that the resultant value of θ is compounded of three parts: (1) a transient oscillation of frequency $f_t = \sqrt{(b - a^2)}/2\pi$; (2) a steady or unvarying angle, T_{av}/K; (3) a series of forced oscillations whose frequencies are ω_1 and multiples thereof. In case the frequency f_t of the transient term happens to coincide with that of any of the forced oscillations, a condition of mechanical resonance will exist, and the resultant amplitude may become so great as to cause the motor to fall out of step. The condition for resonance is obviously

$$f_t = \frac{\sqrt{b - a^2}}{2\pi} = \frac{r\omega_1}{2\pi} \quad (11\text{-}55)$$

THE TWO-REACTION THEORY

11-16. Phasor Diagram. The chief value of the cylindrical-rotor theory as applied to the synchronous motor is that it provides a relatively simple approach to the problem of determining the general nature of the operating characteristics. It has the disadvantage, just as when it is applied to the synchronous generator, that it does not accurately take account of the effects due to salient-pole construction; and since practically all synchronous motors are built with salient poles, it becomes important to analyze their performance in terms of the more exact two-reaction theory. This will be all the more evident when it is realized that much depends upon the accuracy with which the torque angle δ can be determined, and that in the case of the synchronous-impedance method discussed in the preceding sections this in turn depends upon the very uncertain value of Z_s.

The construction of the two-reaction phasor diagram in Fig. 11-25 follows exactly the same reasoning which led to the corresponding diagram for the generator shown in Fig. 10-40. Just as in any motor, the constant impressed terminal voltage V must include as one component an emf $(-E)$ equal and opposite to the counter emf (assumed as due to the

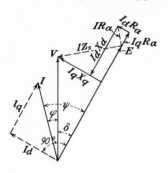

FIG. 11-25. Two-reaction phasor diagram, leading current.

field excitation acting alone), and an additional component to balance the impedance drop. In accordance with the two-reaction theory, the armature current I is resolved into two components, one of which, I_q, magnetizes in the transverse axis and (because of motor action) is in phase opposition to the counter emf E, and therefore in phase with $-E$; the other component, I_d, magnetizes along the main magnetic axis, and is in quadrature with E. The diagram, Fig. 11-25, is drawn to represent the common case of leading current (I ahead of V), but whatever the phase conditions may be, the relation

$$\mathbf{V} = -\mathbf{E} + \mathbf{I}Z_s \qquad (11\text{-}56)$$

must hold.

Just as in the corresponding analysis of the synchronous generator,

$$X_d = X_a + X_{rd}$$
and
$$X_q = X_a + X_{rq}$$

and the relations between R_a, X_d, X_q, Z_d, and Z_q, which are included in Eq. 10-33, are here again valid.

Figure 11-25 shows that

$$V \sin \delta = I_q X_q + I_d R_a \qquad (11\text{-}57)$$
and
$$E - V \cos \delta = I_d X_d - I_q R_a \qquad (11\text{-}58)$$

which are not quite identical with the corresponding equations 10-34 and 10-35, but when they are transformed in the manner explained in Art. 10-18, they lead to the equation

$$Z_s^2 = Z_d^2 \cos^2 (\varphi_d + \psi) + Z_q^2 \sin^2 (\varphi_q + \psi) \qquad (11\text{-}59)$$

which is again the polar equation of an ellipse, the variables being Z_s and ψ. Omitting the step-by-step reductions, which are procedurally identical with those of Art. 10-18, the result is that Z_s turns out to be the same cyclical function which is illustrated in Figs. 10-43b and 10-44.

11-17. Current Locus, Constant Power. It is obvious that without regard to any special theory of synchronous motor operation the power developed is given by

$$P = VI \cos \varphi - I^2 R_a$$

and that Eq. 11-14, which follows from it, is always valid, i.e.,

$$I^2 + \left(\frac{V}{2R_a}\right)^2 - 2I\left(\frac{V}{2R_a}\right)\cos \varphi = \left(\frac{V}{2R_a}\right)^2 - \frac{P}{R_a}$$

Consequently, the phasor **I** may be regarded as one side of a triangle the other two sides of which are $V/2R_a$ and $\sqrt{(V/2R_a)^2 - (P/R_a)}$, as shown in Figs. 11-10 and 11-12. The family of power circles shown in Fig. 11-12 may then be used generally to define the armature current for any given value of P.

Since the impedance Z_s, which appears in the two-reaction theory, cannot be considered as constant, the family of excitation circles illustrated in Figs. 11-11 and 11-12 is not consistent with the facts as they exist in a salient-pole machine. The current locus, subject to the condition of constant excitation, must differ from a circle, thus affecting not only the shape of the V curves but particularly the conditions for unity power factor and for stability. The first point to be determined is therefore the nature of the current locus when the field excitation is held constant.

11-18. Current Locus, Constant Excitation.* Equations 11-57 and 11-58, when solved for I_q and I_d, yield the following relations:

$$I_q = \frac{VX_d \sin \delta - R_a(E - V \cos \delta)}{X_dX_q + R_a^2} = \frac{VZ_d \cos (\delta - \varphi_d) - ER_a}{X_dX_q + R_a^2} \quad (11\text{-}60)$$

$$I_d = \frac{VR_a \sin \delta + X_q(E - V \cos \delta)}{X_dX_q + R_a^2} = \frac{VZ_q \sin (\delta - \varphi_q) + EX_q}{X_dX_q + R_a^2} \quad (11\text{-}61)$$

The form of these two equations suggests a simple geometrical construction for the current locus if E is maintained constant. Thus, in Fig. 11-26, OV represents the fixed terminal voltage, and $(-OE)$ is the excitation voltage, fixed as to magnitude, but displaced from OV by the variable torque angle δ. The lines $OD = VZ_d/(X_dX_q + R_a^2)$ and

$$OC = \frac{VZ_q}{(X_dX_q + R_a^2)}$$

representing the constant coefficients that appear in Eqs. 11-60 and 11-61, are drawn at the fixed angles φ_d and φ_q, respectively, with OV. Accordingly, when perpendiculars are dropped from the points D and C upon the line OE, it follows that

$$OK = \frac{VZ_d}{X_dX_q + R_a^2} \cos (\delta - \varphi_d)$$

$$GC = \frac{VZ_q}{X_dX_q + R_a^2} \sin (\delta - \varphi_q)$$

* Abstracted from article by A. S. Langsdorf, Contributions to Synchronous-machine Theory, *Trans. AIEE*, **56**:41 (1937).

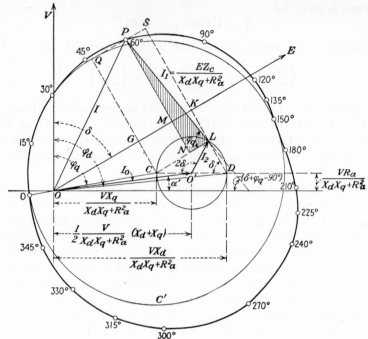

FIG. 11-26. Current locus, fixed excitation, two-reaction theory. $E = \frac{5}{4}V$.

On subtracting from OK the fixed length

$$KM = LN = \frac{ER_a}{X_d X_q + R_a^2}$$

and adding to GC (which must be considered negative in the diagram since $\delta < \varphi_q$) the fixed length

$$CQ = NP = \frac{EX_q}{X_d X_q + R_a^2}$$

it is clear that in accordance with Eqs. 11-60 and 11-61

$$OM = I_q$$
$$MP = I_d$$

and therefore $OP = \sqrt{(OM)^2 + (MP)^2} = \sqrt{I_q^2 + I_d^2} = I$

Now it is apparent from the construction of Fig. 11-26 that no matter what value is assigned to δ, the angle CLD is necessarily a right angle; hence, its locus is a circle having CD as a diameter.   The magnitude and position of CD are readily fixed in terms of the coordinates of points C and D as indicated on the diagram, from which it appears that CD is a horizontal line (or at any rate perpendicular to OV) and that

$$CD = \frac{V(X_d - X_q)}{X_d X_q + R_a^2}$$

The center of the circle CLD is at O', which has the coordinates

$$\left(\frac{V}{X_dX_q + R_a^2}\frac{X_d + X_q}{2}, \frac{VR_a}{X_dX_q + R_a^2}\right)$$

consequently, the line $OO' = I_0$ is fixed in length and is tipped up from the horizontal by the angle α'. Since the angle $CDK = \delta$ by construction, it follows that the radius $O'L = I_2$ is inclined to $O'C$ at an angle 2δ. Finally, the line

$$LP = I_1 = \sqrt{\left(\frac{ER_a}{X_dX_q + R_a^2}\right)^2 + \left(\frac{EX_q}{X_dX_q + R_a^2}\right)^2} = \frac{EZ_q}{X_dX_q + R_a^2}$$

is also of fixed length so long as E remains constant, and it is inclined to the horizontal at an angle $\delta + \varphi_q - 90$, as indicated in the figure.

So we arrive at the remarkably interesting fact that the current $OP = I$ is the phasor sum of three components, two of which, I_0 and I_2, are permanently constant in magnitude, and the third component, I_1, is constant for a fixed excitation, and for different excitations is directly proportional to the excitation. But while the components are constant in magnitude, they are linked together at phase angles which vary with δ in an interesting manner, with the result that the current locus has the irregular form shown in Fig. 11-26, which has been drawn for the condition $E = \frac{5}{4}V$.

Expressed in complex notation,

$$\mathbf{I} = \mathbf{I}_0 + \mathbf{I}_2 + \mathbf{I}_1 \tag{11-62}$$

where

$$\mathbf{I}_0 = \frac{V}{X_dX_q + R_a^2}\sqrt{R_a^2 + \left(\frac{X_d + X_q}{2}\right)^2}\,\epsilon^{j\alpha'} = I_0(\cos\alpha' + j\sin\alpha') \tag{11-63}$$

$$\mathbf{I}_2 = -\frac{V}{X_dX_q + R_a^2}\frac{X_d - X_q}{2}\,\epsilon^{-j2\delta} = -I_2(\cos 2\delta - j\sin 2\delta) \tag{11-64}$$

$$\mathbf{I}_1 = -j\frac{EZ_q}{X_dX_q + R_a^2}\,\epsilon^{-j(\delta+\varphi_q)} = -I_1[\sin(\delta + \varphi_q) + j\cos(\delta + \varphi_q)] \tag{11-65}$$

These results may at this point be compared with those of the cylindrical-rotor theory as previously developed. To do so, it is only necessary to impose the conditions that

$$Z_d = Z_q = Z_s$$
$$X_d = X_q = X_s$$

When this is done, the "double-frequency" phasor $\mathbf{I}_2$ (Eq. 11-64) vanishes; the points O' and D then become coincident with point C, which would then have the coordinates

$$\frac{VX_s}{X_s^2 + R_a^2} = \frac{V}{Z_s}\sin\varphi_s$$

and $VR_a/(X_s^2 + R_a^2) = (V/Z_s) \cos \varphi_s$, which are the same as those of point D in Figs. 11-12 to 11-16, and the irregular current locus of Fig. 11-26 then degenerates to a simple circle of the type shown in Fig. 11-12; it is shown in Fig. 11-26 as a circle (marked C') having its center at C and radius equal to LP.

To construct the current loci for different values of E, it is only necessary to modify the dimensions of the triangle LPN in the desired ratio; otherwise, all construction lines remain the same as in Fig. 11-26. The effect of varying E from zero to $7/2V$ by steps of $1/2V$ is shown in Fig. 11-27.*

Figure 11-27 brings out vividly some extremely interesting peculiarities. Perhaps the most striking one is in connection with the current

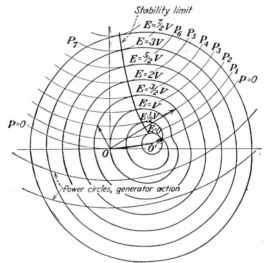

FIG. 11-27. Loci of current for varying excitation and power.

locus for $E = V/2$, which shows a reentrant loop; another point of interest is the proof inherent in the diagram that an unexcited machine ($E = 0$) is capable of carrying a maximum load corresponding to the power circle P_1, whereas the cylindrical-rotor theory (see Fig. 11-12) indicates that an unexcited machine can develop no power whatever, a conclusion which is known from experience to be incorrect.

The reentrant loop that appears in Fig. 11-27 for the case $E = V/2$ is not confined to that particular curve. The same thing occurs for all excitations below a critical value; this is illustrated in Fig. 11-28, where the small shaded triangle, corresponding to triangle LSP of Fig. 11-26, is shown in successive positions for the full range of δ from zero to 360°. The critical value of E, above which the reentrant loops do not appear, is that for which the excitation phasor $I_1 = EZ_q/(X_dX_q + R_a^2)$ is just

* The excitation loci shown in Fig. 11-27 are limaçons.

equal to the diameter of the small circle CLD, i.e.,

$$\frac{EZ_q}{X_dX_q + R_a^2} = \frac{V(X_d - X_q)}{X_dX_q + R_a^2}$$

or
$$E = \frac{V(X_d - X_q)}{Z_q} \tag{11-66}$$

When $E = 0$, which means that the field is not excited, the triangle LSP of Fig. 11-28 vanishes, and the doubly reentrant loop degenerates to two complete traverses of the circle CLD. Accordingly, if the unexcited

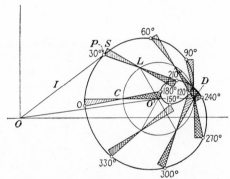

Fig. 11-28. Detail of double-loop locus.

machine is subjected to a slip test, the armature current should oscillate at slip frequency from a minimum value $OO' - O'L$ to a maximum $OO' + O'L$, in the manner shown by curve 1 in Fig. 11-29. Similarly, if a slip test is made with the field partially excited, the current determined by the doubly reentrant loop of Fig. 11-28 should result in a cartesian graph like curve 2 in Fig. 11-29, which has a smaller minimum, and a larger maximum, then curve 1.

In order to check these theoretical deductions, slip tests were made with a three-phase 15-kva laboratory-type alternator, using (a) no field excitation, (b) weak excitation, (c) moderate excitation, and the resulting oscillograms of armature current are shown in Fig. 11-30.

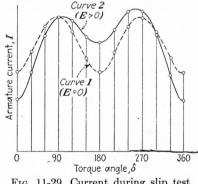

Fig. 11-29. Current during slip test.

Oscillogram (a) shows exactly the type of current variation demanded by a polar diagram like Fig. 11-26 or 11-28, in which the phasor OO', proportional to $X_d + X_q$, is not greatly larger than the diameter of circle CD, proportional to $X_d - X_q$; for with this relation between X_d and X_q the angular interval during which the current is less than its mean value is much smaller than the interval during which the current is greater than the average (see Figs. 10-43b and 10-44).

Oscillogram (b) corresponds to an excitation curve in Fig. 11-27 which is intermediate between the curves marked $E = \frac{1}{2}V$ and $E = V$. Such a curve would call for a current (shown in Fig. 11-30b) which is small for a relatively short angular interval as δ changes, and then remains nearly constant for a much longer interval, but with a dip midway in this range.

Oscillogram (c) corresponds to an excitation between $E = \frac{1}{2}V$ and $E = V$ in Fig. 11-27. The minimum value of current is less than in either of the other of the other two cases, as would be expected, and the maximum value is sustained during the greater part of the double cycle.

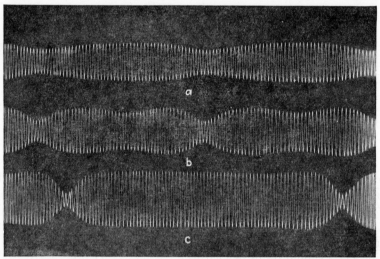

Fig. 11-30. Oscillograms of slip-test current: (a) zero excitation; (b) weak excitation; (c) moderate excitation.

11-19. The V Curves: Two-reaction Theory. The curves of Fig. 11-27 have been drawn for the full range of δ from 0 to 360°. Only those parts of the loops which lie within the zero-power circle ($P = 0$) represent positive motor power; those parts of the excitation loops which lie outside the circle $P = 0$ correspond to negative power, and therefore indicate generator action. The reentrant loop that appears in the curve for $E = V/2$ means, therefore, that if δ were to approach 180°, the motor would become a generator and then, if δ were further increased, would again develop motor power before a still further increase in δ brings the current finally within the zone of generator action. This cyclical change from motor action to generator action actually takes place in making the slip test with the field moderately excited.

The V curves corresponding to Fig. 11-27 may be constructed in precisely the manner described in connection with Fig. 11-12; they are shown in Fig. 11-31, and it is at once apparent that they differ considerably from those based upon the assumption of constant synchronous impedance. The curve H_1, defining the condition of unity power factor, has its smallest abscissa when $E = V$ and $I = 0$, and not, as in Fig. 11-12, when I has a value greater than zero. The difference between the two sets of curves is most marked for the condition of zero excitation, $E = 0$.

For example, the V curve for zero power, P_0, intersects the vertical axis of coordinates in two points instead of only one point as in Fig. 11-12. A further peculiarity is that, in the unstable range shown by the dashed portions of the curves, the curve for zero power lies partly *inside* a curve corresponding to power P_1, which is a little larger than zero, whereas in Fig. 11-12 all curves corresponding to power greater than

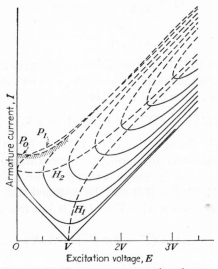

FIG. 11-31. V curves, two-reaction theory.

zero lie wholly inside the curve of zero power, P_0. Verification of the correctness of both of these features is to be found in a set of V curves obtained experimentally by Prof. J. F. H. Douglas.*

11-20. The Condition for Unity Power Factor. Inspection of Fig. 11-25 shows that, under unity-power-factor conditions, $\varphi = 0$ and $\psi = \delta$. Subject therefore to the limitation $\cos \varphi = 1$, the basic equations 11-57 and 11-58 may be written

$$V \sin \delta = IX_q \cos \delta + IR_a \sin \delta \qquad (11\text{-}67)$$
$$E - V \cos \delta = IX_d \sin \delta - IR_a \cos \delta \qquad (11\text{-}68)$$

from which
$$\sin \delta = \frac{EIX_q}{(V - IR_a)^2 + I^2X_dX_q} \qquad (11\text{-}69)$$

$$\cos \delta = \frac{E(V - IR_a)}{(V - IR_a)^2 + I^2X_dX_q} \qquad (11\text{-}70)$$

* Douglas, Engeset, and Jones, *loc. cit.*

Now it will be noted, on inspection of Fig. 11-26, that when the current I is in phase with V, the algebraic sum of the horizontal components of I_0, I_2, and I_1 is zero. Referring to Eqs. 11-63 to 11-65, this condition is expressed by

$$I_0 \cos \alpha' - I_2 \cos 2\delta - I_1 \sin (\delta + \varphi_q) = 0 \qquad (11\text{-}71)$$

The term $I_0 \cos \alpha'$ is seen from Fig. 11-26 to be equal to

$$I_0 \cos \alpha' = \frac{V}{X_d X_q + R_a^2} \frac{X_d + X_q}{2}$$

and we have also from Eqs. 11-64 and 11-65

$$I_2 = \frac{V}{X_d X_q + R_a^2} \frac{X_d - X_q}{2}$$

$$I_1 = \frac{E Z_q}{X_d X_q + R_a^2}$$

From Eqs. 11-69 and 11-70, it is possible to express $\cos 2\delta$ and $\sin (\delta + \varphi_q)$ in terms of E, I, and the machine constants, and on substituting all these relations in Eq. 11-71 the final result is

$$[(V - I R_a)^2 + I^2 X_d X_q]^2 = E^2[(V - I R_a)^2 + I^2 X_q^2] \qquad (11\text{-}72)$$

which is accordingly the equation of curve H_1 in Fig. 11-31. This equation is complete, without any simplifying approximations; it is obviously of the fourth degree, and the curve is therefore not a simple conic as was curve H_1 in Fig. 11-12; but if it may be assumed that $I X_d$ and $I X_q$ are not too large in comparison with $V - I R_a$, it is a reasonable approximation to write

$$E^2 = (V - I R_a)^2 + I^2 X_d X_q \qquad (11\text{-}73)$$

which is the equation of a hyperbola.

11-21. The Condition for Stability. In Fig. 11-27 the power circles P_1, P_2, P_3, . . . have each been drawn tangent to a particular excitation curve. The points of tangency then define a curve which is the dividing line between a condition of stability on the left side of the curve and a condition of instability on the right. At the point of tangency between a particular power circle and a particular excitation loop, the machine is obviously developing the maximum power that it is capable of producing with that excitation; consequently, the condition for defining the stability limit, or the locus of the points of tangency in Fig. 11-27, is that the derivative of the power with respect to a suitable independent variable (such as the torque angle δ) shall be zero; that is, $dP/d\delta = 0$.

In order to express the power developed as a function of δ, two procedures are possible. One* of them makes use of the fact that the power

* Used by R. E. Doherty and C. A. Nickle, *Trans. AIEE*, **45**:912 (1926).

input is

$$P_i = VI \cos \varphi = I_q(V \cos \delta) + I_d(V \sin \delta) \qquad (11\text{-}74)$$

and that the power developed is then

$$P = P_i - I^2 R_a = VI_q \cos \delta + VI_d \sin \delta - (I_q^2 + I_d^2)R_a \qquad (11\text{-}75)$$

On substituting in this equation the values of I_q and I_d given in Eqs. 11-60 and 11-61, there results a long and complicated expression which is too unwieldy for ordinary purposes; so resort is had to the approximation of dropping all terms containing R_a, since within the working range such terms are quite small in a well-designed machine. The result of this approximation is readily found to be

$$P = \frac{VE}{X_d} \sin \delta + \frac{V^2(X_d - X_q)}{2X_dX_q} \sin 2\delta \qquad (11\text{-}76)$$

whence
$$\frac{dP}{d\delta} = \frac{VE}{X_d} \cos \delta + \frac{V^2(X_d - X_q)}{X_dX_q} \cos 2\delta \qquad (11\text{-}77)$$

It is, however, possible to formulate an accurate expression for P in terms of δ, without encountering the difficulty mentioned in the preceding paragraph. This method rests upon the physical concept which underlies the two-reaction theory, namely, that the armature reaction is equivalent to the presence of two sets of poles in addition to the actual set of poles, as illustrated in Fig. 10-31; one of these fictitious sets of poles is in line with the main poles and either magnetizes or demagnetizes them depending upon the phase of the current; the other set of fictitious poles lies midway between the main poles. If the main poles were alone to be considered, their effect would be to generate emf E, and since I_q is in phase with E, the corresponding power developed would be EI_q; however, in this principal magnetic axis there is a magnetizing (or demagnetizing) effect which produces a voltage expressed by I_dX_d, and I_q is in phase with (or in phase opposition to) this voltage. Consequently the total power produced in the main magnetic axis is* $(E - I_dX_d)I_q$. In the same manner, the power developed in the quadrature axis is $(I_qX_q)I_d$, and the total power developed is then

$$P = (E - I_dX_d)I_q + (I_qX_q)I_d$$
$$= EI_q - I_qI_d(X_d - X_q) \qquad (11\text{-}78)$$

Substituting for I_q and I_d from Eqs. 11-60 and 11-61, the complete equation for P is

$$P = \frac{\left[\begin{array}{l} VEZ_dZ_q^2 \cos (\delta - \varphi_d) + VER_aZ_q(X_d - X_q) \sin (\delta - \varphi_q) \\ - V^2Z_dZ_q(X_d - X_q) \sin (\delta - \varphi_q) \cos (\delta - \varphi_d) - E^2R_aZ_q^2 \end{array}\right]}{(X_dX_q + R_a^2)^2} \qquad (11\text{-}79)$$

* The negative sign is used in accordance with the phasor relations embodied in Fig. 11-25.

and the accurate expression for the stiffness or coupling factor is

$$\frac{dP}{d\delta} = \frac{\left[\begin{array}{c} VER_aZ_q(X_d - X_q)\cos(\delta - \varphi_q) - VEZ_dZ_q^2\sin(\delta - \varphi_d) \\ - V^2Z_dZ_q(X_d - X_q)\cos(2\delta - \varphi_d - \varphi_q) \end{array}\right]}{(X_dX_q + R_a^2)^2} \quad (11\text{-}80)$$

These last two equations reduce to 11-76 and 11-77, respectively, on substituting $R_a = 0$, and $\varphi_d = \varphi_q = 90°$.

Doherty and Nickle, in Part II of their papers on synchronous machines, refer to the power term containing the factor $X_d - X_q$ as "reluctance power." This is a very descriptive phrase since the power thus represented has its origin in the difference of reluctance between the principal and transverse magnetic axes, as shown very clearly in Eq. 11-78. It is an interesting fact that the reluctance power is equal to the maximum power that an unexcited motor can develop; i.e., it is the power that corresponds to circle P_1 (Fig. 11-27).

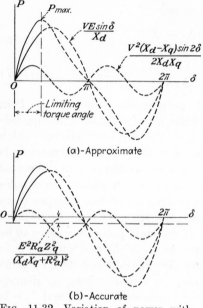

(a)-Approximate

(b)-Accurate

Fig. 11-32. Variation of power with torque angle.

The equation of the stability curve H_2 (Fig. 11-31) can be determined by imposing the condition that

$$\frac{dP}{d\delta} = 0$$

thus fixing values of δ which satisfy this condition. Substituting these values of δ in Eqs. 11-60 and 11-61, there will result the desired relation between E and I. But even when the simplified Eq. 11-77 is used, together with the correspondingly simplified expressions $I_q = (V/X_q)\sin\delta$ and $I_d = -(V/X_d)\cos\delta$, the resultant equation for curve H_2 is quite complicated.

The point of real importance in this analysis is that Eq. 11-76, as well as the accurate expression 11-79, show that the power developed by a salient-pole motor is represented by two parts, one varying as a harmonic function of δ, the other as a harmonic function of 2δ. This is shown in Fig. 11-32, in which part a corresponds to the approximate relation Eq. 11-76 and part b corresponds to the accurate Eq. 11-79. The effect of the term containing $\sin 2\delta$ is to make the maximum power (consistent with a given excitation) occur with a smaller torque angle than would otherwise be the case. In other words, the salient-pole machine has a stiffer coupling than an equivalent cylindrical-rotor machine; this is shown also by the extra term for the stiffness factor appearing in Eq. 11-77. In a cylindrical-rotor machine, the factor $X_d - X_q$ is zero; hence, the curve showing the relation between the power and torque angle of such a motor is the graph of the equation

$$P = \frac{VE \sin \delta}{Z_d} = \frac{VE \sin \delta}{Z_s}$$

One point of difference between parts a and b of Fig. 11-32 is the shift in the axis of ordinates which appears in the latter. The horizontal axis of reference divides the diagram into two parts such that ordinates measured above it represent motor power, and those below it represent generator power.

The stiffer coupling of a salient-pole machine is shown in another way in Fig. 11-26, where the circle marked C' would be the excitation locus of an equivalent cylindrical-rotor machine.

11-22. Excitation of Synchronous Motors. Since the field (rotor) winding of a synchronous motor must be excited by direct current, exactly as in a synchronous generator, the machine must either be constructed with a relatively small d-c generator driven directly by the rotor shaft, or provision must be made for connecting the field winding, through slip rings, to a d-c circuit of suitable voltage. The field winding is commonly designed for 125-volt excitation, though 250-volt circuits are sometimes used. The necessity of an auxiliary exciter is a disadvantage, especially in the case of synchronous motors of small size, but in larger sizes this disadvantage is counterbalanced by such distinctive operating characteristics as constancy of (average) speed and the possibility of power-factor correction of the system to which the motor is connected.

11-23. Starting of Synchronous Motors. It has been pointed out in Art. 11-2 that a synchronous motor is not inherently self-starting, considering only the reaction between the revolving field produced by the armature currents and the field poles themselves. For this reason, in the early history of the art, some synchronous motors were equipped with a special motor designed for use during the starting period only, but this is clearly a clumsy and expensive arrangement, especially in case a high starting torque is required. Moreover, with such a starting motor, the synchronous motor itself must be connected to the line at the moment of synchronism, thus calling for special synchronizing devices.

Induction-motor Start. As now constructed, synchronous motors are generally provided with an amortisseur winding, consisting of copper or bronze bars embedded in slots in the pole faces and short-circuited at both ends by conducting rings, which serve not only to damp out oscillations of speed during normal operation but also, when suitably designed, as a squirrel-cage winding for starting purposes. At the moment of starting, the synchronously rotating field produced by the armature current induces in the bars of the squirrel-cage emfs and currents of line frequency, and the reaction of these induced currents upon the main field produces a torque which accelerates the rotor in the direction of the rotating magnetic field. As the rotor speeds up under the impulsion of the torque, the relative speed or slip of the synchronously rotating armature field, with respect to the rotor bars, falls off, thus reducing not only the magnitude of the induced emfs but also their frequency. Because of the fact that the leakage reactance of the squirrel-cage winding falls off with decreasing slip (i.e., with increasing speed), the lag of the induced currents behind the inducing emfs becomes steadily less than at starting, so that the torque actually increases for a time notwithstanding the reduced magnitude of the current in the rotor bars. The squirrel-cage winding could not of itself accelerate the rotor to full synchronous speed, because as synchronism is approached the small slip reduces the induced emf and current to values much too small for adequate torque.

During the starting period just described, the field poles (not yet excited) are more and more slowly slipping backward through the synchronously rotating armature field. They tend to become magnetized by induction, first with one polarity, then with the other, so that if the field circuit is suddenly energized as synchronism is approached, the stator and rotor fields will lock together provided the impressed polarity of the field is of the proper sign at the instant the field switch is closed. In case the impressed polarity happens to be the reverse of what it should be, the machine suddenly experiences generator action, its speed is momentarily checked, and the field system slips back through a pole pitch, thus again bringing armature and rotor fields to a locking position. The transient conditions during this period of pulling into step are quite complex;* they are obviously conditioned by such factors as:

a. The load on the motor during the starting period and the manner in which it varies with speed; for it is clear that the greater the load to be started the greater will be the time required to accelerate it.

b. The torque (or power) developed by the motor when the field poles are excited, in accordance with curves such as those in Fig. 11-27.

c. The inertial properties of the rotor and its connected load, considered as a torsional pendulum, in accordance with the discussion of Arts. 11-13, 11-14, and 11-15, but especially the latter.

d. The torque-speed characteristics of the squirrel-cage damping winding.

Because of the fact that a salient-pole machine has greater stiffness of

---

* For further particulars concerning this and related features, the student should consult the following references: C. J. Fechheimer, Self-Starting Synchronous Motors, *Trans. AIEE*, **31**:529 (1912); E. B. Shand, Starting Characteristics of Synchronous Motors, *Elec. Jour.*, **18**:309 (1921); H. E. Edgerton and P. Fourmarier, The Pulling-into-Step of a Salient Pole Synchronous Motor, *Trans. AIEE*, **50**:769 (1931).

coupling, other things being equal, than a corresponding cylindrical-rotor type, as has been shown in connection with Fig. 11-32, the salient-pole machine has definitely the better pull-in torque. But in any case the field winding should not be energized until the speed is close to synchronism, if the full benefit of the pull-in torque is to be realized. If, for example, the fields are excited too soon, the machine develops motor power when the poles are appropriately placed with respect to the armature field, and immediately thereafter, when the slip has caused them to drop back through 180 electrical degrees, it becomes a generator; since the only source of energy for generator action is the kinetic energy of the rotating parts, a slowing down results at a time when acceleration is needed. Moreover, when thus acting as a generator, the machine tends to pump current (of subsynchronous frequency) back to the supply circuit, causing a more or less violent disturbance in the supply current.

During the starting period thus described, and while the field winding is still unexcited, the field coils are being cut by the revolving armature flux at a frequency which decreases from line frequency at standstill to zero at full synchronous speed. At standstill, therefore, there is induced in the field winding a voltage which may reach very high values, dangerous both to life and to the insulation. In order to limit this voltage to safe values, the field winding is sometimes interrupted at several points by some form of field breakup switch, but this is difficult in the case of a revolving-field (stationary-armature) machine.*

A better way to limit the induced voltage in the field winding is to reduce the voltage impressed upon the armature terminals to a fraction (one-third to one-half) of normal value; this has the incidental advantage of limiting the initial rush of starting current to a moderate amount, though this reduction of armature current also reduces the starting torque very materially.† The reduced voltage at starting is usually obtained by means of step-down transformers, commonly in the form of autotransformers (starting compensators); the same effect may be obtained by inserting reactance coils in the supply line, thus taking advantage of the inductive drop due to them with no loss of power other than that incidental to their small ohmic resistance.

Instead of leaving the field circuit open during the starting period, it might conceivably be short-circuited on the theory that the current thereby induced would add to the torque contributed by the squirrel-cage damping winding. Tests show that this theory is untenable, the actual torque being less than with the fields open-circuited, up to speeds somewhat beyond half the synchronous speed.

---

* A field sectionalizing switch in a revolving-field machine can be arranged to be operated by a centrifugal device. See reference to paper by M. A. Hyde, Jr., page 506.

† It has been shown in Chap. 6 that the starting torque of an induction motor varies approximately as the square of the impressed voltage.

Resistor in Field Circuit. *   The reduced torque during the early stages of the acceleration period caused by short-circuiting the field is due to the development of negative torque by some of the flux harmonics that exist under these conditions.   The shape of the speed-torque curve during the acceleration period is greatly affected by the magnitude of the field resistance, and if the latter is too low, as with the field short-circuited, the torque, instead of increasing faster than the speed, may tend to fall off, forming cusps or dips in the speed-torque curve, in which case the speed will "hang" at a subsynchronous value.   But if resistance is inserted in series with the field, this additional resistance being of the

FIG. 11-33. Rotor of 225-hp 300-rpm motor, with phase-connected damper winding. (*Courtesy of Westinghouse Electric Corporation.*)

order of 100 times the field resistance, then the starting torque will be large, provided there is also present a damper winding having high resistance and low reactance.   The field resistance is reduced as the motor accelerates until it amounts to three or four times that of the field itself, this reduction having the effect of improving the torque near synchronism.

This method has been used in some machines where large starting torque was required; it has the disadvantage that the voltage induced in the field is large at the moment of starting.   To keep this induced voltage within reasonable bounds, it is necessary to design the field winding with several sections in parallel, thereby likewise reducing the normal excitation voltage.

* M. A. Hyde, Jr., Synchronous Motor with Phase-connected Damper Windings for High-torque Loads, *Trans. AIEE*, **50**:600 (1931).

*Phase-connected Damping Winding.** While a squirrel-cage damping winding provides a starting torque considerably greater than could be attained without this device, the initial torque may fall considerably short of the amount required to start certain loads such as tube mills for making cement. To meet the need for a synchronous motor having a starting torque of the order of 200 per cent of full-load torque, machines have been built which employ the principle of the slip-ring induction motor. The bars of the damper winding embedded in the pole faces are connected to form a balanced three-phase Y-connected winding, with the terminals connected through slip rings to an adjustable rheostat. The starting resistance is then cut out by successive steps, by means of contactors actuated by a centrifugal device as the speed rises, until the winding is completely short-circuited at synchronism. It is then equivalent to the squirrel-cage winding it replaced, and is in condition to serve as a damping winding for suppressing hunting.

Figure 11-33 illustrates a rotor equipped with such a phase-wound damper.

Multiple Armature Windings.† By making the armature winding as two independent windings, normally connected in parallel, each of the constituent windings will have an impedance double that of the winding as a whole; so if only one winding is used during the starting period, the

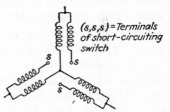

(s,s,s) = Terminals of short-circuiting switch

Fig. 11-34. Multiple-winding starting arrangement.

effect, with full voltage applied to the terminals, is about the same as though half voltage were impressed upon the complete machine. In other words, the starting compensator effect is built into the main armature winding. The diagram of connections is shown in Fig. 11-34.

The *supersynchronous* motor is a term, rather poorly chosen, that has been used to designate a specially constructed machine that is particularly suited for loads requiring a larger starting torque than is attainable with the usual squirrel-cage winding. The armature, instead of being rigidly bolted to the bedplate as in an ordinary motor, is capable of rotating about the rotor shaft on quill bearings, but under normal running conditions it is held stationary by a brake band surrounding the frame of the armature core. The rotor, as in the usual type of machine, is mechanically coupled to the load. When such a machine is to be started, the brake band surrounding the armature is released, and when line voltage is impressed upon the armature terminals (though slip rings), the armature speeds up in a direction opposite to the normal direction of rotation of the rotor; this is due to the fact that the inertia of the rotor and its connected load, or their combined starting friction, calls for a

* *Ibid.*

† D. W. McLenegan and A. G. Ferriss, Multiple Winding Starting Method for Synchronous Motors, *Gen. Elec. Rev.*, **33**:574 (1930).

larger torque than is necessary to start the unloaded armature structure. The armature will quickly reach nearly synchronous speed, and on exciting the rotor fields, the pull-in torque will bring the armature to full synchronous speed. Thereafter, on gradually slowing down the armature by means of the brake band, the rotor will speed up equally gradually, since the relative speed of the armature and the field structure remains constant. In this way, the full pull-out torque of the motor is available to start the load, whereas in the ordinary motor it is not available until full rotor speed has been attained.

11-24. Power-factor Correction. The fact that a synchronous motor can be made to draw either a leading or a lagging current by adjusting its field excitation has been explained on simple physical grounds in Art. 11-5. This characteristic constitutes one of the most valuable features of the synchronous motor, for it may be utilized to correct the power factor of a transmission or distribution system and to hold it at any desired value within the ability of the motor to absorb or supply reactive power.

Suppose, for example, that a distribution system is supplying power to a heavily inductive load at a power factor, say, of 60 per cent. For each ampere of current taken by the load, 0.6 amp represents active power supplied, while 0.8 amp represents reactive power. The quadrature current, though it does no useful work in carrying the load, is nevertheless responsible for ohmic loss just as effectively as though it were truly useful, so that in this example the total ohmic loss is greater than it would be if the quadrature (wattless) current were absent in the ratio

$$\frac{1^2}{0.6^2} = 2.78$$

The gain in efficiency through the suppression or neutralization of the quadrature current is so obvious as to need no comment. Another advantage accrues from its neutralization because of the better voltage regulation of the generators that supply the load; and still another for the reason that when the generating and distributing equipment is relieved of the quadrature current, there is released for other service that portion of the system capacity which would otherwise be unavailable because of the temperature rise due to the useless quadrature current. It is therefore obvious that if a synchronous motor of sufficient size were placed at the center of distribution of the load, its field winding could be so overexcited as to cause it to draw a leading current with a quadrature component equal and opposite to that required by the inductive load, and so raise the power factor of the load as a whole to unity; by still further increasing the excitation, the resultant power factor may correspond to a net leading current, thereby raising the terminal voltage sufficiently to compensate (or to overcompensate) the line drop. Looked at in another way, the synchronous motor used in this manner may be

considered to generate a quadrature current sufficient to supply the lagging quadrature component demanded by the load. For all these reasons, a synchronous machine used for this purpose is called a *synchronous
condenser.*

As another example, consider a generating plant supplying a distribution system over a long transmission line. Such a line may have such
large capacitance that the charging current may be a considerable
percentage of the current-carrying capacity of the generators and
transmission line. In that case, a synchronous machine operated with
underexcited field may be made to draw a lagging current sufficient to
compensate the capacitative effect of the transmission line, and the synchronous machine used in this way is called a *synchronous reactor.* There
are cases where one of the spare generators in a power plant is "floated"
on the line, running idly as a synchronous motor with only the friction
load of its prime mover as mechanical load, for the purpose of relieving
the other generators of the capacitance effect of a lightly loaded feeder.

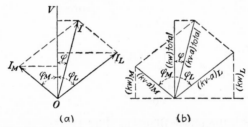

FIG. 11-35. Phasor and power diagrams, power-factor correction.

A synchronous motor used for power-factor correction may, of course,
carry a mechanical load at the same time. In the general case, the problem that arises is to determine the rating of a synchronous motor, which,
when carrying a definite load of its own, and when operated in parallel
with a load of given magnitude and power factor, will adjust the power
factor of the combined load to an assigned percentage. An approximate
solution, sufficiently accurate for practical purposes, follows from the simple diagram (Fig. 11-35a). Phasor OV is the terminal voltage (per phase)
common both to the load to be compensated, whose current (per phase)
and power factor are I_L and $\cos \varphi_L$, and to the motor, whose current and
power factor are I_M and $\cos \varphi_M$. The power factor of the combined load
is to be $\cos \varphi$. The diagram shows that

$$I_M^2 = I^2 + I_L^2 - 2II_L \cos (\varphi_L - \varphi) \tag{11-81}$$

and since the power per phase to be supplied by the motor is approximately

$$P_M = VI_M \cos \varphi_M$$

it follows that

$$VI \cos \varphi = VI_L \cos \varphi_L + P_M$$

whence
$$I = \frac{VI_L \cos \varphi_L + P_M}{V \cos \varphi} \qquad (11\text{-}82)$$

Substituting this value of I in Eq. 11-81,

$$I_M = \left[\left(\frac{VI_L \cos \varphi_L + P_M}{V \cos \varphi} \right)^2 + I_L^2 \right.$$
$$\left. - 2 \frac{VI_L \cos \varphi_L + P_M}{V \cos \varphi} I_L \cos (\varphi_L - \varphi) \right]^{\frac{1}{2}} \qquad (11\text{-}83)$$

whence the power rating of the motor, in volt-amperes, is

$$mVI_M = \left[\left(\frac{mVI_L \cos \varphi_L + mP_M}{\cos \varphi} \right)^2 + (mVI_L)^2 \right.$$
$$\left. - 2 \frac{mVI_L \cos \varphi_L + mP_M}{\cos \varphi} mVI_L \cos (\varphi_L - \varphi) \right]^{\frac{1}{2}} \qquad (11\text{-}84)$$

Since $mVI_L \cos \varphi_L$ is the total power taken by the load and mP_M is the total power supplied by the motor, both expressed in watts, this relation may be put in the convenient form

$$(\text{kva})_M = \left\{ \left[\frac{(\text{kw})_L + (\text{kw})_M}{\cos \varphi} \right]^2 + (\text{kva})_L^2 \right.$$
$$\left. - 2 \frac{(\text{kw})_L + (\text{kw})_M}{\cos \varphi} (\text{kva})_L \cos (\varphi_L - \varphi) \right\}^{\frac{1}{2}} \qquad (11\text{-}85)$$

which checks with the power diagram (Fig. 11-35b), drawn to correspond with the phasor diagram of currents (Fig. 11-35a). The approximation in this derivation is of course due to the fact that the motor load appearing in the equations and in the diagrams is not the output, which actually determines rating, but the input; the difference is of no consequence, however, since in selecting a motor the nearest commercial size must in any case be used.

CHAPTER 12

PARALLEL OPERATION OF SYNCHRONOUS GENERATORS

12-1. Synchronizing. In order that an incoming generator may be connected in parallel with others already in operation, it is necessary (1) that its speed correspond exactly to the frequency of the system to which it is to be connected; (2) that its voltage be numerically equal to that of the system at the bus terminals where the connection is made; and (3) that with respect to the external load circuit its voltage be in phase with that of the bus at the point of connection;* this requirement obviously means that the phase sequence of the incoming machine must be the same as that of the bus.

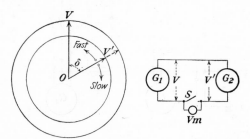

Fig. 12-1. Voltage relations while synchronizing.

If the bus-bar voltage of the system is assumed to have the constant value of V volts per phase, as in Fig. 12-1, the phase voltage V' of the incoming machine will in general differ from V, both as to magnitude and phase, while it is being brought up to the proper speed and excitation. If it be assumed that the incoming machine is slowly accelerating but that its speed falls short of synchronism, the relative angular velocity of phasor V' with respect to that of V is clockwise, in the direction marked "slow" in Fig. 12-1. A voltmeter connected across the terminals of an open switch S will then tend to read the phasor difference between V and V', which varies from $V - V'$ to $V + V'$ at a frequency equal to the difference of the frequencies of V and V'. By regulating the speed of the

* If the voltage of the incoming machine is considered with reference to the local circuit which includes only the other generators to which it is to be connected, its voltage must then be in phase opposition to that of the bus at the point of connection. Otherwise stated, the points to be connected must have the same potential.

incoming machine and adjusting its excitation, V' may be made to have the same magnitude and frequency as V, but it must be made to arrive at this condition when V' is in phase with V. This requires appropriate manipulation of the speed of the prime mover. If the latter is a d-c shunt motor, speed adjustment is most simply obtained by field control of the motor; but in the case of a steam or hydraulic plant the necessary adjustment is obtained by means of a small reversible motor, operated by remote control from the main switchboard, which adjusts the spring tension of the centrifugal governor mechanism and thereby affects the throttle valve.

12-2. Synchronism Indicators. The considerations outlined in Art. 12-1 show the need for a device which will indicate the exact moment for

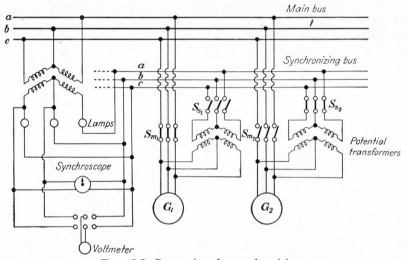

FIG. 12-2. Connections for synchronizing.

connecting the incoming generator to the main bus bars, assuming that the operation is to be performed manually.

Synchronizing Lamps. An early form of synchronism indicator, still used occasionally, calls for the use of incandescent lamps, connected in the manner shown in Fig. 12-2 for the case of a high-voltage three-phase system. Each generator switchboard panel is provided with a pair of potential transformers, connected in open Δ, the secondaries of which may be connected to an auxiliary synchronizing bus by means of plug switches, S_{s1} and S_{s2}. If the generator G_1 is already in operation, its main switch S_{m1} will be in the closed position and S_{s1} will be open. After generator G_2 has been brought up to approximately synchronous speed, switch S_{s2} is plugged in, whereupon the synchronizing lamps will flicker with a frequency equal to the difference between the frequencies of G_1 and G_2. The voltage of G_2 may be adjusted to equality with that of the main bus by the aid of a voltmeter which is connected alternately to the synchronizing bus and to the main bus. When the two voltages are equal, and the frequencies are the same, there may still be a phase difference between the voltages of G_1 and G_2, in which case the lamps will glow steadily; further adjustment of the speed of G_2 will then bring the two voltages into phase, in which case, because the lamps are connected so that the two voltages are in opposition through them, they will remain permanently dark. There-upon, the main switch S_{m2} may be closed and S_{s2} opened, and the paralleling is completed.

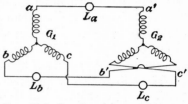

FIG. 12-3. Synchronizing with transposed terminals.

It is of course obvious that the synchronizing lamps must be adapted to operate at a voltage equal to twice the voltage between line and neutral. Since potential transformers are usually designed to give a secondary voltage of 110 volts, the lamps must in that case be rated at 220 volts.

The potential transformers shown in Fig. 12-2 may be omitted if the generators are of the low-voltage type. The synchronizing lamps must, however, be adapted to take up twice the bus voltage in such an installation.

When a generator is to be paralleled for the first time, it is not certain that the phase sequence of its terminals will be identically the same as that of other machines already in service. There is always a possibility

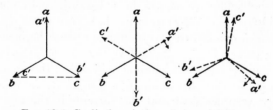

FIG. 12-4. Cyclical variation of phase relations.

that two of its terminals have been interchanged, or if they are correct, an accidental transposition may exist in the external connections to the switchboard; in any case, it is necessary to test the phase sequence and if necessary make a compensating transposition of two of the three terminals. Suppose, for example, that the connection diagrams of generators G_1 and G_2 of Fig. 12-2 are in reality as shown in Fig. 12-3, but that the transposition in G_2 is unsuspected; the synchronizing lamps would then be connected between the pairs of (apparently) homologous terminals aa', bb', cc', exactly as in Fig. 12-2. If the sequence of phase voltages of G_1 is counterclockwise, as shown by phasors a, b, c (Fig. 12-4), the sequence of phase voltages of G_2 will be clockwise, as a', b', c'. When G_2 has reached synchronous speed, phasors a and a' may be coincident, in which case lamp L_a will be dark, but lamps L_b and L_c will be subjected to voltages equal to $\sqrt{3}\, e$, which is 86.6 per cent of the maximum for which they are designed. When the speed of G_2 is just short of synchronism, phasors a', b', c' are slipping slowly in the clockwise direction relative to a, b, c, and in that case, as may be seen from the successive diagrams of Fig. 12-4, the lamps will pass through the dark and light phases in the cyclical order L_a, L_b, L_c. The same reasoning indicates that if G_2 is rotating at greater than synchronous speed, the order of rotation of the lamp phases will be reversed.

The use of lamps in the manner just described serves to "phase out" two three-phase circuits of like frequency and voltage, i.e., to determine corresponding pairs of terminals. In a synchronizing arrangement originally used by Siemens and Halske, the transposition of two of the three lamp terminals was made deliberately in order to make use of the sequence of lamp brightness to determine whether the incoming machine was running below or above synchronism; but when this arrangement is used, the combination of synchronism and the proper phase relationships between the voltages will be indicated only when one particular lamp remains permanently dark. In Fig. 12-3, this lamp would be L_a.

The Synchroscope. The Lincoln synchronizer* has almost entirely supplanted the use of synchronizing lamps, though occasionally the two devices are used jointly. It consists of a small bipolar motor whose laminated field structure is excited from the bus bars, at frequency $f = \omega/2\pi$, through a resistance R_F (Fig. 12-5) which is sufficiently large to ensure that the field current will be substantially in phase with the impressed voltage V. The armature has two windings, R and X, arranged in space quadrature, both supplied from the incoming generator, whose frequency $f' = \omega'/2\pi$ and voltage V' may be greater or less than that of the bus bars; one winding is in series (through slip rings not shown in Fig. 12-5) with a noninductive resistor R, the other is in series with a reactor X so designed that the currents in the two windings are very nearly in time quadrature, and their effective ampere-turns are equal; in other words, the current in winding R is very nearly in phase with V' and the current in winding X lags behind V' by nearly 90°. It will be assumed that the voltage induced in the armature coils R and X by the alternation of the field flux is negligible, and that the voltage induced in F by the fluxes due to windings R and X is also negligible.

Subject to these assumptions, it is possible to consider separately the torque acting on coil R due to the reaction between its current and the flux set up by the field F and the corresponding torque acting on coil X due to its reaction with coil F. The current in coil R is in phase with V', and the flux due to F is in phase with V. While the incoming machine

---

* P. M. Lincoln, Synchronism and Frequency Indication, *Trans. AIEE*, **18**:255 (1901).

is coming up to speed, the phase angle between V and V' is constantly changing (see Fig. 12-1), but if this phase angle is δ at the instant when the axes of windings R and F are mechanically displaced by angle θ (Fig. 12-5), the torque acting on coil R is

$$T_R = K \sin \theta \cos \delta \qquad (12\text{-}1)$$

Similarly, the torque acting upon coil X is

$$T_X = K \sin (\theta + 90) \cos (\delta \pm 90) = \mp K \cos \theta \sin \delta \qquad (12\text{-}2)$$

Neglecting the effect of inertia and friction of the armature as too small to be taken into account, it follows that $T_R + T_X = 0$, whence

$$\sin \theta \cos \delta = \pm \cos \theta \sin \delta$$
$$\tan \theta = \pm \tan \delta$$

or $\qquad \theta = \pm \delta \qquad$ or $\qquad \pm (180 + \delta) \qquad (12\text{-}3)$

The reason for the $\pm$ sign in Eq. 12-2 is the fact that the terminals of coil X can be connected in either of two ways; assuming that the connections are so made that the term

$$\cos (\delta \pm 90)$$

is actually to be taken as $\cos (\delta + 90)$, it follows that

$$\theta = \delta \qquad \text{or} \qquad (180 + \delta)$$

and since only one value need be used, we have

$$\theta = \delta$$

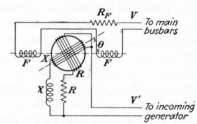

FIG. 12-5. Circuits of Lincoln synchronizer.

The physical meaning of this result is that the armature will align itself so that the axes of windings R and F are inclined at an angle equal to the phase displacement between V and V'. If there is any difference between the frequencies of V and V', a pointer attached to the armature shaft will rotate at slip speed, and the direction of its rotation will indicate whether the incoming machine is running above or below synchronism. At synchronism, the pointer will remain stationary, but it must be brought to the particular position which indicates zero phase displacement ($\delta = 0$) between V and V' before the main switch of the incoming generator is closed.

The synchroscope just described (sometimes called a synchronoscope) is essentially a single-phase instrument, as may also be seen from the connection diagram in Fig. 12-2, where it is associated with one pair of bus bars, b and c. Indication of synchronism is then complete only when it is known from a preliminary phasing-out test that the potentials of all three pairs of terminals are simultaneously the same.

Special Synchronizing Transformer. Figure 12-6 illustrates a special type of transformer for use in connection with a single synchronizing lamp. If the voltages of the bus bars and the incoming generator are in phase with respect to the external load circuit, as they should be for parallel operation, appropriate connections to the exciting windings on the two outer legs of the core will cause their fluxes to neutralize in the middle leg; a lamp connected to the middle winding will then be dark. If there is any phase difference between the voltages of the bus bars and the machine to be synchronized, some flux will pass through the middle core, and the lamp will glow.

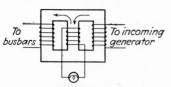

Fig. 12-6. Special synchronizing transformer.

12-3. Automatic Synchronizing. Synchronization by means of manually operated switching served well enough when the individual generators were relatively small, but with the growth of system capacity, and the ratings of the generating units themselves, it became necessary to resort to automatic devices to ensure the closing of the main switch of the incoming machine at the proper instant. Because of the size and inertia of the moving parts of the main switch or circuit breaker, and the time delay in its control mechanism, a finite time, varying from 0.2 to 0.8 sec, is required for the closing of the main contacts after the triggering of its actuating mechanism. It is therefore evident that unless the closing coil of the relay which actuates the circuit breaker is energized at the right moment, the main contacts may close when the voltages V and V' (Fig. 12-7) are so far from phase coincidence that a very large equalizing current may flow and so cause a serious system disturbance.

Specifically, let V and V' in Fig. 12-7 represent the assumed equal voltages of the bus bar and of the incoming machine, respectively, the former alternating at frequency f, the latter at frequency $f' < f$. Phasor V' may then be considered to be rotating slowly in the clockwise direction relative to the stationary phasor V at a frequency $f - f'$; and at the instant represented in the diagram the angle $\alpha = 2\pi(f - f')t$, where t is the time required for the two phasors to be coincident. If t is the over-all time lag of the circuit breaker, then for a given frequency difference $f - f'$ the angle α is the phase displacement between V and V' at the moment when the closing relay should be initially actuated.

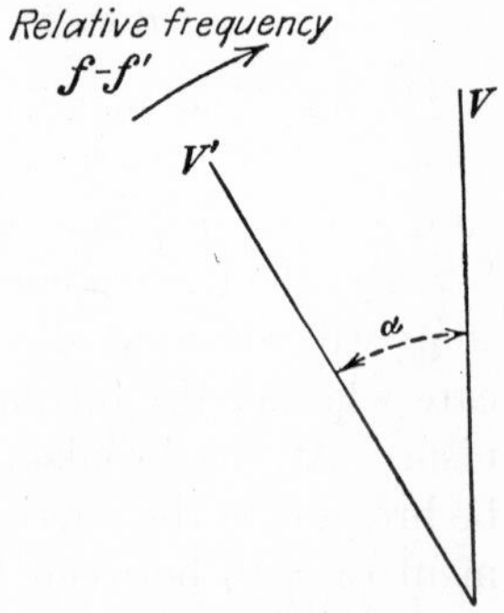

Relative frequency
f-f'

Fig. 12-7. Voltages approaching synchronism.

In order to design equipment which will automatically close the main circuit breaker at the moment when V and V' are in phase (with respect to the external circuit), there must be provided two contact-making relays, II and III, such that one of them, say, III, operates only when angle α has a predetermined value, and the other, II, operates only when $f - f'$ has such a value that $t = \alpha/2\pi(f - f')$ is the time lag of the main breaker.   The contacts of relays II and III, connected in series, will then serve to energize the closing coil of the main circuit breaker only when α and $f - f'$ are simultaneously at the correct values.

Relay III is designed so that it may be set to close its contacts when the phase angle α lies anywhere between definite limits, as indicated in Fig. 12-8, but in such a way that the closure is independent of the frequency difference $f - f'$.   On the other hand, relay II is designed to give a response proportional to $f - f'$, but the slope of its graph in Fig. 12-8 is adjustable.   Simultaneous operation of relays II and III is then determined by the point of intersection of the lines marked II and III.

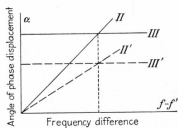

FIG. 12-8. Adjustable settings of relays.

Automatic synchronizers based upon these principles are made in numerous forms.   One of them, made by the Westinghouse Electric Corporation, which utilizes electronic equipment in its control circuits is illustrated schematically in Fig. 12-9.

12-4. Circulating Current and Synchronizing Action of Two Identical Alternators.   If a generator is paralleled with another machine of identical characteristics at the instant when its own voltage is exactly equal to, and in phase with, the bus-bar voltage of the one already under load, it will not relieve the latter of any of its load provided that the speeds of the two machines are also exactly the same; it will merely continue to run without either supplying any current to the bus bars or taking any current from them.   Under these conditions, the voltages V_1 and V_2 of the two generators, measured at their point of connection at switch S in Fig. 12-10a, are equal in magnitude and in exact phase opposition with respect to the local circuit in which they have a series relation.

Suppose, however, that, at the moment of synchronizing generator G_2, its terminal voltage V_2, while numerically equal to the bus-bar voltage V_1, is not exactly opposite in phase* to V_1 but falls short of complete

---

* With respect to the local circuit between G_1 and G_2.

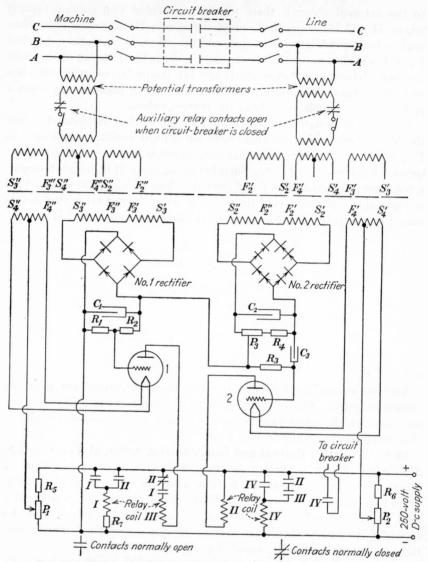

FIG. 12-9. Schematic diagram of Westinghouse automatic synchronizer.

opposition because G_2 is at the moment running slightly slower than G_1. This condition is indicated in Fig. 12-10b; there is then a resultant voltage E_c acting in the local series circuit, which sets up current I_c lagging behind E_c by an angle φ_s such that

$$\tan \varphi_s = \frac{X_{s_1} + X_{s_2}}{R_{a_1} + R_{a_2}} \qquad (12\text{-}4)$$

where $X_{s_1} = X_{s_2} = X_s$ is the synchronous reactance of each of the two iden-

tical machines and $R_{a_1} = R_{a_2} = R_a$ is their common armature resistance.*
The current I_c is

$$\mathbf{I}_c = \frac{\mathbf{E}_c}{2Z_s} = \frac{\mathbf{E}_c}{2(R_a + jX_s)} \tag{12-5}$$

It is plain from Fig. 12-10b that the circulating current I_c, which is in
addition to the load current already being supplied by G_1, has a component in phase with V_1, and therefore implies an additional load on G_1
which tends to slow it down; and that, because I_c has a component in
opposition to V_2, machine G_2 develops motor action which tends to raise
its speed. If, on the other hand, G_2 is running slightly faster than G_1 at
the moment of synchronizing, voltage V_2 will be somewhat ahead of the
position of exact phase opposition, as in Fig. 12-10c, and the resultant
circulating current will cause G_2 to develop generator power, tending to
reduce its speed, while G_1 develops motor
action which tends to raise its speed.

Another aspect of this interchange of generator and motor action is evident from a
consideration of the case of two identical
generators running in exact synchronism
with equal excitations and with their voltages V_1 and V_2 in exact phase opposition
with respect to the local circuit between
them. There will then be no circulating
current, and the two machines will divide
the external load equally. Any change in
the load, say, a sudden increase, will cause a
momentary slowing down of both machines,
but even a slight difference in the sensitivity
of their governing mechanisms will cause
one of the two machines to take more than
its share of the load increment. Suppose,

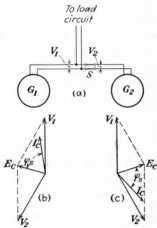

FIG. 12-10. Phasor diagram of
circulating current referred to
local circuit.

for instance, that G_1 takes the greater part of the increased load, thereby
causing it to slow down relative to G_2, so that the latter will relatively
pull ahead until V_1 and V_2 assume the positions indicated in Fig. 12-10c.
The resultant generator action of G_2 will then tend to restore the original
equal division of the load.

It is seen, therefore, that there is an automatic synchronizing action
which tends to hold the machines in step. This inherent synchronizing
power is primarily due to the elastic reaction between the magnetic fields
of the stator and rotor of each machine, which may conveniently be vis-

---

* Equation 12-4 is approximate because under the assumed conditions the frequencies of the two machines are not exactly the same. If the difference in frequencies is
small, as assumed, the error is unimportant.

ualized as due to a tension acting along the lines of magnetic induction in the airgaps. The synchronizing power is therefore measured by the stiffness or coupling factor discussed in Art. 11-13. The synchronizing power vanishes at the stability limit, so that if the two machines swing too far apart they will fall out of step.

12-5. Power Output of Generators in Parallel. It has been shown in Chap. 11 that in accordance with the synchronous-reactance theory the power developed by a cylindrical-rotor machine is given by Eq. 11-33 as

$$P = \frac{VE \cos (\varphi_s - \delta)}{Z_s} - \frac{E^2 \cos \varphi_s}{Z_s} \qquad (11\text{-}33)$$

whereas in the case of a salient-pole machine the power is given by Eq. 11-76 in the form

$$P = \frac{VE}{X_d} \sin \delta + \frac{V^2(X_d - X_q)}{2X_dX_q} \sin 2\delta \qquad (11\text{-}76)$$

In both equations, the power or torque angle δ is the angular displacement between V, the terminal voltage, and E, the voltage induced by the field excitation. The importance of this angle may be better understood by observing from Eq. 11-33 that if $\varphi_s = \tan^{-1}(X_s/R_a)$ is assumed to be practically $90°$ (because R_a is usually very small in comparison with X_s), Eq. 11-33 reduces to the simple form

$$P = \frac{VE}{X_s} \sin \delta \qquad (12\text{-}6)$$

which shows that for given values of V and E the power developed is measured by sin δ.

It will be noted that if in Eq. 11-76 we impose the condition

$$X_d = X_q = X_s$$

which is characteristic of a cylindrical rotor, the expression for P becomes the same as Eq. 12-6. The term involving the angle 2δ in Eq. 11-76 represents the reluctance power (see Art. 11-21); as a rule, it is small in comparison with the term involving sin δ, because the ratio of the two coefficients is of the order $(X_d - X_q)/2X_q$.

Although Eq. 12-6 as here derived stems from consideration of synchronous-motor theory, it is equally applicable to the synchronous generator. It is merely necessary to bear in mind that V is the terminal voltage as fixed by the bus-bar voltage of the system, E is the excitation voltage, and δ is the angle of phase displacement between them, as in Fig. 12-11a. In order that the generator may supply power to the line, the angle δ must take such a value as to satisfy Eq. 12-6, which means that for a given excitation (i.e., for a given value of E) the rotor of the generator must be forced ahead of the position of the field structure of a hypothetical generator of large capacity which maintains the terminal voltage V and which rotates at constant angular velocity. It follows that if the load carried by a synchronous generator is to be increased when it is operating in parallel with others which maintain constant terminal voltage, *additional power must be supplied to it by its prime mover.*

The effect of varying the excitation of a generator which is operating in parallel with others on a constant-potential bus can be understood by considering Fig. 12-11b and c.* In these diagrams, it is assumed that the excitation voltage E is exactly in phase with the bus voltage V, but that in the one case $E > V$, and in the other $E < V$. Neglecting the effect of resistance, the voltage differences $E - V$ and $V - E$ will result in a circulating current I_c in quadrature with both E and V. In the former case, Fig. 12-11b, this current lags behind E and therefore exerts a demagnetizing action to counteract the excessive field excitation; in the other case, Fig. 12-11c, the circulating current leads E and exerts a magnetizing action to compensate for the deficient excitation. But in neither

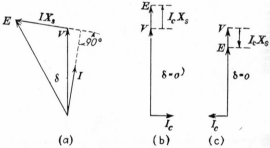

FIG. 12-11. Effect of varying torque angle.

case is there any power developed, a conclusion which follows both because $\delta = 0$ and because the circulating current is in quadrature with the voltage. In general, therefore, adjustment of the field excitation of an alternator will not affect its output when it is in parallel with others which maintain constant bus voltage, but it will result in the production of a circulating quadrature current which is undesirable because of its heating effect.

12-6. Parallel Operation of Two Identical Generators. The preceding discussion of alternators in parallel has been based upon the assumption that the terminal or bus-bar voltage at the point of connection is constant. Let this condition be again assumed for the case of two identical generators which are initially equally excited and in each of which the power supplied by the prime movers is adjusted so that each machine carries half the load represented by an external impedance $Z = R + j2\pi fL$, where R and L are constant. These conditions will then be represented by Fig. 12-12a, where $\mathbf{I} = 2\mathbf{I}_1 = 2\mathbf{I}_2 = \mathbf{V}/Z$.

* See M. Liwschitz-Garik and C. C. Whipple, "Electric Machinery," Vol. II, pp. 341–345, D. Van Nostrand Company Inc., New York, 1946.

Assume now that the excitation voltages of the two machines are simultaneously changed to the magnitudes represented by E_1' and E_2', Fig. 12-12b, in such manner that:

a. The terminal voltage V remains unaltered and therefore $I = V/Z$ remains the same as before.

b. The power developed by each machine remains unchanged at the value

$$P = \frac{VE_1'}{X_s} \sin \delta_1' = \frac{VE_2'}{X_s} \sin \delta_2' = \frac{VE_1}{X_s} \sin \delta$$

It will be seen from Fig. 12-12b that subject to these assumed conditions the current I_1' becomes larger than its original value and at the same time more heavily lagging, while I_2' becomes leading. There is accordingly a demagnetizing action in machine 1, and a magnetizing action in 2.

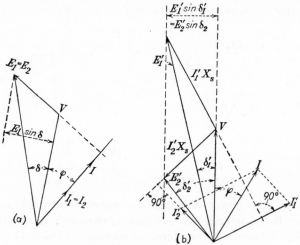

FIG. 12-12. Two identical alternators in parallel.

But the point of prime importance is that if all the stated conditions are to hold true, the changes in E_1 and E_2 cannot be made at random, but must be definitely related, for reasons implicit in Fig. 12-12b. Thus,

$$\mathbf{E}_1' = \mathbf{V} + j\mathbf{I}_1'X_s$$
$$\mathbf{E}_2' = \mathbf{V} + j\mathbf{I}_2'X_s$$

which when added give

$$j(\mathbf{I}_1' + \mathbf{I}_2')X_s = \mathbf{E}_1' + \mathbf{E}_2' - 2\mathbf{V}$$

But since

$$I = \mathbf{I}_1' + \mathbf{I}_2' = \frac{\mathbf{V}}{Z}$$

we have

$$\mathbf{E}_1' + \mathbf{E}_2' = \mathbf{I}(2Z + jX_s) = \text{constant}$$

It follows, therefore, that if E_2 is changed to E_2' without at the same time changing E_1 in the manner called for by the above relation, the terminal voltage V will change to a new value, which will in turn affect the current taken by the external circuit and thereby change the magnitude of the load.   But if these changes occur without a change in the governor settings of the prime movers, the changed load, if it is a decrease, will cause the speed of the two generators to increase; or if the external load increases, the speed will fall.   In either case, the frequency will be correspondingly affected, and this will change the load reactance $2\pi fL$ if L is constant.   It will therefore be seen that the parallel operation of two identical generators presents a highly complex problem, which is even more intricate if the external circuit supplied by them consists of induction motors.

12-7. Effect of Armature Reactance upon Parallel Operation.   The phasor diagrams in Fig. 12-10 bring out clearly that it is the armature reactance of the parallel machines which is responsible for the automatic synchronizing action which holds them in step.   For if there were no reactance, I_c would be in phase with E_c, in which case its projections upon V_1 and V_2 would be equal, and they would represent generator action in both machines, so that there would then be no synchronizing power.   The essential feature of the synchronizing effect is that a machine which momentarily runs ahead of its mean position shall develop generator action tending to make it slow down, while at the same time the machine which has fallen behind its mean position shall develop motor action and so be accelerated.   It is the reactance which accomplishes this result by forcing the current I_c to be nearly in phase with V_2 in the former case, and nearly in phase with V_1 in the latter.

12-8. Division of Load between Alternators in Parallel.   When d-c generators are operated in parallel, the load on any one of them may be increased or decreased by raising or lowering its field excitation.   The preceding discussion shows that this is not the case when an alternator is in parallel with others, the effect of changed excitation being merely to establish a circulating quadrature current without materially affecting the power delivered.   A simple explanation of this behavior is that the electrical power output of an alternator cannot be greater than the difference between the mechanical power input and its own internal losses, so that in general, because the changed excitation affects the losses only to a minor extent, the power output can be varied only by a corresponding change in the mechanical input.   This means that the division of load between alternators in parallel can be controlled only by adjusting the input to the prime movers, i.e., by manipulating the valves controlling the steam supply to an engine- or turbine-driven alternator, or the water supply to a hydraulic unit.

By way of further example of the effect of changing the excitation, other conditions remaining the same, consider Fig. 12-13, where the initial excitation voltage is E_1 and the corresponding impedance drop, current, and power are, respectively, E_{c_1}, I_1, and P.   This diagram is based upon the synchronous-reactance theory which led to Figs. 11-10 to 11-12, the chief difference being that the power circle P now lies outside the zero-power circle because P in the expression $\sqrt{(V/2R_a)^2 - P/R_a}$ must be treated as a negative quantity when the machine is operating as a

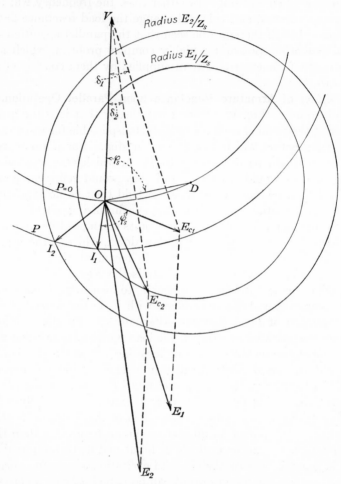

FIG. 12-13. Effect of varying excitation.

generator.   Changing the excitation voltage to E_2 can have no appreciable effect upon the power developed; consequently, the new current phasor I_2 must terminate on the original power circle P, and phasors E_2 and E_{c_2} must adjust themselves to the new conditions by a change in the torque angle from δ_1 to δ_2.   The alteration in the current from I_1 to I_2 means that there is set up a circulating current equal to the phasor difference between I_2 and I_1, and this produces the self-synchronizing effect incident to the hunting which accompanies the change in the torque angle.

A conclusion which follows from this discussion is that the division of load between alternators in parallel does not depend upon their internal impedances, as was found to be the case when transformers are connected in parallel. The load assumed by any one generator depends altogether upon the valve setting of its prime mover, and this in turn depends upon the setting of the governor mechanism.

12-9. Governor Characteristics. The speed-load characteristic of a generator must be a drooping curve (Fig. 12-14), in order that its operation may be stable; for unless the speed drops as the load increases, any increase of load would be accompanied by an increased speed, which would mean the assumption of still more load until the machine had taken the entire load from those with which it is in parallel, after which it would tend to run away. The governors commonly used on the prime movers operate on the centrifugal principle, the momentary drop in speed caused by an increase of load being utilized to make them operate

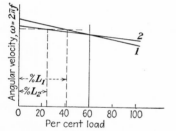

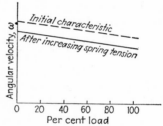

Fig. 12-14. Speed-load governor characteristics.

Fig. 12-15. Shift of speed-load characteristic.

the valve mechanism; such governors therefore automatically impart a drooping speed characteristic, and the design is such that there is ordinarily a difference of 3 to 4 per cent in speed between no load and full load. Usually, the curve showing the relation between the average speed and the load is very nearly a straight line within the limits of normal operation.

If two generating units connected in parallel have dissimilar speed-load characteristics, as indicated by curves 1 and 2 in Fig. 12-14, they will divide the load in proportion to their ratings only at the particular speed at which their characteristics intersect each other. At any other speed, the division of load will depart from this proportion. If the division of load is to remain the same at all loads without the need for special adjustments, both machines must have identical speed-load characteristics.

Notwithstanding differences in the speed-load characteristics in the manner indicated in Fig. 12-14, it is possible to divide the load between alternators in parallel in any desired manner by adjusting the spring tension of the governor mechanism. This has the effect of changing the valve setting, hence the power input corresponding to any particular speed, and causes the speed-load curve to be shifted to a new position nearly parallel to its initial position, as indicated in Fig. 12-15. A decrease of spring tension will decrease the speed corresponding to a particular valve opening, and so lower the entire characteristic.

The drop in speed incident to increased load would, if left to itself, reduce the frequency of the system as the load increases. This is undesirable, and may be prevented by an automatic frequency control which operates by controlling the spring tension of the governor of one of the generating units, raising or lowering its speed as the case may be, until its frequency has the desired value regardless of the load. The frequency thus established determines the constant speed at which all the other units must operate; the load fluctuations are thereby taken by the machine having the controlled governor, all the others retaining the constant loads assigned to them by their original governor settings. Any desired adjustment of load between these "trailing" machines may then be made at pleasure by manual control of their governor springs.

The speed-load curves of Figs. 12-14 and 12-15 relate, of course, to the *average* speed at any load. The instantaneous angular velocity of a generator may vary from point to point during a revolution because of the torque characteristics of its prime mover. If the latter is an internal-combustion engine, the torque, expressed as a function of time, is the sum of a constant and a series of harmonics; the result is that during part of a revolution there is a surplus of torque, causing an angular acceleration of the rotating system, and at other times there is a deficit of torque that brings about a retardation. These changes of instantaneous speed are reflected in phase swinging of the generated emf and consequent oscillations in the magnitude of the circulating current between machines. In case these pulsations, or any of their components, have a periodicity that agrees with the natural frequency of the generator regarded as a torsional pendulum, violent hunting is likely to be induced and so cause the machines to fall out of step if the limit of stability is reached. Such a condition must be prevented by the use of heavy flywheels and powerful damping grids in the pole faces. Somewhat similar variations of torque occur in the case of reciprocating steam-engine drives, but to a lesser extent than in the case of internal-combustion engines. Turbine-driven units (steam and hydraulic) are, of course, free from this cyclic irregularity of torque.

In any case, the governor mechanism will not respond instantly to a change of speed, because of friction and lost motion in its moving parts. It is not desirable that it should be too sensitive, for if it were, a tendency toward violent hunting might be aggravated; for this reason, the governor is equipped with an adjustable dashpot to bring its sensitivity under positive control.   Because of these considerations, the speed-load characteristic is not a mathematical line, as in Figs. 12-14 and 12-15, but is, rather, a band of appreciable width, as in Fig. 12-16, the width being a measure of the sluggishness of governor response.   It is easily seen that the damping of the governor must be sufficient to produce a band of such width that any cyclical variations of engine speed shall lie within it.

12-10. Parallel Operation of Dissimilar Generators.   In small power plants, it is quite common to find that the load must at times be divided between two generating units of different designs and ratings.   For

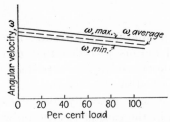

FIG. 12-16. Effect of sluggish governor.

example, one may be a 60-cycle 250-kva unit consisting of an engine-driven alternator having 28 poles, running at 257 rpm (nearly); the other, a turbine-driven alternator having 4 poles, running at 1,800 rpm. In the former, 1 space degree is equivalent to 14 electrical degrees; in the latter, 1 space degree is equivalent to 2 electrical degrees, or only one-seventh as much.   To keep the two machines strictly in phase therefore requires that the actual torque angle of the reciprocating unit must not deviate by more than one-seventh of the corresponding actual torque angle of the turbine unit.   Obviously, this requires careful design of the flywheel of the reciprocating unit.

CHAPTER 13

THE SYNCHRONOUS CONVERTER

13-1. Rectification of Alternating Current. Because the development of d-c generators and motors preceded that of the corresponding a-c machines, numerous commercial and industrial applications of direct current were firmly established by the time that satisfactory a-c appliances, particularly motors, became generally available. This situation was especially pronounced in the case of electric railways and in the power drives for passenger and freight elevators, in both of which fields the d-c motor held undisputed sway for many years. As the advantages of a-c transmission and distribution became better understood, and more and more power plants were equipped with a-c generators, it became necessary to develop machines to serve as a connecting link between them and the established d-c applications by fulfilling the function of converting the alternating current to direct current. There are, of course, certain applications of electrical energy, such as in electrochemical processes, where direct current is required regardless of this historical sequence of development, thus reinforcing the need for suitable converting apparatus.

Several types of rectifiers are available, which may be classified broadly as *mechanical, electronic,* and *electromagnetic.*

Mechanical rectifiers may be dismissed from consideration so far as heavy-power applications are concerned, and they are now obsolete even for such uses as the operation of high-voltage X-ray tubes; they are in effect nothing but segmented commutators driven in synchronism with the alternating current to be rectified.

Electronic rectifiers include those of the electrolytic type in which dissimilar chemical substances (usually having a metallic base), either directly in contact or immersed in an electrolyte, have the property of transmitting current readily in one direction while interposing extremely high resistance to current flow in the opposite direction; and with these may be grouped thermionic tubes of the vacuum and gas-filled types, such as the mercury-vapor rectifier. The latter is now in wide use in the heavy-power field, the original fragile glass bulbs having given way to large steel tanks. Further discussion of the mercury-arc rectifier will be found in Chap. 16.

The important electromagnetic types of rectifiers include the *motor-generator* and the *synchronous converter*. The motor-generator consists of a suitable a-c motor, either of the synchronous or induction type, direct-connected to a d-c generator, usually of the compound-wound type; this type of converting unit has the advantage of complete independence of control of the motor and the generator, but it is more expensive, and requires more floor space, than an equivalent synchronous converter; its operating characteristics will depend upon those of the driving motor and of the generator, considered separately. The remainder of this chapter will be confined to the synchronous converter, ordinarily called the *rotary converter*.

13-2. Construction of the Synchronous Converter. A d-c generator can be converted to an a-c generator by tapping the armature winding and connecting the taps to slip rings. In a multipolar machine having a simplex lap-wound armature and p poles, each slip ring must be connected to p symmetrically spaced points in the armature winding; if only one additional slip ring is to be used so as to make the machine a single-phase generator, the second ring must be connected to a second set of p taps displaced by 180 electrical degrees from the first set. Three slip rings, connected in order to three sets of taps, each displaced from the next by 120 electrical degrees, will result in a three-phase Δ-connected winding. Additional slip rings, when connected to suitable sets of taps, will result in four-phase (or quarter-phase), six-phase, twelve-phase, etc., windings. The two-pole armature of Fig. 13-1 (shown as a ring winding for convenience) may be used as a single-phase, quarter-phase, or three-phase generator.

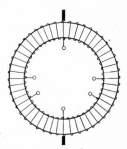

Fig. 13-1. Single-, quarter-, and three-phase taps.

A machine of this kind, provided with a commutator at one end, and slip rings at the other end of the armature core, may be used not only as an a-c generator or as a d-c generator, but simultaneously as a double-current generator, subject, of course, to the limitation that the total power taken from it shall be within the safe thermal limits of operation; for the current in any individual armature element will at any instant be the sum of the corresponding instantaneous values of the two currents and, as will presently appear, the average heating is not the same in all the winding elements. The machine may also be used separately either as a d-c motor or as a synchronous motor; or simultaneously as a synchronous motor and d-c generator, in which case it is called a *synchronous*, or *rotary, converter;* or simultaneously as a d-c motor and an a-c generator, in which case it is called an *inverted converter*. In either of the last two cases, the current in an armature element is at any instant the difference between the corresponding generator and motor currents, with the result that its rating is in general higher than when it is used exclusively as a generator or as a motor.

It must not be assumed, however, that a given design will be equally effective in all these various uses; for if the commutator is adequate for use as a simple d-c generator or motor, it will be too large for the double-current purpose, and too small when the alternating and direct currents are in opposition; in fact, one of the striking features of the rotary converter is the large size of its commutator in comparison with the other dimensions of the machine.   The same thing is true with regard to the slip rings.   But still more important, the commutating conditions are so different in the various possible combinations that the particular conditions under which the machine is to operate determine the design.

13-3. The Voltage Ratio of a Converter:Sinusoidal Flux Distribution. Let Fig. 13-2 represent in diagrammatic form the simplex lap winding of a multipolar armature which is tapped at intervals of $2\pi/m$ electrical degrees, where $m \geqq 3$ is the number of phases and slip rings on the a-c side.   When $m = 4$, the machine is a quarter-phase converter, this being the nearest equivalent to a two-phase arrangement.   When the machine is arranged for single-phase operation, there must be two slip rings tapped into points 180 electrical degrees apart; so the relation $2\pi/m$ fails for this case, and special treatment is required.

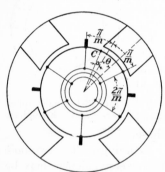

FIG. 13-2. Armature winding of m-phase converter.

In Fig. 13-2, let E_m represent the maximum emf developed in a single conductor at the instant it passes the middle of a pole; on either side of this position, the emf falls off in accordance with a harmonic law; consequently, the average emf per conductor is $(2/\pi)E_m$, and the d-c voltage for the Z/p conductors in series between brushes is

$$E_{dc} = \frac{2}{\pi} \frac{Z}{p} E_m \qquad (13\text{-}1)$$

provided the brushes are in the geometrical neutral axis.

Consider a single conductor C (Fig. 13-2), displaced from the midpoint of a phase belt by angle α, at the instant when the mid-point of the belt is itself displaced from the pole axis by angle θ.   The instantaneous emf in conductor C is then

$$e = E_m \cos (\theta + \alpha)$$

Since the number of conductors between taps is $2Z/pm$, the instantaneous emf for the whole phase belt lying within the limits $\alpha = -\pi/m$ and

$\alpha = +\pi/m$ is

$$e = \frac{2ZE_m}{pm}\frac{m}{2\pi}\int_{-\pi/m}^{+\pi/m}\cos\ (\theta + \alpha)\ d\alpha$$

$$= \frac{2ZE_m}{pm}\frac{\sin\ (\pi/m)}{\pi/m}\cos\ \theta \qquad\qquad (13\text{-}2)$$

In this equation, the quantity $2ZE_m/pm$ is the maximum emf that would be developed in the entire phase belt if all the conductors were concentrated; the quantity $\sin\ (\pi/m)/(\pi/m)$ is therefore the breadth or distribution factor, a result which might have been anticipated from Eq. 4-18.

The effective voltage per phase (i.e., between slip rings) is therefore

$$E_{ac} = \frac{\sqrt{2}\ ZE_m}{pm}\frac{\sin\ (\pi/m)}{\pi/m} \qquad\qquad (13\text{-}3)$$

and the ratio of the a-c to the d-c voltages of the converter is

$$\frac{E_{ac}}{E_{dc}} = \frac{\sin\ (\pi/m)}{\sqrt{2}} \qquad\qquad (13\text{-}4)$$

The last equation may be written

$$\frac{(E_{ac})_{max}}{E_{dc}} = \frac{\sqrt{2}\ E_{ac}}{E_{dc}} = \sin\frac{\pi}{m}$$

Fig. 13-3. Voltage ratio, m-phase converter.

from which it follows (see Fig. 13-3) that if the d-c voltage is represented as the diameter of a circle, the *maximum* value of the a-c voltage is the chord subtended by the central angle $2\pi/m$; these results are valid only on condition that the brushes are in the geometrical neutral and that the airgap flux is sinusoidally distributed.

In the case of a single-phase converter (not used in practice), only two slip rings are required, and the winding is tapped at points 180 electrical degrees apart. Reference to Fig. 13-2 will show that under these conditions the maximum value of the single-phase voltage will then be equal to the steady d-c voltage from brush to brush, i.e.,

$$E_{ac_1} = \frac{E_{dc}}{\sqrt{2}} \qquad\qquad (13\text{-}5)$$

13-4. The Current Ratio of a Converter. It is necessary to distinguish between the line current (I_l) at the a-c end and the coil current (I_c) in the armature winding itself. For example, let Fig. 13-4a represent the winding in diagrammatic form for an m-phase *bipolar* machine; the coil currents in successive phase belts will be equal, under balanced load conditions, but they will differ in phase by $2\pi/m$ electrical degrees, as indicated in Fig. 13-4b. The line current I_l at a tap (or slip ring) will then be the phasor difference between the two adjacent coil currents, or

$$I_l = 2I_c \sin \frac{\pi}{m} \qquad p = 2$$

If the machine is multipolar (p poles) and has the usual simplex lap winding as in Fig. 13-2, the line current subdivides, not once, as in Fig. 13-4a, but $p/2$ times, so that a more general relation between I_l and I_c is

$$I_l = \frac{p}{2} 2I_c \sin \frac{\pi}{m} = pI_c \sin \frac{\pi}{m} \qquad (13\text{-}6)$$

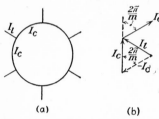

(a)   (b)

FIG. 13-4. Phase relations of line and coil currents, m-phase converter.

In order to fix the relation between the alternating and direct current at the two ends of the converter, let

I_{dc} = total direct current.

I_c = alternating current in the coils.

V_{dc} = terminal voltage on d-c side.

V_{ac} = terminal voltage on a-c side.

η = efficiency of conversion = d-c watts/a-c watts.

$\cos \varphi$ = power factor.

Therefore,

$$\eta \left(m \frac{p}{2} \right) (V_{ac} I_c) \cos \varphi = V_{dc} I_{dc} \qquad (13\text{-}7)$$

Since V_{ac}/V_{dc} is nearly equal to $E_{ac}/E_{dc} = \sin (\pi/m)/\sqrt{2}$, it follows that

$$\frac{I_c}{I_{dc}} = \frac{2 \sqrt{2}}{\eta m p \cos \varphi \sin (\pi/m)} \qquad (13\text{-}8)$$

and

$$\frac{I_l}{I_{dc}} = \frac{2 \sqrt{2}}{\eta m \cos \varphi} \qquad (13\text{-}9)$$

13-5. Resultant Current in Individual Winding Elements. Consider the general case of a multipolar converter having p poles, tapped for m phases, as in Fig. 13-5, and concentrate attention upon a winding element C which is displaced from the center of a phase belt by α electrical degrees. In the diagram as drawn, the center of the phase belt is shown opposite the middle of the pole face, but as the armature rotates, the angular displacement between these two points is in general $\theta = \omega t$, where ω is the constant angular velocity of the armature (in electrical radians per second), and t is the time counted from the instant when the centers of the phase belt and of the pole face are in alignment. At that moment, the alternating emf generated in the phase belt has its maximum value, but the corresponding alternating coil current, being in general out of phase with the emf, is represented by

$$i_c = \sqrt{2} I_c \cos (\omega t - \varphi) \qquad (13\text{-}10)$$

where I_c is the effective value of the individual coil current as given by Eq. 13-6. It is obvious, of course, that this alternating current is the same, at any given moment, in all the winding elements comprising a phase belt, including the element C of Fig. 13-5.

At the same time that element C is carrying current i_c, it is also carrying its share of the direct current, amounting to I_{dc}/p, assuming as before that the armature has a simplex lap winding. The alternating and the direct currents are in general opposite in direction, since one of them is a generator current and the other a motor current. The direct current in coil C reverses its direction each time the coil passes under a brush, and it may therefore be idealized as a rectangular wave* (Fig. 13-6). If the coil C were midway between taps, the middle of one of the

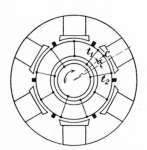

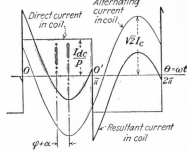

FIG. 13-5. General multipolar converter, m phases.

FIG. 13-6. Phase relations between direct and alternating coil currents, three-phase converter.

positive rectangular loops would coincide with the negative maximum of the emf wave of the phase belt, hence would be out of phase with the negative maximum of the alternating coil current by $\varphi°$; the physical displacement of coil C from the middle of the phase belt therefore brings about an additional phase displacement of $\alpha°$ between the middle of a positive rectangular loop and the negative maximum of alternating coil current, as in Fig. 13-6.

The direct current in the winding element is I_{dc}/p, and the alternating current has a maximum value of $\sqrt{2}\,I_c$; using Eq. 13-8, the ratio is

$$\frac{\sqrt{2}\,I_c}{I_{dc}/p} = \frac{4}{\eta m \cos \varphi \sin (\pi/m)} \tag{13-11}$$

If $\eta = 0.96$, $m = 3$, $\cos \varphi = 1$, this ratio is 1.61, and it becomes larger as the power factor decreases. All of these relations are shown in Fig. 13-6, from which it is seen that the resultant current in coil C is at any instant the algebraic sum of the two components, and that it has the peculiar wave form shown as a heavy line.

* Actually, the d-c wave more nearly resembles a trapezoid because of the time required for commutation to take place, but the difference is so slight that it may here be neglected for the sake of simplicity.

It is convenient to transfer the origin of coordinates, tacitly assumed as point O (Fig. 13-6), to the point O'. It is then possible to write the expression for the instantaneous coil current as

$$i = \sqrt{2}\, I_c \sin\, (\omega t - \varphi - \alpha) - \frac{I_{dc}}{p} \qquad (13\text{-}12)$$

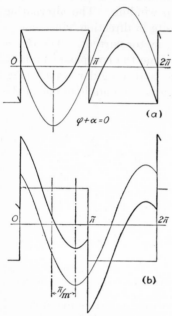

(a)

$\varphi + \alpha = 0$

(b)

$\frac{\pi}{m}$

FIG. 13-7. Coil currents: (a) $\varphi + \alpha = 0$; (b) $\varphi + \alpha = \pi/m$. Three-phase converter.

from which it is apparent that as the angle α varies from $-\pi/m$ to $+\pi/m$ the wave form of the resultant current in the individual winding elements comprising a phase belt changes its shape. Wave forms corresponding to $\alpha = 0$ and $\alpha = \pi/m$ are shown in Fig. 13-7, subject to the above assumption that $\cos \varphi = 1$, or $\varphi = 0$. The diagrams show clearly that the wave form becomes more and more distorted the nearer the winding element approaches the taps, and that the effective value of the resultant current, hence also its heating effect, is greater in the coils adjacent to the taps than at intermediate points.

13-6. Coil Heating. The amount of heat developed in a coil in a given time is proportional to the mean squared value of the current flowing in it during that time. Squaring Eq. 13-12 and integrating the result between $\theta = \omega t = 0$ and $\theta = \omega t = \pi$, the square of the effective current in coil C is

$$I_\alpha^2 = \frac{1}{\pi} \int_0^\pi \left[\sqrt{2}\, I_c \sin\, (\theta - \varphi - \alpha) - \frac{I_{dc}}{p} \right]^2 d\theta \qquad (13\text{-}13)$$

and on substituting the value of I_c (in terms of I_{dc}) from Eq. 13-8, the result is

$$I_\alpha^2 = \frac{I_{dc}^2}{p^2} \left[\frac{8}{\eta^2 m^2 \cos^2 \varphi \sin^2 \dfrac{\pi}{m}} - \frac{16 \cos\, (\varphi + \alpha)}{\pi \eta m \cos \varphi \sin \dfrac{\pi}{m}} + 1 \right] \qquad (13\text{-}14)$$

Inspection of this equation shows that for a given machine under given load conditions (that is, η, m, and φ fixed), the only variable term is $\cos\, (\varphi + \alpha)$, so that the heating effect varies with α; this conclusion has already been qualitatively indicated in Figs. 13-6 and 13-7, but Eq. 13-14 reduces it to a quantitative basis. When the power factor is unity ($\varphi = 0$), the variable term in Eq. 13-14 has its smallest value, and therefore I_α^2 its greatest value when $\alpha = \pm\pi/m$ (i.e., the heating is greatest in the coils adjacent to the taps); and I_α^2 is a minimum when $\alpha = 0$, that is, in the coil midway between taps. But for values of the power factor less than unity the heating effect is not the same in the coils adjacent to the two taps; for example, when $\cos \varphi = 0.866$, or $\varphi = 30°$ (lagging) in a three-phase machine, the heating effect is greater in the coil for which $\alpha = \pi/m = 60°$ than for the coil defined by $\alpha = -\pi/m = -60°$.

Other conclusions which follow at once from Eq. 13-14 are:

1. The coil heating decreases as the number of phases is increased.

2. The coil heating increases as the power factor decreases.

Typical curves defined by Eq. 13-14 are shown in Fig. 13-8 for the case of three-, six-, and twelve-phase machines, assuming in all three cases $\eta = 0.93$, $\cos \varphi = 0.95$. Since these curves give the values of I_α^2 in terms of α, they show the variation of copper loss throughout the phase belts. The reduction in the copper loss is relatively much greater in passing from a three-phase to a six-phase winding than from a six-phase to a twelve-phase winding.

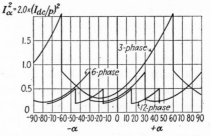

FIG. 13-8. Relative copper losses in 3-, 6-, and 12-phase converters.

Equations 13-13 and 13-14 do not cover the case of a single-phase converter. This type has no commercial importance, but for the sake of completeness the analysis follows:

It has been shown in Art. 13-3 that in a single-phase converter

$$E_{dc} = \sqrt{2}\, E_{ac}$$

consequently, it is approximately true that $V_{dc} = \sqrt{2}\, V_{ac}$; if the alternating current in the individual winding elements of the armature is I_{c1}, the total line current is pI_{c1}, therefore

$$\eta V_{ac}(pI_{c1}) \cos \varphi = V_{dc}I_{dc} \tag{13-15}$$

and
$$\frac{I_{c1}}{I_{dc}/p} = \frac{\sqrt{2}}{\eta \cos \varphi} \tag{13-16}$$

The last equation establishes the relation between the effective alternating current and the direct current in an individual winding element. Proceeding on the same reasoning as before, the instantaneous coil current is

$$i = \sqrt{2}\, I_{c1} \sin (\omega t - \varphi - \alpha) - \frac{I_{dc}}{p}$$

$$= \frac{I_{dc}}{p}\left[\frac{2}{\eta \cos \varphi} \sin (\theta - \varphi - \alpha) - 1 \right] \tag{13-17}$$

whence the mean squared value of current in a coil displaced by angle α from the center of the phase belt is

$$
\begin{aligned}
I_{\alpha 1}^2 &= \frac{I_{dc}^2}{p^2\pi} \int_{\theta=0}^{\theta=\pi} \left[\frac{2}{\eta \cos \varphi} \sin (\theta - \varphi - \alpha) - 1 \right]^2 d\theta \\
&= \frac{I_{dc}^2}{p^2} \left[\frac{2}{\eta^2 \cos^2 \varphi} + 1 - \frac{8 \cos (\varphi + \alpha)}{\pi\eta \cos \varphi} \right]
\end{aligned}
\tag{13-18}
$$

and the limits of α are $-\pi/2$ and $+\pi/2$.

13-7. Rating of Converters. The permissible output of any machine is determined by the consideration that its temperature rise, at the hottest spot, shall not exceed standard limits. The temperature rise is in turn dependent upon the losses and the facilities for cooling. In the case of a converter, it is customary to compute the rating at such a value that the total armature copper loss will be equal to the permissible copper loss of the same machine when operated at the rated speed as a d-c generator. The core losses in the two cases will not differ greatly; so this procedure is equivalent to the assumption that the *average* copper loss of a converter armature may be taken as a measure of the temperature rise. The curves of Figs. 13-6 to 13-8 show clearly that the armature copper loss in a converter is not uniformly distributed around the periphery as it is in a d-c generator, and that coils adjacent to some of the taps heat decidedly more than others. If the cooling facilities are such that the heat thus irregularly liberated can be readily transferred to cooler areas and then dissipated, the use of average coil heating to determine the rating is justified; otherwise it is not. In other words, the rating should depend not only upon the average coil heating but also upon the ability of the machine to transfer heat from the hot spots at the taps. The difficulty of making such a correction is too great for simple calculations, but it may be overcome by making allowances determined by test measurements. It is to be noted, however, that the variation in heating becomes less pronounced as the number of phases is increased.

Assuming, then, that it is sufficiently accurate for ordinary purposes to use average copper loss as a basis for rating, it is necessary only to find the average value of I_α^2, as given by Eq. 13-13, between the limits $\alpha = -\pi/m$ and $\alpha = +\pi/m$. Thus

$$
(I_\alpha)_{\text{av}}^2 = \frac{I_{dc}^2}{p^2} \frac{1}{2\pi/m} \int_{\alpha=-\frac{\pi}{m}}^{\alpha=\frac{\pi}{m}} \left[\frac{8}{\eta^2 m^2 \cos^2 \varphi \sin^2 \frac{\pi}{m}} - \frac{16 \cos (\varphi + \alpha)}{\pi\eta m \cos \varphi \sin \frac{\pi}{m}} + 1 \right] d\alpha
$$

from which it is readily found that

$$
\frac{(I_\alpha)_{\text{av}}^2}{(I_{dc}/p)^2} = \frac{8}{\eta^2 m^2 \cos^2 \varphi \sin^2 (\pi/m)} + 1 - \frac{16}{\pi^2\eta}
\tag{13-19}
$$

Since I_{dc}/p is the direct current per armature conductor, this ratio represents the average copper loss due to the actual current as a fraction of what it would be if the direct current alone were flowing. For equal copper losses in both cases, the rating of the converter may be greater than that of the same machine used as a d-c generator in the ratio

$$\frac{1}{\sqrt{\dfrac{8}{\eta^2 m^2 \cos^2 \varphi \sin^2 (\pi/m)} + 1 - \dfrac{16}{\pi^2 \eta}}} \qquad (13\text{-}20)$$

The rating of a single-phase converter may be found in a similar manner from Eq. 13-17; for

$$(I_{\alpha 1}^2)_{av} = \frac{I_{dc}^2}{p^2} \frac{1}{\pi} \int_{\alpha = -\frac{\pi}{2}}^{\alpha = +\frac{\pi}{2}} \left[\frac{2}{\eta^2 \cos^2 \varphi} + 1 - \frac{8 \cos (\varphi + \alpha)}{\pi \eta \cos \varphi} \right] d\alpha$$

whence

$$\frac{(I_{\alpha 1}^2)_{av}}{(I_{dc}/p)^2} = \frac{2}{\eta^2 \cos^2 \varphi} + 1 - \frac{16}{\pi^2 \eta} \qquad (13\text{-}21)$$

and the ratio of converter capacity to d-c generator capacity is

$$\frac{1}{\sqrt{\dfrac{2}{\eta^2 \cos^2 \varphi} + 1 - \dfrac{16}{\pi^2 \eta}}} \qquad (13\text{-}22)$$

Using the ratios given by expressions 13-20 and 13-22, and assuming 100 per cent efficiency, the following table of relative outputs can be computed:

Number of phases, m	Ratio of converter rating to d-c rating	
	$\cos \varphi = 1$	$\cos \varphi = 0.9$
1	0.854	0.735
3	1.332	1.090
4	1.625	1.396
6	1.933	1.449
12	2.192	1.576

These figures show that the capacity increases as the number of phases is increased, but beyond twelve phases the gain is very slight; in fact, the gain in passing from six to twelve phases is so small that most converters are designed for six-phase operation, the additional cost and complication due to twelve phases being justified only in very large machines. It will be seen that the increased capacity is largely reduced by a change in power factor from unity to 90 per cent; it is therefore important to take advantage of the synchronous-motor characteristics of the converter by adjusting its field excitation to maintain the power factor as close to unity as possible.

13-8. Armature Reaction.   Although the actual current in an armature winding element has the distorted wave shape shown in Figs. 13-6 and 13-7, it is convenient to consider that the direct and alternating component currents have independent existence, and then to compute their separate magnetizing actions.   Since these two component currents are in general oppositely directed, one of them being a motor current and the other a generator current, their magnetizing effects tend to neutralize in the same way as in a dynamotor,* but the neutralization is not complete.   If the magnetizing effect of one current exactly annulled that of the other, there would be no resultant distortion of the main field and therefore no interference with commutating conditions at the brushes; even with the partial neutralization inherent in the performance of a converter, commutation difficulties are less severe than in a simple d-c machine of like design, and the partial neutralization of armature reaction likewise accounts for the fact that the armature ampere-turns of a converter can be much greater in proportion to the field excitation than in a simple d-c machine.

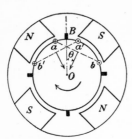

FIG. 13-9. Direct-current magnetizing action.

A superficial analysis indicates that an ideal converter operating at 100 per cent efficiency and at 100 per cent power factor should have no resultant armature reaction.   Consider, for example, a multipolar machine having p poles, as in Fig. 13-9; a pair of conductors such as a and b, separated by a full pole pitch, will produce the centrally directed mmf indicated by the arrow; but for each pair of conductors like a and b there will be another pair, a', b', symmetrically placed on the opposite side of the brush axis OB, so that the components along OB will add, while the components perpendicular to OB will cancel.   Consequently the effective mmf of conductors a and b, each carrying the current I_{dc}/p, is $(I_{dc}/p) \cos \theta$ amp-turns.†   In a double pole pitch there are Z/p such pairs of conductors, to each of which there corresponds a different value of θ, covering the entire range from $\theta = -\pi/2$ to $\theta = +\pi/2$.   The total d-c mmf determined in this way is then

$$A_{dc} = \frac{Z}{p} \frac{I_{dc}}{p} \frac{1}{\pi} \int_{-\frac{\pi}{2}}^{+\frac{\pi}{2}} \cos \theta \, d\theta = \frac{2}{\pi} \frac{Z}{p} \frac{I_{dc}}{p} \text{ amp-turns per pair of poles directed}$$

along the brush axis.

* See A. S. Langsdorf "Principles of Direct-Current Machines," 5th ed., p. 296, McGraw-Hill Book Company, Inc., New York, 1940.
† Angle θ must be expressed in electrical degrees.

Applying the same elementary analysis to the a-c side, the maximum ampere-turns per phase per pair of poles would equal

$$Z/2(m)(\tfrac{1}{2}p) \cdot \sqrt{2}\, I_c = \sqrt{2}\, Z I_c/mp$$

provided the winding were concentrated; actually, the phase spread is $2\pi/m$; so the distribution factor is $\sin (\pi/m)/(\pi/m)$. Dividing the maximum alternating mmf into two rotating components each of half amplitude, the backwardly rotating components of the m phases will cancel, while the forwardly rotating components will add to give a resultant mmf

$$A_{ac} = \frac{m}{2}\frac{\sqrt{2}\, Z I_c}{mp}\frac{\sin (\pi/m)}{\pi/m} \text{ amp-turns per pair of poles}$$

If in this expression there is substituted the value of I_c from Eq. 13-8, but taking $\eta = 1.0$, $\cos \varphi = 1.0$,

$$A_{ac} = \frac{2}{\pi}\frac{Z}{p}\frac{I_{dc}}{p}$$

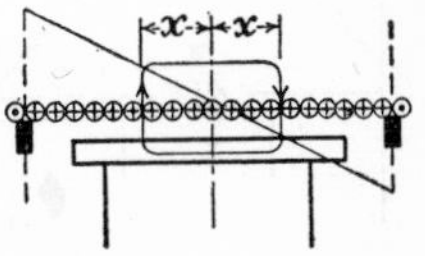

which is the same as the expression for A_{dc}.

The fallacy in this procedure is that the d-c and a-c mmfs are distributed in space in altogether different ways, and a different approach to the problem is

Fig. 13-10. Space distribution of mmf due to direct current.

necessary. So far as the direct current is concerned, the mmf due to the conductors in a belt of width $2x$ (Fig. 13-10) is $Z/\pi d \cdot 2x \cdot I_{dc}/p$ amp-turns (where d is the diameter of the armature), half of this acting on the airgap on each side of the center of the belt. At the brush axis, where $x = \pi d/2p$, the armature mmf is therefore

$$(A_{dc})_{\max} = \frac{1}{2}\frac{Z}{p}\frac{I_{dc}}{p} \text{ amp-turns per pole} \qquad (13\text{-}23)$$

and at the next consecutive brush axis the mmf is equal and opposite to this value, varying linearly between these extreme values.

It has been shown (Eq. 4-44) that the fundamental mmf due to current I_c in the winding is sinusoidally distributed and that its maximum amplitude is

$$A_{ac} = \frac{2\sqrt{2}}{\pi} k_{b_1}k_{p_1}mN_p I_c \text{ amp-turns per pole}$$

where N_p is the number of turns per pole per phase. In the converter, $k_{b_1} = \sin (\pi/m)/(\pi/m)$, $k_{p_1} = 1$, and $N_p = Z/2mp$; substituting these values in the expression for A_{ac}, as well as the value of I_c from Eq. 13-8, but inserting $\eta = 1.0$, $\cos \varphi = 1.0$, there results

$$A_{ac} = \frac{4}{\pi^2}\frac{Z}{p}\frac{I_{dc}}{p} \text{ amp-turns per pole} \qquad (13\text{-}24)$$

It will be recalled, however, that the position of the space fundamental of a-c mmf depends upon the angular displacement ψ between the nominal emf E and the current I_c; if $\psi = 0$, the armature mmf is purely cross-magnetizing, and in that case the graphs of Eqs. 13-23 and 13-24 are as shown in Fig. 13-11. It can be seen from this diagram that under the ideal conditions here assumed the a-c and d-c mmfs do not annul each other at the critical position occupied by the brush; there is a residual excitation because of the greater effect of the direct current at this point. If the efficiency is less than unity, but $\psi = 0$, this difference is reduced, and would disappear if $\eta = \dfrac{4/\pi^2}{2} = 81$ per cent. But for other values of the power factor the transverse mmf due to the alternating current is

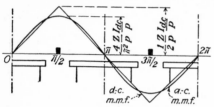

FIG. 13-11. Space distributions of a-c and d-c mmf, cos $\psi = 1$.

proportional to cos ψ, and the residual excitation in the brush axis becomes greater. This residual excitation in the brush axis, though much less than it would be in a simple d-c generator, accounts for the fact that the operation of synchronous converters is improved by the use of commutating poles,

which are almost always used. The residual excitation that remains to be compensated when $\psi = 0$ is only $\dfrac{\frac{1}{2} - (4/\pi^2)}{\frac{1}{2}} = 0.19$ of what it would be if I_{dc} alone constituted the armature current; hence the interpoles and their windings are relatively only about 20 per cent as powerful as in a d-c machine.

The preceding discussion has omitted any reference to the space harmonics of mmf produced by the alternating current. The magnitudes and speeds of these harmonics may be readily determined from Eq. 4-64, and tables similar to Tables 4-2 and 4-3 may then be constructed for six- and twelve-phase machines. The harmonics travel at various speeds relative to the armature winding, some in one direction, others in the opposite direction, and they affect commutating conditions at the brushes.

13-9. Voltage Control; Sinusoidal Flux Distribution. Under the conditions assumed in Art. 13-3, namely, sinusoidal flux distribution and brushes fixed at the geometrical neutral, the ratio of the voltages at the a-c and d-c terminals is definite, so that if the direct voltage requires adjustment to meet changing load conditions, the alternating supply voltage must be changed proportionally. Several methods, described in the following paragraphs, have been developed to provide this type of voltage control.

Tap-changing Supply Transformers. Inasmuch as synchronous converters are always designed to supply direct current at low or moderate voltage, ranging from 550 to 650 volts for railway service down to about 230 volts for general power or lighting purposes, step-down transformers are always required to reduce the relatively high transmission voltage to the comparatively low voltage required at the slip rings. The presence of these transformers provides an opportunity to vary the slip-ring voltage by means of taps in the transformer windings. Such an arrangement is simple and inexpensive, accounting for its extensive use, but it has the disadvantage that the voltage variation takes place by a series of steps instead of by a smooth transition.

Induction Regulator. Absolutely smooth variation of the slip-ring voltage can be obtained by connecting the secondary of a polyphase induction regulator in series between the supply transformers and the slip rings. The secondary of the induction regulator is wound on the stationary outer core, while the movable inner core carries the primary winding, excited through slip rings from the main supply line. This method introduces complications in the wiring and is naturally more expensive than the tap-changing regulator.

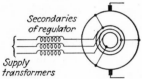

Fig. 13-12. Diagrammatic wiring of voltage regulator.

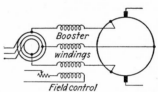

Fig. 13-13. Booster diagram.

The Synchronous Booster Converter. Instead of using an induction regulator to add to (or subtract from) the voltage impressed upon the slip rings, as in Fig. 13-12, it is possible to accomplish the same result by inserting the armature winding of an auxiliary synchronous generator, called a *booster*, in series between the supply transformers and the slip rings. Figure 13-12, though drawn to represent the induction-regulator control, serves equally well to illustrate one way of connecting such a booster for controlling a three-phase converter; the secondaries of the induction regulator become the stationary armature winding of the booster, this winding being distributed in slots around the inner periphery of a stationary core surrounding an extension of the main shaft; the rotating field of the booster, keyed to the main shaft, but not indicated in Fig. 13-12, takes the place of the primary of the induction regulator.

An alternative type of construction is indicated in Fig. 13-13. Here the booster armature is mounted on the main shaft between the slip rings and the converter armature, and it is surrounded by a set of stationary field poles equal in number to those of the main field. The booster must, of course, have the same number of poles as the converter, and for most economical design the two sets of poles should be in exact alignment.

In either case, the field excitation of the booster can be adjusted from zero to a maximum in either direction by means of a reversing rheostat, thus giving smooth control throughout the desired range.

Series Reactance. The terminal voltage of a d-c generator can be varied at pleasure by adjusting its field excitation. This control becomes automatic in the case of a compound-wound generator, which can be made to have any reasonable amount of overcompounding to compensate for line drop. But in the case of a synchronous converter supplied with alternating current at constant voltage, the voltage at the d-c end is fixed regardless of the excitation, and the effect of varying the excitation under these conditions is merely to alter the power factor on the supply side just as in any synchronous motor. In other words, if a synchronous converter is provided with a compound field winding, the series coils being excited by the d-c output (or a part thereof), the effect of increased load is to overexcite the field and to make the machine draw a leading reactive component from the a-c supply transformers. If under these circumstances there were series reactance in the circuit between the slip rings and the constant-voltage terminals of the supply transformers, the inductive drop normally due to this reactance may by proper design be not only neutralized but even overcompensated, thereby resulting in an increase of the slip-ring voltage and a proportional increase in the direct voltage. The effect is the same as connecting a capacitor in series with a reactance coil. In order to take advantage of these facts, it is not necessary to use separate reactors between the transformers and the slip rings, for the same effect can be realized by designing the supply transformers with more than the usual amount of leakage reactance.

The voltage regulation thus effected by the compound field winding is accomplished in a manner quite different from that of an ordinary d-c generator; in the latter machine, the voltage control is brought about by an internal change in the main flux; in the converter, the flux changes but slightly, and the main reactions are external to the converter itself.

This method of voltage control was the first to be used in connection with synchronous converters, but has been virtually superseded by the more flexible methods described in the preceding paragraphs. The series-reactance method, while simple, inherently requires that the power factor must change with the load. In order to limit the coil heating caused by the reactive component of alternating current, the shunt field excitation should be adjusted so that the power factor is unity, or slightly leading, at full load, therefore lagging at light loads when the extra heating due to the reactive current is rendered harmless because of the lower value of the current as a whole.

13-10. Voltage Control by Change of Wave Form. The voltage ratios derived in Art. 13-3 were based upon the twofold assumption of sinusoidal flux distribution and brushes in the geometrical neutral and are

therefore valid only so long as these conditions obtain.   It follows, therefore, that control of the voltage ratio is possible by altering one or the
other of these factors.

The voltage generated in a d-c machine having a given armature winding, whether that of a converter or any other type, depends only upon the
total flux per pole and the speed, provided the brushes are in the neutral
axis; it is not in any way dependent upon the manner in which the flux
is distributed around the airgap.   But
if the same winding is provided with
taps and slip rings, the alternating voltage is definitely dependent upon the flux
distribution.   Thus, let the flux density be distributed in accordance with
the curve of Fig. 13-14a, represented by

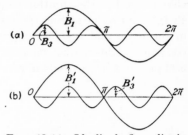

$$b = B_1 \sin \alpha + B_3 \sin 3\alpha \quad (13\text{-}25)$$

so that the flux per pole is

FIG. 13-14.   Idealized flux distribution, split-pole converter.

$$\Phi = \int_0^\pi blr \, d\alpha = 2lr(B_1 + \tfrac{1}{3}B_3) \qquad (13\text{-}26)$$

where r is the radius of the airgap.   If, on the other hand, the flux is
distributed in the manner of Fig. 13-14b, so that

$$b = B_1' \sin \alpha - B_3' \sin 3\alpha \qquad (13\text{-}27)$$

the flux per pole will be

$$\Phi = \int_0^\pi blr \, d\alpha = 2lr(B_1' - \tfrac{1}{3}B_3') \qquad (13\text{-}28)$$

and the flux per pole will be the same in both cases, provided that

$$B_1' - B_1 = \tfrac{1}{3}(B_3' + B_3) \qquad (13\text{-}29)$$

In the first case (Fig. 13-14a), the effective emf developed in each phase
by the flux fundamental will be, say, E_1, and that produced by the third
harmonic will be E_3, both of which may be computed by the use of equations given in Chap. 4 when the details of the winding are known.   The
effective voltage per phase will then be

$$E_a = \sqrt{E_1^2 + E_3^2} \qquad (13\text{-}30)$$

In the second case, the effective voltage per phase will be

$$E_b = \sqrt{E_1'^2 + E_3'^2} \qquad (13\text{-}31)$$

and E_a and E_b will differ because of the differences between B_1 and B_1'
and B_3 and B_3'.

Early forms of converters based upon this principle utilized pole pieces split into three parts, as in Fig. 13-15, whence arose the term *split-pole converter*. The main shunt field winding, which may be made in three parts, one for each leg of the pole, magnetizes all three parts in the same direction, while of the three sections of the regulating winding, all of which are in series, the two outer windings magnetize in opposition to the middle coil. Reversal of the current in the regulating winding will change the flux distribution from the form of Fig. 13-14a to that of Fig. 13-14b, and by adjusting the relative magnitudes of the exciting current in the main and regulating windings the total flux can be maintained constant. This arrangement is capable of producing a variation of several per cent in the voltage ratio.

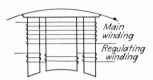

FIG. 13-15. Three-part pole.

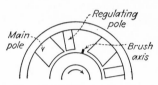

FIG. 13-16. Two-part pole.

13-11. Voltage Control by Brush Shift. A later modification of the split-pole converter is illustrated in Fig. 13-16. In addition to the main pole, there is a smaller regulating pole whose excitation may be independently varied or reversed, thus producing a shift of the axis of the resultant polar flux. This is the equivalent of shifting the brushes; however, whereas the angle through which the brushes could actually be shifted is limited by the requirement of sparkless commutation, the equivalent device of shifting the flux is capable of giving the effect of a considerably increased brush shift since the axis of commutation is permanently in a field controlled by the leading tip of a main pole. This type of machine was designed so that normally only the main poles were excited. The d-c voltage becomes a maximum when the regulating pole is caused to have the same polarity as the main pole, and it is a minimum when their polarities are opposite.

13-12. Harmonics in Split-pole Converters. *Transformer Connections.* The construction of the split-pole converter deliberately introduces harmonics in the flux distribution, whereas every effort is made to suppress them in ordinary synchronous generators and motors. There is a possibility, therefore, that the alternating counter emf developed by the motor action of the converter may introduce disturbing harmonics of emf and current into the local circuits of the machine and even back into the supply line, unless precautions are taken to suppress them. The diagrams of Fig. 13-14 indicate the presence of a considerable third harmonic, but other odd harmonics, though of smaller amplitude, may also be present. The third harmonic of flux will not produce a third harmonic in the phase voltage of a three-phase machine, for the spread of a phase belt is 120°, and the breadth or distribution factor is therefore $\frac{\sin (3 \times \pi/3)}{3 \times \pi/3} = 0$; but in a six-phase machine the breadth factor of the third harmonic is $\frac{\sin (3 \times \pi/6)}{3 \times \pi/6} = 0.635$, and so the third harmonic will appear in the phase voltage. However, even though harmonics may exist in the phase voltages, they will not produce any short-circuit current around the closed d-c winding of the converter armature since their sum, taken around the complete winding, is always zero.

While current harmonics cannot be set up in the local circuit around the armature itself, they may exist in the local circuits between the armature and the supply transformers unless these circuits are so disposed as to present very high impedance to such currents. The only case requiring particular attention is that due to the third harmonic in a split-pole six-phase converter (since there is no third voltage harmonic in a three-phase machine); higher harmonics, if present, will be small, and their effects will be rendered negligible by moderate reactance in the transformers. In the six-phase case, the transformer connections which will provide a short-circuit path for the triple-harmonic current are those in which the secondaries are connected (a) diametrically (Fig. 2-38) or (b) double-Y (Fig. 2-37), provided that the primaries are at the same time connected either (a) in Δ or (b) in Y, with the neutral interconnected with that of the generating system as by common grounding. A double-T connection (Fig. 2-34) with grounded neutral will also provide a low-impedance path for triple-harmonic currents.

If synchronous converters supply direct current to three-wire distribution systems, it is necessary to connect the common return wire to the neutral point of the system. The neutral point is the same on both the d-c and a-c sides, which might at first glance seem to indicate that the common return wire on the d-c side might be tapped into the neutral point of Y-connected secondaries of the supply transformers; this arrangement is not permissible, however, for in case of unbalanced loads on the two sides of the d-c system the return current would divide approximately equally between the three secondaries and thereby produce a condition of magnetic unbalance in the cores. To meet this condition, the double-wound secondaries must be interconnected in the manner shown in Fig. 2-40, for in this case the magnetizing effect of the direct current in each half of a winding neutralizes that of the other.

13-13. The Inverted Converter. When a converter is supplied with alternating current and delivers direct current to the load, its speed is definitely fixed at $120f/p$ rpm; hence the name synchronous converter applied to this type of machine. When supplied with direct current and delivering alternating current to the load, the machine becomes an *inverted converter*, and it then assumes the joint characteristics of a d-c motor and an a-c generator. The speed is no longer constant, but changes with the excitation, as in any d-c motor, and since the a-c and d-c circuits are electrically and magnetically interlinked, changes in the character of the a-c load will react upon the excitation and so affect the speed and the frequency. For example, an inductive load will draw a lagging current, which will weaken the field and raise the speed and frequency, thereby still further increasing the load reactance and tending to increase the speed indefinitely. This instability makes it necessary to provide an inverted converter with some form of speed-limiting device to prevent runaway accidents.

As a matter of fact, every converter, whether synchronous or inverted, should be equipped with overspeed protection. In a case which occurred before the necessity for this precaution had been generally recognized, a synchronous converter, having a compound field winding and supplied from a 4,000-kva turbo-alternator, was connected on the d-c side to the feeder circuits of a large street-railway system, in parallel with other sub-stations and a central 550-volt generating plant. The accidental break-age of a link of the butterfly valve controlling the steam supply to the turbine caused the valve to close, thereby cutting off the a-c power sup-ply to the converter; the latter promptly became an inverted converter taking direct current from the trolley system, running, of course, as a differential-compound motor at increased speed, and driving the turbo-alternator as a synchronous motor at a proportionally increased speed. The converter d-c ammeter on the switchboard of the substation hap-pened to be of the astatic type, hence continued to read positively even though the current had reversed its direction. The switchboard opera-tor happened to be observing the ammeter at the moment this chain of circumstances began, and, noting a sudden increase in the ammeter read-ing, weakened the main field in an attempt to reduce what seemed to him to be an overload. This reduction of excitation, combined with the reduction due to the series field winding, raised the speed of both con-verter and turbo-generator to the runaway limit, and both were wrecked. Accidents of this kind are now prevented in two ways: (1) a centrifugally operated device on the shaft of the converter trips the circuit breakers if the speed increases beyond a predetermined limit; (2) a reverse-current relay on the d-c side performs the same function in case a synchronous converter changes to inverted action.

The tendency of an inverted converter to speed up indefinitely when a highly inductive load is suddenly applied can be partially checked if the initial increase of speed brings about a sufficiently sharp increase of exci-tation; one way that has been proposed is to provide the converter with a direct-connected shunt exciter built with an unsaturated magnetic cir-cuit so that its voltage will respond quickly to a change of speed; but the rate of increase of excitation is determined only in part by the charac-teristics of the exciter, since the time constant of the converter field is an equally important factor. In any case, a converter should not be oper-ated inverted without first disconnecting or short-circuiting the series field winding if one is present. Inverted converters are rarely used, and are not to be recommended. Motor-generator sets are decidedly preferable.

13-14. Hunting and Commutation. Considered from the a-c side, a synchronous converter has all the characteristics of a synchronous motor, including the tendency to hunt or oscillate about its mean torque-angle position. Hunting, of itself, is no more serious than in an ordinary syn-chronous motor, and can be checked by the customary amortisseur wind-ings in the pole faces; but in the case of a converter the situation is com-plicated by the requirement of sparkless commutation at the d-c end of the machine, and for this reason the amplitude of hunting must be held within very narrow limits, thus calling for unusually powerful damping grids.

The intimate connection between hunting and commutation will be understood when it is considered that the fundamental of armature mmf rotates at synchronous (therefore constant) speed with respect to the armature winding, and will be stationary with respect to the poles only if the armature is itself rotating at synchronous speed. When hunting occurs, the armature is moving alternately faster and slower than syn-chronous speed; hence, the armature flux sways back and forth not only across the pole faces but also through the commutating zone; an addi-tional pulsation of armature mmf exists under all conditions because of the space harmonics which move at different speeds and in different directions. If hunting is accompanied by a sudden change of load, the difficulties are increased because of the sudden change in the magnitude of the residual field in the commutating zone (see Fig. 13-11). One or both of these disturbances may produce vicious sparking at the brushes; or, what is worse, the swinging of the flux across the pole faces may induce transient voltages in the winding elements lying between brushes to such an extent as to break down the insulation between commutator segments and so produce a "flashover."* Some converters are equipped with shields or barriers between brushes to minimize the disastrous effects of such a flashover.

Difficulties due to hunting and commutation, of the kind just described, are much more common in 60-cycle converters than in those designed for 25-cycle systems. The fundamental cause of this difference is to be found in the table of synchronous speeds for these two standard frequencies (Art. 4-4), in conjunction with the fact that the peripheral speed of the commutator is limited by considerations of mechanical strength and free-

* See Langsdorf, *op. cit.*, p. 586.

dom from vibration. Early designs of 60-cycle converters were very conservative as to allowable peripheral velocity, with the result that the number of poles was large, while the armature and commutator diameters were relatively small. Because the width of the commutator segments cannot be less than about $3/16$ in., these considerations limited the total number of segments, with consequent large average voltage per segment; and at the same time the poles were crowded close together, thus reducing the width of the commutating zone to such a small amount as to give a steep gradient to the field intensity in this zone. All of these factors conspired to produce a machine highly sensitive to commutating conditions and therefore susceptible to violent sparking and flashover. Later designs stepped up the peripheral speed to nearly twice the original limit, permitting the use of fewer main poles and providing space for commutating poles in addition; the average voltage per commutator segment in 600-volt machines was thereby reduced to less than 15 volts, which compares favorably with ordinary d-c design. The usual range is from 14 poles at 1,500 kw to 6 poles at 500 kw.

Converters for 25-cycle operation are relatively free from these difficulties because of the much more flexible range of speeds with moderate numbers of poles.

13-15. Methods of Starting Converters. *a. As a D-C Motor.* In power stations where an adequate source of direct current is available, converters may be started as d-c shunt motors and synchronized on the high-tension side of the supply transformers in the same manner as an a-c generator. This procedure calls for a suitable starting rheostat and synchronizing device.

In case the converter has a compound field winding, the series winding must be short-circuited or wholly disconnected during the starting period; otherwise, the machine would start as a differential-compound motor, thereby introducing the possibility that it will start in the wrong direction.

Another complication in d-c starting is the fact that the armature winding is in parallel, through the taps and slip rings, with the secondaries of the supply transformers, which are always solidly connected to the slip rings. At the moment of starting, and until the speed has risen considerably, the transformer windings have very small impedance, thereby greatly increasing the starting current. This effect is particularly bad in the case of transformers connected diametrically.

b. By Means of an Auxiliary Motor. In some early converter substations, starting was effected by means of a portable induction motor mounted on a truck which could be clamped to the floor so as to permit the motor to be belted to the converter shaft. The obvious crudity of this arrangement led to the permanent installation of an auxiliary induction motor on the overhanging shaft of each converter. Inasmuch as the full speed of an induction motor is always less than synchronous speed, the starting motor had to be built with two less poles than the converter itself, thereby making its full speed higher than the synchronous speed of the converter. The motor speed was permitted to rise until the converter was running slightly above synchronism, as shown by a synchroscope, after which the motor was disconnected and the converter allowed to coast until the synchroscope showed that the main switch might be closed.

c. Induction-motor Start. Later practice took advantage of the presence of the heavy damping windings to make them function in the same manner as the squirrel-cage rotor of an induction motor. In this case, however, the damping grids are attached to the stationary poles of the converter instead of being part of the rotor as in the usual induction motor. On applying reduced voltage to the slip rings, the armature current sets up a magnetic field rotating at synchronous speed with respect to the initially stationary armature, and therefore rotating at the same speed relative to the stationary poles and damping grids. The reaction between the current induced in the grids and the rotating magnetic field sets the armature in motion, and as its speed increases, the armature field, still rotating synchronously relative to the armature, slows down relative to the poles. When the speed approaches synchronous speed, the locking action between the armature field and the field poles pulls the armature into synchronism.

When a converter is started in this way, it is necessary to keep the shunt field winding open by means of a field breakup switch in order to avoid the danger of excessive induced voltage. And if there is a shunted series field winding, the normally closed circuit represented by this combination must also be opened.

Between the moment of starting and the attainment of full synchronous speed, the armature mmf, rotating at gradually falling speed with respect to the stationary poles, produces a corresponding flux which sweeps across the armature winding, including the coils short-circuited by the brushes. If there are no commutating poles, the high reluctance in the commutating zone limits the flux to such a moderate value that the voltage developed in the short-circuited winding elements is hardly sufficient to give trouble; but if commutating poles are present, the flux in the brush axis is so greatly increased that vicious sparking would occur unless the brushes were removed from contact with the commutator. For this reason, commutating-pole converters designed for induction-motor starting must be provided with a brush-lifting mechanism; this is so designed that by throwing a lever all but one of the brush holders on each stud are rotated sufficiently to lift the brushes; the single brush of each set which is left in contact with the commutator is narrower than the others, and its high resistance limits the short-circuit current to a safe amount.

The single brush of each set left in contact with the commutator during the starting period serves a twofold purpose: one function is to make it possible to observe the polarity of the brushes when synchronous speed has been attained; the other is to provide a source of direct current for energizing the shunt field winding at that moment. There is, of course, no assurance that when the armature field locks with the field poles the polarity of the brushes will be of the right sign. For this reason, it is usual to equip the switchboard with a two-way voltmeter (one in which the zero reading is at the middle of a scale reading both positive and negative voltages); if the polarity comes up reversed, reversing the double-throw field breakup switch will ordinarily cause the machine to slip a pole, whereupon the field switch can again be reversed to restore normal polarity. In case the armature field is too strong to permit the poles to slip back through one pole pitch, the main switch on the a-c side can be opened momentarily.

13-16. Parallel Operation of Synchronous Converters. There are no special problems to be met in operating synchronous converters in parallel unless two or more are supplied from the same set of secondaries of a bank of step-down transformers. In that case, there might be circulating currents between them, but this contingency may be ruled out of consideration for the reason that it is general practice to provide each converter with an independent polyphase transformer or bank of single-phase transformers.

If the field winding is compound, as is usually the case with converters intended for traction service, equalizers must be provided just as with ordinary compound-wound d-c generators, and for the same reasons. Damping windings are required for the reasons previously discussed, and to prevent a machine which may be inherently more sensitive than the others from taking an undue proportion of the load.

The division of the load between several machines in parallel may be controlled by varying the voltage on the d-c side, exactly as in the case of d-c generators in parallel. If the machines are provided with series reactance, an increase of field excitation will raise both the a-c and the d-c voltage and so increase the output. If the voltage is controlled by induction regulators or by synchronous boosters, an increase in the voltage impressed upon the main armature winding will have a like effect.

CHAPTER 14

PHASE AND FREQUENCY CONVERTERS

14-1. Rotary Phase Converters. It has been shown in Chap. 2 that a polyphase circuit having two or more phases can be converted by means of static transformers to another polyphase circuit having a different number of phases. In all such cases, the frequencies of the two systems are necessarily the same. The use of transformers is not possible, however, if it is desired to obtain a polyphase circuit from a single-phase source, and in that case it is necessary to resort to a *rotary phase converter*.

The AIEE Standards define a rotary phase converter as a machine which converts power from an a-c system of one or more phases to an a-c system of a different number of phases, both of the same frequency. Such converters are usually limited to the conversion of single-phase power to three-phase power, as, e.g., in the original electrification of the Norfolk and Western Railway, where the locomotives, equipped with three-phase motors, received power from a single-phase trolley.

The principle underlying the design and operation of such a rotary phase converter rests upon the fact that a single-phase induction motor develops a rotating magnetic field, as explained in Chap. 9. If the motor were to run at synchronous speed, the magnetic field would not only rotate uniformly at synchronous speed, but its magnitude would remain constant; actually the speed falls short of exact synchronism, giving rise to an elliptically rotating field, or, what amounts to the same thing, to two nearly equal component alternating fields, each stationary with respect to the exciting winding, and nearly in quadrature in space and in time. From this it follows that if the stator of a single-phase induction motor is provided with an auxiliary winding occupying slots symmetrically spaced midway between the slots of the main winding, the auxiliary winding will become the seat of an induced voltage which is substantially in time quadrature with the supply voltage. The magnitude of the voltage of the second phase thus created can be made to have any desired value (within reasonable limits) by a suitable choice of the number and distribution of the turns of the auxiliary winding.

Figure 14-1 illustrates the connections of such a machine. The main stator winding of the induction motor is supplied from a step-down transformer which reduces the high trolley voltage to a value more suitable for the motor. The auxiliary winding is designed to develop a voltage equal to 86.6 per cent of the secondary voltage of the transformer; so by the use of the T (or Scott) connection the original single-phase supply is converted to a three-phase circuit available for direct connection to the main motors on the axles of the locomotive.

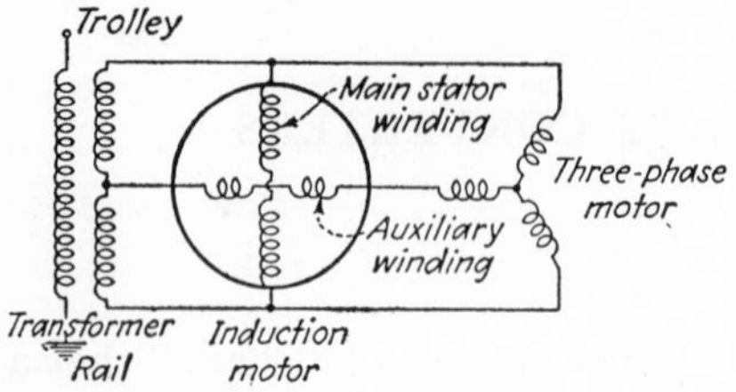

FIG. 14-1. Connections of rotary phase converter.

14-2. Frequency Changers and Converters. Some of the reasons which explain the general use of both 25-cycle and 60-cycle systems have already been outlined. In large urban systems, and in the so-called superpower systems which distribute the combined output of several widely separated generating plants, both frequencies are used to supply particular load requirements, and it then becomes necessary or economically desirable to interconnect circuits of different frequencies in order that the generators of one frequency may be used to help out those of the other frequency.

The simplest device for accomplishing this purpose consists of two synchronous machines with their shafts directly coupled and therefore running at the same speed, each having the proper number of poles to correspond with the frequency of the line to which it is connected. In general, if the frequencies are f_1 and f_2, and the respective numbers of poles are p_1 and p_2, the common speed (n rpm) requires that

$$\frac{120f_1}{p_1} = \frac{120f_2}{p_2} = n$$

or

$$\frac{p_1}{p_2} = \frac{f_1}{f_2}$$

If $f_1 = 60$ and $f_2 = 25$, it follows that

$$\frac{p_1}{p_2} = \frac{60}{25} = \frac{12}{5} = \frac{24}{10}$$

in other words, the smallest number of poles that can be used with these particular frequencies is 24 for the 60-cycle machine and 10 for the 25-cycle machine.

Two synchronous machines mechanically coupled in this way constitute a *synchronous-synchronous frequency changer*. In general, a frequency changer (or converter) is defined by the AIEE Standards as "a machine which converts the power of an a-c system from one frequency to another, with or without change in the number of phases, or in the voltage."

Change of frequency from one value to another, generally from a lower to a higher value, can also be accomplished by taking advantage of the fact that the rotor winding of an induction machine develops emfs and currents having a frequency which differs from the line frequency by an amount depending upon the slip. In this case, the primary and secondary circuits, carrying currents of different frequencies, are linked together by a common magnetic field, whereas in the synchronous-synchronous frequency changer the two circuits have separate and distinct magnetic circuits and the linkage is wholly mechanical. In either case, the term frequency converter is applicable. The characteristic features of these two types, and of various combinations of them, are discussed in the following articles.

14-3. Synchronous-synchronous Frequency Changers. A unit of this type may be used to transfer power from a 60-cycle network to a 25-cycle system, in which case the 60-cycle machine operates as a synchronous motor and the 25-cycle machine as a synchronous generator; or it may transfer power in the opposite direction, in which case the respective motor and generator roles are interchanged. Each of the two machines must be provided with damping or amortisseur windings to provide starting torque if it is used as a motor, and to suppress hunting whether it operates as a motor or as a generator. The operation of such a set is quite simple if the circuit to which power is supplied is not connected to other sources of supply, as, for instance, if power from a 25-cycle circuit is to be converted to 60 cycles for feeding an isolated load having that frequency. Under such circumstances, the frequency changer is nothing more than a motor-generator set. But if there are independent generators connected to, and supplying, both the 60-cycle and the 25-cycle networks, as is usually the case, operating conditions at once become more complicated, as may be seen from the following considerations:

1. Assume that the 25-cycle and the 60-cycle systems are operating independently, and that one of them, the former to be specific, is so overloaded as to call for power available from the more lightly loaded 60-cycle system. The frequency changer would then be started from the 60-cycle end, and brought up to synchronous speed in the usual manner. Before the 25-cycle unit of the frequency changer can be connected to the line, it must be synchronized as a generator so that its frequency and voltage are the same as those of the 25-cycle circuit at the point of connection, and the two voltages must likewise be in phase. Nothing can be done to the frequency changer itself to adjust its speed, since that is fixed by the frequency of the 60-cycle circuit which supplies it. The phase of the 25-cycle voltage of the frequency changer can be controlled to a certain extent by slipping the poles of the 60-cycle motor, but the variations possible by this method take place by discontinuous steps that are too large to permit the fine adjustment required for successful paralleling. It follows that the final adjustment must be made by adjusting the frequency

and phase of either the entire 60-cycle system or the entire 25-cycle system; this, of course, can be accomplished only by adjusting the governor setting of the master generator in one of the two main generating plants. Finally, after the frequency changer has been connected as a link between the two systems, the amount of power that will be transmitted through it is controlled entirely by the governor settings of the master generators in the two systems.

2. Suppose that two frequency changers of the type here under consideration are to be operated in parallel. One of them may be assumed to be connected and in operation when the need for the transfer of additional power calls for the paralleling of the other. When the second machine is brought up to synchronous speed, it will be running at exactly the same speed as the first one, but the generator voltage of the incoming set may still be out of phase with that of the first generator by any one of a considerable number of angles. This is due to the fact that the motors and the generators have different numbers of poles in the ratio of 12:5. This difficulty can be overcome as before, by slipping the poles of the motor of the incoming set. When the two frequency changers are finally paralleled, they may not divide the load in the proper proportion, and if both are of ordinary construction, nothing can be done to correct matters. For when two generators are in parallel, their respective loads can be altered only if one or the other can be made to advance the phase of its voltage relative to that of its companion. To obtain this result, one of the two sets must be so constructed that the stator frame of the generator unit can be turned bodily around the shaft through an arc sufficient to bring about the necessary change of torque angle; in other words, the stator frame must be mounted on a cradle and geared to the base so as to permit angular adjustment either by a handwheel or by a small motor.

3. More important than either of the preceding considerations is the requirement that the two systems linked together by a synchronous-synchronous unit shall maintain the exact frequencies for which the two machines of the frequency changer are designed; or more precisely, that the ratio of these two frequencies shall remain constant. The two electrical systems are in effect like powerful machines geared together, with the frequency changer playing the part of the gears; it is to be understood, however, that while the frequency changer functions as a gear, the coupling has a small amount of elasticity as distinguished from absolute rigidity. This mechanical analogy makes it quite plain that any disturbance which causes one of the interlinked power systems to surge ahead of, or lag behind, the other is certain to impose severe stresses and strains on the linkage between them. In other words, the amount and direction of power flow through the frequency changer are dependent upon the speed regulation of the generators of the interlinked systems, including

under this heading hunting of these systems regarded as two separate units. When two power networks, each of which has large generating capacity behind it, are thus linked together by a frequency changer of relatively moderate rating, any disturbance which materially affects the generator speeds is likely to load the frequency changer beyond the limit of stability, causing it to fall out of synchronism, and at the same time overheating the windings and overstressing the mechanical parts. There is nothing inherent in the nature of the synchronous-synchronous set which enables it to ride through such disturbances without danger.

14-4. The Synchronous-induction Frequency Converter. In discussing the circle diagrams of the polyphase induction motor, attention was called to the fact that for values of the slip greater than unity the machine becomes a brake. This conclusion was based upon the assumption that the rotor circuit remains the same, when operating in the braking range, as within the limits of motor or generator action; i.e., the rotor is assumed to be constructed either with a squirrel-cage or with a polyphase coil winding short-circuited upon itself. The cause of the braking action is clear enough from the physical consideration that the rotor is being driven in a direction opposite to that of the rotating magnetic field, and that the current thereby generated in the closed winding opposes the driving torque which produced it, in accordance with Lenz's law. Analytically, the braking action is indicated by the equations which define the power and torque in terms of the slip, for when the slip is positive and greater than unity, the power becomes negative, while the torque remains positive. The circle diagrams show that as the speed (in the backward direction) increases indefinitely, the stator and rotor currents remain nearly constant in magnitude, notwithstanding the obvious fact that the rotor emf increases in proportion to the speed. This practical constancy of current is due to the fact that the reactance of the fixed rotor circuit, which likewise increases in proportion to the slip, constitutes nearly the whole of the rotor circuit impedance.

Operating conditions will, however, be quite different if the rotor, provided with a polyphase coil winding, is connected through slip rings to an external circuit of variable impedance. When driven backward, in opposition to the forwardly rotating magnetic field produced by the stator excitation, the machine becomes a generator supplying current at slip frequency to the external circuit. The slip frequency may be made to have any desired value, greater than that of the line supplying the stator, by a suitable choice of speed.

Assume, for example, that the stator of the induction machine is supplied with current at frequency f_1 and that its rotor is direct-connected to the shaft of a synchronous motor, likewise supplied at frequency f_1, as in Fig. 14-2. Let the number of poles of these two machines be p_i and p_s, respectively, and let their common speed of rotation be n rpm.

It follows that

$$n = \frac{120f_1}{p_s}$$

and that the frequency developed in the rotor winding of the induction machine is

$$f_2 = sf_1 = \left(1 + \frac{n}{n_1}\right)f_1$$

where n_1 is the speed, in rpm, of the rotating magnetic field set up by the exciting current in the stator of the induction machine. Since

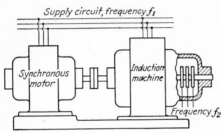

$$n_1 = \frac{120f_1}{p_i}$$

it is readily shown that

$$f_2 = f_1\left(1 + \frac{p_i}{p_s}\right)$$

Thus, if $f_2 = 60$ and $f_1 = 25$, $p_i/p_s = {}^{35}\!/_{25} = {}^{7}\!/_{5}$, whence the minimum number of poles that

FIG. 14-2. Induction frequency converter.

will give the desired frequency change is $p_i = 14$ and $p_s = 10$.

The electrical output from the rotor of the induction converter is supplied in two ways: (1) electrically, from the stator, by transformer action; (2) mechanically, from the shaft of the synchronous motor. The relative magnitudes of the electrical and mechanical power input, both of which come from the supply circuit, may be quite simply computed if the magnetizing current of the converter and its internal losses are neglected; for if secondary voltages and currents are reduced to terms of the primary, the stator and rotor currents may then be considered to be equal, or

$$I_1 = I_2$$

If the primary voltage is V_1, the secondary voltage will be sV_1, provided the internal leakage-impedance drops are neglected. Consequently if the power factor on both primary (stator) and secondary (rotor) circuits are taken as unity, the electrical power from the stator will be

$$P_e = V_1I_1$$

and the electrical output from the rotor will be

$$P = sV_1I_2 = sV_1I_1$$

and this will be greater than P_e since $s > 1$. The difference between P and P_e is then the power P_m that must be supplied mechanically, whence

$$P_m = V_1I_1(s - 1)$$

or
$$\frac{P_m}{P_e} = s - 1 = \frac{p_i}{p_s}$$

Thus, when $f_1 = 25$ and $f_2 = 60$, $p_i/p_s = \frac{7}{5}$, and $P_m/P_e = \frac{7}{5}$, which means that for each kilowatt of secondary load, $\frac{7}{12}$ kw is supplied by the synchronous motor and $\frac{5}{12}$ kw is supplied electrically from the 25-cycle line. These ratios are approximate because of the simplifying assumptions that have been made, but they are sufficiently accurate for practical purposes.

Frequency converters employing the above-described combination of a synchronous motor and an induction machine are called *synchronous-induction frequency converters*.* The synchronous motor may, of course, be replaced by any other form of motor, in which case the unit may be designated merely as an *induction* frequency converter. An adjustable-speed motor makes it possible to obtain a wide range of secondary frequencies; it is to be noted, however, that the secondary voltage will then vary in proportion to the secondary frequency, so that if constant voltage is desired at all frequencies, it is necessary either to provide a regulating transformer or to adjust the voltage applied to the stator of the converter.

14-5. Variable-ratio Frequency Converters. Both the synchronous-synchronous and the synchronous-induction types of frequency converters have the common property of calling for a fixed ratio between the frequencies of the interlinked systems. Any departure from this ratio, such as might be caused by the sudden application or removal of a considerable load from either system, is likely to cause a serious disturbance in the operation of the frequency converter. It has already been pointed out that the frequency converter is equivalent to a gear between the two circuits it links together, so that if moderate variations in the ratio of their frequencies are to be provided for, what is needed must be the analogue of a slipping clutch. It is possible to obtain this characteristic by an assembly of suitable machines as illustrated in Fig. 14-3, the resultant arrangement constituting a *variable-ratio frequency converter*. It is more complicated than the other types and does not possess quite the efficiency of a synchronous-synchronous set, but it has the advantage of being able to ride through system disturbances with less risk of damage to the equipment.

Three frequency converters of this variable-ratio type are in operation at the Page Avenue Station in St. Louis, where they tie together the 25-cycle lines from the Keokuk hydraulic power plant and the 60-cycle lines of the Union Electric Company. Each one of these sets is designed to transfer 20,000 kw (full-load rating) in either direction, allowing for simultaneous and opposite variations of $\frac{1}{2}$ cycle in each system. The extremes of frequency ratios are therefore $60.5/24.5 = 2.47$ and

* O. E. Shirley, A 35,000-kw. Induction Frequency Converter, *Trans. AIEE*, **43**: 1011 (1924).

59.5/25.5 = 2.33.   In other words, full-load power may be transferred from either system to the other if the frequencies are represented by any of the following pairs of limiting values:* 60.5, 24.5; 59.5, 25.5; 60, 24.3; 60, 25.7; 58.3, 25; 61.7, 25.

The converter set shown diagrammatically in Fig. 14-3 consists of seven distinct rotating machines all directly coupled.   Two of them, much larger than the others, serve the main purpose of transferring power from one system to the other, while the five smaller machines serve such auxiliary purposes as starting, excitation, and control of load and power factor.   Of the two main machines, one, of the synchronous type, is connected to the 60-cycle system, while the other, of the wound-rotor induction type, is connected to the 25-cycle system.   In this particular installation, the three-phase synchronous machine is rated at 21,000 kw (30,500 kva at 0.7 power factor), 13,800 volts, 60 cycles, 300 rpm and has 24 poles; the induction machine is rated at 28,700 kva (unity power factor), 13,800 volts, 25 cycles and has 10 poles, corresponding to a synchronous speed of 300 rpm.   Both have forced-air cooling, the former requiring 52,000 cu ft of air per min, the latter 70,000 cu ft per min, at full load.

The Synchronous and Induction Machines.   Before considering the functions of the auxiliary machines, it is necessary to examine the performance that may be expected when a synchronous machine is direct-connected to a wound-rotor induction machine, both having the same synchronous speed, each connected to a circuit of appropriate frequency.

Suppose, first, that the frequencies are exactly 60 and 25 cycles, respectively.   The 60-cycle synchronous machine with its 24 poles will run at exactly 300 rpm, and the rotor of the 10-pole induction machine, necessarily running at the same speed, will be exactly in step with the rotating magnetic field set up by the 25-cycle excitation.   With the rotor winding short-circuited, no current will flow in it, and there will be no transfer of power.   The synchronous machine will draw only enough power from the 60-cycle line to supply its own losses, and the induction machine will draw from the 25-cycle bus its own constant excitation core loss.   With the line frequencies remaining constant at these values, there is only one possible way to effect a transfer of power from one bus to the other, and that is to introduce into the rotor winding of the induction machine *continuous* (zero-frequency) *current*.   Continuous current, if of the proper magnitude in each of the distributed phase windings, will produce consequent poles distributed around the rotor periphery; but since the air-gap flux must remain constant in a constant-voltage induction machine, the result will be to cause the flow of stator current just sufficient to neutralize the rotor mmf.   The direction of flow of the continuous exciting

* Computed by dividing the higher frequency by 2.47 or 2.33, according to circumstances.

current will naturally determine whether the stator current will correspond to energy flow from or toward the 25-cycle line. The power thus transferred can accordingly be controlled as to magnitude and direction of flow by varying the magnitude and direction of the continuous exciting current. It is to be understood, of course, that in order to introduce the continuous-current excitation into the rotor winding, the short circuit or jumper connection at the slip rings must be removed, and the slip rings connected to a suitable source of d-c excitation.

Let it now be assumed that the frequency of the 60-cycle line remains unchanged, but that the frequency of the other system is reduced, say, to 24.5 cycles. The shaft speed remains at 300 rpm because the synchronous machine must remain in step with its supply; consequently, the rotor of the induction machine, running at the same speed, is slipping ahead of the revolving magnetic field produced by the 24.5-cycle excitation, and generator action results. The rotor slip, expressed in terms of the synchronous speed of the revolving magnetic field (now 294 rpm), amounts to $(300 - 294)/294 = 0.0204$, or 2.04 per cent. If under these conditions the rotor were still short-circuited at the slip rings, it would be possible to determine the amount of electrical power delivered to the 24.5-cycle bus by using a circle diagram based upon the above slip, with the rotor constants adjusted to the reduced frequency of 24.5 cycles. In general, this amount of power will not be the same as the rated capacity of the machine, and means must be found to adjust the output to the desired amount. Furthermore, in the converter here under discussion, it is desired to provide for *motor* action, as well as generator action, of the induction machine at the frequencies that have been assumed for illustrative purposes.

Under the conditions considered in the preceding paragraph, the slip frequency of the rotor current is $\frac{1}{2}$ cycle. This current is exclusively due to the emf developed in the short-circuited winding by rotating through the stator field. If the short circuit is removed and the slip rings are connected to a source of voltage alternating at $\frac{1}{2}$ cps, the resultant current in the rotor winding will be more or less than the original amount, and may even have reversed flow, depending upon the magnitude and phase of the auxiliary voltage thus injected into the circuit.

No matter what combination of bus frequencies is studied, the conclusion always follows that control of the stator current of the induction machine may be secured by connecting in series with the rotor a slip-frequency (including zero-frequency) voltage the magnitude and phase of which can be adjusted at will. It is the function of two of the auxiliary machines of the converter set to provide this slip-frequency voltage and current.

The Auxiliary Regulating Machines. The two machines shown at the left of Fig. 14-3 are of special construction. The one marked "A-C

Exciter" somewhat resembles a rotary converter. The "Regulating Machine," which resembles a d-c generator so far as the rotating armature is concerned, has a stator carrying two distinct three-phase windings, one of which provides load control, the other power-factor control.

Consider first the small a-c exciter, whose speed (normally 300 rpm) is fixed by that of the main 60-cycle synchronous machine of the frequency converter proper. Six slip rings, tapped into the armature winding to provide six-phase supply, are connected to the main 25-cycle bus through a three-phase to six-phase step-down transformer. The coils of the armature winding are designed with a pitch corresponding to 10 poles, so that if the voltage applied to the slip rings has a frequency of 25 cycles, the armature field will rotate at 300 rpm relative to the winding, and can be made to be stationary in space if the armature is itself rotating at 300 rpm in the opposite direction. It must be remembered that the speed of

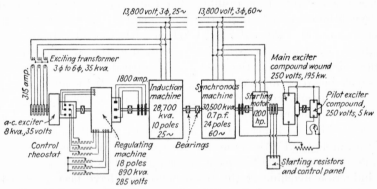

Fig. 14-3. Connection diagram of variable-ratio frequency converter.

the entire set of machines will change if the frequency of the nominal 60-cycle circuit changes, and that any change in the 25-cycle frequency will alter the speed of the armature field of the a-c exciter relative to that winding. But whatever these changes of frequency may be, the armature field of the a-c exciter will rotate in space at a speed that agrees exactly with the slip frequency of the main induction converter.

The validity of this conclusion can be checked in the following manner: Let the frequencies of the 60-cycle and the 25-cycle systems be designated as f_{60} and f_{25}, respectively, with the understanding that the symbols represent frequencies that actually vary within restricted limits. The speed of the common shaft is then

$$n = \frac{120f_{60}}{p_s} = \frac{120f_{60}}{24} = 5f_{60}$$

and the speed of the revolving field of the induction machine is

$$n_i = \frac{120f_{25}}{10} = 12f_{25}$$

The slip speed in the induction machine is then the difference between n_i and n, or $12f_{25} - 5f_{60}$, and the slip of the induction machine, in terms of its synchronous speed as unity, is

$$s = \frac{12f_{25} - 5f_{60}}{12f_{25}} = 1 - \frac{5}{12}\frac{f_{60}}{f_{25}}$$

In the a-c exciter, the speed of the armature is necessarily $n = 5f_{60}$, and the oppositely rotating magnetic field produced by its winding is $120f_{25}/10 = 12f_{25}$. The difference, which is the speed of the armature field in fixed space, is $\pm(12f_{25} - 5f_{60})$, the direction of rotation depending upon which of the two components is the greater. This difference is seen to agree exactly with the value of slip in the induction machine.

The fact that the armature field of the a-c exciter may rotate slowly in either direction (except when $s = 0$, when it is stationary in space) precludes the possibility of using as a stator the customary salient-pole field structure, and such construction is, moreover, unnecessary. All that is required is a laminated cylindrical stator, concentric with the rotor and without any winding whatever, which serves merely to provide a path of low reluctance for the slowly moving armature field. The a-c exciter is, in fact, the Leblanc exciter which has been described in Art. 8-7.

The armature winding of the a-c exciter, which when regarded from the commutator end is like that of an ordinary d-c generator, is therefore seen to be subjected to the inductive influence of a magnetic field (having 10 poles) which is stationary in space when $s = 0$, and which moves slowly in one direction or the other when s differs from zero. Accordingly, when $s = 0$, that is when $f_{60}/f_{25} = 1\frac{2}{5} = 2.4$, the brushes of the machine will deliver continuous (zero-frequency) current, and at any other value of slip they will deliver current alternating at slip frequency s. But whereas in any ordinary d-c generator the voltage at the commutator will be proportional to the armature speed, the brush voltage of this machine is independent of the speed and bears a fixed ratio to the 25-cycle voltage impressed upon the slip rings, just as in the usual rotary converter.

Since the commutator output of the a-c exciter has exactly the right frequency for insertion in the rotor winding of the main induction machine, it would at first glance appear that the brushes of the exciter might be electrically connected to the slip rings of the induction machine; and that regulation of the voltage of this slip-frequency control current might be obtained by an induction regulator or a tap-changing transformer in the 25-cycle line supplying the exciter. However, because of the large current required by the induction machine, the exciter would have to be very large, and the control would be very awkward; moreover, such an arrangement would not permit control of the power factor of the 25-cycle side of the system.

For these reasons, the exciter as actually constructed is quite small

(8 kva) and is used to excite the field of the main *regulating machine* (Fig. 14-3). The latter, as has been previously stated, has an armature similar to that of a d-c generator; but the field (stator) resembles the stator of an induction motor and has two distinct three-phase windings distributed in slots in the usual manner. One winding receives current directly from the brushes of the a-c exciter; the other receives current from the same source, but through regulating rheostats in order to control the magnitude of this auxiliary excitation.

The output of the a-c exciter is either continuous current if $s = 0$, or it is alternating current of slip frequency if s differs from zero. Consequently, when $s = 0$, the excitation of the regulating machine produces a magnetic field stationary in space, and the machine differs in no way from a d-c generator. Its output is therefore supplied as continuous current to the rotor of the main induction machine just as has been found to be necessary when $s = 0$. When s differs from zero, the excitation produces a magnetic field rotating in space at slip speed, the effect being the same as though the d-c armature winding were subjected to a field alternating at slip frequency, so that the commutator voltage alternates at the same slip frequency, regardless of the armature speed. So whatever the relative frequencies of the main circuits may be, the frequency of the voltage injected into the rotor of the main induction machine has just the right magnitude.

But in addition to assuring correct frequency to the regulating current, it is necessary to have control of its magnitude and phase. This is accomplished by a combination of brush shifting at the commutators of the a-c exciter and the regulating machine, and by rheostatic control of the auxiliary field winding of the latter. The brush shifting is effected by small d-c motors (not shown in Fig. 14-3) geared to the rocker rings of the brushes and operated by remote control from the switchboard; the control rheostat is similarly motor-operated.

Starting Motor and Exciters. The remaining machines in the set of seven include a wound-rotor induction motor for starting purposes; a main exciter for supplying the field winding of the 60-cycle synchronous machine; and a small pilot exciter to supply the shunt field of the main exciter.

Each of the sets that have been described is 60 ft long, 19 ft wide, and weighs 709,000 lb. The control equipment, none of which is shown in Fig. 14-3, is fully automatic, so that by pushing a single button the set can be started, synchronized, and loaded. Relays are provided for the purpose of holding the load at any predetermined amount. The entire equipment was built by the General Electric Company.

CHAPTER 15

COMMUTATOR MOTORS

15-1. Introduction. Some of the basic physical considerations underlying the operation of commutator motors have been outlined in Chap. 5, where it was shown that by suitable connections of the stator and rotor circuits it is possible to impart to the motor either series or shunt characteristics. It is the purpose of this chapter to examine some of the more important types of connections in greater detail than was there attempted, to the end that their working characteristics may be better understood; and at the same time to consider the problem of commutation, which is always a matter of vital concern whenever a commutator and brushes are used. Series-type motors will be considered first, and shunt-type motors last.

15-2. The Series Motor. An ordinary d-c series motor will run in the same direction regardless of the polarity of the supply circuit, but it does not follow from this simple fact that the same motor will operate successfully when supplied from an a-c circuit. The diagram of connections (Fig. 15-1) indicates that there is no inductive coupling between the stator and rotor windings, since their axes are in space quadrature; consequently, both windings may be regarded as the primaries of transformers which have no associated secondaries. Each winding will accordingly have large reactance, and the resultant current will be small and lagging heavily behind the impressed terminal voltage.

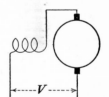

Fig. 15-1. Simple series motor.

Moreover, the alternation of the magnetic field through the solid pole cores and yoke of the usual d-c structure will give rise to excessive heating which absorbs so much of the power input, already limited by the low power factor, as seriously to impair the efficiency and so still further restrict the output.

To overcome these difficulties, it is essential that the stator core shall be fully laminated and that the reactances of the stator and rotor windings shall be reduced to a minimum. So far as the rotor winding is concerned, the latter requirement can be met by means of a compensating winding C (Fig. 15-2) connected in series with the armature winding; the number of turns per pole (N_c) in winding C is so chosen that the mmf it produces is equal and opposite to that of the armature, so that if the armature has Z conductors arranged in a parallel paths,

$$N_c = \frac{Z}{2pa}$$

The compensating winding alone cannot entirely neutralize the armature field in the commutating zone, for its space distribution is not identical with that of the armature winding; there will be a residual armature field owing to the armature turns lying between the pole tips, and the only way to neutralize or overcompensate this flux in the commutating zone is to introduce commutating poles.

The stator flux cannot, of course, be neutralized for the purpose of improving the power factor, for its presence is essential to produce the working torque; nevertheless, the stator winding reactance must be kept as low as possible if the power factor is to be reasonably high, and this requirement calls for the minimum possible number of field-exciting turns per pole and the minimum flux per pole. This is exactly opposite to the requirements in a simple, uncompensated d-c motor, where the field must be "stiff" to prevent undue distortion or skewing because of armature reaction. But when the field flux is thus deliberately reduced, the development of the required torque calls for a correspondingly increased number of armature conductors, thereby still further emphasizing the fact that in an a-c series motor the ratio of armature ampere-turns per pole to field ampere-turns per pole is greatly in excess of that ratio in a simple d-c motor. The combination of a magnetically powerful armature and a relatively weak field is not objectionable because the armature mmf must in any case be neutralized by a compensating winding in the pole faces.

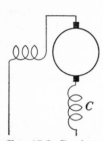

Fig. 15-2. Conductively compensated series motor.

There is, however, a limit to the number of armature ampere-turns that can be accommodated on a given core, this limit being fixed by considerations of heating. For it has been shown in Art. 7-1 that the ratio

$$\frac{\text{Amp-conductors per in. of periphery}}{\text{Cir mils per amp in armature copper}}$$

is equal to the armature copper loss per square inch of cylindrical surface, and these quantities are fixed by the ventilating conditions and the allowable rise of temperature. The only way open, then, to develop the desired torque in motors of considerable rating is to use numerous poles, thus introducing an additional difference between an a-c series motor and the usual four-pole d-c railway motor. The use of numerous poles, each with relatively few turns, has the further advantage of reducing the inductance of the field winding as compared with that of a winding having fewer poles and more turns per pole; but the principal advantage is concerned with the improvement of commutation.

15-3. The Phasor Diagram of the Series Motor. The phasor diagram of the simple series motor, including the compensating winding, has the form shown in Fig. 15-3. The current I, being common to the entire circuit, is chosen as the axis of reference. The main flux Φ is nearly, but not quite, in phase with I, the displacement being the angle of hysteretic advance. The subscripts f, c, and a refer to the main field winding, the compensating winding, and the armature, respectively. The reactances X_f, X_c, and X_a are due to the leakage fluxes associated with the several windings and, except for the disturbing effects of saturation, may be considered to be constant. Phasor E_a is the component of the impressed voltage V which balances the counter emf developed by rotation of the armature winding through the flux Φ, and it is therefore in phase with Φ, and so very nearly in phase with I.

The product of E_a and I, multiplied by the cosine of the angle between them, is the power developed by the motor. Since E_a is practically in phase with the ohmic drops in the windings, it is itself equivalent to the drop in a fictitious resistance which by its variation simulates the effect of the mechanical load. It is

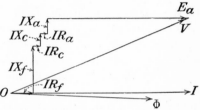

FIG. 15-3. Phasor diagram of compensated series motor.

therefore possible to construct an equivalent circuit consisting of a series connection of resistances and reactances, of which the former only are variable (neglecting saturation), so that the locus of the current phasor is a circle.

15-4. Commutation.* At first glance, it would appear to be no more difficult to commutate an alternating current than a direct current; for the time interval available for reversing the current in the winding element undergoing commutation is so small in comparison with the duration of a complete cycle of the alternating current itself that for all practical purposes the main armature current does not change materially while commutation is taking place. For example, consider a 12-pole motor having a commutator 18 in. in diameter, running at 1,250 rpm, the brush width being $\frac{3}{8}$ in. and the mica insulation between commutator segments being 0.030 in. thick. The peripheral velocity of the commutator is

$$v = \pi \times 18 \times {}^{1250}\!/_{60} = 1,180 \text{ in. per sec}$$

---

* B. G. Lamme, The Single-phase Commutator-type Railway Motor, *Trans. AIEE*, **27**:137 (1908). Felix Konn, The Single-phase Commutator-type Traction Motor, *Gen. Elec. Rev.*, **35**:206, 275, 397 (1932).

and the time during which a coil is short-circuited is

$$\frac{0.375 - 0.030}{1,180} = 0.000292 = \frac{1}{3,250} \text{ sec}$$

If the frequency of the current is 25 cps, the time of commutation then

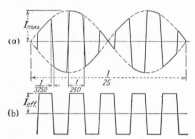

corresponds to an angular interval of only $^{25}\!/_{3250} \times 360 = 2.77$ electrical degrees. The wave form of the current in a single winding element would then have the form shown in Fig. 15-4a. Comparing this with the wave form (Fig. 15-4b) in an equivalent d-c machine carrying a current equal to the effective value of the alternating current, it is seen that the difference between the two cases is due

FIG. 15-4. Variation in magnitude of commutated current.

to the varying amplitude of the commutated current in the individual winding elements of the a-c machine.

There is, however, another difference between the a-c and the d-c motors which is the cause of the real commutation difficulty. It is due to the fact that while the coil undergoing commutation is short-circuited by a brush, it constitutes the closed secondary of a transformer with the field winding playing the part of the primary, as shown diagrammatically

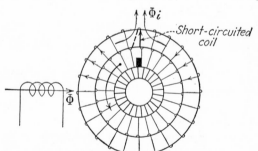

FIG. 15-5. Conditions in short-circuited coil.

in Fig. 15-5. The transformer voltage thereby induced in the short-circuited coil is a quarter period behind the phase of the main flux Φ; at the same time, the motion of the coil causes it to cut the resultant flux* Φ_i in the commutating zone, giving rise to a rotational voltage in phase opposition* to Φ_i. Since Φ and Φ_i are almost in phase coincidence because they are both produced by the same current, the two voltages

* Flux Φ_i is shown as an upwardly directed flux in Fig. 15-5, as though due to commutating poles whose mmf opposes that of the armature. In accordance with the conventions described in Chap. 5, counterclockwise rotation through Φ_i generates a negatively directed emf.

developed in the short-circuited coil are in time quadrature, and their resultant is greater than either component alone.

The immediate effect of the resultant voltage in the short-circuited coil is to produce a circulating current which completes its path through the brush. At the moment of starting, the current through the main circuit of the motor has its greatest magnitude; consequently, the field flux Φ and the transformer voltage in the commutated coil are likewise greatest at that time, while the rotational voltage is zero. Motors of this type are always constructed with a single turn per armature winding element in order to keep the transformer voltage as small as possible, but this construction is not alone sufficient to keep the short-circuited circulating current within proper bounds. To accomplish this result, it is necessary to limit either the main flux Φ or the frequency, or both at the same time, since the transformer voltage is proportional to their product. The same flux which links with the short-circuited armature element also links with each turn of the main field winding (ignoring the effect of magnetic leakage); this consideration reinforces the earlier conclusion that the field winding should have relatively few turns, for it is obvious from Fig. 15-3 that the field winding should absorb only a small part of the total impressed voltage in order that the working voltage at the armature terminals shall be as large as possible. The armature voltage itself cannot be very large in this type of motor, even though it is relatively much greater than the field drop, for the average voltage per commutator segment must be kept low, and the number of segments is limited by considerations of the physical size of the machine. Hence, these motors are inherently low-voltage machines, the maximum operating voltage being approximately 300 volts.

In the absence of methods for the neutralization of the transformer voltage in the coil undergoing commutation, conditions can be improved by using a low-frequency supply;* this accounts for the fact that in European practice the rather low frequency of $16\frac{2}{3}$ cycles was adopted for single-phase railway electrification; the same frequency was used in the original electrification of the Washington, Baltimore, and Annapolis Railway.† Later improvements have made it possible to design such motors for 25-cycle systems, but higher frequencies are still impracticable.

Among the earlier devices for the limitation of circulating current in the short-circuited coils, the simplest was the use of high-resistance leads between the winding elements and the commutator segments, as in Fig. 15-6. If only one coil is commutated at a time,‡ two of these leads are

---

* The late Dr. Steinmetz once facetiously remarked that the optimum frequency is zero (implying a d-c motor).

† B. G. Lamme, The Washington, Baltimore, and Annapolis Single-phase Railway, *Trans. AIEE*, **20**:15 (1902).

‡ Present practice limits this number to two.

in series so far as the circulating current is concerned, but they are in parallel with respect to the working current. As actually constructed, these leads were made of material of high resistivity placed in the bottom of the armature slots, so that the commutator was at the end opposite its customary position. The ohmic loss in these leads was more than offset by the reduction of the copper loss, which, without them, would have occurred in the commutated coils. Devices of this kind are open to the criticism that they merely abate the trouble and do not eliminate the cause. The best remedy is to reduce the magnitude of the transformer voltage in the short-circuited coils by minimizing the field flux Φ at the moment of starting, and then to select brushes of such quality that the circulating current at starting will be least harmful during this period. Some reliance can then be placed on the circumstance that the starting period is only a small part of the complete duty cycle.

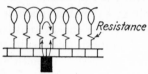

FIG. 15-6. Resistance leads.

15-5. Commutating Poles. Mere inspection of Fig. 15-5 is sufficient to show that ordinary commutating windings connected directly in series with the armature are entirely ineffective for the purpose of neutralizing the transformer voltage in the short-circuited armature elements. This is certainly true at the moment of starting, for commutating poles function because of the rotational emf they produce in the armature coils, and at the moment of starting this emf is zero. Under running conditions, the transformer voltage and the rotational voltage are in time quadrature, as explained previously; so the effect is still worse than at starting. The obvious remedy, at least under running conditions, is to alter the phase of Φ_i with respect to that of Φ (see Fig. 15-5) so that Φ_i will contain one component in phase with Φ and another in quadrature with Φ; the latter component can then be so disposed that the rotational emf it produces will be in opposition to the transformer voltage, and the former component will be effective in the usual manner for reversing the current in the short-circuited coil.

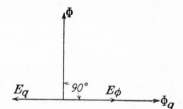

FIG. 15-7. Phase relations for neutralizing transformer voltage.

Assuming the instantaneous direction of fluxes and currents indicated in Fig. 15-5, it may be asserted that the transformer voltage E_ϕ in the short-circuited coil, lagging 90° behind Φ as shown in Fig. 15-7, is positive with respect to the coil. In accordance with the conventions previously adopted, rotation through the flux Φ_i in the commutating zone develops an emf directed negatively through the coil; consequently, if the rotational emf is to be opposite in phase to E_ϕ, the flux Φ_i must include a component Φ_q, as shown in Fig. 15-7, which lags 90° behind Φ and which gives rise to the voltage E_q.

Numerous devices have been proposed and used to secure the desired component Φ_q in the commutating flux. The simplest one, due to Behn-Eschenberg, now used in practically all motors of this type, employs a noninductive resistor shunted around the commutating winding, as in

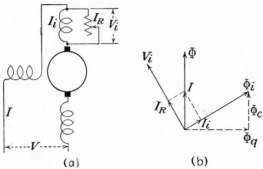

(a)   (b)

Fig. 15-8. Establishment of quadrature commutating flux by noninductive interpole shunt.

Fig. 15-8a. It is apparent that if V_i (Fig. 15-8b) is the drop of potential around the interpole circuit (V_i is usually about 10 volts), the current I_R through the resistor will be in phase with V_i, and the current I_i through the interpole or commutating windings will lag by nearly 90° behind V_i; the resultant of I_R and I_i is necessarily the current through the motor; hence, it is practically in phase with Φ. Current I_i then sets up a flux Φ_i

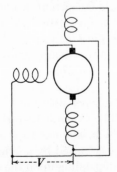

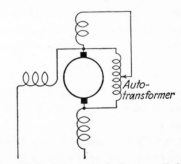

Fig. 15-9. Interpole winding shunted across line voltage.

Fig. 15-10. Interpole winding supplied by part of armature voltage.

almost in phase with itself, including therefore the quadrature component Φ_q and the in-phase component Φ_c, as shown in Fig. 15-8b.

Other methods involve connecting the interpole windings across the main terminals, as in Fig. 15-9; or, as in Fig. 15-10, connecting them across the whole, or a part, of the armature voltage, by means of an adjustable-ratio autotransformer.

15-6. The Effect of Varying Speed upon Commutating Conditions. In a lap-wound drum armature such as is used in motors of the type considered, the flux linking with a full-pitch winding element will vary harmonically in accordance with the relation

$$\phi = \Phi \cos \omega t$$

where Φ is the flux per pole, and since there is one turn per element, the emf due to transformer action is

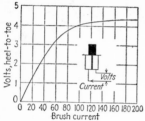

FIG. 15-11. Typical volt-ampere brush characteristic.

$$e = -\frac{d\phi}{dt} = \omega\Phi \sin \omega t$$

and the effective voltage is

$$E = \frac{\omega\Phi}{\sqrt{2}}$$

which at 25 cycles becomes

$$E_{f=25} = 111 \times \text{webers per pole} \quad (15\text{-}1)$$

This is the voltage which at standstill produces the circulating current through the brush.

It is found by experiment that the relation between brush circulating current and the heel-to-toe voltage measured across the brush has the form shown* in Fig. 15-11 (for 25 cycles). The net voltage producing circulating current must be kept well below the knee of the curve, for at and above that point the brush will glow violently. The curve of Fig. 15-11 represents conditions without any working current through the brushes; when both working current and circulating current exist simultaneously, as in normal running, the heating effect of the load current lowers the brush resistance because of its negative temperature coefficient, thus increasing the circulating current above what it would otherwise be.

Equation 15-1 brings out clearly that the flux per pole must be kept quite small as compared with d-c practice. The General Electric Company limits the heel-to-toe brush voltage, which is equal to the transformer voltage times the number of coils short-circuited by a brush (not more than two), to 3 volts or less at starting, depending upon the quality of the brushes.

Series motors for traction purposes must maintain substantially constant torque during the acceleration period, so that both the current I and the flux Φ likewise remain nearly constant during this period, therefore also the transformer voltage in the short-circuited coils. On the other hand, the rotational emf which opposes the transformer voltage increases in direct proportion to the speed, in the manner illustrated in

* F. Konn, *Gen. Elec. Rev.*, **35**: 209 (1932).

Fig. 15-12. At the point marked P, the two voltages are equal, and at the corresponding speed the commutation is at its best. The diagram represents two distinct settings of the shunt around the interpole winding, one being used for slow-speed, the other for high-speed operation. The change of the shunt setting is accomplished automatically by means of a relay-operated contactor. The high-speed setting of the shunt, as developed by the General Electric Company, involves the insertion of a

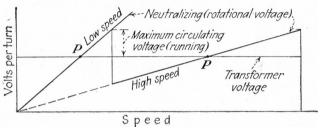

FIG. 15-12. Effect of speed on neutralizing voltage with double setting of shunt.

reactor in the shunt circuit, and the simultaneous reduction of the resistance in order to obtain the desired impedance in the shunt circuit; the switching arrangement for the two settings is shown in Fig. 15-13.

15-7. Structural Features of Series Traction Motors. Figure 15-14 shows a segment of the stator and rotor punchings of a 10-pole General Electric motor. The interpole faces are shaped to distribute the commutating flux most effectively, and the cross section is sufficient to prevent saturation, which if present would destroy the desired proportionality between excitation and flux. The armature slots are half-closed,

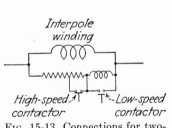

FIG. 15-13. Connections for two-speed shunt setting.

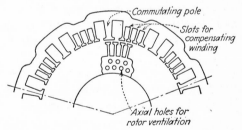

FIG. 15-14. Sector of 10-pole General Electric series traction motor.

this design being a compromise between open slots, which minimize the inductance of the short-circuited coils, and fully closed slots, which minimize the airgap reluctance. The holes in the armature core below the slots serve as ducts for the cooling air which is forced through the motor by means of motor-driven blowers.

The number of armature slots per pair of poles is an odd number in order to minimize flux pulsations. The number of winding elements per slot is chosen as an odd number so that commutation does not occur simultaneously at all the brushes, and the winding pitch is fractional in order to reduce the mutual inductance of simultaneously short-circuited coils. The winding is also provided with equalizing connections between the several parallel paths.

The brushes used in single-phase traction motors have no "pigtail" connections, but consist of plain pieces of carbon to which the current is conveyed from a tip held against the top of the brush by spring pressure.

The commutators of a-c traction motors have considerably greater axial length than in corresponding d-c construction. This is due in part to the fact that the brush width is limited by the requirement that not more than two armature elements may be simultaneously short-circuited at a single brush set, therefore calling for increased axial length of the brushes. Brush current densities at starting run as high as 100 to 150 amp per sq in. But notwithstanding the relatively long commutator, the motors are not unduly large; this is because the torque flux per pole is low, so that the section of the stator iron behind the slots may be small, and also because the large number of poles decreases the angular pitch of the armature winding elements and therefore the axial length of the end connections of the coils.

15-8. Operating Characteristics, Losses, and Efficiency of Series Traction Motors.

The single-phase series traction motor includes all the principal electrical features of the corresponding d-c motor, but developed to a degree of refinement not necessary in the latter machine; accordingly, a well-designed a-c motor is at the same time a superior d-c motor and will operate on direct current as well as, or better than, on the frequency for which it was designed. This property is utilized, for example, in the case of the single-phase locomotives of the New York, New Haven, and Hartford Railroad, which in the vicinity of New York City operate on the d-c electrification of the New York Central Railroad. When running on alternating current, the motors receive current from the 11,000-volt trolley through a step-down transformer; on entering the d-c zone, the transformer is cut out of circuit, and two motors in series operate on the third rail at 650 volts.

The presence of a step-down transformer to reduce the high trolley voltage to a value suitable for the inherently low-voltage motors makes it possible to vary the motor voltage during the acceleration period by means of taps in the secondary winding of the transformer instead of by means of the resistors used in d-c practice. It is, however, necessary to use a special tap-changing device in order that the connections may be changed under load conditions without short-circuiting portions of the transformer secondary. The tap changer operates in the manner shown in Fig. 15-15, where part a shows a number of taps, 1, 2, 3, etc., and part b shows five successive steps in the process of changing from tap 1 to tap 2. Coil C is wound on an iron core and has a connection at its middle point;

in the first and fifth positions, the two halves of the coil magnetize in opposite directions, hence the reactance is zero (or a minimum); in the third (middle) position, the coil presents its full reactance to what would otherwise be the short-circuit current of the section of the transformer secondary across which it is bridged, and at the same time it presents zero (or a minimum) reactance to the main working current supplied to the motors.

The losses in the a-c motor itself are somewhat greater than when the same machine is operated on direct current. This is due to the iron losses in the stator core; copper loss, in the coils short-circuited by the brushes, caused by unbalanced transformer voltage; and local core losses caused by pulsations of leakage flux. The economics of a-c vs. d-c electrification is too highly specialized and too extensive to be considered here, but it is evident that against the increased weight of the a-c motors and their associated transformer must be credited the greater simplicity of substations and the trolley feeder circuits.

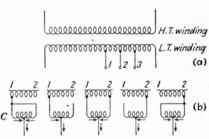

FIG. 15-15. Successive connections in changing taps.

15-9. The Universal Motor. The development of innumerable appliances for use in homes, offices, stores, and factories, all requiring fractional-horsepower drive, led to the demand for a motor adapted for use on both a-c and d-c circuits. The considerations outlined in the preceding articles indicate that the series motor best meets the requirement of universality, particularly because of its high starting torque, which is generally three to four times its full-load torque.

Universal motors are designed for voltages ranging from 32 to 250 volts, frequencies from zero to 60 cycles, and ratings below ¾ hp. The average speed is high, generally in the neighborhood of 7,000 rpm at normal load, which accounts for the fact that in these motors the ratio of horsepower output to the weight is much higher than in ordinary motors.

Universal motors must be designed with weak fields to minimize commutation difficulties, and the stator core must be laminated. High-resistance carbon brushes are used to limit the circulating current due to the transformer voltage in the short-circuited coils. Compensating windings are sometimes used, but in motors of small power rating they are not needed since the armature current is so small as to eliminate serious commutation trouble, and the low power factor is not a serious matter.

In common with all series motors, the universal motor will race when the load is removed, but in small motors the friction and windage losses are sufficient to limit the no-load speed to safe values, though the no-load speed may rise as high as 15,000 to 20,000 rpm. The normal speed of 7,000 rpm is too high for some applications, and in those cases a gear reduction is built into the frame of the motor. The variable speed char-

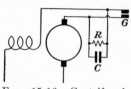

FIG. 15-16. Centrifugal governor.

acteristic of the series motor can be controlled within reasonable limits by means of a governor arranged as in Fig. 15-16; it consists of a pair of contacts G mounted on springs that rotate with the shaft, so adjusted that at the upper limit of the desired speed range the contacts open and introduce into the motor circuit a sufficient resistance R to reduce the current and so reduce the speed. The capacitor C tends to reduce the sparking at the governor contacts.

Characteristic curves* of a ¹⁄₁₆-hp universal motor are shown in Fig. 15-17.

15-10. The Repulsion Motor. The qualifying adjective employed to designate this type of motor is a hopeless misfit, but the term has been

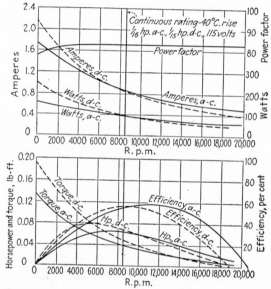

FIG. 15-17. Characteristic curves of universal motor.

in use for such a long time that it is generally accepted. It appears to have been used for the first time in the specification of U.S. patent 363,185, issued to Elihu Thomson in 1887, to describe the machine shown in elementary form in Fig. 15-18a, and in modified form in Fig. 15-18b. The distinctive feature of this machine which differentiates it sharply from the types now in use is the open-circuited armature winding; the

* W. H. Fromm, Why Use Universal Motors, *Elec. Mfg.*, July, 1936.

individual armature coils of Fig. 15-18b successively experience a torque when they are short-circuited by the pair of brushes displaced from the axis of the stator winding, the direction of the torque being in the direction of the brush displacement. It is perfectly clear that such an arrangement as Fig. 15-18a or b will not develop torque if the brush axis is in the plane of the stator coil, for in that case the active rotor coil constitutes merely the short-circuited secondary of a transformer linking with the stator flux; and if the brushes are displaced by 90°, there is likewise no torque since there is then no rotor current.

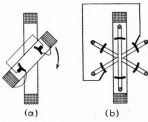

It is only in intermediate positions of the brushes that torque is developed. But it is to be noted that if the brushes are in the plane of the stator coil, and if the plane of the active rotor coil is parallel to, but slightly displaced from, the stator coil, there will be a force of repulsion between the coils acting in the direction of the displacement; this is in accordance with the experimental fact

(a)   (b)

Fig. 15-18. Elementary repulsion motor of Elihu Thomson.

(discovered by Ampère in 1820) that parallel conductors carrying currents in opposite directions repel each other, this phenomenon being utilized in the constant-current transformer described in Art. 2-27. It is probable that this particular behavior of parallel coils gave rise to the term "repulsion" in connection with the motor of Fig. 15-18, but the genuine repulsion between parallel coils has nothing whatever to do with the operation of the so-called repulsion motor.

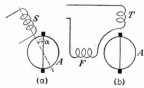

(a)   (b)

Fig. 15-19. Connections of singly fed repulsion motor.

Whatever its origin may have been, the phrase "repulsion motor" is used to designate the arrangement shown diagrammatically in Fig. 15-19a. It consists of a closed-type commutated drum-armature winding entirely similar to that of a d-c machine, the brushes being short-circuited along an axis displaced by an angle α from the axis of the single-phase stator winding. The latter is disposed in slots around the inner periphery of a laminated ring similar to the stator frame of an induction motor.

It is readily apparent that the single-phase alternating mmf supplied by the stator winding S of Fig. 15-19a can be resolved into two components, cophasal with respect to time, but displaced in space by 90°, so that one component is in line with the brush axis and the other is perpendicular thereto; or, what amounts to the same thing, the actual single stator winding may be regarded as equivalent to the two windings F and T of Fig. 15-19b, as has already been indicated in Chap. 5. Winding T then plays the part of the primary of a (series) transformer with the short-circuited armature winding acting as the secondary; and the reaction between the inductively supplied rotor current and the magnetic field due to F develops the torque.   Since the current taken by the motor clearly varies with the load, and the flux due to winding F is proportional to the current (ignoring possible saturation), the motor is characterized by variable field flux and will therefore have the series characteristic of variable speed.   One further fact evident from Fig. 15-19b is that the magnetic field due to the armature mmf is largely neutralized by the mmf of winding T, which therefore serves as a compensating winding functioning by induction, instead of by conduction as in the series traction motor discussed in previous articles.

15-11. Starting Conditions in the Repulsion Motor.   Replacing the sketch of Fig. 15-19b by the more detailed diagram of Fig. 15-20, it will

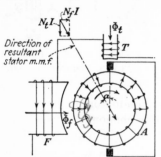

FIG. 15-20. Instantaneous current flow.

be seen that the brushes are shifted clockwise with respect to the resultant stator mmf compounded of the separate mmfs produced by windings F and T.   With the stator currents having the instantaneous direction indicated, the rotor current must by Lenz's law magnetize in opposition to T, thus fixing the instantaneous current direction in the armature winding.   On applying Fleming's left-hand rule, the direction of the torque due to the field of F is found to be clockwise, i.e., in the direction of brush shift.

It is readily shown that the torque (if any exists) is always in the direction of brush shift, regardless of the sense of the windings.

For convenience, suppose that the rotor is blocked.   Winding T, together with the rotor winding, then constitutes a short-circuited transformer which is in series with the stator winding F.   The latter is equivalent to a simple choke coil since there is no other circuit in inductive relation with it.   The equivalent circuit of the combination therefore

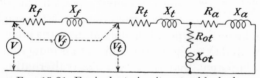

FIG. 15-21. Equivalent circuit, rotor blocked.

has the form shown in Fig. 15-21, where X_t and X_a are the leakage reactances of windings T and A, respectively, both of them being very small in comparison with X_f, which is the reactance due to the entire flux linked with winding F.   The current taken by the motor will therefore be determined largely by the magnitude of X_f; much the greater part of the impressed voltage V will be absorbed by winding F, and only a small part by the short-circuited transformer consisting of winding T

and the rotor winding A; and the phasor sum of these voltages, V_f and V_t, must be equal to V.

To construct the phasor diagram under standstill conditions (Fig. 15-22), it is then only necessary to observe (see part a) that V_t corresponds to the leakage-impedance drop in the short-circuited transformer, and that Φ_t, the flux in the brush axis, is quite small. With a 1:1 ratio of turns in T and in the armature A, the armature current I_a is nearly equal and in phase opposition to the stator current I which flows both in windings T and F; the phasor sum of I_a and I is the very small magnetizing current I_0 required to maintain the mutual flux Φ_t in the brush axis.

In Fig. 15-22b, the flux Φ_f is shown displaced by the small angle α_f (the hysteretic angle) from the current I. The flux Φ_f is really that part of the entire flux linked with F which finds its way into the rotor core, and

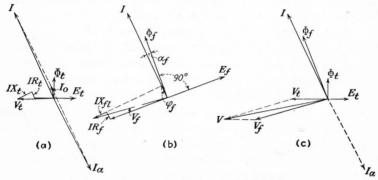

Fig. 15-22. Phasor diagram, rotor blocked.

it corresponds with what has been called the mutual flux of a transformer; there is an additional flux linked with F which does not enter the rotor core, and this corresponds to the leakage flux φ_f of winding F regarded as the primary of a transformer; this leakage flux, being mainly in air, is in phase with I, and it gives rise to a leakage-reactance drop IX_{fl}. Accordingly, V_f is the phasor sum of (1) an emf equal and opposite to E_f induced in winding F by Φ_f; (2) the ohmic drop IR_f in phase with I; and (3) IX_{fl} in quadrature with I. If V_f is projected upon I, it is apparent that V_f may be regarded as made up of two components, one in phase with I, the other leading I by $90°$; the former is the drop due to the effective resistance R_f' of F, including the core loss in that axis; the latter is the total reactive drop IX_f due to the combined inductive effect of Φ_f and φ_f.

Figure 15-22c is a combination of parts a and b. It will be observed that Φ_f and I_a are nearly opposite in time phase, and since their space axes are in quadrature, the conditions for the development of torque are most advantageous.

Reference to Fig. 15-19a shows that the effect of increasing the angle of brush shift is to increase the component field winding F and to decrease the component winding T. There will be no torque when $\alpha = 0$ and again when $\alpha = \pi/2$; consequently, there will be an intermediate value of α for which the torque is a maximum.

15-12. Phasor Diagram of Repulsion Motor, Running Conditions. If the rotor is permitted to accelerate under the influence of the starting torque, the immediate result is the development of an emf E_{fr} in the brush axis (Fig. 15-20), and since this emf is due to rotation of the armature winding through the flux Φ_f, it will be in phase with the latter. Fleming's right-hand rule is sufficient to show that this rotational emf is directed in opposition to the current produced by transformer action; consequently, the rotational emf E_{fr} corresponds to the counter emf of an ordinary motor, while the voltage E_t due to transformer action is equivalent to an inductively impressed terminal voltage.

The rotational emf E_{fr} is in any case proportional to the product of the speed S and the flux Φ_f, and it will increase with increasing speed unless Φ_f decreases at a greater rate than the speed rises. Any increase in E_{fr} must be accompanied by an increase in E_t, for their resultant must be the voltage E_a which maintains the armature current I_a through the leakage impedance $R_a + jX_a$ of the rotor winding. But if E_t increases, V_t must also increase, and since the phasor sum of V_t and V_f is equal to the (assumed) constant voltage V impressed upon the stator terminals, it follows that V_f and Φ_f must decrease with rising speed. The speed will therefore approach a limiting value such that the current I_a and the flux Φ_f will react to yield the torque demanded by the load on the motor.

The phasors representing the various voltages, currents, and fluxes when the motor is operating at a steady load must then be related in the manner shown in Fig. 15-23. Taking Φ_t as a vertical phasor, E_t will lag 90° behind it, and the phase of E_{fr} must be nearly opposite to that of E_t. The resultant of E_t and E_{fr}, namely, E_a, sets up the rotor current I_a such that the phase angle between E_a and I_a is $\varphi_a = \tan^{-1}(X_a/R_a)$. To maintain the flux Φ_t, there must be a resultant magnetizing current I_0 leading the flux Φ_t by the small angle of hysteretic advance α_t; and just as in any transformer, I_0 is the resultant of the secondary current I_a and the primary current I (assuming a 1:1 ratio of transformation, or that all secondary quantities have been reduced to terms of the primary). At this point, the diagram must check with the consideration that I must be ahead of the flux Φ_f by the small angle of hysteretic advance α_f caused by the core losses in the speed axis. Finally, the voltage drop V_t across winding T must include $-E_t$ as one component and $\mathbf{I}Z_t = \mathbf{I}(R_t + jX_t)$ as the other; and when to $\mathbf{V}_t$ there is added $\mathbf{V}_f$ the resultant is $\mathbf{V}$.

The phasor diagram (Fig. 15-23), together with the physical facts upon which it is based, shows that the motor is equivalent to a circuit consisting of a loaded transformer in series with a choke coil. It remains to be shown that the load on the transformer is a noninductive resistance whose variation with the speed simulates the effect of the actual mechanical load, in much the same way as in the polyphase induction motor.

15-13. Analytical Relations in the Repulsion Motor. From the diagram, Fig. 15-23, certain quantitative relations may be seen at a glance. For instance, E_a is the phasor sum of E_t and E_{fr}, whence

$$\mathbf{E}_t + \mathbf{E}_{fr} = \mathbf{E}_a = \mathbf{I}_a(R_a + jX_a) = \mathbf{I}_a Z_a \qquad (15\text{-}2)$$

Also, I_0 is the phasor sum of I and I_a, whence

$$\mathbf{I} + \mathbf{I}_a = \mathbf{I}_0 \qquad (15\text{-}3)$$

and because of the transformer conditions in the brush axis, coinciding with the axis of the stator winding T, it is possible to write

$$\mathbf{I}_0 = -\mathbf{E}_t Y_{0t} \qquad (15\text{-}4)$$

where Y_{0t} is the exciting admittance in that axis.

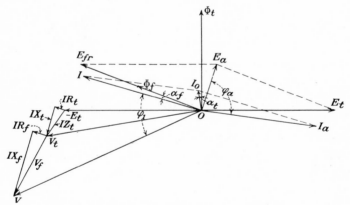

FIG. 15-23. Phasor diagram, motor running.

Again, V_t is the phasor sum of E_t (reversed) and the drop in the leakage impedance $Z_t = R_t + jX_t$, from which

$$\mathbf{V}_t = -\mathbf{E}_t + \mathbf{I}(R_t + jX_t) = -\mathbf{E}_t + \mathbf{I}Z_t \qquad (15\text{-}5)$$

and it is further evident that

$$\mathbf{V} = \mathbf{V}_t + \mathbf{V}_f \qquad (15\text{-}6)$$

In the speed axis, coincident with the axis of winding F, the conditions are those of an open-circuited transformer. The flux Φ_f, alternating through winding F, will induce a transformer voltage E_f lagging 90° behind Φ_f, as indicated in Fig. 15-24a; and since current I is the equivalent of the exciting current of the open-circuited transformer of which F is the primary, we have by analogy with Eq. 15-4

$$\mathbf{I} = -\mathbf{E}_f Y_{0f} \tag{15-7}$$

where Y_{0f} is the exciting admittance in the speed axis.   Finally, in accordance with Fig. 15-24a,

$$\mathbf{V}_f = -\mathbf{E}_f + \mathbf{I}(R_f + jX_{fl}) \tag{15-8}$$

where R_f is the resistance and X_{fl} is the leakage reactance of winding F, considering as leakage flux those lines of induction which link with F but

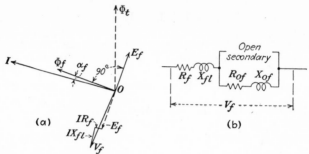

FIG. 15-24. Phase relations and equivalent circuit, speed field.

which do not enter the rotor core.   Equations 15-7 and 15-8 yield the result

$$\mathbf{V}_f = \frac{\mathbf{I}}{Y_{0f}} + \mathbf{I}(R_f + jX_{fl})$$

or, since $1/Y_{0f} = Z_{0f} = R_{0f} + jX_{0f}$,

$$\mathbf{V}_f = \mathbf{I}[(R_{0f} + R_f) + j(X_{0f} + X_{fl})] = \mathbf{I}(R'_f + jX_f) = \mathbf{I}Z_f \tag{15-9}$$

which shows that the winding F is equivalent to a simple choke coil, indicated in Fig. 15-24b.

Now it is evident both from the diagram, Fig. 15-23, and from physical considerations that E_{fr} is in phase with Φ_f and that it is proportional to Φ_f, to the speed* S, and to the number and distribution of the armature turns; but since we are here dealing with the armature as the secondary of a transformer in which all secondary quantities are reduced to terms of the primary, it is possible to write

$$\mathbf{E}_{fr} = kS\mathbf{\Phi}_f N_t \tag{15-10}$$

where N_t is the number of turns in winding T, and k is a proportionality constant which takes into account the pitch and distribution factors of the stator winding.   The assumption is, of course, implicit that the flux is sinusoidally distributed around the airgap.

* The speed S is expressed in terms of synchronous speed as unity.

It is likewise to be noted that since flux Φ_f induces the transformer voltage E_f in the N_f turns of winding F, and since E_f is 90° behind Φ_f and proportional to it,

$$\mathbf{E}_f = -jk\Phi_f N_f \tag{15-11}$$

so that from Eqs. 15-10 and 15-11 there is obtained

$$\frac{\mathbf{E}_{fr}}{\mathbf{E}_f} = jS\frac{N_t}{N_f} \tag{15-12}$$

Equations 15-2 to 15-12 may now be used to express V in terms of I and the constants of the machine, thereby evaluating the equivalent impedance and defining the equivalent circuit. Thus, substituting 15-5 and 15-9 in 15-6,

$$\mathbf{V} = -\mathbf{E}_t + \mathbf{I}(Z_f + Z_t) \tag{15-13}$$

From Eqs. 15-4, 15-3, and 15-2,

$$-\mathbf{E}_t = \frac{\mathbf{I}_0}{Y_{0t}} = \frac{\mathbf{I} + \mathbf{I}_a}{Y_{0t}} = \frac{\mathbf{I}}{Y_{0t}} + \frac{\mathbf{E}_t + \mathbf{E}_{fr}}{Y_{0t}Z_a}$$

whence, using Eq. 15-12,

$$-\mathbf{E}_t\left(1 + \frac{1}{Y_{0t}Z_a}\right) = \frac{\mathbf{I}}{Y_{0t}} + \frac{jS\mathbf{E}_f(N_t/N_f)}{Y_{0t}Z_a}$$

and from Eq. 15-7

$$-\mathbf{E}_t = \mathbf{I}\,\frac{Z_a - jS\dfrac{N_t}{(N_f Y_{0f})}}{1 + Y_{0t}Z_a} \tag{15-14}$$

Substituting 15-14 in 15-13,

$$\mathbf{V} = \mathbf{I}\left[Z_f + Z_t + \frac{Z_a - jSZ_{0f}(N_t/N_f)}{1 + Z_a Y_{0t}}\right] \tag{15-15}$$

and the expression in the brackets is then the equivalent impedance Z_e of the motor. It may readily be modified to the form

$$Z_e = Z_f + Z_t + \frac{1}{Y_{0t} + \dfrac{1 + jSZ_{0f}Y_{0t}(N_t/N_f)}{Z_a - jSZ_{0f}(N_t/N_f)}} \tag{15-16}$$

The last two equations may be simplified by dropping the term $Z_a Y_{0t}$, which is quite small; furthermore, since

$$-jZ_{0f} = -j(R_{0f} + jX_{0f}) = -jR_{0f} + X_{0f}$$

is nearly equal to X_{0f}, Eq. 15-15 becomes

$$\mathbf{V} = \mathbf{I}\left(Z_f + Z_t + Z_a + SX_{0f}\frac{N_t}{N_f}\right) \tag{15-17}$$

and 15-16 reduces to

$$\mathbf{V} = \mathbf{I}\left[Z_f + Z_t + \cfrac{1}{Y_{0t} + \cfrac{1}{Z_a + SX_{0f}(N_t/N_f)}} \right] \qquad (15\text{-}18)$$

The last equation is of the same form that has been encountered in the cases of the transformer and the polyphase induction motor. It indicates that the equivalent circuit has the form shown in Fig. 15-25. Equation 15-17 points to a circuit which differs from that of Fig. 15-25 only in that the exciting admittance of the transformer circuit is omitted. The variable load on the motor is represented by the term $SX_{0f}(N_t/N_f)$, which represents a *noninductive resistance*, since X_{0f}, in the absence of the operator j, is a pure resistance expressible in ohms.

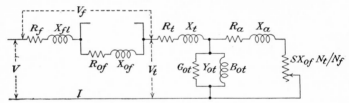

Fig. 15-25. Equivalent circuit of repulsion motor.

The ratio N_t/N_f that appears in the preceding equations has the physical meaning, deducible from Fig. 15-20, that

$$\frac{N_t}{N_f} = \cot \alpha \qquad (15\text{-}19)$$

where α is the angle of brush shift from the axis of the actual single stator winding. N_t and N_f are further related by the equation

$$\sqrt{N_t^2 + N_f^2} = N \qquad (15\text{-}20)$$

where N is the number of turns (corrected for pitch and spread) in the actual stator winding.

The theory here outlined is predicated upon the assumption of a sinusoidally distributed field, whereas the mmf distribution due to the stator winding actually includes a number of the higher space harmonics. Some discrepancies between the predictions of the theory and the results of tests may therefore be anticipated, and they do occur. Since the stator has a single-phase winding, it cannot economically be distributed over the entire periphery, the result being a trapezoidal distribution of mmf which may be analyzed by the aid of formulas derived in Chap. 4. It is the fundamental full-pitch distribution which is concerned in the preceding analysis, and all of the ampere-turns which enter into the calculation are those which are associated with this fundamental.

A somewhat different method of approaching the theory of the motor is outlined in a paper* by V. A. Fynn. Those parts of the armature winding lying with the angle $360 - 4\alpha$ (shown in heavy lines in Fig. 15-26) may be regarded as the secondary of a transformer of which the stator winding S is the primary. The remaining armature turns, within the double angle of brush shift, then set up a field indicated by Φ, which reacts with the induced armature current in the other belt to produce the torque. Because of the manner in which energy is inductively conveyed to the rotor, with the latter then exciting the field Φ, Fynn designates this machine as a "self-excited single-phase series induction motor with rotor excitation."

15-14. The Circle Diagram and Performance Characteristics of the Repulsion Motor.

The equivalent circuit of Fig. 15-25 shows clearly that the repulsion motor is equivalent to a transformer in which both the primary resistance and leakage reactance are greater than normal. It shows, further, that if the exciting admittance Y_{0t} is small enough to be negligible (in other words, if I and I_a are equal and in phase opposition) the circuit consists of a simple series grouping made up of a fixed reactance and a variable resistance, from which it follows that the locus of the stator current is a semicircle of diameter $V/(X_f + X_t + X_a)$ drawn perpendicular to the phasor representing the impressed voltage V. This diagram may then be made to incorporate† the phasors representing the remaining currents and voltages that have been considered in connection with Fig. 15-23, but this is left as an exercise for the student.

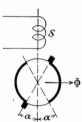

Fig. 15-26. Resolution of armature mmf into demagnetizing and crossmagnetizing components.

Neglecting the exciting admittance shown in Fig. 15-25, the current taken by the motor will be

$$I = \frac{V}{\sqrt{\left(R_f' + R_t + R_a + SX_{0f}\dfrac{N_t}{N_f}\right)^2 + (X_f + X_t + X_a)^2}} \qquad (15\text{-}21)$$

and the mechanical power developed (including friction and windage) will be equal to the power absorbed by the variable resistance that simulates the load; i.e.,

$$P = I^2 S X_{0f} \frac{N_t}{N_f} \qquad (15\text{-}22)$$

The actual speed of the motor, n rpm, is given by

$$n = n_1 S \qquad (15\text{-}23)$$

* Classification of Alternating-current Motors, *Trans. AIEE*, **34**:1362 (1915).

† A. S. McAllister, "Alternating Current Motors," McGraw-Hill Book Company, Inc., New York, 1909. John M. Bryant and Elmer W. Johnson, "Alternating Current Machinery," McGraw-Hill Book Company, Inc., New York, 1935.

where n_1 is the so-called synchronous speed of the machine, or

$$n_1 = \frac{120f}{p}$$

where f is the impressed frequency and p is the number of poles. Since the repulsion motor has series characteristics, the actual speed is variable and has no close relation to the synchronous speed, the latter being introduced for convenience only.

The torque, in synchronous watts, is given by

$$2\pi n_1 S T = P$$

whence

$$T = \frac{V^2 X_{0f}(N_t/N_f)}{2\pi n_1 \left[\left(R_f' + R_t + R_a + S X_{0f} \frac{N_t}{N_f} \right)^2 + (X_f + X_t + X_a)^2 \right]} \qquad (15\text{-}24)$$

which shows that the torque is greatest at starting $(S = 0)$ and that it decreases with increasing speed. The form of the torque-speed curve has already been indicated in Fig. 9-25; as a matter of fact, with the exception noted in the next paragraph, the repulsion-motor principle is used mainly in connection with single-phase induction motors for starting purposes when large starting torque is required.

The *repulsion induction* motor,[*] described in the references below as a new type, really dates back to 1907, when it was patented by Edward Bretch. It has a single-phase stator, and a rotor which combines in one structure the usual repulsion-motor winding with commutator and brushes, and also a squirrel-cage winding. The commutated d-c type of winding occupies slots in the periphery of the rotor, and the bars of the squirrel-cage lie below the commutated winding. The shape of the slots is quite similar to that used in double-cage induction motors.

Both rotor windings of this motor remain in circuit at all times. At starting, the torque is due principally to the commutated winding, since the large reactance of the deeply buried squirrel cage limits to a very small amount the torque it can develop. With increasing speed, the resultant magnetic field in the airgap, while in general elliptical, tends to become a uniformly rotating field as synchronism is approached; under these circumstances, the slip becomes so small that the greatly reduced reactance of the squirrel cage permits the flow of considerable current, with correspondingly increased torque due to induction-motor action. The resultant torque-speed characteristic is therefore compounded of the drooping characteristic of the repulsion motor and the rising characteristic of the induction motor, somewhat in the manner shown in Fig. 9-25;

[*] S. R. Bergman, A New Type of Single-phase Motor, *Trans. AIEE*, **43**:1039 (1924). H. R. West, Theory and Calculation of the Squirrel-cage Repulsion Motor, *Trans. AIEE*, **43**:1048 (1924).

however, there is no sharp break as in that diagram, since there is here no sudden transition from the one characteristic to the other.

15-15. Commutation in Repulsion Motors. An interesting feature of the operating conditions in a repulsion motor is the manner in which V_f and V_t change with the load. Their variation may be most simply investigated by referring to the equivalent circuit, Fig. 15-25, ignoring the exciting admittance Y_{0t} except at standstill or at low speeds. At standstill ($S = 0$) the variable load resistance constitutes a short circuit of the transformer; hence, V_t will be small and V_f correspondingly large; this fact is exemplified in Fig. 15-22. As the speed rises, V_t increases and V_f decreases, as indicated in Fig. 15-23, which should be compared with Fig. 15-22 for the purpose of visualizing the changing relative magnitudes of these two voltages. (No attempt has been made to draw these two diagrams to any particular scale or to represent any particular loads.)

Figure 15-20 shows clearly that the coils short-circuited by the brushes are subjected to the full inductive effect of the speed field Φ_f, and a transformer voltage will be induced in them in the manner discussed in Art. 15-4. At the moment of starting, there is no rotational emf to balance the transformer voltage; so the conditions are then entirely comparable with those in the straight series motor. But as the motor speeds up, Φ_t increases and Φ_f decreases, and the phase angle between these two fluxes approaches 90° as synchronous speed is approached. This is exactly what is required for good commutation; hence, the commutating conditions in the repulsion motor, at speeds near synchronism, are much superior to those in the series motor; beyond synchronous speed this superiority vanishes, for both Φ_t and the speed become so large as greatly to overbalance the transformer voltage due to the diminishing Φ_f.

An interesting corollary that follows from inspection of Fig. 15-23 is that the resultant airgap field is an elliptically rotating one; for the component fields Φ_f and Φ_t are in space quadrature, and their time phases are displaced, tending toward 90° displacement at synchronous speed.

15-16. The Compensated Repulsion Motor. One of the principal disadvantages of the repulsion motor, in the form described in the preceding articles, is its relatively poor power factor. The chief factor contributing to this drawback is the considerable impedance of the field winding F, which introduces the large quadrature drop IX_f, as shown in Figs. 15-23 and 15-25. This effect is due to the fact that winding F plays the part of a choke coil, or what amounts to the same thing, the primary of a transformer which has no secondary. It cannot be provided with a compensating winding on the main magnetic circuit for the purpose of neutralizing its field, for it is this very field which produces the torque; but the problem of improving the power factor raises the question whether it is possible partially to neutralize the inductive drop

V_f in some other way, thereby obtaining a motor with relatively high power factor in addition to the advantageous commutating conditions inherent in the repulsion type of motor.

Among the numerous arrangements that have been proposed and used, one of the earliest was the compensated repulsion motor due to M. Latour and to Winter and Eichberg (1903), and developed for railway purposes by the Allgemeine Elektrizitäts-Gesellschaft of Berlin. Alternative forms of the diagram of connections are shown in Fig. 15-27. In all three parts of that diagram, the working current is transferred inductively to the transformer axis t, t, the rotor current in that axis being the mirror image of the primary or line current. In part a, the line current itself is conductively supplied to the speed axis by means of brushes f, f on the same commutator which serves axis t, t, and in the rotor speed axis the line current sets up the torque field, which reacts with the inductively supplied working current in axis t, t; in parts b and c, the rotor current in the speed axis f, f is supplied inductively from the

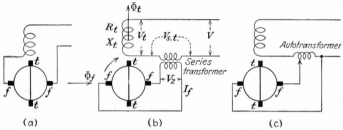

FIG. 15-27. Connections of compensated repulsion motor.

line, in the former case by means of a series transformer, in the latter case by means of an autotransformer. Basically, all three methods are alike in that the torque field is proportional to the line current, or a part thereof, so that series operating characteristics will result; minor differences may be anticipated because of the slight phase shifts that will be introduced by the transformers in cases b and c.

Comparison of Fig. 15-27a with Fig. 15-19b indicates that they differ with respect to the manner in which the torque field is produced. In the former case, the excitation is supplied by the line current flowing in the rotor winding; in the latter, by the line current flowing in the stator winding F. But whereas in Fig. 15-19b the voltage drop across winding F cannot be compensated since there is no possibility of a counter emf in its circuit, in Fig. 15-27a the voltage impressed upon brushes f, f can be partially balanced by the emf generated in that axis by rotation through the flux Φ_t in the t, t axis, without at the same time neutralizing the essential torque flux Φ_f. This is explained in the next article.

15-17. Phasor Diagram of the Compensated Repulsion Motor. Referring to Fig. 15-27b, it is apparent that the flux Φ_t induces in the rotor transformer axis an emf E_{tt} which corresponds* to the voltage impressed upon the terminals of an ordinary motor. When the motor is running, any flux Φ_f in the speed axis will produce a second voltage in the t, t axis of the rotor, proportional to Φ_f and to the speed, and this voltage E_{fr} must be in approximate phase opposition to E_{tt} since it corresponds to the counter emf. Their resultant E_T is then the voltage which drives the rotor current I_t through the leakage impedance in the transformer axis t, t. These considerations lead at once to the proper placement of the phasors representing these quantities, starting arbitrarily with Φ_t (Fig. 15-28) as a vertical phasor. The maintenance of the flux Φ_t calls for a magnetizing current I_{0t}, which must be the resultant of I_t and the line current I flowing in the stator winding. This consideration fixes the magnitude and phase position of I; and thereafter the phasor sum of $-E_{tt}$, IR_t, and IX_t fixes the voltage drop V_t across the stator winding in accordance with usual transformer theory.

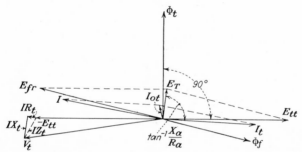

Fig. 15-28. Phase relations in transformer axis t, t.

One feature of the diagram (Fig. 15-28) calls for special comment, namely, that E_{fr} and I must be nearly in phase, the slight discrepancy being due in part to core loss in the speed axis; for since E_{fr} is due to rotation through Φ_f, it must be taken to be in phase opposition to the latter; and the current that produces Φ_f, being derived from the secondary of the series transformer, must be practically the mirror image of the line current I.

Again referring to Fig. 15-27b, it will be seen that, in the closed circuit that includes the speed brushes f, f and the secondary of the series transformer, the phasor sum of all emfs and voltages, taken with due regard to the direction through this circuit, must be zero in accordance with Kirchhoff's second law. Considering the series transformer first, its phasor diagram (Fig. 15-29b) must be similar in form to that of any other transformer, but in this case subject to the condition that its primary current I must be the same in magnitude and phase as the current I in

* The double subscripts assigned to the various voltages follow the convention used in Chap. 9; i.e., the first subscript indicates the flux to which it is due; the second indicates whether it is due to transformer action (t) or to rotational generation (r).

Fig. 15-28. Its secondary terminal voltage V_2 must therefore be equal to the terminal voltage at brushes f, f. The latter may be considered to be the phasor sum of three voltages; one of these, Fig. 15-29a, is E_{tr}, generated by rotation through Φ_t and opposite in phase to the latter; another is E_{ft}, induced by the alternation of Φ_f through the rotor winding in axis f, f, and therefore lagging behind Φ_f by 90°; the third is the leakage-impedance drop $I_f(R_f + jX_f)$ in the rotor speed axis.

Combining V_t and V_{st} as shown in Fig. 15-29a (which ties together in one diagram the essential phasors of Figs. 15-28 and 15-29b), it is seen that the resultant line voltage V is less than in a simple repulsion motor, and the over-all power factor is decidedly improved. This result is due

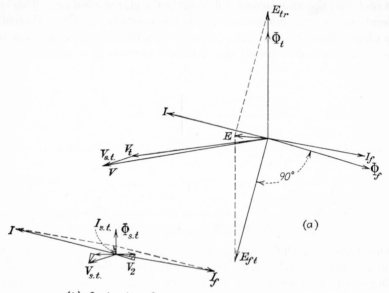

(b) Series transformer

Fig. 15-29. Phase relations, compensated repulsion motor.

to the fact that the relatively large voltage V_f of Figs. 15-21 and 15-23 is replaced by the much smaller drop V_{st} across the series transformer of Fig. 15-27b. Looked at in another way, the voltage V_f of Fig. 15-21 which adversely affects the power factor of the simple repulsion motor is due to the reactance of the speed-field winding F (Fig. 15-20); there is no such field winding in the compensated repulsion motor, but its place is taken by the speed axis of the rotor winding itself, and the reactance voltage of the rotor winding is E_{ft} (Fig. 15-29a). It is this reactance voltage which is largely neutralized by the emf E_{tr}, owing to rotation of the armature through the transformer flux Φ_t. The conditions as a whole have a marked resemblance to those involved in Figs. 9-26 and 9-27, in connection with the power-factor compensation of the single-phase induction motor. It will be observed that in the case of the induction motor, which has the constant-flux characteristic of the shunt motor, the compensating voltage is derived from a shunt across the line, whereas in the compensated repulsion motor, having series characteristics, the compensating voltage is derived from a transformer in series with the line.

15-18. Doubly Fed Series and Repulsion Motors. It has been pointed out in Art. 15-5 that improvement of the inherently poor commutating characteristics of the simple series motor can be effected by the presence of a commutating field which includes a component in time quadrature with the main (torque) field. Among the methods for securing such a commutating field, the connections indicated in Figs. 15-9 and 15-10 were included. In both these cases, the energy from the line is transferred to the armature both *conductively* and *inductively;* for it is clear that while the primary purpose of the auxiliary commutating winding is to provide the desired commutating flux, the auxiliary winding is inductively related to the brush axis of the armature as a whole, the two standing to each other in the roles of primary and secondary of a transformer. Motors of

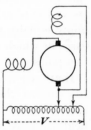

FIG. 15-30. Doubly fed series motor.

the types shown in Figs. 15-9 and 15-10 are accordingly designated as *doubly fed* motors. The fact that energy is supplied both conductively and inductively is an incidental rather than a primary consideration; the basic reason for the combination is the improvement of commutating conditions. Refinement and improvement of commutating conditions in the simple compensated series motor have largely removed the need for these more elaborate devices.

Figure 15-30 is a diagram of connections of a doubly fed series motor. Its electrical identity with Fig. 15-9 should be noted.

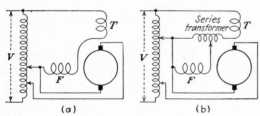
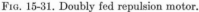

FIG. 15-31. Doubly fed repulsion motor.

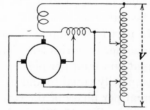

FIG. 15-32. Doubly fed compensated repulsion motor.

Doubly fed repulsion-motor diagrams are shown in Fig. 15-31. Part *a* differs from the elementary diagram of Fig. 15-19 only in that the brush circuit has injected into it a voltage proportional to the line voltage, while in part *b* the current through the speed-field winding is independently variable by means of a series transformer.

Compensated repulsion motors of the Winter-Eichberg type shown in Fig. 15-27c are convertible to the doubly fed type by opening the armature circuit in the transformer axis and introducing an additional conduction voltage from the line, in the manner shown in Fig. 15-32.

15-19. Polyphase Series Motors.   It has been shown in Chap. 5 that if a gramme-ring armature is supplied with balanced m-phase current through m brushes symmetrically spaced around its commutator, there will be produced a bipolar magnetic field rotating at synchronous speed around its periphery.   So long as the brushes remain stationary, the speed of the magnetic field relative to the surrounding space is independent of the rotational speed of the armature itself.   The same conclusions apply equally to any closed-coil d-c armature winding, including those cases in which the winding is so disposed as to correspond to more than two poles.

If attention is concentrated upon the conditions at a particular instant, the sum of the instantaneous values of the brush currents (with due regard to sign) must necessarily be zero; and at this instant the magnetic field will have a definite position relative to the stationary brushes.   The conditions at this moment are then in fact the same as they would be permanently if all the currents were held continuously at these instantaneous values; from this it follows that rocking the brushes will cause the magnetic field to move with them.   It is therefore clear that when the brush currents are alternating, the effect of shifting the brushes is to shift the space phase of the revolving magnetic field by a like amount.

These basic properties of a commutated d-c winding when supplied with polyphase currents through suitable brushes were first applied by Görges* in 1891 to a *polyphase series motor*.   The stator, similar in construction to that of an ordinary induction motor, was provided with a polyphase winding, while the rotor, entirely similar to the armature of a d-c machine, was connected in series with the stator in the manner indicated in Fig. 15-33.   In part a of this diagram, the phase windings of the stator together with those of the rotor constitute a Y-Δ arrangement.   In part b, the stator and rotor windings, each connected in Δ, are linked together by series transformers, from which it follows that the rotor current and mmf per phase, when reduced to terms of the primary, are substantially equal to and in time phase with the corresponding current and mmf per phase of the stator.

If in Fig. 15-33b the brushes are so placed that angle α is zero, the space direction of the mmf of any phase of the rotor will be the same as that of the corresponding stator phase; in that event, there could be no torque developed by the rotor, just as in any motor there can be no torque if the space axes of field and armature mmfs coincide.   Pursuing the same line of reasoning, it becomes clear that if the brushes are displaced from this zero-torque position, torque will be developed which is

* Mitteilungen über neuere Untersuchungen an Wechselstrommotoren, *Elektrotech. Z.*, **52**:699 (1891).

directed one way for a given brush displacement, and in the opposite direction for a reversed brush displacement.

In the case of the polyphase series motor, the mmfs of the several stator phases combine to produce a synchronously rotating resultant mmf which will be sinusoidally distributed in space if attention is confined to the space fundamental only. Let it be assumed that the stator windings are so arranged that this resultant mmf rotates clockwise, as indicated by the arrow in Fig. 15-33b. Then if the brushes are displaced backward by an angle α, the space fundamental of the rotating mmf produced by the rotor currents will follow in step with the stator mmf, but trailing behind it by angle α, and the resultant torque and direction of rotation of the armature will be in the same direction as the motion of

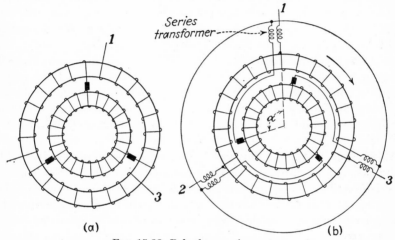

Fig. 15-33. Polyphase series motor.

the stator mmf. Under these conditions, the rotor conductors will move at slip speed through the resultant synchronously rotating magnetic field, with the result that when the rotor is running at synchronous speed, the winding elements short-circuited by the brushes are not cutting flux, and commutating conditions are at their best. At any other speed, the short-circuited elements have emfs of slip frequency induced in them, and when the resulting circulating current passes a definite limit, there will be sparking at the brushes. Commutating conditions will be particularly poor at starting.

Shifting the brushes forward instead of backward will cause a reversal of torque and direction of rotation of the armature, but the direction of the resultant magnetic field continues to be clockwise. The slip of the rotor is then greater than unity, and commutation difficulties become so great as to make operation impracticable under these conditions.

This polyphase series type of motor has no commercial importance, and the only reason for considering it is that the physical relations between the stator and rotor fields, which have here been briefly noted, find more useful application in types to be described later.

15-20. The Commutated Single-phase Induction Motor. This type of motor has been discussed both in Chaps. 5 and 9, and its shunt characteristics have there been sufficiently elaborated. To complete the analysis, it is necessary to consider the commutating conditions at the two sets of brushes t, t and r, r (Fig. 9-2).

Coils short-circuited by the brushes t, t generate an emf by rotation through the transformer flux Φ_t, and at the same time there is induced in them another emf because of their linkage with the alternating speed field Φ_r. At the nearly synchronous speed which characterizes the operation of this type of motor within its normal working range, these two fluxes are nearly equal in magnitude, and they are very nearly in time quadrature. It follows, therefore, that the two coil emfs are practically equal in magnitude and opposite in phase, this conclusion being supported by the same reasoning which fixes the relative magnitudes and phase positions of the voltage phasors of Fig. 9-6; since the two coil voltages almost neutralize each other, the circulating current in the short-circuited coil will be kept within limits which can be taken care of by the brush contact resistance, and satisfactory commutation will result. Similar conditions obtain in the coils short-circuited by the brushes r, r.

15-21. The Heyland Induction Motor.* The wide popularity of the polyphase induction motor, owing to its practically constant-speed characteristic and to the simplicity and ruggedness of its construction, was alloyed in the early years following its invention by dissatisfaction with its rather poor power factor. Among the numerous attempts to correct this shortcoming, a method developed by Alexander Heyland† in 1901 presents features of sufficient technical interest to warrant a brief description, even though this type of machine is no longer in use.

Figure 15-34 shows a portion of a rotor which is provided with a squirrel-cage winding in the tops of the slots and a commutated winding in the bottoms of the slots. Brushes bearing upon the commutator are supplied with balanced polyphase current at line frequency either from an autotransformer or from taps in the stator winding. In either case, the mmf produced by these currents in the commutated winding rotates at synchronous speed around the airgap irrespective of the speed of the rotor itself, but its space phase depends upon the position of the brushes. The resultant airgap flux will then be due to the combined effect of the synchronously rotating mmfs of the stator winding, the squirrel-cage

---

* C. A. Adams, A Study of the Heyland Machine as Motor and Generator, *Trans. AIEE*, **21**:519 (1903). A. S. Langsdorf, The Heyland Induction Motor, *Jour. Assoc. Eng. Soc.*, **31**:63 (1903).

† *Elektrotech. Z.*, **32**(pt. 2):633 (1901).

winding, and the commutated winding, and since the space phase of the latter is adjustable by moving the brushes, the space phase of the resultant flux can be controlled at will.

In the Heyland motor, just as in an ordinary induction motor, the magnitude of the resultant rotating field must remain nearly constant at all loads provided the primary leakage-impedance drop is relatively small; but whereas in an ordinary motor this flux is produced by the phasor

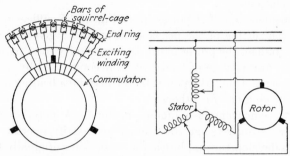

FIG. 15-34. Heyland compensated induction motor.

sum of the stator mmf and the single rotor mmf, in the Heyland motor the flux is due to the phasor sum of the primary mmf and the mmfs of the two rotor windings. Consequently, in the diagram, Fig. 15-35, the equivalent exciting current I_0 which produces the flux Φ is the resultant of (a) the rotor current I_2 in the squirrel-cage winding; (b) the rotor current I_3 in the commutated winding; and (c) the stator current I_1. It is clear from this diagram that by suitably controlling the magnitude and

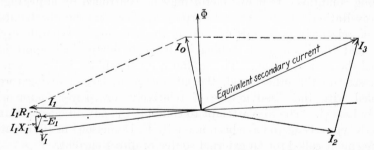

FIG. 15-35. Phasor diagram of Heyland motor.

phase of I_3 the stator current and voltage (I_1 and V_1) may be brought into phase coincidence, or the current may even be made to lead the voltage. In effect, the commutated winding of the rotor has been made to supply the excitation which in the ordinary motor must be derived from the stator alone.

The only feature of this analysis which requires comment is the apparently subtle shift of emphasis from the *space* phase of the excitation contributed by the commutated winding of Fig. 15-34 to the *time* phase of that excitation in Fig. 15-35.   In reality, there is nothing mysterious about this transition, for it is exactly the same in character as the analogous interchanges which were used in setting up the phase relations in alternators and synchronous motors where the space changes in the relative positions of stator windings and poles were reflected in corresponding time-phase changes of stator and rotor voltages and currents.   In the present case, the brush movements play a similar role in affecting time-phase relations.

A brief consideration of the diagram of Fig. 15-35 suffices to show that if, with a given setting of the brush position and a given adjustment of the exciting voltage, the power factor becomes unity for a particular load on the motor, any change of load will be accompanied by an alteration of power factor; and that the power factor may be a leading one for some loads and a lagging one for others.

15-22. The Synchronous-induction Motor.*   A polyphase induction motor having a squirrel-cage rotor must necessarily operate with some slip if it is to develop torque; but if the rotor core, originally fully cylindrical, is notched out to form the equivalent of unwound polar projections, it will lock into synchronous speed provided the load is sufficiently small.   As a matter of fact, such a motor is exactly equivalent to an unexcited synchronous motor, and the maximum power it can develop is the reluctance power discussed in Art. 11-21.   Some fan motors of small size are built on this principle; they start as induction motors, and run as unexcited synchronous motors.

The ordinary synchronous motor has the great advantage that under running conditions its power factor may be controlled by adjusting the field excitation; but for general-purpose applications the disadvantages include relatively poor starting torque, the necessity of separate excitation, and the liability of stalling if the load fluctuations appreciably exceed the normal rating.   The wound-rotor polyphase induction motor possesses, on the other hand, the advantage of large starting torque, coupled with the disadvantage of relatively low power factor when lightly loaded.   The first attempt to combine the advantageous features of both types seems to have been made by E. Danielson† in 1901, but his arrangement called for an external source of direct current.

The Fynn-Weichsel motor made by the Wagner Electric Corporation is a completely self-contained motor which starts as a wound-rotor induction motor, and when up to speed runs as a synchronous motor, therefore

---

* V. A. Fynn, A New Self-excited Synchronous-induction Motor, *Trans. AIEE*, **43**:660 (1924).   H. Weichsel, A New A-C General-purpose Motor, *Trans. AIEE*, **44**:7 (1925).   V. A. Fynn, Another New Self-excited Synchronous-induction Motor, *Trans. AIEE*, **44**:64 (1925).   J. K. Kostko, Self-excited Synchronous Motors, *Trans. AIEE*, **44**:447 (1925).

† E. Danielson, Der Asynchronmotor als Synchronmotor, *Elektrotech. Z.*, **52**:1065 (1901).

combining the characteristics of high starting torque and power-factor compensation under running conditions.

Structurally, the slotted rotor is provided with a small capacity d-c winding occupying the bottoms of the slots, this winding being equipped with a commutator and brushes in the usual manner. In the upper part of the slots, and occupying the greater part of the space is a standard polyphase winding connected to slip rings. This polyphase winding constitutes the primary circuit of the motor, and is connected directly to the supply circuit, as in Fig. 15-36.

The laminated and slotted stator carries two windings which are in space quadrature, and at the moment of starting each of them (in the case of the larger sizes) is placed in series with a resistor, as in Fig. 15-36a.

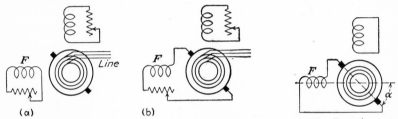

(a)   (b)

FIG. ⌊15-36. Starting connections, Fynn-Weichsel motor.   FIG. 15-37. Running connections, Fynn-Weichsel motor.

The machine is therefore in all respects a wound-rotor induction motor having a three-phase primary (on the rotor) and a two-phase secondary (on the stator), and maximum torque may be attained at starting by a suitable choice of the starting resistance. In small and moderate-sized machines, the starting connections are arranged as in Fig. 15-36b, which results in improved torque as the speed rises, because of the additional voltage injected into stator winding F; and this additional torque assists in bringing about automatic synchronization. It is readily seen that the brush voltage has the same frequency as that induced in winding F.

When synchronism is reached, the connections are changed to the form shown in Fig. 15-37. The angle α between the axes of the brushes and field winding F is less than 90°. The machine then becomes a true synchronous motor.

CHAPTER 16

THE MERCURY-ARC RECTIFIER

16-1. Basic Principles. The conversion of an alternating current to a direct current obviously requires that the rectifying device act as a valve in much the same manner as the valve mechanism of a pump converts the reciprocating effect of the piston into a unidirectional discharge. The electrical equivalent of valve action is an inherent property of rectifiers of the copper-oxide and selenium types, which are characterized by the fact that they conduct current readily in one direction, but very poorly, or not at all, in the reverse direction. Otherwise expressed, the effective resistance of such rectifiers is nonlinear, in the sense that the graph of the relation between voltage and current is not a straight line as in materials like copper and silver.

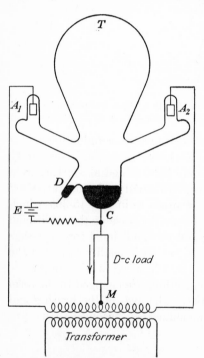

FIG. 16-1. Single-phase full-wave mercury-arc rectifier.

While it had long been known that the electric arc in general possessed nonlinear properties, it was not until 1905 that the particular characteristics of the arc in mercury vapor were applied to the conversion of single-phase alternating current to direct current in the device illustrated in Fig. 16-1. It consisted of a highly evacuated glass bulb, T, provided with a mercury-pool cathode, C, and two anodes, A_1 and A_2, made of iron or graphite. The anodes are connected to the terminals of a transformer secondary the mid-point of which is connected through the d-c load to the cathode C. On energizing the transformer with the tube in its normal vertical position, nothing happens because the potential difference between anode and cathode must clearly be less than the striking voltage which would jump a spark between them through the vacuum. In order

596

that current may flow at all, there must be a conducting bridge of mercury vapor between anode and cathode.

To initiate the operation of the rectifier, the tube T is tipped until contact is established between the mercury in the cathode pool C and in the offset arm D, thereby setting up a current from the auxiliary source E. On restoring the tube T to its normal position, the conducting bridge between C and D is broken, an arc occurs at the break, and the resultant local rise of temperature vaporizes some of the mercury and permits electrons to be emitted from the cathode and be driven by the electric field toward that one of the anodes, say, A_1, which at the moment is positive with respect to the cathode. Collisions between the electrons and the mercury-vapor molecules create positive ions which move within the tube from the anode A_1 to the cathode C, that is, in the direction opposite to the motion of the electrons. There is accordingly set up in the load circuit a current which in terms of the usual convention flows from the cathode C to M and then back to the anode A_1, which at the time is positive.

The bombardment of the mercury pool by the positive ions is in part the cause of the formation of the *cathode spot*, a restricted area of high temperature which wanders erratically over the surface, and which is responsible for the replenishment of the vapor as condensation takes place on the cooler walls of the dome-shaped bulb. The cooling effect of the tube walls must be so adjusted that the rates of evaporation and condensation steady down to equality under normal operating conditions. Overload currents of large magnitude will not cause injury provided their duration is short enough to allow the condensed mercury to trickle back to the cathode receptacle in sufficient quantity to prevent exhaustion of the supply in the cathode pool.

When the potential of anode A_1 falls to zero, the arc stream would be extinguished were it not for the fact that the current persists for a brief interval thereafter. This time lag of the current is due to the deliberately exaggerated leakage inductance of the transformer winding (or, as in some early models, to an auxiliary reactor inserted in the load circuit between points C and M). The effect of this residual current is to sustain the ionization of the vapor until the increasing positive potential of anode A_2 brings about a transfer of the electron stream from C to A_2, equivalent to a current flowing through the load from C to M and back to A_2. It will therefore be seen that the current through the load remains unidirectional as the polarities of the anodes alternate. Because of the persistence of vision, the greenish glow in both arms of the tube appears to be continuous, but by viewing the tube through a suitable stroboscopic device the successive transfers of the arc stream from one anode to the other become clearly visible.*

---

* If a 60-cycle rectifier is used, a satisfactory stroboscope can be improvised by

Continuous operation of the converter in Fig. 16-1 requires that the load be of such nature that the current through it does not fall below about 1 amp, for in that case the arc stream would be extinguished because of insufficient ionization.   To overcome this difficulty, the tube may be provided with two auxiliary anodes, A_1' and A_2', Fig. 16-2, supplied from a separate source of alternating voltage, and feeding sufficient current through an auxiliary resistor, by way of cathode C, to maintain a cathode spot if the principal load is momentarily disconnected.

The fact that the arc stream associated with one anode persists for a brief interval after the other anode becomes operative implies the possibility that the two arcs may merge, particularly because when one anode begins to conduct the other anode is strongly negative with respect

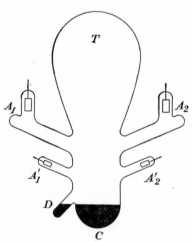

FIG. 16-2. Single-phase rectifier with auxiliary anodes.

to it.   In such a case, there would be a conducting bridge of vapor between anodes A_1 and A_2, thereby producing a short circuit of the supply transformer and a current flow of large magnitude through the tube.   Such a condition is referred to as *backfire*, or *arc back*, and must so far as possible be prevented by suitably shielding the anodes; backfires occur occasionally even in much more highly developed designs, where anode baffles and shields are always used.   Backfire was particularly objectionable in the glass-bulb rectifier because of damage to the anode seal caused by the concentration of heat, and in many cases the glass bulb was itself shattered.   Backfire may also be caused by the formation, on an anode, of a hot spot of sufficiently high temperature to liberate electrons in the same manner as at the cathode C; it is therefore necessary, in units of large capacity, to make adequate provision for cooling the anodes.

16-2. Voltage Drop in the Arc Stream.   Early experiments with the electric arc showed that in general its apparent resistance decreased with increasing current.   In the case of the mercury-vapor arc, it was found that the voltage drop between terminals remained substantially constant at about 13 to 15 volts so long as the current remained moderate, thus implying that the apparent resistance is inversely proportional to the

---

attaching a circular cardboard disk to the shaft of a small d-c motor the speed of which can be adjusted to slightly less than 1,200 rpm.   Three peepholes, 120° apart, on a circle near the edge of the disk, enable an observer to see the arc stream at slowly advancing moments in its cyclical variation.

current. Actually, however, the voltage required to maintain the arc is only in part attributable to resistance, most of it being required to overcome the counter emf due to the cloud of negatively charged electrons and positively charged mercury-vapor ions in the arc stream. Measurements of the potentials from point to point between cathode and anode show the type of distribution sketched in Fig. 16-3.

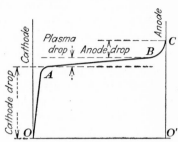

The total drop, indicated by $O'C$, consists of three clearly defined parts: (1) the *cathode drop*, from O to A, amounting to 7 to 10 volts, characterized by relatively large potential gradient, which serves to liberate electrons from the mercury pool and to accelerate them through the narrow *cathode sheath* until they attain sufficient kinetic energy to ionize

FIG. 16-3. Distribution of potential in arc stream.

the mercury vapor; (2) the *anode drop*, from B to C, through the *anode sheath*, which accounts for about 5 volts when the current reaches fairly large values; and (3) the drop in the *plasma*, characterized by a low potential gradient of 0.1 volt per cm from A to B, where the electrons

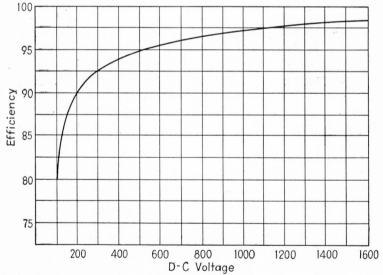

FIG. 16-4. Approximate over-all efficiency of single-anode rectifiers, 10,000 amp output.

moving toward the anode are about equal in number to the positive ions moving toward the cathode; the total drop from A to B becomes greater as the distance between cathode and anode is increased, and as baffles and shields are provided around the anodes to minimize the chance of backfire.

The total drop in the arc stream varies from a minimum of approximately 15 volts when the rectifier has a single anode, to a maximum of 25 to 30 volts when several anodes are operated in conjunction with a single cathode in one and the same tube or tank, and which for that reason requires increased arc length. The drop of voltage in the arc is a measure of the loss in the rectifier (neglecting the losses in auxiliary appliances); hence, the efficiency of conversion increases with increased system voltage. This is illustrated in Fig. 16-4.

16-3. Steel-enclosed Polyphase Rectifiers. The glass-bulb rectifier for single-phase circuits, illustrated in Figs. 16-1 and 16-2, was limited to small sizes because of its lack of mechanical strength as well as by the difficulty of dissipating its heat losses and maintaining a vacuum-tight seal at the anodes. It was therefore natural that one of the first improvements substituted a steel tank for the fragile glass bulb, and that the problems of providing permanent anode seals and protection against backfire likewise received intensive study.*

At the same time that these structural improvements were in process of development, polyphase systems for the generation and distribution of electrical energy were rapidly replacing the single-phase systems which had been in general use at the turn of the century. It was this fact which led to the development, in Europe, of steel-tank rectifiers equipped with three equally spaced anodes and a common cathode adapted for use with Y-connected secondaries of transformers supplied from a three-phase circuit, in the manner indicated in Fig. 16-5b. This arrangement has the obvious advantage that the rectified voltage wave, shown by the full line, has a greater average value, and a smaller ripple, than that of the single-phase arrangement shown in Fig. 16-5a. The extension of this idea to six-phase circuits, as in Fig. 16-5c, indicates a still further smoothing of the rectified voltage and current. Rectifiers of the multianode type have been built with 12 anodes, and in a few cases with 24, but in general the number of anodes is limited to 6 or 12.

While rectifier research and development continued steadily in Europe after 1910, very little was undertaken in the United States between 1910 and 1920. This was due in part to the distractions incident to World War I, but in larger measure because in this country attention was concentrated upon the conversion of alternating to direct current by means of the synchronous converter. Since 1920, however, the mercury-arc rectifier has received much attention, with the result that there are now extensive installations for traction purposes and for use in the electro-chemical, steelmaking, and mining industries.

---

* For a comprehensive history and description of the efforts to overcome the structural defects of the early forms of the rectifier, see O. K. Marti and H. Winograd "Mercury Arc Power Rectifiers," McGraw-Hill Book Company, Inc., New York, 1948.

16-4. Multianode and Single-anode Rectifiers. The limitations upon size and rating inherent in the original glass-bulb rectifier were overcome by the use of a steel-tank enclosure, but difficulties were initially encountered in designing vacuum-tight seals and in getting rid of occluded gas

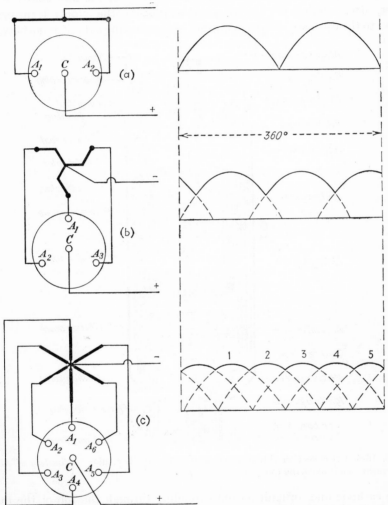

Fig. 16-5. Rectified voltage waves: (a) single-phase; (b) three-phase; (c) six-phase.

in the metal enclosure; it became necessary, therefore, to provide auxiliary pumps to maintain the vacuum. The dissipation of the heat of the arc required the use of water jackets and cooling coils, and in addition the provision of heating coils at the anodes to keep them above the condensation temperature of the mercury vapor during periods of light load. But the chief difficulty with the multianode type of construction, especially as the number of anodes became six or more, was that the arc length had to be increased in order to minimize the danger of backfire, and this in turn meant increased arc drop and reduced efficiency. Even with an elaborate system of anode baffles and shields, the possibility of backfires was not entirely overcome. Starting of the multianode rectifier, after making the electrical connections to the supply transformer and to the d-c load, was accomplished by impressing a d-c voltage between

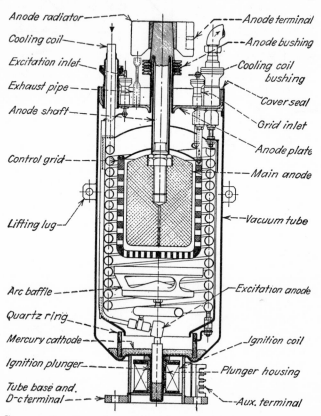

Fig. 16-6. Cross section through sealed excitron rectifier tube. (*Courtesy of Allis-Chalmers Manufacturing Company.*)

the cathode and an ignition rod extending through the top of the tank into the cathode pool, and then withdrawing the rod by means of an electromagnet (or otherwise) so as to strike an arc.

Present practice tends strongly toward the use of single-anode tanks, each with its own cathode, connected in groups of 6 or 12 for operation on a three-phase supply circuit. An important advantage of the single-anode tank is that the risk of backfire is greatly reduced; but equally or more important are the facts (1) that its arc length can be made much shorter than in a multianode converter, thereby ensuring reduced arc drop and appreciably higher efficiency; and (2) that failure of an individual tank can be simply and quickly remedied by replacing it by a spare unit, whereas the failure of a single anode in a multianode rectifier means that the entire unit must be removed from service.

Each individual tank in an assembly of single-anode tubes becomes deionized within a very short time after the end of its firing period, so that means must be provided for reigniting the arc at the instant its conducting period is due to recur, i.e., when the anode again becomes sufficiently positive. The particular point in the cycle at which the firing is initiated can be controlled by a suitable design of the firing circuit, and as will be shown later, it thus becomes possible to regulate the d-c output voltage within reasonable limits.

Single-anode rectifiers made by the Allis-Chalmers Manufacturing Company have been given the trade name of *excitron* rectifier tubes.

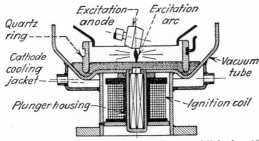

Fig. 16-7. Ignition coil energized and excitation established. (*Courtesy of Allis-Chalmers Manufacturing Company.*)

The principal construction features are shown in Fig. 16-6. The ignition device, shown in greater detail in Fig. 16-7, maintains a continuous excitation arc once the ignition coil has been energized, so that the cathode is always ready to conduct current when the anode fires. The anode is surrounded by a perforated basket-shaped grid, the positive potential of which can be so controlled (by means of a phase-control circuit independent of the cathode excitation circuit) that the anode will fire when its potential reaches the particular positive value, with respect to the cathode, at which conduction is to be initiated.

The *ignitron* rectifier, manufactured under that name by the Westinghouse Electric Corporation and by the General Electric Company, is illustrated in Figs. 16-8 and 16-9. Its distinguishing feature is the means employed for starting the arc, which depend upon the discovery* that if a rod of high resistivity, such as carborundum, is partly immersed in mercury, the passage of a current from the rod to the mercury will within a few microseconds create an arc at the junction of the rod with the surface of the mercury.

* J. Slepian and L. R. Ludwig, A New Method of Starting an Arc, *Elec. Eng.*, **52**:605 (September, 1933).

Mercury-arc rectifiers of the single-anode type can be assembled in sets of 6 or 12 tanks each, for almost any d-c voltage, though the maximum thus far found possible is about 25,000 volts.   The usual range for the electrochemical applications is from 250 to 750 volts, though for traction purposes, as in the case of the Delaware, Lackawanna, and Western

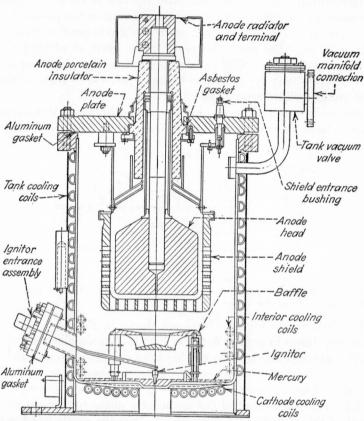

FIG. 16-8. Cross section of ignitron, showing construction.   (*Courtesy of Westinghouse Electric Corporation.*)

Railroad, the voltage is 3,000.   Individual sets with a continuous rating of 4,500 kw have been built, and assemblies of such sets have been placed in operation which deliver over 100,000 kw.

The table on page 606 has been suggested* as a rule of thumb for determining the approximate number of phases for installations of the specified kilowatts-capacity.

* W. E. Gutzwiller, The Application of Mercury Arc Rectifiers in the Electrolytic Industry, a paper presented before the AIEE Middle Eastern District Meeting, Oct. 1, 1953.

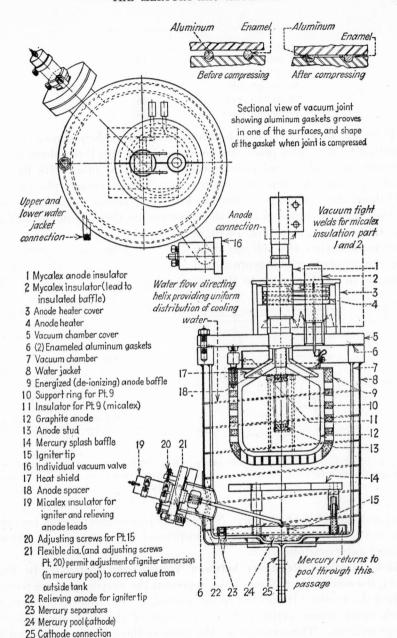

Aluminum   Enamel   Aluminum
                              Enamel
Before compressing   After compressing

Sectional view of vacuum joint
showing aluminum gaskets grooves
in one of the surfaces, and shape
of the gasket when joint is compressed

Upper and
lower water
jacket
connection

Anode
connection

Vacuum tight
welds for micalex
insulation part
1 and 2

1 Mycalex anode insulator
2 Mycalex insulator (lead to
   insulated baffle)
3 Anode heater cover
4 Anode heater
5 Vacuum chamber cover
6 (2) Enameled aluminum gaskets
7 Vacuum chamber
8 Water jacket
9 Energized (de-ionizing) anode baffle
10 Support ring for Pt. 9
11 Insulator for Pt. 9 (micalex)
12 Graphite anode
13 Anode stud
14 Mercury splash baffle
15 Igniter tip
16 Individual vacuum valve
17 Heat shield
18 Anode spacer
19 Micalex insulator for
   igniter and relieving
   anode leads
20 Adjusting screws for Pt. 15
21 Flexible dia. (and adjusting screws
   Pt. 20) permit adjustment of igniter immersion
   (in mercury pool) to correct value from
   outside tank
22 Relieving anode for igniter tip
23 Mercury separators
24 Mercury pool (cathode)
25 Cathode connection

Water flow directing
helix providing uniform
distribution of cooling
water

Mercury returns to
pool through this
passage

Fig. 16-9. Cross section of individual tank for General Electric ignitron rectifier.
(Courtesy of General Electric Company.)

Kw capacity	Number of phases
1,000– 2,000	6
2,000– 6,000	12
6,000–20,000	24
20,000–30,000	30
30,000–50,000	36
50,000 and over	48

Reference to Fig. 2-41 will show how twelve secondary phases may be obtained from a three-phase source by means of two three-phase transformers, one with its primaries connected in Δ, the other with its primaries in star. In order to obtain twenty-four secondary phases, two additional three-phase transformers, with their primaries similarly connected, may be supplied from the same source through phase-shifting autotransformers, as in Fig. 16-10, in such manner that the voltages upon these transformer primaries are shifted through 15° with respect to the pri-

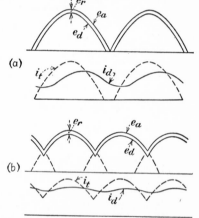

(a)

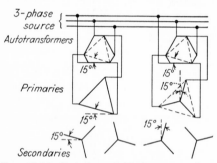

Fig. 16-10. Rotation of 12-phase secondary voltages through 15°.

(b)

Fig. 16-11. Elementary voltage and current relations. (a) Full-wave single-phase rectifiers. (b) Three-phase rectifier.

mary voltages of the first pair. Numbers of phases greater than twenty-four can be obtained by the use of additional transformers and phase-shifting autotransformers.

16-5. Idealized Relations between Voltage and Current. In Fig. 16-11, the rectified curves marked e_a represent the varying positive potentials of the anodes with respect to the neutral, (a) for the case of the two-anode single-phase rectifier; (b) for the case of the three-anode three-phase rectifier. These curves are the same as those in Fig. 16-5a and b. The d-c voltage at any instant, marked e_d in Fig. 16-11, is then equal to the difference between e_a and the nearly constant drop, e_r, in the arc stream.

If the d-c circuit were without inductance, the unidirectional current through it would be at every instant directly proportional to e_d, in which case its wave form would have the shape indicated by the dashed line marked i_t; actually, however, the leakage inductance of the transformer secondaries will round off the sharp corners and at the same time cause the alternating component to lag behind the voltage wave e_d. The effect is therefore to smooth out the d-c wave form more and more as the number of phases is increased.*

For the sake of simplicity in deriving relations between the direct and alternating currents and voltages, it is customary to assume as a first approximation that:

1. The d-c wave is a straight line.
2. The voltage drop in the arc is constant at all loads.
3. The leakage reactance of the transformer may be neglected.

Let it be further assumed that

E_a = rms value of alternating voltage to neutral of each of transformer secondary windings

E_d = average value of rectified voltage

e_r = constant drop in arc

I_a = rms value of a-c input to each anode

I_d = constant d-c output

n = number of anodes (equal to number of secondary phase windings)

Subject to these assumptions, the anodes will fire one at a time, in regular sequence, and each in turn will deliver to the load the constant current I_d during an interval of $2\pi/n$ electrical degrees. During this firing period, the voltage from anode to cathode will be represented by

$$e_a = \sqrt{2}\,E_a \cos\theta \qquad (16\text{-}1)$$

provided that the emf wave is referred to origin O in Fig. 16-12, and the d-c voltage will be

$$e_d = \sqrt{2}\,E_a \cos\theta - e_r \qquad (16\text{-}2)$$

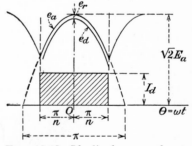

FIG. 16-12. Idealized wave shapes, n phases.

The average value of e_d between the limits $+\pi/n$ and $-\pi/n$ will then be equal to E_d; hence,

$$E_d = \frac{1}{2\pi/n} \int_{-\pi/n}^{+\pi/n} (\sqrt{2}\,E_a \cos\theta - e_r)\,d\theta$$

$$= \sqrt{2}\,E_a \frac{\sin(\pi/n)}{\pi/n} - e_r \qquad (16\text{-}3)$$

* It is important to note in passing that the return current from the d-c circuit must flow through the windings of the three-phase transformer secondaries in Fig. 16-5b and that the zigzag connection there indicated must accordingly be used.

If e_r is neglected, the ratio E_d/E_a takes the form

$$\frac{E_d}{E_a} = \sqrt{2}\,\frac{\sin{(\pi/n)}}{\pi/n} \tag{16-4}$$

and from this expression the following table may be obtained:

n	2	3	6	12	24	∞
E_d/E_a	0 9	1.17	1.35	1.40	1.41	1.414

The table shows, as might have been anticipated from Fig. 16-5, that as n is indefinitely increased the average value of the d-c voltage approaches the maximum (crest) value of the secondary a-c voltage per phase.

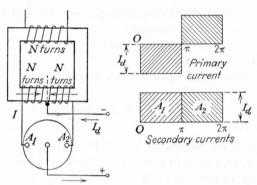

FIG. 16-13. Primary and secondary currents, two-anode single-phase rectifier.

Under the assumed conditions, the alternating current supplied to the anode has the square-shouldered wave form shown in Fig. 16-12, which persists only through the angular interval $2\pi/n$; hence, its effective value is by definition the square root of its mean squared value during a complete cycle 2π, so that

$$I_a = \sqrt{\frac{1}{2\pi}\left(\frac{2\pi}{n}\,I_d^2\right)} = \frac{1}{\sqrt{n}}\,I_d \tag{16-5}$$

16-6. Idealized D-C and A-C Power Ratings. *Case 1. Single-phase Full-wave Rectifier.* Referring to Fig. 16-13, let it be assumed that there is a 1:1 ratio between the turns of the primary of the supply transformer and the turns in each half of the secondary; also, that the magnetizing current of the transformer may be neglected. It follows that when the anode A_1 is firing, the primary current is numerically equal, and opposite in direction, to the anode current, or $I_a = I_d$. During the next half cycle, when anode A_2 is in operation, the primary current must reverse its direction in order to balance the reversed mmf of the current through anode A_2.

The primary current therefore has the square-shouldered form indicated in Fig. 16-13, and its effective value is accordingly equal to I_d. Because of the assumed 1:1 ratio of transformation, the primary voltage is equal to E_a; hence, the primary volt-ampere rating is

$$P_1 = E_a I_d \qquad (16\text{-}6)$$

The d-c power output is obviously $P_d = E_d I_d$, and if the drop in the arc is neglected, it follows from Eq. 16-3 that

$$P_d = \sqrt{2}\, E_a \frac{\sin (\pi/2)}{\pi/2} I_d = \frac{2\sqrt{2}}{\pi} E_a I_d \qquad (16\text{-}7)$$

Hence,
$$\frac{P_d}{P_1} = \frac{2\sqrt{2}}{\pi} = 0.90 \qquad (16\text{-}8)$$

is the apparent power factor.

Case 2. *Six-phase Rectifier Supplied by Three-phase Transformer Connected in* Δ*-Double Star.* Subject to the same assumptions as before, the

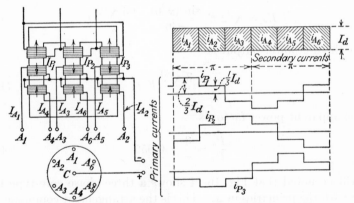

Fig. 16-14. Primary and secondary currents, six-phase rectifier.

six anode currents from the corresponding secondaries will be represented by the symbols i_{A_1}, i_{A_2}, . . . , i_{A_6}, each of which is successively equal to the d-c output current I_d, as indicated in Fig. 16-14. Since the resultant mmfs on the several legs of the transformer core must all be equal, and the number of turns is the same in all the coils,

$$i_{P_1} - i_{A_1} + i_{A_4} = i_{P_2} - i_{A_3} + i_{A_6} = i_{P_3} - i_{A_5} + i_{A_2} \qquad (16\text{-}9)$$

where i_{P_1}, i_{P_2}, and i_{P_3} are the corresponding instantaneous values of the currents in the primary windings. But since the primary windings form a three-phase Δ circuit, the sum of the instantaneous primary currents must be zero at all times; hence,

$$i_{P_1} + i_{P_2} + i_{P_3} = 0 \qquad (16\text{-}10)$$

The simultaneous solution of Eqs. 16-9 and 16-10 yields the relations

$$i_{P_1} = \tfrac{2}{3}i_{A_1} + \tfrac{1}{3}i_{A_2} - \tfrac{1}{3}i_{A_3} - \tfrac{2}{3}i_{A_4} - \tfrac{1}{3}i_{A_5} + \tfrac{1}{3}i_{A_6}$$
$$i_{P_2} = -\tfrac{1}{3}i_{A_1} + \tfrac{1}{3}i_{A_2} + \tfrac{2}{3}i_{A_3} + \tfrac{1}{3}i_{A_4} - \tfrac{1}{3}i_{A_5} - \tfrac{2}{3}i_{A_6} \quad (16\text{-}11)$$
$$i_{P_3} = -\tfrac{1}{3}i_{A_1} - \tfrac{2}{3}i_{A_2} - \tfrac{1}{3}i_{A_3} + \tfrac{1}{3}i_{A_4} + \tfrac{2}{3}i_{A_5} + \tfrac{1}{3}i_{A_6}$$

which, when plotted as in Fig. 16-14, give the stepped wave forms which show a three-phase relationship, and likewise the presence of harmonics.

The effective or rms value of the primary current is the square root of the average squared values in the angular interval π, and is given by

$$I_1 = \sqrt{\frac{1}{\pi}\left[\frac{\pi}{3}\left(\frac{2}{3}I_d\right)^2 + \frac{\pi}{3}\left(\frac{1}{3}I_d\right)^2 + \frac{\pi}{3}\left(\frac{1}{3}I_d\right)^2\right]} = \frac{\sqrt{2}}{3}I_d \quad (16\text{-}12)$$

Hence, the total primary input is

$$P_1 = 3E_aI_1 = \sqrt{2}\,E_aI_d \tag{16-13}$$

The average d-c voltage, by Eq. 16-3, is

$$E_d = \sqrt{2}\,E_a\frac{\sin(\pi/6)}{\pi/6} = \frac{3\sqrt{2}}{\pi}E_a \tag{16-14}$$

so that the d-c power output is

$$P_d = \frac{3\sqrt{2}}{\pi}E_aI_d \tag{16-15}$$

and the apparent power factor is

$$\frac{P_d}{P_1} = \frac{3}{\pi} = 0.955 \tag{16-16}$$

It will be noted that Fig. 16-14 shows a three-phase core-type transformer with the primaries in Δ. This is the arrangement commonly used when a single transformer is used to obtain the six secondary phases, for it avoids the disturbing effect of a possible d-c component superposed upon the normal a-c component in each of the secondary windings. If there is such a d-c component exerting an mmf in each leg of the core, it would be represented by an additional term in each of the three expressions in Eq. 16-9, but the equalities there indicated would remain in effect with the core-type assembly, and these residual terms would accordingly cancel out. This would not be the case if three single-phase transformers, or a three-phase shell-type transformer, were used; hence, these latter combinations must not be used, for the resultant d-c excitation would introduce objectionable bias into the core magnetization.

16-7. The Effect of Transformer Inductance. Since the transformer windings possess inductance, the current at an anode cannot instantly increase from zero to the full value I_d, nor can it suddenly decrease to

zero when the next anode becomes operative.   There is accordingly a
period of overlap, the duration of which is indicated in Fig. 16-15a by the
angle φ, during which the first anode is carrying the decreasing current
i_1 while the second anode is carrying the increasing current i_2, as sketched
in Fig. 16-15b.

For purposes of analysis, it will be assumed that the total inductance
in the d-c circuit is sufficiently large to justify the approximation that

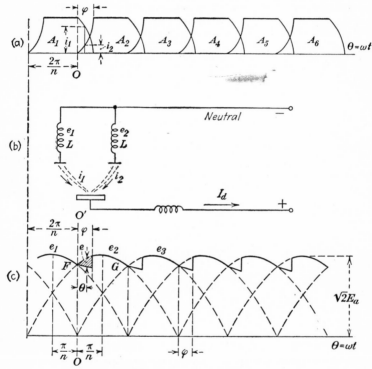

Fig. 16-15. Effect of overlap upon d-c voltage.

the load current I_d remains constant; in other words,

$$i_1 + i_2 = I_d = \text{constant} \tag{16-17}$$

The transformer secondary voltage waves which correspond to the
anode current waves A_1, A_2, A_3, . . . , are shown in Fig. 16-15c as e_1,
e_2, e_3, . . . ; but because of the overlap of the currents the d-c voltage,
during the overlap period φ, may be taken to be the average of the corresponding instantaneous values of e_1 and e_2 (provided the arc drop is
neglected), and similarly as successive anodes take over.   The resultant
d-c voltage therefore takes the saw-tooth form shown by the heavy line.

In order to determine i_1 and i_2 as functions of time, it will be observed
from Fig. 16-15b that since the two branches simultaneously in operation are in parallel, the difference of potential between the transformer

neutral and the cathode must be the same for each of them. Accordingly, if the resistance of the transformer windings is neglected,

$$e_1 - L \frac{di_1}{dt} - e_r = e_2 - L \frac{di_2}{dt} - e_r \qquad (16\text{-}18)$$

from which

$$e_1 - e_2 = L \left(\frac{di_1}{dt} - \frac{di_2}{dt} \right) \qquad (16\text{-}19)$$

But from Fig. 16-15c it will be seen that the emf waves e_1 and e_2, referred to an origin in axis OO', are represented by

$$e_1 = \sqrt{2}\, E_a \cos \left(\omega t + \frac{\pi}{n} \right)$$
$$e_2 = \sqrt{2}\, E_a \cos \left(\omega t - \frac{\pi}{n} \right) \qquad (16\text{-}20)$$

so that from Eq. 16-19

$$L \left(\frac{di_1}{dt} - \frac{di_2}{dt} \right) = -2 \sqrt{2}\, E_a \sin \frac{\pi}{n} \sin \omega t \qquad (16\text{-}21)$$

From Eq. 16-17,

$$\frac{di_1}{dt} + \frac{di_2}{dt} = 0 \qquad (16\text{-}22)$$

Hence, by combining Eqs. 16-21 and 16-22,

$$\frac{di_2}{dt} = \frac{\sqrt{2}\, E_a}{L} \sin \frac{\pi}{n} \sin \omega t$$

and therefore

$$i_2 = \int_0^{i_2} di_2 = \frac{\sqrt{2}\, E_a}{L} \sin \frac{\pi}{n} \int_0^t \sin \omega t \, dt$$

$$= \left(\frac{\sqrt{2}\, E_a}{\omega L} \sin \frac{\pi}{n} \right) (1 - \cos \omega t) \qquad (16\text{-}23)$$

and

$$i_1 = I_d - \left(\frac{\sqrt{2}\, E_a}{\omega L} \sin \frac{\pi}{n} \right) (1 - \cos \omega t)$$

The last two equations for i_1 and i_2 can be simplified by observing from Fig. 16-15a that when $\omega t = \varphi$, $i_1 = 0$, so that

$$1 - \cos \varphi = \frac{I_d \omega L}{\sqrt{2}\, E_a \sin (\pi/n)} \qquad (16\text{-}24)$$

or

$$\frac{\sqrt{2}\, E_a \sin (\pi/n)}{\omega L} = \frac{I_d}{1 - \cos \varphi} \qquad (16\text{-}25)$$

and when this relation is substituted in Eq. 16-23, the result is

$$i_1 = I_d \left(1 - \frac{1 - \cos \omega t}{1 - \cos \varphi} \right)$$
$$i_2 = I_d \frac{1 - \cos \omega t}{1 - \cos \varphi} \qquad (16\text{-}26)$$

The effect of the overlap is to reduce the average d-c voltage by an amount proportional to the area of the crosshatched triangular figure in Fig. 16-15c. Thus, the area under curve e_2 between the points F and G, divided by the base $2\pi/n$, would be the average d-c voltage if there were no overlap, and if the arc drop is neglected, this is equal to $\sqrt{2}\,E_a\dfrac{\sin\,(\pi/n)}{\pi/n}$ as given by Eq. 16-3. From this value must be subtracted an amount e_φ equal to the crosshatched area divided by $2\pi/n$; hence, if curves e_1 and e_2 are referred to origin O, the ordinate e at a point $\theta°$ to the right of the origin is

$$e = e_2 - \tfrac{1}{2}(e_1 + e_2) = \tfrac{1}{2}(e_2 - e_1)$$

and

$$e_\varphi = \frac{1}{2\pi/n}\int_0^\varphi e\,d\theta$$

But we have

$$e_1 = \sqrt{2}\,E_a\,\cos\left(\theta + \frac{\pi}{n}\right)$$

$$e_2 = \sqrt{2}\,E_a\,\cos\left(\theta - \frac{\pi}{n}\right)$$

whence

$$e = \sqrt{2}\,E_a\,\sin\frac{\pi}{n}\,\sin\,\theta$$

and

$$e_\varphi = \frac{E_a}{\sqrt{2}}\frac{\sin\,(\pi/n)}{\pi/n}\int_0^\varphi \sin\,\theta\,d\theta = \frac{E_a}{2}\,(1 - \cos\,\varphi) \qquad (16\text{-}27)$$

The net average value of E_d is therefore

$$(E_d)_{\text{net}} = E_d - E_d\frac{1 - \cos\,\varphi}{2} = \sqrt{2}\,E_a\frac{\sin\,(\pi/n)}{\pi/n}\left(1 - \frac{1 - \cos\,\varphi}{2}\right)$$
$$(16\text{-}28)$$

and since Eq. 16-25 shows that

$$1 - \cos\,\varphi = \frac{\omega L I_d}{\sqrt{2}\,E_a\,\sin\,(\pi/n)}$$

Eq. 16-28 can be written

$$(E_d)_{\text{net}} = \sqrt{2}\,E_a\frac{\sin\,(\pi/n)}{\pi/n} - \frac{n\omega L}{2\pi}\,I_d \qquad (16\text{-}29)$$

thereby showing that the d-c voltage decreases linearly as the load current increases, and that the decrease becomes greater in direct proportion to the number of anodes, n. In the absence of voltage-regulating devices, the drop in the d-c output voltage is usually 5 to 7 per cent of rated value, provided that the a-c supply voltage is kept constant.

The overlap likewise affects the magnitude of the effective (rms) anode current, which in terms of the symbols in Fig. 16-15a is given by

$$I_a = \sqrt{\frac{1}{2\pi}\left(\int_0^\varphi i_2^2\,d\theta + \int_\varphi^{2\pi/n} I_d^2\,d\theta + \int_0^\varphi i_1^2\,d\theta\right)} \qquad (16\text{-}30)$$

Substituting the values of i_1 and i_2 from Eq. 16-26 (where $\omega t = \theta$), the result is

$$I_a = \frac{I_d}{\sqrt{n}}\sqrt{1 - n\frac{(2 + \cos\varphi)\sin\varphi - (1 + 2\cos\varphi)\varphi}{2\pi(1 - \cos\varphi)^2}} \qquad (16\text{-}31)$$

On substituting in Eq. 16-31 the expanded values of $\sin\varphi$ and $\cos\varphi$ as determined by Maclaurin's theorem, it is found that

$$I_a = \frac{I_d}{\sqrt{n}}\sqrt{1 - n\frac{2\varphi}{15\pi}\left(1 + \frac{\varphi^2}{84} + \cdots\right)} \qquad (16\text{-}32)$$

where the angle of overlap is expressed in electrical radians. The resultant current is less than the idealized value determined by Eq. 16-5, and the reduction becomes greater as n and φ are increased.

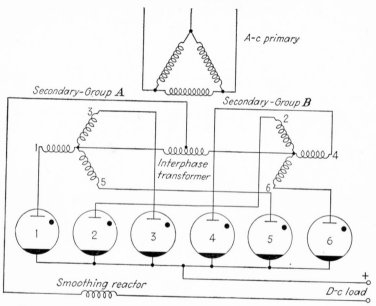

FIG. 16-16. Δ to double-star connection with interphase transformer.

16-8. Interphase Transformer. Figure 16-16 illustrates the most widely used arrangement for rectifiers operating with six-phase secondaries supplied from a three-phase source. It differs from the double-star connection diagram shown in Figs. 16-5 and 16-14 in that the common junctions of the two sets of secondaries, instead of being directly connected, are tied together through the center-tapped *interphase transformer*, which is actually a reactor or autotransformer.

Whereas the direct connection of the two neutrals, as in Fig. 16-14, causes the six anodes to fire in sequence, each for one-sixth of a cycle (neglecting overlap), the effect of the interphase transformer in Fig. 16-16 is to establish a parallel connection between, say, a secondary such as winding 2 in group B, first with winding 1, then with winding 3, of group A, and similarly thereafter with other combinations. The result of this paralleling is that two anodes are always simultaneously in operation, instead of only one as in Figs. 16-5 and 16-14, and the duration of the current flow from each anode is at the same time increased from one-sixth to one-third of a cycle, as indicated in the idealized diagram of Fig. 16-17. The d-c voltage is therefore represented by the heavy line in Fig. 16-17, its value at any instant (neglecting the arc drop) being the average of the corresponding instantaneous values of the two alternating voltages which are at the moment in parallel through the interphase transformer.

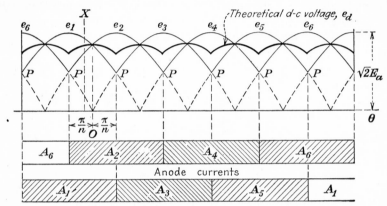

FIG. 16-17. Idealized voltages and currents in Fig. 16-16.

The average value of the d-c voltage, which is shown as the heavy line in Fig. 16-17, may therefore be obtained by finding the average ordinate of one loop of the curve between the limits $-\pi/n$ and $+\pi/n$ on either side of the origin marked O in Fig. 16-17. The equation giving the instantaneous value of e_d is

$$e_d = \frac{1}{2}\left[\sqrt{2}\,E_a \cos\left(\theta + \frac{\pi}{n}\right) + \sqrt{2}\,E_a \cos\left(\theta - \frac{\pi}{n}\right)\right]$$

$$= \sqrt{2}\,E_a \cos\left(\frac{\pi}{n}\right)\cos\theta$$

so that $\qquad E_d = \dfrac{1}{2\pi/n}\displaystyle\int_{-\pi/n}^{+\pi/n} e_d\,d\theta = \sqrt{2}\,E_a\,\dfrac{\sin(\pi/n)}{\pi/n}\cos\dfrac{\pi}{n}$ $\qquad$ (16-33)

which is less than the value given by Eq. 16-4 by the factor $\cos(\pi/n)$. When $n = 6$, as in the diagram, this factor is 0.866.

The operation of the interphase transformer is explained in an ingenious manner in the book entitled "Applied Electronics"* in somewhat the following manner:

* Written by members of the staff of the Department of Electrical Engineering, Massachusetts Institute of Technology (John Wiley & Sons, Inc., New York,

In Fig. 16-18, let the two sets of phasors, E_1, E_3, E_5, and E_2, E_4, E_6, each rotating at synchronous speed about the centers O and O', represent the spokes of rimless wheels the centers of which are connected by the rigid bar OO'. Let the motions of the two wheels be so constrained that the terminal points P and Q of two of the spokes are in contact with a fixed guide XY, which likewise represents the assumed fixed potential of the cathodes in Fig. 16-16. If E_1, E_2, . . . , E_6 represent the maximum values of the secondary voltages, the projections marked e_1 and e_2 in Fig. 16-18 then represent the instantaneous differences of potential between the cathode and the corresponding anodes. The rigid bar OO' is the analogue of the interphase transformer, and the perpendicular distance e_d from its mid-point to the reference line XY then represents the d-c voltage. It is obvious that in the mechanical model the axes O and O' will move up and down, and also to and fro, and that the magnitude of e_d will pulsate accordingly. The vertical displacement between O and O' will be a measure of the difference of potential between the two trans-

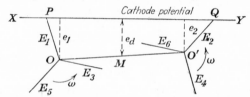

FIG. 16-18. Model of voltage phasors in Fig. 16-16.

former neutrals, and therefore of the voltage impressed upon the interphase transformer.

At the particular instant when voltages e_1 and e_2 in Fig. 16-18 have the indicated values, the conditions correspond to those shown at ordinate X in Fig. 16-17. The difference of potential between the neutrals O and O' in Fig. 16-18 magnetizes the interphase transformer in such manner that the induced emf opposes the impressed voltage, thereby opposing the voltage of anode A_1, and aiding that of anode A_2, thus tending to equalize the potentials of O and O' so that the two anodes are effectively in parallel.

Inspection of the curve showing the variation of e_d in Fig. 16-17 indicates that in each half cycle of the impressed alternating voltage there are three maximum and three minimum values of e_d, which implies that the voltage impressed upon the interphase transformer has a frequency triple that of the supply source.

16-9. Phase Control of D-C Voltage. Effect of Delayed Firing. Figure 16-17 was constructed by assuming that the anode currents do

1943). For details of this reference, see pp. 365–367, where it is stated that the elements of the explanation were suggested by Mr. B. D. Bedford of the General Electric Company.

not overlap, and that the initiation and termination of the firing periods occur at the points marked P in that illustration. It is possible, however, by means of auxiliary circuits, to delay the point in the cycle at which a tube is fired. In the case of the ignitron rectifier, this is accomplished by energizing the igniter at an adjustable interval later than that corresponding to point P; and in the case of the excitron rectifier, the same result can be obtained by adjusting the bias of the anode grid.

In either case, the effect upon the d-c voltage is shown in Fig. 16-19, where point P corresponds to the phase angle $\theta = 0$ at which voltage e_2 would normally become operative. Let it now be assumed that the firing of anode A_2 is delayed by the angular interval α, and that because of the transformer inductance the current through A_2 does not attain its full value until after a further period of overlap, indicated by φ.

It is then evident from inspection of Fig. 16-19 that within the angular interval α the d-c voltage (neglecting the arc drop) is the average of voltages e_6 and e_1, that is, it is $\frac{1}{2}(e_6 + e_1)$, which is the same condition that prevails just before $\theta = 0$. It is also seen that within the period of overlap (φ), anodes A_6 and A_2 are in parallel, their resultant voltage being $\frac{1}{2}(e_6 + e_2)$; but at the same time anode A_1 is in parallel with them, and so the resultant d-c voltage is the average of e_1 and of $\frac{1}{2}(e_6 + e_2)$, i.e., it is equal to $\frac{1}{2}[e_1 + \frac{1}{2}(e_6 + e_2)]$. Thereafter, and until anode A_3 is activated, the d-c voltage is the average of e_1 and e_2.

The average value of the resultant d-c voltage will therefore be given by the average ordinate of the crosshatched area in Fig. 16-19, or

$$E_d = \frac{1}{2\pi/n} \left\{ \int_\alpha^{\alpha+\varphi} \frac{1}{2} \left[e_1 + \frac{1}{2}(e_6 + e_2) \right] d\theta + \int_{\alpha+\varphi}^{2\pi/n+\alpha} \frac{1}{2}(e_1 + e_2)\, d\theta \right\}$$

$$(16\text{-}34)$$

Since

$$e_1 = \sqrt{2}\, E_a \cos \theta$$
$$e_2 = \sqrt{2}\, E_a \cos (\theta - 2\pi/n)$$
$$e_6 = \sqrt{2}\, E_a \cos (\theta + 2\pi/n)$$

it is readily found that on substituting these values in Eq. 16-34 and performing the indicated operations the result is

$$E_d = \frac{E_a}{\sqrt{2}} \frac{\sin (2\pi/n)}{2\pi/n} [\cos \alpha + \cos (\alpha + \varphi)]$$

$$= \sqrt{2}\, E_a \frac{\sin (2\pi/n)}{2\pi/n} \cos \frac{\varphi}{2} \cos \left(\alpha + \frac{\varphi}{2} \right) \qquad (16\text{-}35)$$

It will be noted that if α and φ are both zero, i.e., if there is no overlap and no time delay, Eq. 16-35 becomes the same as Eq. 16-33.

Example. If $\varphi = 20°$ and $\alpha = 30°$,

$$\cos \frac{\varphi}{2} \cos \left(\frac{\varphi}{2} + \alpha \right) = \cos 10° \times \cos 40° = 0.754$$

whereas if $\alpha = 0$,

$$\cos \frac{\varphi}{2} \cos \left(\frac{\varphi}{2} + \alpha\right) = \cos^2 10° = 0.970$$

so that the effect of phase control is in this case to reduce the d-c voltage to $(0.754/0.970) \times 100 = 77.7$ per cent of the value it would have in the absence of phase control.

Equation 16-35 shows furthermore that if $(\varphi/2) + \alpha$ exceeds 90°, the value of E_d becomes negative, but the significance of this fact will be considered in detail in Art. 16-11.

Since the d-c terminal voltage decreases linearly with increasing load, as shown by Eq. 16-29, it follows that if the angle of delay, α, is decreased as the load increases, the voltage regulation can be so controlled, either by manual or by automatic means, as to hold the output voltage constant.

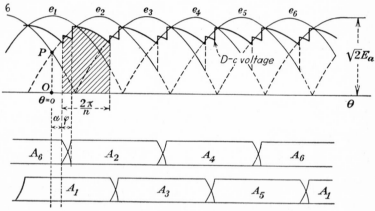

Fig. 16-19. Combined effect of phase control and overlap.

16-10. Regulation of D-C Voltage. Since the output (d-c) voltage of a rectifier bears a definite relation to the alternating voltage impressed upon the anodes, it is obvious that changes in the former can be made by a proportional change in the latter. The alternating voltage can be raised or lowered by means of tap changers in the primaries of the supply transformers, or by means of an induction regulator. It is also possible to insert saturable reactors in the leads to the anodes in such manner that a variable d-c excitation superimposed upon the a-c excitation will change the inductance and thereby affect both the period of overlap and the voltage drop which appears in Eq. 16-29.

Present practice is, however, based upon the fact that the desired regulation can be most economically obtained by varying the time delay in the firing point of the anodes, as illustrated in Fig. 16-19 and indicated in analytical form in Eq. 16-35. Two of the methods commonly employed in this country are described in the following paragraphs.

In the excitron type of rectifier, an anode will not become conducting if there is applied to its control grid a potential that is negative with respect to the cathode, even though the anode potential is at the time more highly positive than that of others in the same group of tubes; but if the potential of the grid is made sufficiently positive, it will enable its anode to become conducting at any moment in the cycle when the anode potential is higher than that of other anodes which are permitted to conduct because of their grid potentials. When an arc has thus been established, the grid has no further control, and the anode will continue to

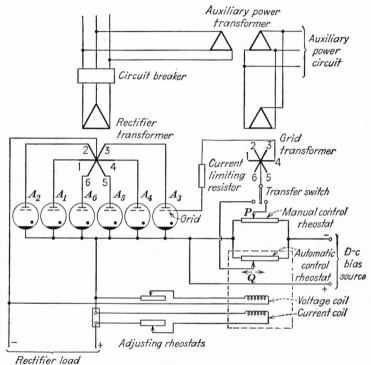

Fig. 16-20. Grid bias control of six-tube excitron rectifier.

conduct until the next anode in the phase sequence takes over because of its higher positive potential. Otherwise stated, the grid takes control only during the nonconducting part of the anode cycle. The grid can only delay the instant at which the anode becomes conducting, but it cannot advance the point of pickup ahead of its normal position (point P in Fig. 16-19).

Figure 16-20* illustrates one of several possible methods for controlling the instant when the grid potential is changed from negative to positive. The potential of the neutral of the grid transformer can be

* Based upon diagrams in *Bull.* 12S6436 and 12X7894, published by the Allis-Chalmers Manufacturing Company.

biased, either by manual manipulation of the contact P of the manually operated potentiometer rheostat or by the automatic setting of point Q, the movement of which is controlled by an electromagnetic device which responds to changes in the output voltage and current. The original patents for this arrangement were issued to the Brown-Boveri Company of Switzerland.

In the case of the ignitron rectifier, the instant of firing can be controlled in several ways. One simple method utilizes a small thyratron tube between the anode and the igniter electrode; the thyratron may be made conducting at the desired moment by adjusting the phase of its grid voltage in accordance with the same general principle described in connection with Fig. 16-20. The principal objection to this method is the necessity of making tube renewals in case of failure of the thyratron.

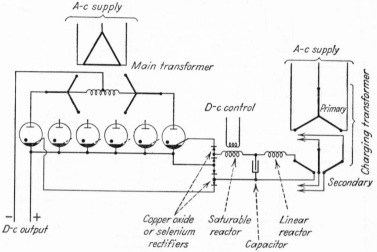

FIG. 16-21. Ignitron ignition circuit.

A firing circuit which utilizes purely electromagnetic devices* is illustrated in Fig. 16-21. An auxiliary charging transformer, supplied by the same source to which the main rectifier is connected, is phased out so that its secondary voltages are 30° behind those of the main transformer secondaries. These auxiliary voltages are applied to special firing circuits, one for each of the three phases; they serve to charge a capacitor through a linear reactor, i.e., one which has substantially constant reactance throughout its normal operating range, and which controls the rate at which the capacitor charges. The capacitor voltage is impressed alternately upon two circuits which include, in series, copper-oxide or selenium rectifiers, an igniter rod, and a saturable reactor. The latter has a core of highly permeable material, such as Hypernik,† the magnetiza-

* *Bull.* B-3024-A, Westinghouse Electric Corporation.
† Developed by the Westinghouse Electric Corporation.

tion curve of which is a straight line until saturation is reached, after which it flattens off with no material further increase of flux. The result is that on reaching the saturation point the inductance of the reactor decreases sharply, thereby permitting the capacitor to discharge a pulse of current through the igniter and so establish a cathode spot. The moment at which saturation is reached is controlled by the d-c biasing current, which can be adjusted either manually or automatically by means similar to those previously explained.

16-11. The Mercury-arc Inverter and Frequency Changer. The basic fact upon which the operation of the rectifier depends is that electrons must first be liberated at the cathode spot, thereby ionizing the mercury vapor and imparting to it the conductivity necessary for the flow of current (in the conventional sense) from the anode to the cathode within the tube or tank. The application of this fact to the case of normal conversion from alternating to direct current means that the flow of energy

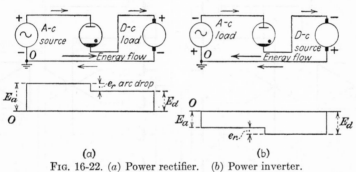

Fig. 16-22. (a) Power rectifier. (b) Power inverter.

is from the a-c source to the d-c load, as in the upper part of Fig. 16-22a; assuming that the potential of point O is arbitrarily taken as zero, the distribution of potential through the circuit, while conduction is taking place, will then have the form shown in the lower part of the diagram.

The same basic fact implies that energy may be made to flow from a d-c source to an a-c load, as in the upper part of Fig. 16-22b, provided only that the polarities of source and load are the reverse of those shown in Fig. 16-22a, but with the direction of current flow remaining the same as before. It will be noted that in case (a) $E_a > E_d$, while in case (b) $E_a < E_d$; but in both cases the anode is more positive than the cathode.

Figure 16-22 is diagrammatic only, for in practice 6 or 12 tubes of such a *power inverter* would be connected to the multiphase windings of a transformer in the same general manner as has already been described in connection with the power rectifier. The essential difference between the rectifier and the inverter* is that in a power rectifier the tubes conduct

* Harold Winograd, Electronic Frequency Changer Used as Nonsynchronous Tie between A-C Power Systems, *Trans. AIEE* (Communications and Electronics) **7**:263 (July, 1953).

during the positive half cycles of their phase voltages, so that the average
d-c voltage is positive and in the same direction as the current, whereas
in a power inverter the tubes conduct during the negative half cycles of
their phase voltages, so that the average d-c voltage is negative and
opposite to the direction of the current.

The application of these fundamental considerations is illustrated in
Fig. 16-23, which shows in elementary form a six-phase star-connected
rectifier supplying a six-phase star-connected inverter. In this form, the
combination will function as a frequency converter, for the frequency of
the output circuit may, by the use of suitable controls, be made to have
any desired value, either higher or lower than the frequency of the supply circuit. Moreover, the combined units may be made to transfer
energy in either direction by interchanging the roles of rectifier and

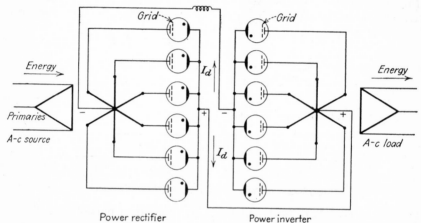

FIG. 16-23. Rectifier and inverter connected as frequency changer.

inverter. In actual practice, the connections of both the rectifier and
inverter include interphase transformers, as in Fig. 16-16, in order to
obtain the benefit of the doubled conducting period of the anodes.

It will be readily understood, however, that if the anodes and control
grids of an inverter were connected to a *passive* a-c network there would
be nothing to fix the frequency of its output. It is therefore necessary
that the receiver circuit of the inverter include the equivalent of synchronous generators the frequency of which is the same as that of the desired
inverter output. Moreover, since the d-c input to the inverter cannot
supply the reactive power normally associated with an a-c network, the
receiver circuit must include a synchronous machine, floating on the line,
the excitation of which can be adjusted to supply the reactive component
of the load current.

It will be apparent, therefore, that the combination of a rectifier and
an inverter will serve as a nonsynchronous tie between two a-c systems

having different frequencies, even though these frequencies are themselves subject to variations from their nominal values. Two units of this type, each having a rating of 8,000 kw, and with a combined 2-hr rating of 20,000 kw, were installed in 1948 and 1949 as a tie between 60-cycle and 25-cycle systems supplying the Gary Sheet and Tin Mill of the United States Steel Corporation.* It is interesting to compare this installation with the elaborate set of rotating machines described in Art. 14-5 and illustrated in Fig. 14-3.

More recently, the Swedish State Power Board has installed mercury-arc equipment having a capacity of 20,000 kw to serve as a tie between the three-phase 132-kv network in southern Sweden and the 33-kv primary distribution system on the island of Gotland in the Baltic Sea.†

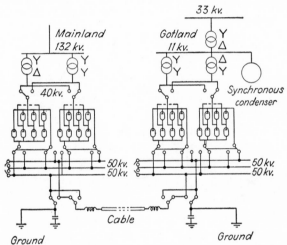

Fig. 16-24. Connection diagram, 100-kv d-c transmission.

The rectifier station near the city of Västervik on the mainland converts the a-c supply to direct current at 100 kv, which is fed into a single-conductor submarine cable extending 60 miles to a point near the town of Visby on the island of Gotland. The d-c return circuit is through the ground and sea water by way of two electrode stations near the cable terminals, but in order to prevent the return current from following the cable armor and thereby causing corrosion, the grounded electrodes are located more than 6 miles south of the cable.

Figure 16-24 is a diagram of the principal connections of this Swedish installation. At the mainland, the incoming 132-kv voltage is stepped down by two three-phase transformers to an intermediate voltage of

---

* See footnote, p. 621.

† B. G. Rathsman, 100-kv Direct-current Circuit Completed in Sweden, *Elec. Light and Power*, Mar. 25, 1954, p. 74.

about 40 kv which is fed into each of the two series-connected valve sets. The latter each delivers direct current at 50 kv, or 100 kv total, to the cable. At the Visby station, the valves, acting as inverters, deliver three-phase alternating voltage at 11 kv, which is stepped up to 33 kv. The reason for the relatively low intermediate voltage of 11 kv is the necessity of inserting a 30,000-kva synchronous condenser at the Visby station to supply the reactive power required by the Gotland network, and to assist in the conversion of the direct current to alternating current at the proper frequency.

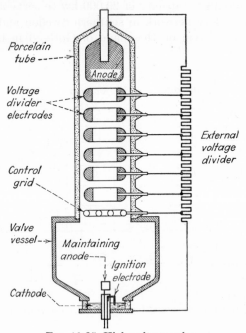

Fig. 16-25. High-voltage valve.

It will be seen that Fig. 16-24 shows an extra, or seventh, tube in each of the valve sets. Under normal conditions, only six tubes conduct current, and the seventh comes into operation only in case of faults in any of the others. Thus, if a backfire and a resultant partial short circuit occur, provision is made for blocking the six valves by means of their control grids, whereupon the extra valve momentarily opens a parallel path for the current; this cuts off the current from the affected six-valve group and provides an opportunity for them to regain their working capacity. Shortly thereafter, the six valves are unblocked, and normal operation is resumed after a total interval of less than ½ sec.

The construction of the individual tubes is indicated in Fig. 16-25. Because of the high voltage per tube, approximately 25,000 volts, special precautions are required to ensure proper distribution of potential in the arc stream, and this is accomplished by the voltage dividers indicated in the diagram.

In conclusion, it is of interest to examine in somewhat more detail the transition from rectification to inversion by means of phase control of the grids. For the sake of simplicity, it will be assumed that the phase voltages are those of the six-phase star-connected unit shown in Fig. 16-23. In such a circuit, each anode conducts for one-sixth of a cycle, and it will be further assumed that there is no overlap.

Referring to Fig. 16-26, part a represents the conditions in a rectifier with zero time delay, where each anode in turn begins to conduct when its potential exceeds that of its predecessor; anode 1, for example, takes over at point P, and similarly for each of the others, the result being that the d-c voltage (neglecting the arc drop) has the average value E_{d_0}.

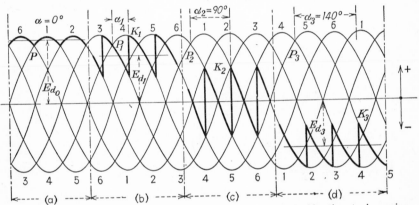

FIG. 16-26. Effect of phase control upon transition from rectification to inversion.

In part b of the diagram, the firing point of each anode, No. 4 for example, is delayed by an angle $\alpha_1 < 90°$, from point P_1 to point K_1 of the cycle, the result being that the average d-c voltage is reduced to the value indicated by E_{d_1}; but the anodes continue to fire on the positive half cycle of the alternating voltage, and the d-c voltage likewise remains positive.

In part c, the angle of delay is 90°, so that the firing point of anode 1, instead of occurring at point P_2, is shifted to point K_2. The d-c voltage then becomes alternately equally positive and negative, with an average value equal to zero. It is assumed that the circuit contains sufficient inductance to maintain the direct current at a constant value.

In part d, the angle of delay is increased to $\alpha_3 = 140°$, so that anode 5, for example, instead of firing at point P_3, as in case a, begins to conduct at point K_3 on the negative half wave. The average d-c voltage become E_{d_3}, and is also negative; hence, part d is characteristic of operation as an inverter.

PROBLEMS

Chapter 1

1-1. The magnetic circuit of a 5,000-kva 60-cycle 60,000/30,000-volt transformer has a mean length of 350 cm and a gross cross section of 3,200 sq cm. The core, made of U.S.S. Transformer 52, 29 gage, has a stacking factor of 0.9. With rated voltage impressed upon the primary, the unloaded transformer takes 30 kva from the supply circuit. Neglecting the no-load copper loss, and assuming that there are no airgaps in the joints of the core, find (*a*) the maximum flux density in the core; (*b*) the number of turns in the primary and secondary windings.

1-2. Figure P1-1 shows the core dimensions of a 60-cycle single-phase shell-type transformer rated at 3,300 kva, 33,000/6,600 volts. The core is built of U.S.S. Transformer 52, 29 gage. The H.T. winding has 440 turns. Assuming that the primary induced emf may be taken as 33,000 volts, determine (*a*) the maximum flux density,

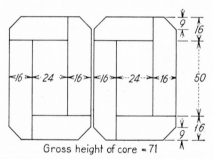

Gross height of core = 71

Fig. P1-1. Core dimensions in centimeters.

assuming that the stacking factor is 0.9 and that the joints in the laminations are equivalent to an airgap of 0.5 mm at each corner; (*b*) the magnetizing component of the no-load current; (*c*) the core loss and the core-loss component of the no-load current.

1-3. The primary leakage reactance of the transformer of Prob. 1-2 is 13.2 ohms, and the primary resistance is 1.65 ohms. (*a*) Compute the primary impressed voltage in order that the secondary terminal voltage may be 6,600 volts at no load; (*b*) construct the corresponding phasor diagram, and label the numerical magnitude of each phasor.

1-4. A 5-kva 60-cycle single-phase distribution transformer is rated at 2,300/230 volts. The no-load iron loss is 40 watts, and the no-load current is 0.3 amp. The a-c resistance of the primary is 5 ohms, and the primary leakage reactance is 25 ohms. Determine (*a*) the no-load power factor; (*b*) the no-load secondary voltage if the primary impressed voltage is 2,300; (*c*) the corresponding phasor diagram, indicating the numerical magnitude of each phasor.

1-5. A 60-cycle core-type transformer rated at 100 kva, 4,400/220 volts, has the following constants: $R_1 = 0.85$; $R_2 = 0.002$; $X_1 = 8$; $X_2 = 0.02$. The magnetizing susceptance referred to the H.T. side is 0.00025, and the core loss conductance is 0.000045 mho.

If the load is adjusted to take rated current at rated voltage at the secondary terminals, the power factor being 0.707, lagging, determine (a) the voltage drops in the secondary; (b) the secondary induced emf; (c) the primary induced emf; (d) the primary impressed voltage and power factor; (e) the regulation. (f) Construct the complete phasor diagrams for both primary and secondary.

1-6. Using the data of Prob. 1-5, make the corresponding calculations for a secondary load which has a power factor of 0.707 leading.

1-7. (a) A 50-cycle single-phase core-type transformer is required to give 4 volts and 700 volts when supplied at 240 volts. Calculate the number of turns in each winding if the flux is not to exceed 0.3 megaline. (b) A transformer for a radio set supplies 1 amp at 4 volts to the rectifier, 6 amp at 4 volts to the filaments, and 120 ma at 700 volts for H.T. purposes. Neglecting the losses, calculate the approximate current taken from the 240-volt supply.

1-8. A 50-cycle transformer rated at 50 kva at 32,000/400 volts has the following constants: $R_1 = 120$; $R_2 = 0.024$; $X_1 = 440$; $X_2 = 0.1$. The iron loss is 600 watts, and the no-load power factor angle is 78°. When used as a step-up transformer with an 80 per cent power-factor load taking rated current at 32,000 volts, (a) determine the impressed voltage and current on the L.T. side and the corresponding power factor; (b) determine the regulation and over-all efficiency; (c) construct the complete phasor diagram, showing the magnitude of each phasor.

1-9. A 10-kva 440/110-volt 60-cycle single-phase transformer has the following data: $R_1 = 0.50$; $R_2 = 0.032$; $X_1 = 0.90$; $X_2 = 0.06$. At no load, the current on the 440-volt side is 0.5 amp, and the core loss is 100 watts. Compute the change in primary voltage required to maintain the rated secondary terminal voltage when the secondary carries a 25 per cent overload current at 80 per cent power factor, lagging.

1-10. A 1,000-kva 60-cycle transformer, 66,600/3,330 volts, has the following parameters: $R_1 = 30$; $R_2 = 0.08$; $X_1 = 150$; $X_2 = 0.42$. With 3,330 volts impressed upon the L.T. side while the H.T. side is open-circuited, the power component of the no-load current is 2.8 amp, and the magnetizing component is 14.5 amp. The transformer, supplied by a 3,330-volt generator, is used to step up the voltage to the constant value of 66,600 volts. Determine the generator terminal voltage when (a) the transformer delivers rated load at 100 per cent power factor; (b) the rated transformer load is fully inductive; (c) the rated transformer load is fully capacitive; (d) the transformer delivers three-fourths of rated load at a power factor of 80 per cent, lagging.

1-11. A 50-cycle single-phase transformer has a ratio of transformation 6. The resistances of primary and secondary are 0.9 and 0.03 ohm, respectively, and the corresponding leakage reactances are 5 ohms and 0.13 ohm. Neglecting the exciting admittance, find (a) the voltage that must be impressed upon the H.T. winding to circulate full-load current of 200 amp through the short-circuited secondary; (b) the power factor at short circuit.

1-12. A 100-kva 10,000/400-volt transformer takes 1,000 watts at no load. Full-load current is produced in the windings when 500 volts is impressed upon the H.T. winding, and the L.T. winding is short-circuited; and the corresponding power input is 1,200 watts. Find (a) the efficiency at full load and at half load at unity power factor; (b) the per cent voltage regulation at full-load rating, the power factor being 80 per cent, lagging.

1-13. A 1,000-kva transformer is connected to the supply circuit for 12 hr per day. The iron loss is 7,000 watts, and the copper loss at full-load current is 18,000 watts.

During 4 hr it delivers 700 kw at 0.7 power factor, during 5 hr it delivers 500 kw at 0.85 power factor, and it is idle during the remaining period. What is the all-day efficiency?

1-14. A 75-kva 10,000/5,000-volt transformer has a calculated full-load copper loss of 2.8 per cent and an iron loss of 1.2 per cent. The load cycle of the transformer is as follows:

	No load	¼ load	½ load	Full load
Hr duration......	8	4	4	8
Power factor......	..	0.95	0.7	0.8

Determine the all-day efficiency.

1-15. A 100-kva transformer, 3,800/230 volts, was subjected to an open-circuit and a short-circuit test with the following results, all readings having been taken on the low-voltage side:

	Volts	Amp	Watts
Open circuit..........	230	42	615
Short circuit.........	7	435	1,120

Calculate the input and efficiency of this transformer when the primary voltage is 3,800 and the secondary load takes 300 amp at 0.8 power factor.

1-16. The test data shown in the table on page 630 were taken on single-phase transformers.

Determine (a) the constants of transformer A; (b) its regulation at full-load rating, 80 per cent power factor, lagging; (c) its efficiency at full load and at half load, power factor 80 per cent, lagging.

1-17. Determine (a) the constants of transformer B in the table on page 630; (b) the regulation at half load and at power factors of 80 per cent, both lagging and leading; (c) the efficiencies corresponding to part b.

1-18. Transformer C of the table on page 630 is reconnected to transform from 60,000 to 6,000 volts. Find its regulation and efficiency first as originally connected and then as reconnected, the load in both cases being full load at 70 per cent power factor.

1-19. What would be the short-circuit test readings for transformer E if they were made with full rated current?

1-20. What would be the short-circuit test readings of transformer F if the instruments were connected on the H.T. side and rated current were used?

1-21. Conventional open-circuit and short-circuit tests are made on the transformer specified in Prob. 1-5. Calculate the readings of all instruments.

1-22. At what load would the efficiency of transformer D (table, page 630) be a maximum if operated at rated voltage and frequency?

1-23. A 200-kva 6,600/384-volt single-phase transformer, when carrying a load of unity power factor, has an efficiency of 98 per cent at full load and at one-half of full load. The no-load power factor is 0.2, and the full-load voltage regulation at a lagging power factor of 0.8 is 4 per cent. Draw the equivalent circuit referred to the L.T. side, and insert all values of the parameters.

1-24. A 200-kva single-phase transformer has an efficiency of 98 per cent at full load. If the maximum efficiency occurs at three-fourths of full load, calculate (a) the iron loss; (b) the copper loss at full load; (c) the efficiency at half load. Neglect the magnetizing current, and assume a power factor of 0.8 at all loads.

Trans-former	Name-plate data			Open-circuit test			Short-circuit test			Remarks
	Kva	Volts ratio	Cps	Volts	Amp	Kw	Volts	Amp	Kw	
A	5	$\dfrac{2,300}{230}$	60	230	1.01	0.04	142	Rated	0.11	Instruments connected conventionally
B	100	$\dfrac{13,200}{2,300}$	60	2,300	2.4	0.57	660	Rated	1.00	Instruments connected conventionally
C	5,000	$\dfrac{2\times30,000}{6,000}$	25	6,000	13.2	15.0	1,800	Rated	67.0	Instruments connected conventionally*
D	10,000	$\dfrac{132,000}{66,000}$	25	66,000	4.1	48.5	9,400	Rated	121.00	Instruments connected conventionally
E	15,000	$\dfrac{66,000}{13,200}$	60	13,200	20.4	58.0	5,000	90% rated	60.0	Instruments connected conventionally
F	10,000	$\dfrac{63,000}{2\times6,300}$	60	63,000	2.5	35	63,000	110% rated	60.0	Instruments in both tests on 63,000-volt side

* Primary coils in parallel.

1-25. A 15,000-kva 60,000/15,000-volt transformer has the following parameters: $R_1 = 0.56$; $R_2 = 0.026$; $X_1 = 9.25$; $X_2 = 0.44$. The iron-loss conductance measured on the 60,000-volt side is 1.3×10^{-5} mho, and the magnetizing susceptance is 13.0×10^{-5} mho. What will be the corrected values of the voltmeter, ammeter, and wattmeter readings (a) when the transformer is tested on open circuit with the instruments on the L.T. side and (b) when the L.T. terminals are short-circuited and the instruments are on the H.T. side?

1-26. Express the parameters of the transformer in Prob. 1-5 in per-unit values, and draw (a) the exact equivalent circuit with all magnitudes expressed in per-unit terms; (b) the simplified equivalent circuit in per-unit terms.

1-27. Express the parameters of the transformer in Prob. 1-8 in per-unit magnitudes. Tabulate the mks values of all parameters in Probs. 1-5 and 1-8 and their per-unit values.

1-28. A 1,000-kva 13,200/600-volt single-phase transformer has the following per-unit constants: $R_1 = 0.0055$; $R_2 = 0.005$; $X_1 = 0.03$; $X_2 = 0.029$; iron-loss conductance 0.0035; magnetizing admittance 0.0175. Find the constants of the transformer in mks units.

1-29. Determine the per-unit parameters of transformer B in Prob. 1-16 from the open- and short-circuit test data. Assume that primary and secondary copper losses are equal in both windings and that the per-unit reactances of the two windings are also equal. Convert the per-unit values to the equivalent mks values.

1-30. Solve Prob. 1-22, using per-unit quantities throughout.

1-31. The following measurements were made on an iron-cored choke coil: (a) input when connected across 200 volts at 60 cycles, 10 amp and 500 watts; (b) input when connected across 400 volts at 120 cycles, 10 amp and 900 watts; (c) current when connected across 20 volts d-c, 10 amp. Calculate the approximate values of the hysteresis and eddy-current losses in case a.

Chapter 2

2-1. A 500-kva 60-cycle 2,400/240-480-volt single-phase transformer has the following per-unit constants: $R_1 = 0.008$; $R_2 = 0.007$; $X_1 = 0.025$; $X_2 = 0.025$; iron-loss conductance 0.004; magnetizing admittance 0.02. Find the constants of the transformer in mks units (a) when the two secondary windings are connected in series for 480 volts; (b) when the two secondary windings are connected in parallel for 240 volts.

2-2. The transformer of Prob. 2-1 is operated at full voltage on the L.T. side with a 10 per cent overload at a lagging power factor of 0.8. Using the per-unit method and the simplified equivalent circuit, find (a) the H.T. voltage in per-unit value and in actual value; (b) the regulation; (c) the efficiency.

2-3. Two 500-kva 25-cycle 11,000/2,200-volt transformers are operated in parallel. Short-circuit tests of these transformers when operated at rated current with the L.T. windings short-circuited yielded the following results:

Transformer	Applied voltage	Power input, watts
A............	260	3,300
B............	945	3,980

What is the largest load at power-factor unity that can be carried by the two transformers in parallel without overloading either of them? Assume that the terminal voltage on the L.T. side is 2,200 volts.

2-4. Transformers E and F of Prob. 1-16 are connected in parallel on both high- and low-voltage sides. They supply a load of 25,000 kva at 0.8 power factor, lagging, at a terminal voltage of 12,600 volts. Calculate the over-all efficiency of the transformer bank.

2-5. The high- and low-voltage windings of a 1,000-kva transformer each consists of two identical halves which may be connected in series or in parallel. With both sets of coils in series, the transformer is rated at 66,000/6,600 volts at 60 cycles, and when so connected the results of open-circuit and short-circuit tests were:

	Open circuit	Short circuit
Current...	9.1	15.15
Voltage...	6,600	3,200
Power...	9,300	7,500

Assuming that the copper loss is the same in primary and secondary windings, and that the leakage reactances are also equal when both are referred to the same side, construct the exact equivalent circuit, indicating the numerical values of all parameters (a) when primary and secondary windings are each in series; (b) when they are each in parallel.

2-6. The transformer of Prob. 2-5 is reconnected to step up the voltage from 3,300 to 66,000 volts. Determine the six parameters in terms of the low-voltage side.

2-7. The transformer of Prob. 2-5 is reconnected to step down from 33,000 to 3,300 volts. Determine the six parameters in terms of the high-voltage side.

2-8. The secondary of the transformer of Prob. 2-5 delivers full-load current at 0.8 power factor, lagging, at a terminal voltage of 6,700 volts. Assuming that the magnetizing current is directly proportional to the induced emf and that the core loss varies as the square of the induced emf, calculate (a) the regulation; (b) the efficiency.

2-9. Two single-phase transformers rated at 600 kva and 400 kva, 2,300/230 volts, are connected in parallel on both high- and low-voltage sides. They supply a load of 1,000 kva at 0.8 power factor, lagging. The per-unit values of their parameters are:

Transformer	Resistance	Reactance
600-kva...	0.016	0.07
400-kva...	0.025	0.06

The supply voltage being held constant at 2,300 volts, calculate the kva loading and the power factor of each transformer.

2-10. Two single-phase transformers have open-circuit secondary voltages of 440 volts and 430 volts when their primary windings are connected in parallel to a common source. The impedance of each transformer, referred to the secondary side, is $0.02 + j1.0$. The secondaries are now connected in parallel, and a total load of 500 amp, lagging by an angle $\cos^{-1} 0.8$ behind the open-circuit secondary voltages, is applied. Determine the load voltage.

2-11. Two single-phase tap-changing transformers, A and B, rated at 3,000 kva and 2,000 kva, respectively, are to operate in parallel to supply a load having a resistance of 22 ohms and a reactance of 16 ohms. The nominal no-load voltage of each transformer is 33,000/11,000 volts, but the tap changers are set incorrectly, and the secondary voltages, with 33,000 volts on the primary, are 11,200 volts on A and

10,800 volts on B. The per cent voltage drops at rated load and at the nominal voltage ratio are:

Transformer	Resistance, %	Leakage reactance, %
A	1	6
B	1	5

Calculate the load in kilovolt-amperes on transformer A.

2-12. Three identical single-phase shell-type transformers, each rated at 15,000 kva, 60 cycles, have their primaries connected in Y to 132-kv lines. The Δ-connected secondaries supply a 35-kv three-phase system. The primary resistance of each transformer is 0.9 ohm, and the primary leakage reactance of each transformer is 8 ohms. The magnetizing current of each transformer is 12 per cent of its rated current, and the no-load core loss is 80 kw. (*a*) Calculate the line-to-line primary voltage at no load, assuming rated voltage on the secondary of the transformer bank; (*b*) sketch the phasor diagram for each transformer in its proper phase relation to each of the others.

2-13. A bank of three transformers, with primaries in Δ and secondaries in Y, is connected between a 10,000-volt transmission line and a 400-volt distribution circuit. Another similar bank steps down from 10,000 volts to 2,000 volts and the 2,000-volt terminals are connected to another Δ-Y bank which steps down from 2,000 to 400 volts. If two similarly placed terminals of the two 400-volt lines are connected, what potential difference will exist between the correspondingly placed terminals of the other pairs of terminals? Illustrate by means of a phasor diagram.

2-14. A single-phase load is connected across one pair of terminals of the secondaries of a transformer bank the primaries of which are Y-connected and the secondaries Δ-connected. Draw the phasor diagram, showing the distribution of the current in the primary and secondary windings. Neglect the exciting current.

2-15. What precautionary measures must be taken before connecting in Δ the secondaries of a three-phase transformer bank? If the phase voltages are each equal to V, what emf would act around the Δ if one phase were reversed?

2-16. A bank of transformers with primaries in Δ and secondaries in Y reduces a three-phase voltage of 22,000 volts between lines to 400 volts between lines. Another bank of transformers with zigzag connections of the primaries (broken-star) and with secondaries in Y gives the same line-to-line voltages. Can the two banks of transformers be paralleled? What is the turn ratio of the transformers in the second group?

2-17. Two three-phase transformers, each having a no-load ratio of 6,600/400 volts, are connected in parallel to 6,600-volt mains. Transformer A has a full-load rating of 1,000 kva, a resistance drop of 1 per cent, and a leakage-reactance drop of 3 per cent at full-load current. Transformer B has a full-load rating of 500 kva, a resistance drop of 2 per cent, and a leakage-reactance drop of 2 per cent at full load. Determine the load and power factor of each transformer and the secondary terminal voltage when the total load is 1,200 kva at 0.85 power factor, lagging.

2-18. A bank of three single-phase transformers, connected in Δ on the H.T. side and in Y on the L.T. side, steps down from a line voltage of 66,000 volts to a line voltage of 6,600 volts at no load. A second group of transformers, also connected in Δ-Y, steps down from a line voltage of 6,600 volts to a line voltage of 420 volts at no load. The secondaries of the first bank are connected to the primaries of the second bank by lines each of which has an impedance of $0.1 + j0.15$ ohm. Test data on the two banks are:

Group	Volts	Amp	Watts
66,000/6,600	300	130	4,500
6,600/420	520	70	4,000

With 66,000 volts impressed upon the first bank, what will be the terminal voltage on the secondary side of the second bank if the balanced load on the second bank takes 2,000 kva at a power factor of 0.8, lagging? Neglect the exciting current.

2-19. A three-phase 2,000-kva 6,600/33,000-volt transformer has a Δ-connected primary and a Y-connected secondary. The resistance and leakage reactance of each phase of the primary winding are 0.5 ohm and 2.6 ohms, respectively; and the corresponding values of each phase of the secondary winding are 4.3 ohms and 21.7 ohms. Calculate the secondary terminal voltage at full load when the primary is supplied at 6,600 volts. Neglect the magnetizing current and the core losses.

2-20. The primaries of a bank of three single-phase transformers, designated as OA, OB, and OC, have the O terminals connected together and the terminals A, B, and C connected to a balanced three-phase supply. The corresponding secondaries, respectively designated oa, ob, and oc, have their o terminals connected together. Windings oa and ob are tapped at points a' and b' such that the turns ratio $oa'/oa = ob'/ob = 1/\sqrt{3}$. A noninductive resistance R is connected between points o and c, and an equal noninductive resistance is connected between a' and b'. Will the voltages on the two resistors be equal and in quadrature? Explain.

2-21. Two Scott-connected transformers transform from 6,600-volt three-phase to 400-volt two-phase. The load on one of the two secondary phases is 200 kva, and on the other it is 300 kva, both at 400 volts, unity power factor. Neglecting the losses, determine the currents in the transformer windings and in the 6,600-volt three-phase supply lines. Use either of the two possible secondary load connections.

2-22. Two electric furnaces are supplied with single-phase current at 80 volts from a three-phase 11,000-volt system by means of two single-phase Scott-connected transformers with similar secondary windings. When the load on one furnace is 500 kw and on the other 800 kw, what current will flow in each of the three-phase lines (a) at unity power factor; (b) at 0.5 power factor, lagging? Neglect the exciting currents and impedance drops.

2-23. A three-phase four-wire distribution network with 240 volts between the line and neutral is supplied from a 5,000-volt two-phase circuit by means of single-phase step-down transformers. Show by connection and phasor diagrams how this result is accomplished, and calculate the number of turns in each secondary winding if there are 2,000 turns on each primary winding.

2-24. A 2,300-volt generator delivers 5,000 kw at 0.707 power factor, lagging, to a three-phase bus having 23,000 volts between lines. What should be the kva rating and voltage rating of the step-up transformers when connected (a) Δ-Δ; (b) Y-Y; (c) Y-Δ; (d) T-T; (e) open V to open V?

2-25. What are the ratios of output to installed capacity in Prob. 2-24?

2-26. Three identical 100-kva transformers are available. The no-load loss of each transformer is 780 watts, and the full-load copper loss is 2,100 watts. The load to be supplied is balanced three-phase, 170 kva at 0.9 power factor, lagging. Calculate the total losses (a) if all three transformers are used and are connected in Δ; (b) if two transformers, connected in open V, are used.

2-27. A six-phase synchronous converter takes 1,200 kva from a three-phase 6,600-volt bus through step-down transformers. The six-phase line-to-line voltage is 230 volts. What should be the kva rating and voltage ratio of the transformers when connected (a) primaries in Δ, secondaries in double Δ; (b) primaries in Y, secondaries in double Δ?

2-28. Three transformers, each rated at 100 kva, are connected in Δ on both H.T. and L.T. sides. These transformers have the following per-unit values of equivalent impedance: No. 1, $0.008 + j0.045$; No. 2, $0.008 + j0.045$; No. 3, $0.009 + j0.035$. If these transformers supply a balanced load of 250 kva at 0.8 power factor, lagging, and a single-phase load of 40 kva at unity power factor across transformer 3, what per cent of its rated kva does each transformer supply?

2-29. A six-phase synchronous converter takes 1,500 kw from a three-phase 6,600-volt transmission line through three single-phase transformers. The primaries are connected in Y, and the secondaries are (a) in double Y; (b) in diametrical star. Determine the current and voltage rating of each winding, assuming 230 volts between lines on the secondary six-phase side.

2-30. A six-phase synchronous converter takes 500 kw from a two-phase 5,000-volt circuit through step-down transformers in double-T connection. The six-phase line-to-line voltage is 200 volts. What should be the current and voltage ratings of the transformers?

2-31. A potential transformer rated at 200 va, 60 cycles, 10,000/110 volts, has the following constants, determined by test: primary resistance 7,500 ohms; secondary resistance 0.62 ohm; primary leakage reactance 8,100 ohms; secondary leakage reactance 0.65 ohm. The no-load input is 20 watts at 0.4 power factor. Calculate the actual voltage ratio and the correction factor when a 150-volt full-scale deflection voltmeter of 120 ohms per volt is connected to the secondary, the reading of the voltmeter being 100 volts.

2-32. A current transformer having a nominal ratio of transformation of 10:1 and a 5-amp secondary has the following constants: primary turns 25; secondary turns 245; secondary a-c resistance 0.62 ohms; secondary leakage reactance 0.6 ohm at 60 cycles. The uniform magnetic circuit has a length of 50 cm and a cross section of 25 sq cm. The core material has a density of 7.75 g per cu cm and the following saturation and loss data at 60 cycles:

B webers per sq m	H amp-turns per m	Core loss, watts per 1,000 g
0.0450	25.5	0.0196
0.0400	25.0	0.0164
0.0350	24.3	0.0134
0.0300	23.1	0.0104
0.0240	20.6	0.0072
0.0180	17.7	0.0042
0.0120	13.7	0.0016
0.0060	8.1	0.0003

This transformer is used on a 60-cycle circuit with a 5-amp ammeter which has a resistance of 0.18 ohm and a reactance of 0.055 ohm at 60 cycles. Assuming that the magnetizing current is sinusoidal, what is (a) the actual ratio of transformation when the instrument reads 5 amp; (b) the phase angle of the transformer when the instrument reads 5 amp?

2-33. A current transformer has a turns ratio of 2:100 and an impedance of $1.05 + j0.30$ ohm referred to the secondary. Calculate the primary current, the ratio error, and the phase-angle error when the transformer supplies a current of 3 amp to an ammeter of impedance $0.6 + j0.3$ ohm, if the magnetizing ampere-turns for the transformer are 30 for iron losses and 40 for magnetization.

2-34. Derive an expression for the current ratio, and for the phase angle, of a current transformer. What factor is chiefly responsible for the ratio error, and what factor or factors for the phase angle?

2-35. The transformer of Prob. 1-5 is reconnected as an autotransformer to supply a 4,620-volt load from a 4,400-volt line. (a) Determine the maximum kva load the transformer can supply without being overloaded; (b) draw a circuit diagram, and show all line and winding currents with a load of 2,000 kw, and 0.9 lagging power factor on the secondary terminals; (c) what is the equivalent impedance viewed from the 4,400-volt terminals? (d) Draw the phasor diagram.

2-36. A 500-kva 60-cycle two-winding transformer designed for 13,200/2,500 volts is reconnected to supply 13,200 volts from a 15,700-volt line. Open- and short-circuit tests on the transformer yielded the following results:

Circuit	Volts	Amp	Watts
Open..........	2,500	6.5	2,190
Short..........	600	37.9	4,320

(a) What is the maximum power the autotransformer can handle at 0.8 power factor? (b) What will be the efficiency and voltage regulation for the case of full-load power flow at 0.8 power factor from the 15,700-volt side to the 13,200-volt side? (c) If a short circuit occurs near the transformer terminals on the 13,200-volt side, what will be the steady short-circuit current flowing into the transformer from the 15,700-volt line (neglecting the exciting current)? (d) If a short circuit occurs on the 15,700-volt side near the terminals, what steady short-circuit current will flow into the 13,200-volt terminals (neglecting the exciting current)?

2-37. A 100-kva two-winding transformer has a 6,600-volt and a 2,200-volt winding. How many different voltage ratios may be obtained without exceeding the voltage rating of the winding at normal operating conditions? What will be the kva capacity of the transformer in each case?

2-38. Deduce the ratio between the weights of copper needed for an autotransformer and for a two-winding transformer, for the same rating in each case. Assume that the ratio of primary to secondary voltage is a.

2-39. A two-pole 110-volt induction regulator is designed to give a nominal voltage of 100 to 120 volts. The primary winding has a rating of 20 amp, the secondary of 220 amp. Assuming that the connections are those of Fig. 2-64 and that the equivalent impedance viewed from the output terminals is $0.001 + j0.04$ ohm, determine (a) the rated output in the 100-, 110-, and 120-volt positions; (b) the full-load efficiency in the 100- and 120-volt positions, the iron loss being constant at 1.5 kw.

2-40. An induction regulator gives an output voltage ranging from 100 to 300 volts, the input voltage being 200. Calculate the greatest possible current in the compensating winding when the output current is 50 amp. What is the output voltage under this condition? Assume that the primary and compensating windings have the same number of turns.

2-41. One corner of the Δ formed by the secondaries of a three-phase transformer bank is opened. A voltmeter connected to the open ends of the winding gives a reading between 50 and 60 per cent of the rated voltage. What is the cause of this voltage reading?

2-42. The currents in lines A, B, and C of a three-phase system are represented by $40 + j60$, $-j90$, and -80, respectively. If the line reactances per phase are 20 ohms for the positive-sequence and for the negative-sequence currents, and 50 ohms for the zero-sequence current, find the voltage drop in line A.

Chapter 3

3-1. A constant current of 835 amp is passed through a No. 4 bare copper wire which is initially at room temperature of 25°C. The length of the wire is sufficient to eliminate the necessity of considering the cooling effect of the terminal connections. Three seconds after the current is established, the rise of temperature of the wire is found to be one-half of its ultimate rise. Assuming that the resistance of the wire has the constant value of 0.292 ohm per 1,000 ft, find (a) the value of α (watts radiated per square inch of radiating surface per degree centigrade difference between the wire and the air); and (b) the ultimate rise of temperature.

3-2. Assuming that the temperature of the wire has attained its final steady value, what will be its temperature 6 sec after interrupting the current supply?

3-3. When the wire has been allowed to cool for the 6 sec specified in Prob. 3-2, a steady current of 1,000 amp is reestablished. Compute the final temperature of the wire thereafter.

3-4. A transformer coil made of No. 6 copper wire has a full-load hot resistance 20 per cent greater than its resistance measured at 25°C. The full-load current density in the wire is 800 cir mils per amp. The readings for the hot resistance were taken 2 min after interrupting the current. Calculate the temperature at the moment of shutdown.

3-5. The coil of Prob. 3-4 is part of the winding of a transformer having 4 per cent impedance. Using Eq. 3-12, calculate its temperature after a short circuit of 2 sec duration, following normal operation under full-load conditions.

3-6. Two identical 10-kva 2,400/240-volt transformers having 4 per cent impedance are to be subjected to a heat run at 25 per cent overload. What is the voltage of the auxiliary circuit which supplies the circulating current?

Chapter 4

4-1. The flux density in the airgap of a synchronous machine is represented by

$$B = B_1 \sin \alpha + B_3 \sin 3(\alpha - \varphi_3) + B_5 \sin 5(\alpha - \varphi_5)$$

where α is the angle in electrical degrees measured from an origin midway between poles. There are p poles, the armature diameter is d, and the axial length of the core is l, all quantities being expressed in mks units. (a) Derive an expression for the flux per pole, and (b) specify the values of φ_3 and φ_5 for which the flux per pole will be independent of the flux harmonics.

4-2. If in Prob. 4-1 φ_3 and φ_5 have the values determined by part b thereof, and if the flux per pole is 0.0112 weber, $B_3 = 0.3B_1$, and $B_5 = 0.1B_1$, what is the rms voltage induced per conductor of the armature winding if the machine is designed for 25-cycle operation?

4-3. The maximum ordinate of a symmetrical flux wave has the constant value B_m between $\alpha = \pi/3$ and $\alpha = 2\pi/3$. Between $\alpha = 0$ and $\alpha = \pi/6$, the ordinates increase linearly from zero to $\frac{3}{4}B_m$; and between $\alpha = \pi/6$ and $\alpha = \pi/3$, they increase linearly from $\frac{3}{4}B_m$ to B_m. Beyond $\alpha = 2\pi/3$, the decreasing ordinates repeat in reverse order the wave shape on the rising side of the loop. Compute the amplitudes of the fundamental and the third harmonic in terms of B_m.

4-4. If the flux density in the airgap of a synchronous machine is represented by a trapezoid, the ordinates of which are equal to B_m between $\alpha = 30°$ and $\alpha = 150°$, what are the amplitudes of the fundamental and the third, fifth, and seventh harmonics, expressed in terms of B_m?

4-5. Using the amplitudes computed in Prob. 4-4, plot the resultant curve which they define. Plot the differences between the ordinates of this resultant curve and the ordinates of the original trapezoid, and determine the maximum per cent difference between them (in terms of the ordinates of the trapezoid).

4-6. A six-pole 60-cycle synchronous generator has a sinusoidally distributed flux of 0.018 weber per pole. The armature has 72 equally spaced slots. The two-layer armature winding consists of 36 full-pitch coils of one turn each disposed (a) in alternate slots; (b) in sets of three adjacent slots. Calculate the rms value of the emf induced in the winding.

4-7. The two-layer winding of a six-pole 60-cycle synchronous generator consists of individual full-pitch coils, each of which has six turns, disposed in the 36 armature slots. The flux per pole is 0.0144 weber, sinusoidally distributed. Determine the open-circuit terminal voltage (line to line) if (a) the coils are connected to form a balanced two-phase winding; (b) they are arranged as a Y-connected three-phase winding.

4-8. The pole faces of the generator of Prob. 4-7 are changed so that the flux distribution in the airgap, instead of being sinusoidal, is represented by

$$B = B_1(\sin \alpha + 0.3 \sin 3\alpha + 0.1 \sin 5\alpha)$$

but the total flux per pole remains the same as before. Determine the open-circuit line-to-line voltage (a) for the two-phase winding; (b) for the Y-connected three-phase winding, and sketch their corresponding wave forms.

4-9. The armature winding of the generator of Prob. 4-8 is modified by using coils each of which has a spread of two-thirds of the pole pitch. Calculate the no-load line voltages for the same two-phase and three-phase groupings, and sketch their wave forms.

4-10. What will be the no-load voltages for the two-phase and three-phase groupings if the coils of the machine of Prob. 4-8 have a spread of five-sixths of the pole pitch? Sketch the wave forms of these voltages.

4-11. What frequencies due to tooth ripples may be expected to appear in the emf wave form of the machine specified in Prob. 4-8?

4-12. A 10-pole machine has a two-layer three-phase fractional-slot winding arranged in 72 slots, the coil span being 6 slots. Construct the winding diagram, and calculate the breadth and pitch factors.

4-13. A 28-pole three-phase 60-cycle generator has a two-layer fractional-slot winding occupying 192 slots. Calculate the breadth and pitch factors if the coil span is (a) 5 slots; (b) 6 slots; (c) 7 slots.

4-14. Assume that in Prob. 4-13 the length of the end connections of the coils which span seven slots is 1.8 times the embedded length and that the lengths of the end connections of the smaller coils are proportional to the peripheral span of the coils. If the speed and field excitation remain constant and all three windings are to supply the same kva rating, what will be their relative copper losses?

4-15. The rotor bars of a four-pole 59-slot squirrel-cage induction motor are skewed through an angle equivalent to one slot pitch. How does the emf per bar compare with that of a similar unskewed rotor, assuming sinusoidal distribution of the airgap flux?

4-16. Construct diagrams similar to Fig. 4-35 for two-phase and three-phase full-pitch windings of a machine which has six slots per pole. Choose positions for the current phasors which differ by steps of 30 electrical degrees.

4-17. A three-phase 375-kva 50-cycle Y-connected generator running at 300 rpm is designed to develop 4,160 volts between terminals. The two-layer armature winding consists of 150 coils, connected series star, each coil having nine turns and a spread of six slots. Determine the armature mmf in ampere-turns per pole when the machine is delivering its rated current.

4-18. A stator frame having 40 slots is provided with a two-pole distributed winding in the manner shown in Fig. 5-13, the two middle slots on each side being left unwound. (a) Calculate the relative amplitudes of the third and fifth space harmonics of mmf in terms of the fundamental amplitude. (b) Repeat the calculations for the case where the four middle slots on each side are left unwound.

4-19. What is the ratio of the amplitudes of the third, fifth, and seventh space harmonics of mmf to the fundamental mmf in the case of a smooth-core d-c winding?

4-20. (a) Check the values given in Table 4-2 for the seventh, fifteenth, and seventeenth space harmonics of mmf due to the time fundamental of the exciting current. (b) Check the values given in Table 4-3 for the third, seventh, and eleventh space harmonics of mmf due to the time fundamental of the exciting current.

Chapter 5

5-1. The bipolar ring-wound machine of Fig. 5-1 is constructed with a completely laminated magnetic circuit. The field winding, energized from a 60-cycle circuit, develops a maximum flux of 0.02 weber per pole, sinusoidally distributed. The armature has 300 face conductors, uniformly spaced, and runs at 1,200 rpm. What are the magnitude and frequency of the brush voltage, assuming that the brushes are in the geometrical neutral?

5-2. The pole faces of the machine of Prob. 5-1 are so changed that they embrace two-thirds of the pole pitch and are so shaped that the maximum flux of 0.02 weber per pole is uniformly distributed within their span. Other conditions remaining the same as before, what are the magnitudes of the fundamental, third, and fifth harmonics of the brush voltage?

5-3. If the brushes of the machine specified in Prob. 5-1 are shifted through 90°, what voltage will appear between them?

5-4. The brushes of the machine of Prob. 5-1 are connected to an external circuit which draws a current of 22 amp at a lagging power factor of 80 per cent. Calculate the torque in pound-feet.

5-5. The brushes of the machine of Prob. 5-1 are shifted clockwise through an angle of 15° in the manner indicated in Fig. 5-7. The 60-cycle excitation produces a flux of 0.02 weber per pole (sinusoidally distributed) which may be assumed to be represented by a vertical phasor. A difference of potential represented by $V = 115/\underline{60°}$ impressed upon the brushes produces a current of 10 amp through the armature which has an impedance of $0.2 + j1.0$ ohms. Find the speed of rotation in rps.

5-6. Referring to Fig. 5-11, assume that the winding F has three times as many turns as winding C and that with the brushes in the position there indicated the speed of rotation is n_1 and the torque is T_1. The line current remaining the same as before, what will be the speed and torque in terms of their initial values when the brushes are shifted through 90°? Neglect the effect of armature leakage impedance.

Chapter 6

6-1. What are the number of poles of polyphase induction motors which operate at the following frequencies and synchronous speeds: (a) 60 cycles, 3,600, 1,800, and 1,200 rpm; (b) 50 cycles, 3,000 rpm; 25 cycles, 750 rpm?

6-2. A 60-cycle polyphase induction motor has six poles and runs at 1,165 rpm when fully loaded. Find (a) the slip; (b) the frequency of the rotor current. Express speed of the rotating field and that of the rotor in electrical radians per second. What is the slip speed in electrical degrees per second?

6-3. A two-pole 60-cycle polyphase induction motor has a primary induced voltage of 110 volts per phase. The secondary induced voltage per phase is 3.2 volts. Both stator and rotor have three-phase windings having equal effective number of turns per phase. Determine (a) the slip in per cent; (b) the frequency of the rotor current; (c) the speed of the motor in rpm.

6-4. A 50 hp four-pole 60-cycle induction motor has a stator winding designed for 440 volts, with Δ connection. The winding consists of 24 conductors per slot, arranged in the 60 stator slots, each phase having two parallel circuits, and the coil pitch is 80 per cent. The rms value of the current per phase is 34 amp. Plot the distribution of the mmf per pole (a) at the instant when the current in phase 1 has its maximum value; (b) one-sixth period later; (c) one-third period later than in (a). Indicate the scale used for the mmf in ampere-turns per pole.

6-5. A 200-hp 440-volt 1,460-rpm three-phase 25-cycle induction motor has 36 slots per pole, with two turns per coil in the double-layer winding. Each coil spans 21 slots, and the phases are Y-connected. The full-load efficiency is 92.3 per cent, and the full-load power factor is 0.933. Calculate (a) the mmf in ampere-turns per pole at the center of phase 1 when the current has maximum value in phase 2; (b) a quarter period later than in (a).

6-6. A 50-hp eight-pole 60-cycle 440-volt induction motor has the following winding data: The stator coils, each having two turns and a spread of 75 per cent of the pole pitch, are arranged as a double-layer Y-connected winding in four slots per pole per phase. The Y-connected wound rotor consists of coils each having two turns and $\frac{8}{9}$ pitch, arranged in three slots per pole per phase. Calculate the reduction factors for converting (a) secondary voltages, (b) secondary currents, (c) and secondary impedances into terms of the primary.

6-7. The motor of Prob. 6-6 is reconnected as a two-phase motor to operate on a 60-cycle circuit supplying 550 volts per phase. The rotor remains unchanged. Determine the reduction factors for converting secondary voltages, currents, and impedances into terms of the primary.

6-8. Determine the reduction factors for converting secondary voltages, currents, and impedances into terms of the primary for a four-pole 1,250-hp three-phase 4,160-volt 60-cycle induction motor which has the following winding data: The double-layer three-phase Y-connected stator has 96 coils, each having seven turns and 91.6 per cent pitch, each phase consisting of two circuits in parallel. The squirrel-cage rotor has 89 bars, not skewed.

6-9. A six-pole 15-hp 600-volt 60-cycle three-phase Y-connected wound-rotor induction motor has the following data, all quantities being expressed in terms of the primary: $R_1 = 0.76$, $R_2 = 0.9$, $X_1 = 2.1$, $X_2 = 2.0$ ohms; $G_0 = 1.4 \times 10^{-3}$,

$$B_0 = 2.1 \times 10^{-2} \text{ mho}$$

Draw the exact equivalent circuit, and indicate the circuit constants for 1.5 and 2 per cent slip; determine the primary and secondary currents when the slip is 2 per cent; determine the primary power factor, the output, efficiency, and torque at 2 per cent slip; also, the torque at 1.0 and 1.5 per cent slip.

6-10. A four-pole 3-hp 440-volt 60-cycle Y-connected induction motor having a squirrel-cage rotor has the following parameters: $R_1 = 2.4$, $X_1 = 5$, $R_2 = 2.3$, $X_2 = 4.6$, all expressed in primary ohms per phase; $G_0 = 3.2 \times 10^{-3}$, $B_0 = 1.0 \times 10^{-2}$ mho per phase. Indicate in primary terms, for a slip of 3 per cent, (a) the exact equivalent circuit; (b) the primary and secondary currents per phase; (c) the primary power factor; (d) the power output in watts and the torque in pound-feet; (e) the efficiency. Construct the phasor diagram.

6-11. The 200-hp motor specified in Prob. 6-5 has the following calculated design data: Primary d-c resistance between terminals 0.0682 ohm (a-c resistance is 1.32 times the d-c resistance). Primary leakage reactance per phase 0.12 ohm. Secondary resistance per phase, in terms of primary, 0.033 ohm. Secondary leakage reactance per phase, in terms of primary, 0.111 ohm. No-load impedance at 440 volts 8.5 ohms. No-load power factor 0.025.

If the motor is running at 1,460 rpm, determine by means of the exact equivalent circuit (a) the input current and power factor; (b) the horsepower output and efficiency; and (c) construct the phasor diagram for these conditions.

6-12. Using the data given in Prob. 6-9, repeat all calculations, using the simplified equivalent circuit. Compare the results with those of Prob. 6-9.

6-13. Repeat the calculations specified in Prob. 6-10, using the simplified equivalent circuit. Discuss the reasons for any discrepancies.

6-14. Solve Prob. 6-10 by using the simplified equivalent circuit, and compare results.

6-15. Calculate the starting torque and the maximum torque for the motor of Prob. 6-9. At what slip will maximum torque occur? What will be the power factor and output when the machine develops maximum torque?

6-16. Determine the maximum torque of the motor specified in Prob. 6-10. Discuss the influence of the primary and secondary resistance upon the maximum torque.

6-17. The maximum torque of a six-pole three-phase induction motor occurs at 18 per cent slip. Neglecting the stator impedance, determine (a) the secondary power factor at maximum torque; (b) the per cent resistance which should be inserted in the rotor circuit in order that maximum torque may occur at 26 per cent slip.

6-18. How much resistance should be inserted into the rotor circuit of the motor of Prob. 6-11 in order that maximum torque may occur at standstill? Express the resistance in terms of the primary.

6-19. A four-pole 60-cycle three-phase induction motor has a rotor resistance of 4 ohms per phase and a standstill reactance of 10 ohms per phase. With no added resistance in the rotor circuit, the total starting torque of the motor is 70 lb-ft. (a) What is the rotor voltage at standstill? (b) What would be the starting torque if 2 ohms resistance were added to each rotor phase? (c) Neglecting the voltage drop in the primary, what would be the induced secondary voltage and the torque at 2.5 per cent slip?

6-20. A six-pole 60-cycle three-phase wound-rotor induction motor has its maximum torque of 250 per cent at 18 per cent slip. Rotor and stator are Y-connected. The rotor resistance per phase, measured by direct current, is 0.7 ohm, and its a-c resistance is 1.00 ohm at 60 cycles. Assuming constant reluctance, determine (a) the minimum voltage to be impressed so that the motor can still supply its rated torque; (b) the resistance to be inserted into the rotor circuit so that the motor will develop full-load starting torque at the reduced voltage.

6-21. The full-load slip of a 200-hp three-phase induction motor is 2 per cent. The motor has 12 poles and is supplied from a 2,000-volt 25-cycle circuit. The d-c resistance of the rotor is 0.43 ohm per phase, and the standstill resistance is 25 per cent greater. What is the starting torque of the motor if the applied potential is adjusted so that the rotor current is twice its full-load value?

6-22. Two 60-cycle induction motors, which have synchronous speeds of 600 and 720 rpm, respectively, are mechanically coupled. If both motors are connected to the supply lines, what will be the approximate speed at which they will run? (Assume that the torque-slip curve in the vicinity of synchronism is a straight line).

6-23. A 50-hp 440-volt 25-cycle six-pole squirrel-cage induction motor is used to determine the power required to drive a certain machine. The following tests were made: (*a*) with the load connected, the motor took 43.5 amp and 30.5 kw; (*b*) with the load disconnected, the motor took 16.3 amp and 1.16 kw; (*c*) with the rotor blocked, the motor took 2.1 kw, 44.3 amp at 52.5 volts. Find the horsepower rating of the load.

6-24. The following test data were taken on a 30-hp three-phase four-pole 60-cycle squirrel-cage motor. The stator winding is Δ-connected and has a rated voltage of 515 volts:

Test	Line voltage	Line current	Wattmeter 1	Wattmeter 2
No-load................	515	8.6	−1.50	3.15
Short-circuit............	140	44.8	−1.50	4.65

The friction and windage loss is 0.9 kw, and the effective value of the stator resistance is 0.68 ohm per phase. Determine the constants of the motor, sketch the exact equivalent circuit, and label impedances numerically.

6-25. A 5-hp six-pole three-phase 60-cycle squirrel-cage induction motor having a Y-connected stator yielded the following test results: At no load, with normal line voltage of 220 volts, the current was 5.25 amp, and the power input was 460 watts; with the rotor blocked, the current input was 16 amp, and the power was 1,100 watts at a power factor of 0.4; friction and windage loss was 108 watts; the primary d-c resistance per phase was 0.44 ohm, and its effective resistance at 25°C was 40 per cent greater. Draw the equivalent circuit of the motor for a slip of 3 per cent, assuming that the reduced value of secondary reactance is equal to that of the primary.

6-26. A four-pole 250-hp 440-volt three-phase Δ-connected 60-cycle squirrel-cage induction motor yielded the following test readings:

Running-light test at 60 cycles			Blocked-rotor test at 60 cycles		
Volts (line-to-line)	Amp	Kw	Volts (line-to-line)	Amp	Kw
550	100	7.7	20	58	0.55
500	73	6.12	35	100	1.7
440	56.8	5.05	50	146	3.2
360	43	3.98	70	205	6.52
280	32.5	3.15	100	308	14.75
200	24	2.45	120	388	22.9
100	17	1.92	128	420	26.5
65	10	1.85			

Plot (*a*) the no-load current and losses against applied voltage and (*b*) the short-circuit current and losses against applied voltage. Separate the losses on graph *a*, and determine the friction and windage loss. Calculate the parameters of the motor, and establish an approximate equivalent circuit for a slip of 1.8 per cent. Assume that the secondary reactance referred to the primary is equal to the primary reactance.

6-27. The following test data were obtained on a four-pole 30-hp three-phase 440-volt 60-cycle Y-connected squirrel-cage motor:

Line volts	Line amp	Wattmeter 1	Wattmeter 2
Running-light test			
490	11.3	−2,000	3,620
445	9.9	−1,500	3,000
415	8.9	−1,180	2,580
277	6.2	− 200	1,350
140	5.17	230	740
65	3.05	310	650
Blocked-rotor test			
52	21.4	− 220	980

The d-c stator resistance is 0.28 ohm per phase at 75°C, and its a-c resistance is 40 per cent greater. Separate the losses, find the parameters of the motor, and draw the equivalent circuit for a slip of 1.8 per cent. Calculate the currents, torque, output, and efficiency at 1.8 per cent slip.

6-28. A six-pole 60-cycle 220-volt squirrel-cage motor with Y-connected stator is rated at 6 hp. The d-c stator resistance, measured line to line, is 1.22 ohm, and the a-c resistance is 30 per cent greater. Test readings gave the following results:

	Volts	Amp	Watts
Running light.........	220	9.8	540
Blocked rotor.........	60	20.2	1,080

Determine the parameters of the motor, and draw the equivalent circuit for 2.5 per cent slip. Primary and secondary leakage reactances may be assumed to be equal.

6-29. From the data given in Prob. 6-26, construct the simplified circle diagram, and from the diagram determine (a) the full-load input current, power factor, and efficiency; (b) the secondary current and power factor; (c) the slip at which the motor develops 250 hp; (d) the slip and speed at which the torque has maximum value; (e) the maximum torque in pound-feet; (f) the starting torque in lb-feet.

6-30. Construct the circle diagram for a four-pole 50-hp 440-volt 60-cycle three-phase motor which yields the following test results:

	Line volts	Line amp	Watts
No-load................	440	8.90	2,090
Rotor blocked...........	200	182.0	26,400

From the diagram determine (a) the slip, efficiency, input, and output when the line current input is 80 amp; (b) the slip at which the motor delivers maximum output; (c) the overload capacity of the motor.

6-31. The following test measurements were obtained from a 3-hp four-pole 440-volt 60-cycle three-phase motor having a Y-connected stator:

	Line volts	Line amp	Total input, watts
No-load test............	440	2.2	202
Blocked rotor.........	110	5.9	490

The primary d-c resistance is 1.4 ohms per phase; the a-c resistance is 40 per cent greater. Construct the circle diagram of the motor, and from it find (a) the point at which the motor delivers 5 hp; (b) the power factor and efficiency at this point; (c) the maximum torque and the slip at which it occurs; (d) the starting torque in pound-feet and the starting current at full voltage; (e) the slip at which the motor has maximum power factor; (f) the line current if the motor operates with a power factor of 60 per cent.

6-32. Calculate the slip at which the motor of Prob. 6-26 will develop full rated load. Compare this value with the result obtained graphically in Prob. 6-29.

6-33. Determine the slip at which the motor of Prob. 6-27 will deliver 110 per cent of full load.

6-34. Determine the exact circle diagram for the motor of Prob. 6-31, and find the values of power factor, efficiency, and line current at full load. Compare the results with those of Prob. 6-31.

6-35. The motor of Prob. 6-11 is started with a resistance in the rotor circuit. What must be the value of this resistance in order that full-load starting torque may be developed with the smallest possible stator current, the impressed voltage having its rated value?

6-36. From the circle diagram determined in Prob. 6-29, find the resistance which should be inserted in the rotor circuit so that full-load torque may be developed at 10 per cent slip.

6-37. A three-phase six-pole 60-cycle 6,600-volt induction regulator has an effective turns ratio of 6:1 and is in an angular position to give a voltage of 6,000 volts. Neglecting voltage drops and losses, calculate (a) the angular displacement between the phase axes of the stator and rotor; (b) the secondary terminal voltage if the angular displacement is 10 mechanical degrees and the primary voltage is 6,600 volts.

6-38. The following data were obtained from a three-phase four-pole 220-volt 60-cycle induction motor with Y-connected stator: $R_1 = 0.118$, $X_1 = 0.208$ ohm; R_2 and X_2 (in terms of the primary) = 0.102 and 0.208 ohm, respectively; core loss 407 watts; windage and friction loss 400 watts; no-load current 11.9 amp at 0.2 power factor. The motor is operated as a brake by driving the rotor at 1,800 rpm against its field. (a) How are the stator iron losses supplied? (b) What is the braking effort, expressed in watts? (c) What is the braking torque?

6-39. The rotor of Prob. 6-10 is operated as a brake at a slip of 1.5 per cent. Determine (a) the speed of the machine; (b) the primary input; (c) the total copper loss in the rotor; (d) the braking effect at the pulley, expressed in pound-feet.

6-40. The motor of Prob. 6-29, when operated as a brake, develops a braking effect of 15 hp. From the circle diagram, determine the approximate values of (a) the slip and speed; (b) the primary current and power factor; (c) the total copper loss in the rotor.

Chapter 7

7-1. The following facts are known with respect to a 200-hp three-phase 25-cycle 440-volt induction motor: When running at full load, the speed is 1,460 rpm, the efficiency is 92.3 per cent, and the power factor is 0.933. The Y-connected stator winding is disposed in 36 slots per pole, each coil having two turns, the cross section of the conductors being 0.0884 sq in., and the stator resistance, measured from line to line at 75°C, being 0.0682 ohm. Each coil has a spread of 21 slots. The squirrel-cage rotor has 55 bars, each of which has a cross section of 0.299 sq in. The length of the airgap is 0.05 in.

Estimate the most favorable values of the stator bore and the axial length of core (in inches), assuming that the average flux density in the airgap does not exceed 50,000 lines per sq in. From these results, compute the number of ampere conductors per inch of periphery.

7-2. Estimate the exciting current and the exciting reactance of the motor specified in Prob. 7-1.

7-3. A 5-kva three-phase four-pole 60-cycle salient-pole machine rated at 110 volts between terminals has an armature which has a diameter of 8.06 in. and an axial length of 4.25 in. There are 48 slots, each 1.15 by 0.35 in. The winding consists of 16 No. 11 AWG conductors per slot, arranged Y-Y, the coil pitch being equal to the pole pitch. The mean length of turn is 30.5 in. Estimate the slot leakage reactance per phase, making allowance for a fiber wedge $\frac{3}{32}$ in. thick at the top of the slots.

7-4. If the armature coils of the machine of Prob. 7-3 had a pitch of 10 slots, by what per cent would the slot leakage reactance be changed? If, under these conditions, the terminal voltage is to remain the same as before, by what per cent must the flux per pole be increased?

7-5. A three-phase machine has a winding which is disposed in four slots per pole per phase, the coil pitch being $\frac{5}{6}$. Compute the value of the term $(k_{br}k_{pr}/r)^2$ in Eq. 7-27 to an accuracy of 5 per cent.

7-6. From the data given in Prob. 7-1, compute the actual full-load current per rotor bar.

Chapter 8

8-1. A 15-hp 440-volt three-phase Y-connected 60-cycle squirrel-cage induction motor has an efficiency of 89 per cent and a power factor of 90 per cent when running at full load. The starting current at full voltage is 7 times full-load current and is to be reduced to 2.5 times full-load current by means of a starting compensator. Compute the percentage tapping of an autotransformer necessary for this result. Neglect saturation and no-load admittance.

8-2. A 50-hp 400-volt 50-cycle 10-pole squirrel-cage motor has the following data: $R_1 = 0.2$ ohm; $X_1 = 1.10$ ohms; R_2 (in terms of the primary) $= 0.3$ ohm; X (in terms of the primary) $= 1.10$ ohms. A star-Δ switch is used to start the motor at full voltage. Calculate the speed at which this switch is to be operated so that the current peak in the supply line is not larger than the initial current on starting the Y-connected motor.

8-3. Compute the relative current densities at the bottom, middle, and top of a deep-bar copper conductor if $w_b/w_s = 0.9$ and $f = 60$.

8-4. A polyphase induction motor has a double squirrel-cage rotor. The impedance of the outer cage in terms of the primary is $0.5 + j0.08$ ohm, while that of the inner one is $0.05 + j0.4$ ohm. Determine the starting torque of the motor in terms of the rated torque, assuming that the motor develops its rated torque at 1.8 per cent slip. Neglect saturation, magnetizing current, and mutual inductance between the two cages.

8-5. The induction motor of Prob. 6-9 is started at no load. What resistance should be added to the rotor circuit in order that the starting current may not exceed 45 amp?

8-6. What resistance should be inserted in the rotor circuit of the motor of Prob. 6-9 so that the speed is reduced to 100 rpm at full-load torque?

8-7. The speed regulation called for in Prob. 8-6 is to be obtained by injecting a suitable voltage into the slip rings. Calculate the magnitude, frequency, and phase of this voltage.

8-8. The following data apply to a 1,000-hp 2,200-volt three-phase Y-connected 25-cycle 12-pole wound-rotor induction motor: Effective rotor resistance per phase, 0.0992 ohm; rotor reactance at 25 cycles, 0.12 ohm per phase. At a slip of 0.018, the current flowing in the rotor is 330 amp, and the motor develops a torque of 22,500 lb-ft. Calculate, or read from a phasor diagram, the effective value of the voltage to be impressed upon the slip rings in order that the motor may develop the same torque (a) at 225 rpm; (b) at 300 rpm.

8-9. A 60-cycle six-pole induction motor is connected in cascade with an eight-pole motor. Calculate the synchronous speed if the two shafts are coupled by a reduction gear having a 2:1 ratio.

8-10. Two selsyns are used for the synchronous operation of two identical diesel engines. At a speed of 600 rpm, one of the engines has a load of 134 hp, while the other has a load of 110 hp. The selsyns are connected to a 25-cycle three-phase supply line and have 6 poles each. Assuming negligible losses in the selsyns, find the power flow in the selsyns (a) if they are running in the direction of their rotating fields; (b) if they are running in the direction opposite to that of their rotating fields.

8-11. A load of 800 kw at 80 per cent power factor is shared by two generators, of which one is an induction generator which develops 300 kw at a power factor of 90 per cent. What are the kva output and the power factor of the other generator?

8-12. The induction motor of Prob. 6-11 is used as an induction generator and is connected to a 25-cycle system supplying 440 volts. It is driven by a hydraulic turbine at 1,545 rpm. Calculate (a) the power in kilowatts flowing into the supply system; (b) the reactive kilovolt-amperes supplied to the induction generator by the supply system.

8-13. The 250-hp induction motor of Prob. 6-26 is driven as an induction generator and delivers 250 amp to a distribution system the voltage of which is held constant at 440 volts by 60-cycle synchronous generators. Using a circle diagram, determine (a) the speed of the prime mover of the induction generator; (b) the power delivered to the supply circuit; (c) the power supplied to the shaft of the induction generator; (d) the reactive power taken by the induction machine from the supply circuit; (e) the capacitance required in order that the induction generator, running at the speed determined in (a), may operate at unity power factor.

Chapter 9

9-1. Using the data given in Art. 9-6, construct the simplified circle diagram of the single-phase induction motor, and from the circle construct characteristic curves showing the variation of primary current, power factor, torque, speed, and efficiency as functions of output.

9-2. Prove that the starting torque of a split-phase motor is proportional to the product of the ampere-turns of the two stator windings and to the sine of the angle of phase displacement between the currents in the two windings.

9-3. A two-phase motor tested at standstill shows a resistance of R ohms and a reactance of X ohms per phase. Derive a formula for finding the magnitude of an additional resistance r which, when added to the circuit through one of the stator windings, will yield maximum torque when the motor is operated as a split-phase motor on a single-phase supply.

9-4. If in Prob. 9-3 the values of R and X are 6.6 and 8.8, respectively, how will the maximum starting torque, when used as a split-phase motor, compare with the starting torque of the original two-phase motor?

9-5. The two-phase motor of Prob. 9-4 is modified by the insertion of a capacitor in series with one of the stator windings. If the reactance of this capacitor is X_c ohms at line frequency, what should be its magnitude in order that the torque shall be a maximum when the machine is used as a split-phase motor? How will this torque compare with that of the original two-phase motor? How will the voltage across the capacitor compare with the normal line voltage?

9-6. A two-phase 110-volt 60-cycle induction motor has a standstill impedance of $6.6 + j8.8$ ohms per phase. It is to be converted into a capacitor-type motor by substituting for one of its phases a new winding in series with a capacitor. The new winding is to be made of wire having smaller cross section than that of the original winding, but the total weight of copper is to remain the same as before (assuming that any desired size of wire is obtainable). The new winding is to be so designed that the starting torque of the capacitor motor will be one-half that of the original two-phase motor. Determine (a) the number of turns in the new winding in terms of the original number; (b) the total line starting current; (c) the capacitance required; (d) the voltage drop across the capacitor.

Chapter 10

10-1. The open-circuit characteristic of a three-phase 50-cycle synchronous machine is determined by the following data:

Field amp...........	20	40	60	84	105	133
Terminal volts.......	850	1,700	2,460	3,000	3,300	3,600

Under short-circuit conditions at normal speed, a field excitation of 50 amp develops full-load stator current. The resistance drop is 2 per cent, and the leakage reactance drop is 15 per cent at normal full-load current. Determine the excitation necessary for full-load operation at a terminal voltage of 3,000 and a leading power factor of 90 per cent, using the general method.

10-2. Estimate the exciting current required by a three-phase 3,300-volt synchronous generator which supplies 1,000 kw at 80 per cent power factor, lagging, if its open-circuit characteristic is given by the following data:

Field amp..............	80	96	118
Terminal volts..........	3,300	3,600	3,900

The stator winding has a per phase resistance of 0.15 ohm and a leakage reactance of 1.2 ohms per phase. There are 16 poles, each wound with 108 turns. The armature winding is arranged in 144 slots, five conductors per slot, each phase consisting of a single circuit with coils of full pitch, and the three phases are Y-connected.

10-3. The following data characterize a 10,000-kva 6,600-volt 50-cycle three-phase turbo-generator:

Field amp-turns......	60,000	80,000	100,000	120,000	145,000	220,000
Open-circuit volts....	4,250	5,450	6,000	7,300	8,000	9,000

The field excitation required to circulate full-load current at short circuit is 117,000 amp-turns. The inductive drop in the stator winding at full-load current is 15 per cent. Find the voltage regulation at full load, 80 per cent power factor, lagging. Specify the method used in making the calculation.

10-4. The following data define the open-circuit characteristic and the zero-power-factor load characteristic of a 15,000-kva 11,000-volt three-phase 50-cycle Y-connected turbo-generator:

Field amp-turns $\times 10^{-3}$	10	18	24	30	40	45	50
Open-circuit volts, kv		4.9	8.4	10.1	11.5	12.8	13.3	13.65
Full load, zero-power-factor line voltage, kv	....	0	....	....	....	10.2	

Find the armature reaction in ampere-turns per pole, the armature leakage reactance, and the synchronous reactance. Calculate the regulation for full load, 80 per cent power factor, lagging, by the general, emf, and mmf methods.

10-5. Explain the reasons for the superiority of two-layer windings over single-layer windings for a-c generators. How may tooth ripples be minimized in salient-pole alternators?

10-6. A 3,750-kva 4,150-volt 3,600-rpm 60-cycle turbo-generator has 18 slots per pole and a two-layer winding forming a double-circuit Y-connected arrangement. (a) Draw a developed winding diagram for one phase of the winding; (b) tabulate the beginning and ending leads of each phase, and indicate the connections so that the resultant Y-Y circuits are balanced.

10-7. A 450-hp synchronous motor for 2,300 volts, 60 cycles, 1,200 rpm has 12 slots per pole. The double-layer lap winding, in which the coils span 10 slots, is arranged for Y connection. (a) Draw a developed winding diagram for one phase; (b) tabulate all coil connections and group connections, and show which of the coil ends are to be connected to form the common neutral and the line terminals.

10-8. A 2,500-kva three-phase 60-cycle 257-rpm synchronous generator develops 2,400 volts in each of the Y-connected phases. The stator has 324 slots, with two coil sides per slot, the coil span being 8 slots. The coils are lap-connected and form four parallel circuits per phase. (a) Draw the developed winding diagram for one pole group of one circuit of a particular phase; (b) tabulate the coil connections for the other circuits of the same phase used in part a; (c) tabulate the phase connections.

10-9. A 300-kva 60-cycle 48-pole two-phase generator has an armature with three slots per pole per phase. It is rated at 3,300 volts between lines. The flux per pole is 0.025 weber, and the magnetization curve is expressed by the equation

$$\text{Volts per phase} = \frac{6,000 I_f}{20 + I_f}$$

where I_f is the field current. The coil span is five-sixths of the pole pitch. The machine is reconnected as a three-phase Y-connected generator to yield 3,300 volts between lines. What percentage of the two-phase excitation will be required?

10-10. A 5,000-kva two-pole 60-cycle synchronous generator has a rated terminal voltage of 4,160 volts between lines. There are 48 slots, in which are disposed a double-layer winding of three turns per coil, the coil pitch being $1\frac{3}{24}$, and the coils are connected in double-circuit Y. The armature resistance, measured with direct current between terminals at 75°C, is 0.023 ohm, and the effective resistance with alternating current is 40 per cent greater. The leakage reactance is 0.078 ohm per phase. There are 202.5 turns per pole on the rotor. The open-circuit characteristic is given by the following data:

Field amp..........	20	40	60	80	100	120	140	160	180	200
Terminal volts.......	1,250	2,500	3,650	4,450	4,950	5,150	5,300	5,440	5,530	5,600

Calculate the regulation of this generator and the field current necessary to maintain rated terminal voltage (a) for full load at unity power factor; (b) for full load at 80 per cent power factor, lagging; (c) for full load at 80 per cent, leading; (d) for full-load current at zero power factor, lagging.

10-11. The generator of Prob. 10-10 when tested at full-load current at zero power factor showed that an exciting current of 84 amp was required at short circuit and that the field current was 164 amp when the terminal voltage was 4,160. Determine (a) the Potier reactance; (b) the armature reaction in terms of field amperes; (c) the zero-power-factor characteristic; (d) the short-circuit characteristic.

10-12. Using the values of Potier reaction and armature reaction determined in Prob. 10-11, compute the regulation of the generator of Prob. 10-10 (a) at half load and at full load for a lagging power factor of 0.707; (b) at half load and at full load for a leading power factor 0.707.

10-13. A three-phase Δ-connected synchronous generator rated at 1,875 kva, 480 volts, 60 cycles, 3,600 rpm has an open-circuit characteristic determined by the following data:

Field amp........	20	30	40	50	60	70	80	90	100	110	120	130	140
Line volts........	222	340	435	500	553	582	600	615	625	634	642	649	656

The stator winding, consisting of single-turn coils of $\frac{2}{3}$ pitch, is disposed in 15 slots per pole. The stator d-c resistance, measured between two terminals, is 0.00145 ohm at working temperature, and the leakage reactance is 0.098 ohm per phase. The field winding has 214 turns per pole. Assuming, first, full-load current at a power factor of 0.707, lagging, and, second, full-load current at a power factor of 0.707, leading, calculate (a) the regulation; (b) the field current required to maintain rated terminal voltage; (c) the angle between the terminal voltage and the airgap voltage.

10-14. The generator of Prob. 10-13, when operated at zero power factor with full rated current, requires a field current of 120 amp to develop rated terminal voltage. When short-circuited, a field current of 50 amp produces a line current of 2,000 amp. Determine (a) the Potier reactance; (b) the armature reaction in terms of the field amperes; (c) the zero-power-factor characteristic at full-load and half-load current. (d) Explain the reason for any discrepancy between the leakage reactance and the Potier reactance.

10-15. A 625-kva three-phase Y-connected two-pole 60-cycle turbo-generator, rated at 600 volts line to line, has a per-unit resistance of 0.005 per phase. The open-circuit characteristic is given by the following data:

Per-unit field current..	0.25	0.50	0.75	1.00	1.25	1.50	1.75	2.00
Per-unit line voltage...	0.28	0.56	0.83	1.00	1.085	1.16	1.2	1.235

On short circuit, a field current of 1 per unit produces 1 per-unit armature current. One point on the zero-power-factor characteristic corresponds to a field current of 2.4 per unit and 1 per-unit voltage. Determine (a) the per-unit Potier reactance and its mks value; (b) the armature reaction in terms of the normal field excitation; (c) the per-unit induced voltage corresponding to rated terminal voltage when the balanced three-phase load is 1.1 per unit at a power factor of 80 per cent, lagging; also the mks value of this voltage; (*d*) the field excitation, expressed in terms of the normal excitation, for the load in part *c*; (*e*) the regulation corresponding to part *c*.   (In parts *c* and *d*, use the general method, employing the values calculated in parts *a* and *b*.)

10-16. Using the data given in Probs. 10-10 and 10-11, assume that the airgap characteristic passes through a point corresponding to a field current of 80 amp and a line voltage of 5,700 volts.   (*a*) Find the unsaturated synchronous reactance; (*b*) plot the ratio of no-load voltage to short-circuit current against field amperes, and discuss the influence of saturation on the synchronous reactance; (*c*) the regulation and field current by the emf method when the machine carries full load at rated voltage and a power factor of 80 per cent, lagging; (*d*) compare the results with those of Prob. 10-10.

10-17. From the data in Probs. 10-13 and 10-14, determine the regulation by the emf method, using the unsaturated value of synchronous impedance.

10-18. Using the data given in Prob. 10-15, (*a*) determine the per-unit synchronous impedance and its ohmic value; (*b*) determine the per-unit armature-reaction reactance, using the synchronous impedance and the Potier reactance as previously calculated; (*c*) compare this value with the per-unit armature reaction, and discuss any discrepancies.

10-19. From the data given in Probs. 10-10 and 10-11, calculate the regulation and the field current for full load at 80 per cent power factor, lagging and leading, (*a*) by the mmf method; (*b*) by the saturated synchronous impedance method; (*c*) by the ASA method; (*d*) compare the results with those obtained from Prob. 10-10.

10-20. Repeat the calculations called for in Prob. 10-19, but using the data given in Probs. 10-13 and 10-14.

10-21. Repeat the calculations called for in Prob. 10-19, but using the data given in Prob. 10-15.

10-22. A 3,500-kva slow-speed three-phase generator, rated at 4,160 volts at 60 cycles, has 32 salient poles each of which has a pole arc of 73 per cent of the pole pitch.   The airgap has uniform length.   The armature winding, occupying 288 slots, is of the double-layer lap-wound type, each coil having 16 turns and a $\frac{7}{9}$ pitch.   The coils are connected to form a four-circuit Y connection.   The d-c resistance measured between terminals at 75°C is 0.125 ohm, and the a-c resistance is 30 per cent greater. The leakage reactance is 15.9 per cent.   Each pole has 50 turns and a resistance of 0.28 ohm at 40°C.   The open-circuit characteristic is given by the following data:

Field current.....	50	100	150	200	250	300	350	400	450
Terminal volts...	1,620	3,150	4,160	4,754	5,130	5,370	5,550	5,650	5,750

At a zero-power-factor load of 495 amp at 4160 volts, the field current was 410 amp; and on short circuit a field current of 200 amp produced a current of 680 amp.

Determine the armature reaction and its direct- and quadrature-axis components as functions of the load and the angle between the no-load voltage and the load current.

10-23. A 300-kva three-phase 60-cycle synchronous generator has 28 poles and is rated at 440 volts between lines.   The double-layer armature winding occupies six slots per pole, and the coils of $\frac{5}{6}$ pitch, each having three turns, are connected as a lap winding to form a two-circuit Y connection.   The d-c resistance measured between terminals is 0.925 ohm, and the leakage reactance is 20.3 per cent.   The ratio of pole arc to pole pitch is 0.72, and the airgap is uniform.   Each field pole has 112 turns. The open-circuit characteristic is given by the following data:

Field amp...........	5	10	15	20	25	30	35	40	45	50
Terminal volts.......	120	240	345	432	497	537	566	582	608	625

The 400-amp zero-power-factor characteristic is defined by a point the coordinates of which are 440 volts and 57.5 field amperes. The short-circuit characteristic passes through a point the coordinates of which are 400 armature amperes and 24 field amperes. Determine the full-load armature reaction and the direct- and quadrature-axis components as functions of the angle between the armature current and the no-load voltage.

10-24. A three-phase Y-connected 60-cycle, salient-pole laboratory generator is rated at 20 kva at 440 volts and 1,200 rpm. The poles, each having 400 turns, embrace 70 per cent of the pole pitch, and the airgap is uniform. The armature winding, disposed in 72 slots with eight conductors per slot, consists of coils which span 10 slots. The effective armature resistance per phase is 0.1 ohm, and the leakage reactance per phase is 0.3 ohm. The open-circuit characteristic is given by the following data:

Field amp..............	1	2	3	4	5	6	7
Volts per phase..........	70	140	205	255	290	312	330

Determine (a) the full-load armature reaction in the direct and the quadrature axes as functions of the angle between the load current and the no-load voltage; (b) the regulation at full load, 80 per cent power factor, lagging; (c) the field current required to maintain the terminal voltage at the above load; (d) the unsaturated values of the synchronous reactance in the direct and the quadrature axes; (e) the short-circuit characteristic.

10-25. Determine the regulation and the necessary field excitation of the machine defined by Prob. 10-24 (a) for full load at unity power factor; (b) for full load at a power factor of 0.707, leading.

10-26. The 3,500-kva generator specified in Prob. 10-22 supplies a 2,500-kw load at 0.8 power factor, lagging. Using the per-unit method throughout, (a) determine the regulation and the per-unit field current to maintain 1.05 per-unit volts at the terminals; (b) transform the results into mks values.

10-27. The 300-kva synchronous machine specified in Prob. 10-23 is used as a generator to supply a 440-volt bus bar with 200 kw at 0.8 power factor, lagging. (a) What field excitation is required for this load? (b) What will be the per cent voltage rise if this load is disconnected, assuming no change in speed? (c) What will be the change in the phase angle of the terminal voltage when the load is disconnected?

10-28. The measured values of the direct- and quadrature-axis synchronous reactances of the generator of Prob. 10-22, obtained by a slip test, are 5.6 and 3.4 ohms, respectively, both being unsaturated values. Neglecting armature resistance, determine the regulation, and the field current needed to maintain 4,368 volts at the terminals, when the load is 2,500 kw at 0.8 power factor, lagging. Compare the results with those of Prob. 10-26.

10-29. The 300-kva machine specified in Prob. 10-23, when subjected to a slip test, yielded the values $X_d = 0.825$ and $X_q = 0.555$ ohm. Using these values, solve Prob. 10-27 by the Doherty-Nickle method, and compare the results with those of Prob. 10-27.

10-30. A 350-kva 60-cycle 1,200 rpm Y-connected salient-pole alternator, rated at 2,300 volts between terminals, has an open-circuit characteristic determined by the following data:

Per-unit field current.....	0.25	0.50	0.75	1.00	1.25	1.50	1.75	2.00	2.25	2.50	2.75	3.00
Per-unit terminal volts.	0.317	0.635	0.855	1.00	1.07	1.125	1.17	1.205	1.23	1.258	1.281	1.301

The airgap characteristic is defined by a point which has the coordinates field current = 1 per unit and terminal volts = 1.31 per unit. The short-circuit characteristic passes through a point which has the coordinates field current = 1 per unit and armature current = 0.83 per unit. X_d = 1.205 per unit, X_q = 0.82 per unit, and the armature leakage reactance is 0.091 per unit. The armature resistance is negligible. Assuming rated voltage at the terminals, (a) determine the regulation, field current, and power angle for full load at 0.707 power factor, lagging, using the Doherty-Nickle method; (b) find the same quantities by the ASA method.

10-31. The 3,500-kva generator specified in Prob. 10-22 has the no-load core losses given in the following table:

No-load terminal volts.......	2,000	2,500	3,000	3,500	4,000	4,500	5,000	5,500
Core loss, kw..............	8	12.2	17	23.2	32	44	59	82

The windage and friction loss is constant at 15.2 kw. Find the efficiency of the generator for the operating conditions specified in Prob. 10-22.

10-32. The 300-kva generator of Prob. 10-23 has the following core-loss characteristic:

No-load terminal volts...........	200	300	400	500	600
Core loss, kw....................	2.5	5	8	12.7	21.5

The windage and friction loss is constant at 22 kw. Find the efficiency for the load conditions specified in Prob. 10-27.

Chapter 11

11-1. A 6,000-hp three-phase 60-cycle synchronous motor running at 3,600 rpm is used to drive a high-speed wind-tunnel fan. The stator winding, designed as a two-circuit double-layer Y-connected arrangement, occupies 54 slots. There are two conductors per slot, and the coil pitch is 16 slots. The effective armature resistance is 0.0042 ohm per phase, and the leakage reactance is 0.05 ohm per phase. The operating voltage is 2,400 volts between terminals.

The open-circuit saturation curve is defined by the following data:

Field amp.............	50	75	100	125	150	175	200	225	250	300
Terminal volts........	760	1,130	1,500	1,840	2,140	2,440	2,650	2,860	3,040	3,320

Two points on the zero-power-factor characteristic for 1,500 amp have the following coordinates: terminal volts = 0, field current = 167 amp; terminal volts = 2,400, field current = 345 amp.

The fan blades are so adjusted that the motor delivers 80 per cent of its rated output. Calculate the field current if the motor is to operate (a) at 0.8 power factor, lagging, assuming an efficiency of 92 per cent; (b) at unity power factor, assuming an efficiency of 93 per cent; (c) at 0.8 power factor, leading, assuming an efficiency of 92 per cent. Use the Potier method, and construct the phasor diagram corresponding to each case. Calculate the power angle for each case.

11-2. Repeat the calculations of Prob. 11-1, using the emf method, first calculating the unsaturated value of the synchronous impedance.

11-3. A 1,000-hp four-pole 60-cycle 4,200-volt Y-connected cylindrical-rotor synchronous motor has an effective armature resistance of 0.15 ohm per phase and a synchronous reactance of 1.1 ohms per phase. Neglecting saturation, calculate the excitation voltage necessary (a) for full output at unity power factor, assuming 91 per cent efficiency; (b) for 10 per cent overload at 0.9 power factor, leading, assuming 89.5 per cent efficiency. Construct the phasor diagram for each case.

11-4. The 20-kva salient-pole machine specified in Prob. 10-24 is used as a synchronous motor. Assuming an efficiency of 84 per cent, determine the excitation for an output of 20 hp at (a) 0.8 power factor, lagging; (b) 0.8 power factor, leading, using the two-reaction method. Construct the phasor diagram for each case, and determine the power angles.

11-5. The synchronous machine specified in Prob. 10-30, when used as a synchronous motor, delivers 450 hp. Calculate the per-unit excitation necessary for the machine to operate (a) at unity power factor with an efficiency of 95.6 per cent; (b) at 0.8 power factor, lagging, with an efficiency of 94 per cent; (c) at 0.8 power factor, leading, with an efficiency of 94 per cent. Draw the phasor diagram for each case, and determine the corresponding power angles.

11-6. A 1,000-kva three-phase 60-cycle 2,300-volt Y-connected synchronous motor has negligible armature resistance and a synchronous reactance of 1.65 ohms per phase. (a) What is the value of the excitation voltage if the power angle is 10° and the motor takes rated current at a lagging power factor? (b) What is the developed power per phase? (c) What is the power factor of the motor? (d) At what power angle will the motor operate if it develops an output of 500 kw at rated line voltage and with an excitation voltage of 2,000 volts? Draw the phasor diagram, and determine whether the motor draws leading or lagging current.

11-7. A 440-volt three-phase Y-connected synchronous motor has a rated armature current of 26.3 amp. The synchronous reactance is 6.06 ohms per phase, and the armature resistance is negligible. Assuming a constant input power of 15 kw, determine (a) the power angle δ for excitation voltages of 200, 250, 300, and 400 volts; (b) the power factor and line current for an excitation voltage of 300.

11-8. The transformers and cables supplying an industrial plant have a rating of 1,500 kva and are fully loaded by the plant, which draws 1,500 kva at a power factor of 0.7, lagging. (a) A 250-hp synchronous motor having an efficiency of 90 per cent is to be added to the plant load without increasing the transformer or cable capacity. At what power factor must the motor operate? (b) If, instead of the synchronous motor, there were added an equivalent induction motor load at 80 per cent power factor, what rating of synchronous condenser connected to the bus would avoid the necessity of increasing the transformer and cable capacity? (Neglect the losses in the synchronous condenser.)

11-9. A manufacturing plant takes 350 kw at a lagging power factor of 0.6. Calculate (a) the rating of a synchronous motor which would deliver 140 kw and at the same time make it possible for the plant to operate without overloading its 600-kva supply transformer; (b) the resultant power factor of the plant; (c) the power factor of the synchronous motor.

11-10. A cylindrical-rotor synchronous machine is rated at 500 kva at 3,000 volts, Y-connected. The armature resistance is 0.435 ohm per phase; the synchronous reactance is 1.740 ohms per phase. The core loss is 8 kw, and the friction and windage loss is 7 kw. (a) Draw power circles for shaft outputs of 485 kw and 735 kw (scale 500 amp per in.) and excitation circles for 25, 50, 75, 100, 125, 150, 175, and 200 per cent of normal excitation. (b) Construct a V curve for an output of 735 kw at the shaft, showing the stability limits. (c) Determine the maximum and minimum per cent excitation for a shaft output of 485 kw. (d) What excitation will result in minimum line current when the shaft output is 735 kw, and what is the corresponding power angle?

11-11. A three-phase Y-connected cylindrical-rotor synchronous motor is rated at 1,500 kva at 4,240 volts. The per-phase resistance and synchronous reactance of the armature winding are 0.22 and 0.9 ohm, respectively. (a) Construct power circles for 1,000, 1,500, and 2,000 kw developed power and excitation circles for per cent excitations of 25, 50, 75, 100, 125, 150, 175, and 200 per cent (scale 1,000 amp per in.). (b) Draw the V curve for no load and for a developed power of 1,500 kw, and show the stability limits. (c) Determine the maximum and minimum per cent excitations for a developed power of 1,000 kw. (d) When the motor develops 2,000 kw, what must be the per cent excitation in order that the line current may be a minimum, and what are the corresponding values of the power angle and the power-factor angle?

11-12. A three-phase Y-connected synchronous motor is designed for a terminal voltage of 3,300 volts, and its synchronous impedance is $0.25 + j2.00$ ohms per phase. The excitation is adjusted to a value which corresponds to an open-circuit terminal voltage of 3,500 volts. Determine the current and power factor for an output of 750 kw.

11-13. A six-pole three-phase 2,000-volt 25-cycle synchronous motor has an armature impedance of 10 ohms and a resistance of 0.5 ohm per phase. The field excitation is adjusted so that the corresponding open-circuit voltage is 1,600 volts. Calculate the maximum total torque in pound-feet that the machine can develop before it drops out of step.

11-14. A synchronous motor has an equivalent armature reactance of 3.3 ohms. The exciting current is adjusted to such a value that the open-circuit emf is 950 volts. Find the power factor at which the motor would operate when it takes 80 kw from 800-volt supply lines.

11-15. A three-phase synchronous machine, when driven at its rated speed, has a magnetization curve determined by the following data:

Exciting current.........	5	10	15	20	25
Line voltage.............	370	655	830	950	1,050

An exciting current of 10 amp produces a short-circuit current of 200 amp. What will be the power factor of this machine when operating as a synchronous motor on 800-volt mains, developing 75 kw, the exciting current being 20 amp?

11-16. If a synchronous motor is brought up to speed without any field excitation and is then connected to the supply circuit, will it remain in step? State reasons, and indicate the type to which the machine must belong.

11-17. Calculate the rotational inertia (in lb-ft² units) of the rotor of a 10,000-kva 6,600-volt four-pole turbo-alternator driven at 1,500 rpm in order that the machine may have a natural period of 1 sec when running in parallel with a large number of other machines. The steady short-circuit current of the alternator is five times the normal full-load current.

11-18. A 5,000-kva three-phase 10,000-volt machine running at 1,500 rpm on a 50-cycle supply line has a rotor which has a moment of inertia of 150 ton-ft² and the steady short-circuit current, when operated as a generator, of five times the normal full-load current. What is the time of one complete period if hunting occurs?

11-19. A 30-pole 240-rpm three-phase Y-connected machine is rated at 5,000 kva at 6,600 volts (line to line). The armature has 360 slots with two conductors per slot, the coils having ⅔ pitch. The field winding has 67.5 turns per pole. The effective resistance of the armature winding is 0.042 ohm per phase, and the leakage reactance is 1.01 ohms per phase. Open- and short-circuit tests give the following data:

Exciting current..........	100	150	200	250
No-load volts.............	4,800	6,550	7,500	8,000
Short-circuit current.......	676	1,014		

The ratio of pole arc to pole pitch is 0.6. A slip test shows that the ratio of X_d to X_q is 5:3, and it may be assumed that the average of X_d and X_q is equal to the synchronous reactance. Using the two-reaction method, construct the phasor diagram of the machine running as a synchronous motor when the input is 4,000 kw at 85 per cent power factor, leading, and indicate the magnitude of each phasor.

11-20. Construct the V curves of the machine specified in Prob. 11-19, and indicate the portions within the limits of 25 per cent overload current

Chapter 12

12-1. Calculate the torque angle of the 5,000-kva generator specified in Prob. 10-10 for the loads given in parts *a* to *d*. Plot the power angle against power factor, and discuss the influence of power factor upon the power angle subject to the condition that the load remains constant.

12-2. Determine the torque angle of the generator in Prob. 10-10 when it carries full load at 0.8 power factor, lagging and leading, using the emf method in constructing the phasor diagram. The synchronous reactance has the value found in Prob. 10-16. Discuss the influence of saturation on the power angle.

12-3. The generator of Prob. 10-10 is connected to an infinite bus. Calculate the synchronizing torque per radian for the loads specified in Prob. 10-10, using the emf method. Calculate also the synchronizing torque at zero power factor, leading, with full-load current.

12-4. Plot the torque angle characteristic of the generator of Prob. 10-10, assuming constant excitation equivalent to 2,400 volts per phase and with rated terminal voltage. Neglect saturation, and use the synchronous impedance determined in Prob. 10-16.

12-5. Calculate and plot the torque angle characteristic of the generator of Prob. 10-22, using the synchronous impedances given in Prob. 10-28, assuming a constant excitation corresponding to 2,400 volts per phase and at rated terminal voltage. Determine the torque angle at which the output is a maximum.

12-6. The generator of Prob. 10-22 is connected to an infinite bus. Determine the synchronizing torque per radian if the generator is loaded as in Prob. 10-28. What would be the synchronizing power if the power angle were changed by 1 mechanical degree and all voltages are assumed to be constant?

12-7. A synchronous generator with cylindrical rotor is rated at 1,000 kva, 3,300 volts, 60 cycles, at 600 rpm. The synchronous reactance has a per-unit magnitude of 0.2, the resistance being negligible. Calculate the synchronizing power in kilowatts per mechanical degree of displacement when the machine is running at full load at a power factor of 0.8 (both leading and lagging).

12-8. The 20-kva salient-pole machine defined in Prob. 10-24 was supplying 2 kw at 0.9 power factor to the laboratory supply circuit, which was also supplied by the city power system. The d-c excitation of the laboratory generator was interrupted during this operation. Using the values of the direct and quadrature impedances corresponding to the calculations of Prob. 10-24*d*, determine (*a*) the power angle before the failure of the d-c supply, assuming normal voltage at the terminals of the machine; (b) the power angle after the interruption of the excitation; (c) the synchronizing power per mechanical degree for the conditions in (b).

12-9. Two identical three-phase Y-connected alternators operating in parallel are driven by prime movers which have identical speed-load characteristics. The effective armature resistance and the synchronous reactance of each machine are 2.18 and 62 ohms per phase, respectively. The alternators supply 1,830 kw at 13,800 volts to a load which has a power factor of 0.8. The excitations of the alternators are adjusted in such a way that one of them supplies a current of 40 amp lagging behind its terminal voltage by an angle $\cos^{-1} 0.8$. (a) What current does the other machine supply? (b) What are the excitation emfs of the two machines and the angular displacement between them?

12-10. Two identical 1,000 kva three-phase 60-cycle 6,600-volt Y-connected alternators are operating in parallel and supply a load which has a power factor of 0.9. The power input to the first machine is 800 kw, and the power input to the other is 400 kw. The excitation of the first machine is so adjusted that it corresponds to an open-circuit voltage of 5,000 volts per phase. Each machine has a synchronous reactance of 17 ohms per phase. Neglecting resistance and all losses, find (a) the power angle at which the first machine is operating; (b) the magnitude of the current and the power factor of the first machine; (c) the magnitude of the circulating current. (d) Explain how the circulating current can be reduced to zero.

12-11. Two alternators rated at 350 kw and 700 kw, respectively, are driven by prime movers which have straight-line speed characteristics, both being adjusted to a no-load speed of 1,800 rpm. The former has a speed regulation of 3.4 per cent, the latter a speed regulation of 2.8 per cent. (a) When the two units are in parallel, how will they divide a total load of 1,000 kw? (b) What change should be made in order that the combined load of 1,000 kw may be divided in proportion to the ratings of the machines?

12-12. Each of two identical generators is rated at 20,000 kva at 11,000 volts, and the synchronous reactance of the Y-connected winding is 15 per cent. When operating in parallel, they supply an 80 per cent power-factor load of 30,000 kw at rated terminal voltage. They operate at the same power factor, and the power inputs are adjusted for equal loads. Determine for each machine the no-load voltage, the power angle, and the kilovolt-amperes and reactive kilovolt-amperes supplied.

12-13. The total load on the two machines of Prob. 12-12 remains at 30,000 kw at 80 per cent power factor at 11,000 terminal volts. The no-load voltage of one machine is adjusted to 10,650 volts per phase, and the prime movers are adjusted so that the first delivers 12,000 kw to the load, and the second machine delivers 18,000 kw. Determine the excitation voltage of the second machine, and for each machine the power angle, the current, and the power factor.

12-14. Calculate the synchronizing torque per unit mechanical angle of phase displacement for a 5,000-kva alternator running at 1,500 rpm when connected to a 6,600-volt 50-cycle supply line. The armature has a short-circuit reactance of 15 per cent.

12-15. Two identical three-phase Y-connected 50-cycle alternators are paralleled with a phase displacement of 2 electrical degrees, the terminal voltage being 6,600, there being no connected load. The synchronous reactance of each machine is 8.5 ohms, the resistance being negligible. Calculate approximately the synchronizing current.

12-16. Two three-phase synchronous machines, mechanically coupled, operate in parallel on the same load. Determine the kilowatts output and power factor of each machine if the synchronous impedance of each generator is $0.2 + j2.0$ ohms and the equivalent impedance of the load is $3 - j4$ ohms per phase. The induced emf per phase of generator 1 is $2,000 + j0$, and that of generator 2 is $2,200$ volts.

12-17. Two similar, 6,600-volt three-phase generators are operated in parallel on bus bars which maintain constant voltage and frequency. Each machine has an effective resistance and reactance of 0.05 ohm and 0.5 ohm, respectively, and supplies one-half of a total load of 10,000 kw and 80 per cent power factor, lagging, the two machines being equally excited. If the excitation of one generator is adjusted until the armature current is 438 amp, and the steam supply of its driving turbine remains unaltered, find the armature current, the emf, and the power factor of the other generator. Construct the phasor diagram illustrating the conditions.

12-18. A three-phase Y-connected alternator connected to 6,600-volt bus bars has a synchronous impedance of 10 ohms per phase and a resistance of 2 ohms per phase. The excitation corresponds to an open-circuit emf of 6,000 volts. What is the maximum load the machine can supply to the external circuit before dropping out of synchronism, and what are the corresponding values of armature current and power factor?

Chapter 13

13-1. Does Eq. 13-4 apply to lap-wound armature windings having fractional pitch? State reasons.

13-2. A six-pole lap-wound armature has 144 commutator segments. Prepare a table showing the segments to which connections should be made to obtain (a) single-phase, (b) quarter-phase, (c) three-phase output.

13-3. What is the effective value of the alternating voltage between slip rings which corresponds to 220 volts at the commutator end of synchronous converters for (a) single-phase, (b) three-phase, (c) six-phase operation? In each case, determine the alternating line current corresponding to a direct current of 1,000 amp if the power factor is 0.9 and the efficiency of conversion is 95 per cent.

13-4. A synchronous converter supplies a d-c load of 750 kw at 230 volts. It is in turn supplied from a three-phase source having 6,600 volts between lines. The excitation is adjusted to correspond to a leading power factor of 95 per cent, and the efficiency of conversion is 96 per cent. If the converter has three slip rings, what will be the voltage and current ratings of the windings of three single-phase transformers, connected Y-Δ, which supply the converter?

13-5. If the converter of Prob. 13-4 has six slip rings and is to be supplied by three single-phase transformers with primaries in Y, secondaries in Δ-Δ, what should be the voltage and current ratings of the transformer windings?

13-6. The turns ratio in each phase of a transformer connecting a six-ring converter (with diametral tapping) to an 11,000-volt three-phase network is 60.5:1. The transformer primaries are Δ-connected. What is the commutator brush voltage on open circuit?

13-7. A six-ring synchronous converter with diametral tappings is supplied from a 33-kv three-phase source. The transformer is Δ-connected on the primary side and has a turns ratio of 77 and an equivalent secondary reactance of 0.2 ohm. If the d-c load remains constant at 500 amp, find the change in commutator voltage when the power factor at the slip rings is increased from 0.8 (leading) to unity. Assume constant efficiency at 92 per cent.

13-8. A six-ring 12-pole lap-wound synchronous converter with diametral tapping runs at 600 rpm and supplies a d-c load of 2,000 amp. There are 1,200 armature conductors, and the flux per pole is 0.05 weber. The transformer is Δ-connected to a 6,600-volt three-phase supply circuit. Assuming a leading power factor of 0.95 and an efficiency of 96 per cent, find (a) the turns ratio of the transformer and the voltage between adjacent rings; (b) the current per ring; (c) the current in the armature winding adjacent to a tapping point.

13-9. Find the d-c output and voltage of a six-ring converter with diametral tapping when it takes 500 amp at a leading power factor of 80 per cent, measured at the slip rings, from a transformer supplied at 6,600 volts from a 50-cycle source. The turns ratio of the transformer is 12, and its reactance, considered as concentrated in the secondary, is 0.06 henry. The efficiency of conversion is 90 per cent.

13-10. A four-pole 500-kw 500-volt converter is supplied from a three-phase 25-cycle source having 110,000 volts between lines. Specify the voltage and current ratings of the required three-phase supply transformer, if it is connected Y-Δ, and the machine is to operate at unity power factor at its a-c end, and at 93 per cent efficiency at full load.

13-11. Draw the wave form of the current in a tap coil of a four-pole 500-kw converter supplying direct current at 500 volts, when connected directly to a three-phase 60-cycle source. Assume normal excitation and an efficiency of 92 per cent when operating at a power factor of 0.9, (a) lagging; (b) leading.

13-12. A 2,000-kw 25-cycle six-phase synchronous converter delivers power to a three-wire d-c system having 125 volts between the neutral and each outer wire. Show the transformer connections and specify the voltage and current ratings of the transformer windings if the primaries are connected to a 6,600-volt three-phase line. What current flows in each a-c and d-c lead with full balanced load on the d-c side, the excitation being normal and the efficiency 95 per cent?

13-13. A four-pole 500-kw 550-volt six-ring synchronous converter has 15 slots per pole and four conductors per slot. The efficiency is 94 per cent. Construct curves showing the a-c and d-c mmf distribution over two adjacent pole pitches. How would the values of mmf from these curves be used to determine the number of turns required on interpoles?

13-14. The simplex lap winding of a three-phase synchronous converter is designed with winding elements of $\frac{5}{6}$ pitch. The pole arc is 70 per cent of the pole pitch. If the airgap flux is trapezoidally instead of sinusoidally distributed, what will be the ratio of a-c and d-c voltages, assuming the same total flux per pole in both cases?

13-15. A compound-wound synchronous converter is to have a d-c voltage of 600 volts at no load and 625 volts when delivering the rated d-c output of 500 kw. Alternating current is to be supplied from three single-phase transformers, the primaries of which are Y-connected to a 6,600-volt feeder, and the secondaries of which are connected diametrically to six slip rings. The full-pitch simplex lap winding of the armature is disposed in 96 slots with six conductors per slot, and its hot resistance, measured between main terminals, is 0.00975 ohm. The series field winding, having $4\frac{1}{2}$ turns per pole, has a hot resistance of 0.000625 ohm. The shunt field winding of 600 turns per pole has a hot resistance, including the regulating rheostat, of 13.9 ohms. The friction, windage, and core losses may be assumed constant at 12.5 kw. The open-circuit characteristic of the machine, considered from the d-c side, is represented by the equation $E = 1{,}200 i_s/(13.4 + i_s)$, where i_s is the shunt field current. Assuming that the synchronous-reactance drop in the armature amounts to 6 per cent, what must be the per cent leakage reactance of the transformers, neglecting the resistance of the transformers and their connecting leads?

Chapter 14

14-1. A three-phase induction motor designed to operate at a terminal voltage of 460 volts is to be supplied from an 11,000-volt single-phase circuit. Specify the turns ratio of the supply transformer and the turns ratio of the stator windings of the required rotary phase converter.

14-2. A 60-cycle synchronous motor running at 600 rpm is mechanically coupled to a 500-hp load. A 10-pole 60-cycle induction motor is coupled mechanically to the synchronous motor and is electrically connected to the same supply circuit. How is the load divided between the two machines?

14-3. Two synchronous machines are mechanically coupled to transfer power from a 60-cycle system to a 25-cycle system. A duplicate frequency-changer set is synchronized on the 60-cycle side. If the machines of both sets have the minimum number of poles consistent with the system frequencies, in how many ways may the 25-cycle machine of the second set fail to be in synchronism with the 25-cycle system? Make a sketch of the circuits and instrumentation required for paralleling the two sets, and outline the procedure to be followed.

Chapter 15

15-1. A compensated series a-c motor, when supplied at constant impressed voltage, develops its rated power with an efficiency of 88 per cent and at a power factor of 80 per cent. Under these conditions, the corresponding values of current input, speed, and flux per pole have their normal unit values. Assuming that the magnetic circuit of the machine is unsaturated and that the resistances and leakage reactances of the windings are constant, plot the per-unit values of the speed and developed power in terms of the per-unit current input.

Chapter 16

16-1. A full-wave single-phase mercury-arc rectifier supplies a d-c load of 25 amp at 110 volts, the arc drop being 16 volts. Neglecting overlap of the anode currents, what are the rms values of voltage and current which must be supplied by the transformer secondary?

16-2. A 440/220-volt single-phase transformer with center-tapped secondary supplies a full-wave mercury-arc rectifier which has a constant arc drop of 16 volts. When the d-c load current is 40 amp and the angle of overlap is 20°, what is the d-c voltage?

16-3. Transformers having Δ-connected primaries and zigzag-connected secondaries supply a three-phase mercury-arc rectifier which has a constant arc drop of 18 volts and which delivers 200 amp at 250 volts to a d-c load. The angle of overlap is 20°. Neglecting losses in the transformers, what must be the ratio of primary turns to the turns of each secondary if the transformers are supplied from a 2,300-volt circuit?

16-4. If in Prob. 16-3 the load losses in the supply transformers amount to 1,000 watts, and if there is an impedance drop of 6 per cent, how would the results be modified?

16-5. Six single-anode rectifier tubes are supplied from a 2,300-volt three-phase source by transformers which have Δ-connected primaries and Y-connected secondaries the neutral points of which are connected by an interphase transformer. The rectifiers have a constant arc drop of 16 volts and supply a d-c load of 1,000 kw at 230 volts. The corresponding losses in the supply transformers amount to 18 kw, and there is an impedance drop of 8 per cent. The rectifier operates with an angle of overlap of 20°, and at the load indicated the firing point is retarded by 25°. Calculate the ratio of primary turns to the turns of each secondary.

16-6. The d-c load specified in Prob. 16-5 is decreased by 25 per cent, and the d-c voltage is to be held constant at 230 volts. The load losses in the transformers may be assumed to vary as the square of the d-c current output. By how much must the firing angle be changed, and in which direction?

16-7. Calculate the over-all efficiency of the units specified in (*a*) Prob. 16-5; (*b*) Prob. 16-6.

INDEX

Date Due